STUDENT SOLUTIONS MANUAL

DANIEL S. MILLER

Niagara County Community College

5TH EDITION

INTRODUCTORY ALGEBRA

for College Students

BLITZER

PEARSON

Prentice
Hall

Upper Saddle River, NJ 07458

Editorial Director: Christine Hoag
Editor-in-Chief: Paul Murphy
Editorial Project Manager: Dawn Nuttall
Assistant Editor: Christine Whitlock
Senior Managing Editor: Linda Mihatov Behrens
Associate Managing Editor: Bayani Mendoza de Leon
Project Manager: Barbara Mack
Art Director: Heather Scott
Supplement Cover Manager: Paul Gourhan
Supplement Cover Designer: Victoria Colotta
Operations Specialist: Ilene Kahn
Senior Operations Supervisor: Diane Peirano

© 2009 Pearson Education, Inc.
Pearson Prentice Hall
Pearson Education, Inc.
Upper Saddle River, NJ 07458

The author and publisher of this book have used their best efforts in preparing this book. These efforts include the development, research, and testing of the theories and programs to determine their effectiveness. The author and publisher make no warranty of any kind, expressed or implied, with regard to these programs or the documentation contained in this book. The author and publisher shall not be liable in any event for incidental or consequential damages in connection with, or arising out of, the furnishing, performance, or use of these programs.

Printed in the United States of America

10   9   8   7   6   5   4   3   2

ISBN-13:   978-0-13-603146-8   Standalone

ISBN-10:   0-13-603146-3   Standalone

ISBN-13:   978-0-13-603147-5   Component

ISBN-10:   0-13-603147-1   Component

Pearson Education Ltd., London
Pearson Education Singapore, Pte. Ltd.
Pearson Education Canada, Inc.
Pearson Education—Japan
Pearson Education Australia PTY, Limited
Pearson Education North Asia, Ltd., Hong Kong
Pearson Educación de Mexico, S.A. de C.V.
Pearson Education Malaysia, Pte. Ltd.
Pearson Education Upper Saddle River, New Jersey

TABLE OF CONTENTS for STUDENT SOLUTIONS

INTRODUCTORY ALGEBRA FOR COLLEGE STUDENTS 5E

Chapter 1
Variables, Real Numbers, and Mathematical Models

1.1 Check Points

1. a. $6 + 2x = 6 + 2(10) = 26$

b. $2(x + 6) = 2(10 + 6) = 32$

2. a. $7x + 2y = 7 \cdot 3 + 2 \cdot 8 = 21 + 16 = 37$

b. $\dfrac{6x - y}{2y - x - 8} = \dfrac{6 \cdot 3 - 8}{2 \cdot 8 - 3 - 8} = \dfrac{10}{5} = 2$

3. a. $6x$

b. $4 + x$

c. $3x + 5$

d. $12 - 2x$

e. $\dfrac{15}{x}$

4. a. $\quad 9x - 3 = 42$
$\qquad 9(6) - 3 = 42$
$\qquad 54 - 3 = 42$
$\qquad\qquad 51 = 42, \text{ false}$
6 is not a solution.

b. $\quad 2(y + 3) = 5y - 3$
$\qquad 2(3 + 3) = 5(3) - 3$
$\qquad\quad 2(6) = 15 - 3$
$\qquad\qquad 12 = 12, \text{ true}$
3 is a solution.

5. a. $\dfrac{x}{6} = 5$

b. $7 - 2x = 1$

6. a. $d = 4n + 5$
$d = 4(15) + 5 = 65$
65% of marriages end in divorce after 15 years when the wife is under 18 at the time of marriage.

b. According to the line graph, 60% of marriages end in divorce after 15 years when the wife is under 18 at the time of marriage.

c. The mathematical model overestimates the actual percentage shown in the graph by 5%.

1.1 Exercise Set

1. $x + 8 = 4 + 8 = 12$

3. $12 - x = 12 - 4 = 8$

5. $5x = 5 \cdot 4 = 20$

7. $\dfrac{28}{x} = \dfrac{28}{4} = 7$

9. $5 + 3x = 5 + 3 \cdot 4 = 5 + 12 = 17$

11. $2(x + 5) = 2(4 + 5) = 2(9) = 18$

13. $\dfrac{12x - 8}{2x} = \dfrac{12 \cdot 4 - 8}{2 \cdot 4} = \dfrac{48 - 8}{8} = \dfrac{40}{8} = 5$

15. $2x + y = 2 \cdot 7 + 5 = 14 + 5 = 19$

17. $2(x + y) = 2(7 + 5) = 2(12) = 24$

19. $4x - 3y = 4 \cdot 7 - 3 \cdot 5 = 28 - 15 = 13$

21. $\dfrac{21}{x} + \dfrac{35}{y} = \dfrac{21}{7} + \dfrac{35}{5} = 3 + 7 = 10$

23. $\dfrac{2x - y + 6}{2y - x} = \dfrac{2 \cdot 7 - 5 + 6}{2 \cdot 5 - 7} = \dfrac{14 - 5 + 6}{10 - 7} = \dfrac{15}{3} = 5$

25. $x + 4$

27. $x - 4$

29. $x + 4$

31. $x - 9$

33. $9 - x$

35. $3x - 5$

37. $12x - 1$

39. $\dfrac{10}{x} + \dfrac{x}{10}$

41. $\dfrac{x}{30} + 6$

43. $x + 14 = 20$

$6 + 14 = 20$

$20 = 20$, true

The number is a solution.

45. $30 - y = 10$

$30 - 20 = 10$

$10 = 10$, true

The number is a solution.

47. $4z = 20$

$4(10) = 20$

$40 = 20$, false

The number is not a solution.

49. $\dfrac{r}{6} = 8$

$\dfrac{48}{6} = 8$

$8 = 8$, true

The number is a solution.

51. $4m + 3 = 23$

$4(6) + 3 = 23$

$24 + 3 = 23$

$27 = 23$, false

The number is not a solution.

53. $5a - 4 = 2a + 5$

$5(3) - 4 = 2(3) + 5$

$15 - 4 = 6 + 5$

$11 = 11$, true

The number is a solution.

55. $6(p - 4) = 3p$

$6(8 - 4) = 3(8)$

$6(4) = 24$

$24 = 24$, true

The number is a solution.

57. $2(w + 1) = 3(w - 1)$

$2(7 + 1) = 3(7 - 1)$

$2(8) = 3(6)$

$16 = 18$, false

The number is not a solution.

59. $4x = 28$

61. $\dfrac{14}{x} = \dfrac{1}{2}$

63. $20 - x = 5$

65. $2x + 6 = 16$

67. $3x - 5 = 7$

69. $4x + 5 = 33$

71. $4(x + 5) = 33$

73. $5x = 24 - x$

75. First find x.

$x = 7y + 2$

$x = 7(5) + 2 = 37$

Evaluate the expression.

$\dfrac{x - y}{4} = \dfrac{37 - 5}{4} = \dfrac{32}{4} = 8$

77. First find x.

$x = \dfrac{y}{4} - 1$

$x = \dfrac{12}{4} - 1 = 3 - 1 = 2$

Evaluate the expression.

$4x + 3(y + 5) = 4(2) + 3(12 + 5)$

$= 8 + 3(17)$

$= 8 + 51$

$= 59$

79. a. $2(x + 3y) = 2(4 + 3 \cdot 1) = 2(7) = 14$

b. $5z - 30 = 40$

$5(14) - 30 = 40$

$70 - 30 = 40$

$40 = 40$, true

Yes, it is a solution.

81. a. $6x - 2y = 6 \cdot 3 - 2 \cdot 6 = 18 - 12 = 6$

b. $7w = 45 - 2w$

$7(6) = 45 - 2(6)$

$42 = 45 - 12$

$42 = 33$, false

No, it is not a solution.

83. a. $p = 16 - n$

$p = 16 - 5$

$= 11$

The percentage of African American players was 11% in 2002.
The model overestimates the actual percentage shown in the bar graph by 1%.

b. $p = 16 - n$

$p = 16 - 7$

$= 9$

The percentage of African American players was 9% in 2004.
The model gives the actual percentage shown in the bar graph in 2004.

85. a. $p = 7.4h + 6$

$p = 7.4(4) + 6$

$= 35.6$

The percentage of U.S. adults that got 8 or more hours of sleep was 35.6% in 1998.
The model overestimates the actual percentage shown in the bar graph by 0.6%.

b. $p = 3.7h + 15$

$p = 3.7(4) + 15$

$= 29.8$

The percentage of U.S. adults that got 8 or more hours of sleep was 29.8% in 2005.
The model overestimates the actual percentage shown in the bar graph by 3.8%.

87. a. $H = 0.8(200 - A)$

$H = 0.8(200 - 145)$

$= 44$

A bowler with an average score of 145 will have a handicap of 44.

b. The bowler's final score will be $120 + 44,$ or 164.

89. – 97. Answers will vary.

99. makes sense

101. makes sense

103. true

105. true

107. Choices of variables may vary.
Let $h =$ hours worked.
Let $s =$ salary.

$s = 20h$

109. a. O'Donnell: $p = \dfrac{s}{w} = \dfrac{2}{3.1} \approx \$0.65$

Vieira: $p = \dfrac{s}{w} = \dfrac{10}{5.6} \approx \$1.79$

Couric: $p = \dfrac{s}{w} = \dfrac{15}{7.3} \approx \$2.05$

b. Using the magazine's criterion, O'Donnell was the best buy.

110. $\dfrac{3}{7} \cdot \dfrac{2}{5} = \dfrac{3 \cdot 2}{7 \cdot 5} = \dfrac{6}{35}$

111. $\dfrac{2}{3} \div \dfrac{7}{5} = \dfrac{2}{3} \cdot \dfrac{5}{7} = \dfrac{2 \cdot 5}{3 \cdot 7} = \dfrac{10}{21}$

112. $\dfrac{9}{17} - \dfrac{5}{17} = \dfrac{9 - 5}{17} = \dfrac{4}{17}$

1.2 Check Points

1. $2\dfrac{5}{8} = \dfrac{2 \cdot 8 + 5}{8} = \dfrac{16 + 5}{8} = \dfrac{21}{8}$

2. 5 divided by 3 is 1 with a remainder of 2, so $\dfrac{5}{3} = 1\dfrac{2}{3}.$

3. Begin by selecting any two numbers whose product is 36.
Here is one possibility: $36 = 4 \cdot 9$
Because the factors 4 and 9 are not prime, factor each of these composite numbers.
$36 = 4 \cdot 9$

$= 2 \cdot 2 \cdot 3 \cdot 3$

Notice that 2 and 3 are both prime. The prime factorization of 36 is $2 \cdot 2 \cdot 3 \cdot 3.$

4. a. $\dfrac{10}{15} = \dfrac{2 \cdot \cancel{5}}{3 \cdot \cancel{5}} = \dfrac{2}{3}$

b. $\dfrac{42}{24} = \dfrac{\cancel{2} \cdot \cancel{3} \cdot 7}{2 \cdot 2 \cdot \cancel{2} \cdot \cancel{3}} = \dfrac{7}{4}$

When reducing fractions, it may not be necessary to write prime factorizations. We can use the greatest common factor to reduce this fraction.

$\dfrac{42}{24} = \dfrac{7 \cdot \cancel{6}}{4 \cdot \cancel{6}} = \dfrac{7}{4}$

c. $\dfrac{13}{15}$; Because 13 and 15 share no common factors (other than 1), $\dfrac{13}{15}$ is already reduced to its lowest terms.

d. $\dfrac{9}{45} = \dfrac{1 \cdot \cancel{9}}{5 \cdot \cancel{9}} = \dfrac{1}{5}$

5. a. $\dfrac{4}{11} \cdot \dfrac{2}{3} = \dfrac{4 \cdot 2}{11 \cdot 3} = \dfrac{8}{33}$

b. $6 \cdot \dfrac{3}{5} = \dfrac{6}{1} \cdot \dfrac{3}{5} = \dfrac{18}{5} = 3\dfrac{3}{5}$

c. $\dfrac{3}{7} \cdot \dfrac{2}{3} = \dfrac{3 \cdot 2}{7 \cdot 3} = \dfrac{6}{21} = \dfrac{2 \cdot \cancel{3}}{7 \cdot \cancel{3}} = \dfrac{2}{7}$

Remember that you can divide numerators and denominators by common factors before performing multiplication.

$\dfrac{3}{7} \cdot \dfrac{2}{3} = \dfrac{\cancel{3}}{7} \cdot \dfrac{2}{\cancel{3}} = \dfrac{2}{7}$

d. $\left(3\dfrac{2}{5}\right)\left(1\dfrac{1}{2}\right) = \dfrac{17}{5} \cdot \dfrac{3}{2} = \dfrac{51}{10} = 5\dfrac{1}{10}$

6. a. $\dfrac{5}{4} \div \dfrac{3}{8} = \dfrac{5}{4} \cdot \dfrac{8}{3} = \dfrac{5}{\cancel{4}} \cdot \dfrac{\cancel{4} \cdot 2}{3} = \dfrac{10}{3} = 3\dfrac{1}{3}$

b. $\dfrac{2}{3} \div 3 = \dfrac{2}{3} \div \dfrac{3}{1} = \dfrac{2}{3} \cdot \dfrac{1}{3} = \dfrac{2}{9}$

c. $3\dfrac{3}{8} \div 2\dfrac{1}{4} = \dfrac{27}{8} \div \dfrac{9}{4} = \dfrac{27}{8} \cdot \dfrac{4}{9}$

$= \dfrac{\cancel{9} \cdot 3}{\cancel{4} \cdot 2} \cdot \dfrac{\cancel{4}}{\cancel{9}} = \dfrac{3}{2} = 1\dfrac{1}{2}$

7. a. $\dfrac{2}{11} + \dfrac{3}{11} = \dfrac{5}{11}$

b. $\dfrac{5}{6} - \dfrac{1}{6} = \dfrac{4}{6} = \dfrac{2}{3}$

c. $3\dfrac{3}{8} - 1\dfrac{1}{8} = \dfrac{27}{8} - \dfrac{9}{8} = \dfrac{18}{8} = \dfrac{9}{4} = 2\dfrac{1}{4}$

8. $\dfrac{2}{3} = \dfrac{2 \cdot 7}{3 \cdot 7} = \dfrac{14}{21}$

9. a. $\dfrac{1}{2} + \dfrac{3}{5} = \dfrac{1 \cdot 5}{2 \cdot 5} + \dfrac{3 \cdot 2}{5 \cdot 2} = \dfrac{5}{10} + \dfrac{6}{10} = \dfrac{11}{10}$

b. $\dfrac{4}{3} - \dfrac{3}{4} = \dfrac{4 \cdot 4}{3 \cdot 4} - \dfrac{3 \cdot 3}{4 \cdot 3} = \dfrac{16}{12} - \dfrac{9}{12} = \dfrac{7}{12}$

c. $3\dfrac{1}{6} - 1\dfrac{11}{12} = \dfrac{19}{6} - \dfrac{23}{12} = \dfrac{19 \cdot 2}{6 \cdot 2} - \dfrac{23}{12}$

$= \dfrac{38}{12} - \dfrac{23}{12} = \dfrac{15}{12}$

$= \dfrac{5}{4} = 1\dfrac{1}{4}$

10. $10 = 2 \cdot 5$
$12 = 2 \cdot 2 \cdot 3$
$LCD = 2 \cdot 2 \cdot 3 \cdot 5 = 60$
$\dfrac{3}{10} + \dfrac{7}{12} = \dfrac{3 \cdot 6}{10 \cdot 6} + \dfrac{7 \cdot 5}{12 \cdot 5} = \dfrac{18}{60} + \dfrac{35}{60} = \dfrac{53}{60}$

11. a.
$$x - \frac{2}{9}x = 1$$

$$1\frac{2}{7} - \frac{2}{9}\left(1\frac{2}{7}\right) = 1$$

$$\frac{9}{7} - \frac{2}{9}\left(\frac{9}{7}\right) = 1$$

$$\frac{9}{7} - \frac{2}{7} = 1$$

$$\frac{7}{7} = 1$$

$$1 = 1, \text{ true}$$

The given fraction is a solution.

b.
$$\frac{1}{5} - w = \frac{1}{3}w$$

$$\frac{1}{5} - \frac{3}{20} = \frac{1}{3}\left(\frac{3}{20}\right)$$

$$\frac{4}{20} - \frac{3}{20} = \frac{1}{20}$$

$$\frac{1}{20} = \frac{1}{20}, \text{ true}$$

The given fraction is a solution.

12. a. $\dfrac{2}{3}(x - 6)$

b. $\dfrac{3}{4}x - 2 = \dfrac{1}{5}x$

13. $C = \dfrac{5}{9}(F - 32)$

$$C = \frac{5}{9}(77 - 32) = \frac{5}{9}(45) = 25$$

77°F is equivalent to 25°C.

1.2 Exercise Set

1. $2\dfrac{3}{8} = \dfrac{2 \cdot 8 + 3}{8} = \dfrac{16 + 3}{8} = \dfrac{19}{8}$

3. $7\dfrac{3}{5} = \dfrac{7 \cdot 5 + 3}{5} = \dfrac{35 + 3}{5} = \dfrac{38}{5}$

5. $8\dfrac{7}{16} = \dfrac{8 \cdot 16 + 7}{16} = \dfrac{128 + 7}{16} = \dfrac{135}{16}$

7. 23 divided by 5 is 4 with a remainder of 3, so
$$\frac{23}{5} = 4\frac{3}{5}.$$

9. 76 divided by 9 is 8 with a remainder of 4, so
$$\frac{76}{9} = 8\frac{4}{9}.$$

11. 711 divided by 20 is 35 with a remainder of 11, so
$$\frac{711}{20} = 35\frac{11}{20}.$$

13. composite; $22 = 2 \cdot 11$

15. composite; $20 = 4 \cdot 5 = 2 \cdot 2 \cdot 5$

17. 37 has no factors other than 1 and 37, so 37 is prime.

19. composite; $36 = 4 \cdot 9 = 2 \cdot 2 \cdot 3 \cdot 3$

21. composite; $140 = 10 \cdot 14 = 2 \cdot 5 \cdot 2 \cdot 7$
$$= 2 \cdot 2 \cdot 5 \cdot 7$$

23. 79 has no factors other than 1 and 79, so 79 is prime.

25. composite; $81 = 9 \cdot 9 = 3 \cdot 3 \cdot 3 \cdot 3$

27. composite; $240 = 10 \cdot 24$
$$= 2 \cdot 5 \cdot 2 \cdot 12$$
$$= 2 \cdot 5 \cdot 2 \cdot 3 \cdot 4$$
$$= 2 \cdot 5 \cdot 2 \cdot 3 \cdot 2 \cdot 2$$
$$= 2 \cdot 2 \cdot 2 \cdot 2 \cdot 3 \cdot 5$$

29. $\dfrac{10}{16} = \dfrac{\cancel{2} \cdot 5}{\cancel{2} \cdot 8} = \dfrac{5}{8}$

31. $\dfrac{15}{18} = \dfrac{\cancel{3} \cdot 5}{\cancel{3} \cdot 6} = \dfrac{5}{6}$

33. $\dfrac{35}{50} = \dfrac{\cancel{5} \cdot 7}{\cancel{5} \cdot 10} = \dfrac{7}{10}$

35. $\dfrac{32}{80} = \dfrac{\cancel{16} \cdot 2}{\cancel{16} \cdot 5} = \dfrac{2}{5}$

37. $\dfrac{44}{50} = \dfrac{\cancel{2} \cdot 22}{\cancel{2} \cdot 25} = \dfrac{22}{25}$

39. $\dfrac{120}{86} = \dfrac{\cancel{2} \cdot 60}{\cancel{2} \cdot 43} = \dfrac{60}{43}$

41. $\dfrac{2}{5} \cdot \dfrac{1}{3} = \dfrac{2 \cdot 1}{5 \cdot 3} = \dfrac{2}{15}$

43. $\dfrac{3}{8} \cdot \dfrac{7}{11} = \dfrac{3 \cdot 7}{8 \cdot 11} = \dfrac{21}{88}$

45. $9 \cdot \dfrac{4}{7} = \dfrac{9}{1} \cdot \dfrac{4}{7} = \dfrac{9 \cdot 4}{1 \cdot 7} = \dfrac{36}{7}$ or $5\dfrac{1}{7}$

47. $\dfrac{1}{10} \cdot \dfrac{5}{6} = \dfrac{1 \cdot 5}{10 \cdot 6} = \dfrac{5}{60} = \dfrac{5 \cdot 1}{5 \cdot 12} = \dfrac{1}{12}$

49. $\dfrac{5}{4} \cdot \dfrac{6}{7} = \dfrac{5 \cdot 6}{4 \cdot 7} = \dfrac{30}{28} = \dfrac{2 \cdot 15}{2 \cdot 14} = \dfrac{15}{14}$ or $1\dfrac{1}{14}$

51. $\left(3\dfrac{3}{4}\right)\left(1\dfrac{3}{5}\right) = \dfrac{15}{4} \cdot \dfrac{8}{5} = \dfrac{120}{20} = \dfrac{20 \cdot 6}{20 \cdot 1} = 6$

53. $\dfrac{5}{4} \div \dfrac{4}{3} = \dfrac{5}{4} \cdot \dfrac{3}{4} = \dfrac{5 \cdot 3}{4 \cdot 4} = \dfrac{15}{16}$

55. $\dfrac{18}{5} \div 2 = \dfrac{18}{5} \cdot \dfrac{1}{2}$

$\qquad = \dfrac{18 \cdot 1}{5 \cdot 2} = \dfrac{18}{10} = \dfrac{2 \cdot 9}{2 \cdot 5} = \dfrac{9}{5}$ or $1\dfrac{4}{5}$

57. $2 \div \dfrac{18}{5} = \dfrac{2}{1} \cdot \dfrac{5}{18} = \dfrac{10}{18} = \dfrac{2 \cdot 5}{2 \cdot 9} = \dfrac{5}{9}$

59. $\dfrac{3}{4} \div \dfrac{1}{4} = \dfrac{3}{4} \cdot \dfrac{4}{1} = \dfrac{3 \cdot 4}{4 \cdot 1} = \dfrac{12}{4} = 3$

61. $\dfrac{7}{6} \div \dfrac{5}{3} = \dfrac{7}{6} \cdot \dfrac{3}{5} = \dfrac{7 \cdot 3}{6 \cdot 5} = \dfrac{21}{30} = \dfrac{3 \cdot 7}{3 \cdot 10} = \dfrac{7}{10}$

63. $\dfrac{1}{14} \div \dfrac{1}{7} = \dfrac{1}{14} \cdot \dfrac{7}{1} = \dfrac{7}{14} = \dfrac{7 \cdot 1}{7 \cdot 2} = \dfrac{1}{2}$

65. $6\dfrac{3}{5} \div 1\dfrac{1}{10} = \dfrac{33}{5} \div \dfrac{11}{10}$

$\qquad = \dfrac{33}{5} \cdot \dfrac{10}{11} = \dfrac{11 \cdot 3}{5} \cdot \dfrac{5 \cdot 2}{11} = \dfrac{6}{1} = 6$

67. $\dfrac{2}{11} + \dfrac{4}{11} = \dfrac{2+4}{11} = \dfrac{6}{11}$

69. $\dfrac{7}{12} + \dfrac{1}{12} = \dfrac{8}{12} = \dfrac{4 \cdot 2}{4 \cdot 3} = \dfrac{2}{3}$

71. $\dfrac{5}{8} + \dfrac{5}{8} = \dfrac{10}{8} = \dfrac{2 \cdot 5}{2 \cdot 4} = \dfrac{5}{4}$ or $1\dfrac{1}{4}$

73. $\dfrac{7}{12} - \dfrac{5}{12} = \dfrac{2}{12} = \dfrac{2 \cdot 1}{2 \cdot 6} = \dfrac{1}{6}$

75. $\dfrac{16}{7} - \dfrac{2}{7} = \dfrac{14}{7} = \dfrac{7 \cdot 2}{7 \cdot 1} = 2$

77. $\dfrac{1}{2} + \dfrac{1}{5} = \dfrac{1}{2} \cdot \dfrac{5}{5} + \dfrac{1}{5} \cdot \dfrac{2}{2}$

$\qquad = \dfrac{5}{10} + \dfrac{2}{10} = \dfrac{5+2}{10} = \dfrac{7}{10}$

79. $\dfrac{3}{4} + \dfrac{3}{20} = \dfrac{3}{4} \cdot \dfrac{5}{5} + \dfrac{3}{20}$

$\qquad = \dfrac{15}{20} + \dfrac{3}{20}$

$\qquad = \dfrac{18}{20} = \dfrac{2 \cdot 9}{2 \cdot 10} = \dfrac{9}{10}$

81. $\dfrac{3}{8} + \dfrac{5}{12} = \dfrac{3}{8} \cdot \dfrac{3}{3} + \dfrac{5}{12} \cdot \dfrac{2}{2}$

$\qquad = \dfrac{9}{24} + \dfrac{10}{24} = \dfrac{19}{24}$

83. $\dfrac{11}{18} - \dfrac{2}{9} = \dfrac{11}{18} - \dfrac{2}{9} \cdot \dfrac{2}{2} = \dfrac{11}{18} - \dfrac{4}{18} = \dfrac{7}{18}$

85. $\dfrac{4}{3} - \dfrac{3}{4} = \dfrac{4}{3} \cdot \dfrac{4}{4} - \dfrac{3}{4} \cdot \dfrac{3}{3}$

$\qquad = \dfrac{16}{12} - \dfrac{9}{12} = \dfrac{7}{12}$

87. $\dfrac{7}{10} - \dfrac{3}{16} = \dfrac{7}{10} \cdot \dfrac{8}{8} - \dfrac{3}{16} \cdot \dfrac{5}{5}$

$\qquad = \dfrac{56}{80} - \dfrac{15}{80} = \dfrac{41}{80}$

89. $3\dfrac{3}{4} - 2\dfrac{1}{3} = \dfrac{15}{4} - \dfrac{7}{3}$

$\qquad = \dfrac{15}{4} \cdot \dfrac{3}{3} - \dfrac{7}{3} \cdot \dfrac{4}{4}$

$\qquad = \dfrac{45}{12} - \dfrac{28}{12} = \dfrac{17}{12}$ or $1\dfrac{5}{12}$

91. $\quad \dfrac{7}{2}x = 28$

$$\dfrac{7}{2}\cdot 8 = 28$$

$$\dfrac{7}{2}\cdot\dfrac{8}{1} = 28$$

$$\dfrac{7}{\cancel{2}}\cdot\dfrac{4\cdot\cancel{2}}{1} = 28$$

$$28 = 28,\ \text{true}$$

The given number is a solution.

93. $\quad w - \dfrac{2}{3} = \dfrac{3}{4}$

$$1\dfrac{5}{12} - \dfrac{2}{3} = \dfrac{3}{4}$$

$$\dfrac{17}{12} - \dfrac{2}{3} = \dfrac{3}{4}$$

$$\dfrac{17}{12} - \dfrac{8}{12} = \dfrac{3}{4}$$

$$\dfrac{9}{12} = \dfrac{3}{4}$$

$$\dfrac{3}{4} = \dfrac{3}{4},\ \text{true}$$

The given number is a solution.

95. $\quad 20 - \dfrac{1}{3}z = \dfrac{1}{2}z$

$$20 - \dfrac{1}{3}\cdot 12 = \dfrac{1}{2}\cdot 12$$

$$20 - \dfrac{1}{3}\cdot\dfrac{12}{1} = \dfrac{1}{2}\cdot\dfrac{12}{1}$$

$$20 - 4 = 12$$

$$16 = 12,\ \text{false}$$

The given number is not a solution.

97. $\quad \dfrac{2}{9}y + \dfrac{1}{3}y = \dfrac{3}{7}$

$$\dfrac{2}{9}\cdot\dfrac{27}{35} + \dfrac{1}{3}\cdot\dfrac{27}{35} = \dfrac{3}{7}$$

$$\dfrac{2}{\cancel{9}}\cdot\dfrac{\cancel{9}\cdot 3}{35} + \dfrac{1}{\cancel{3}}\cdot\dfrac{\cancel{3}\cdot 9}{35} = \dfrac{3}{7}$$

$$\dfrac{6}{35} + \dfrac{9}{35} = \dfrac{3}{7}$$

$$\dfrac{15}{35} = \dfrac{3}{7}$$

$$\dfrac{3\cdot\cancel{5}}{7\cdot\cancel{5}} = \dfrac{3}{7}$$

$$\dfrac{3}{7} = \dfrac{3}{7},\ \text{true}$$

The given number is a solution.

99. $\quad \dfrac{1}{3}(x-2) = \dfrac{1}{5}(x+4)$

$$\dfrac{1}{3}(26-2) = \dfrac{1}{5}(26+4)$$

$$\dfrac{1}{3}(24) = \dfrac{1}{5}(30)$$

$$8 = 6,\ \text{false}$$

The given number is not a solution.

101. $\quad (y\div 6) + \dfrac{2}{3} = (y\div 2) - \dfrac{7}{9}$

$$\left(4\dfrac{1}{3}\div 6\right) + \dfrac{2}{3} = \left(4\dfrac{1}{3}\div 2\right) - \dfrac{7}{9}$$

$$\left(\dfrac{13}{3}\div\dfrac{6}{1}\right) + \dfrac{2}{3} = \left(\dfrac{13}{3}\div\dfrac{2}{1}\right) - \dfrac{7}{9}$$

$$\left(\dfrac{13}{3}\cdot\dfrac{1}{6}\right) + \dfrac{2}{3} = \left(\dfrac{13}{3}\cdot\dfrac{1}{2}\right) - \dfrac{7}{9}$$

$$\dfrac{13}{18} + \dfrac{2}{3} = \dfrac{13}{6} - \dfrac{7}{9}$$

$$\dfrac{13}{18} + \dfrac{12}{18} = \dfrac{39}{18} - \dfrac{14}{18}$$

$$\dfrac{25}{18} = \dfrac{25}{18},\ \text{true}$$

The given number is a solution.

103. $\quad \dfrac{1}{5}x$

105. $\quad x - \dfrac{1}{4}x$

107. $\quad x - \dfrac{1}{4} = \dfrac{1}{2}x$

109. $\dfrac{1}{7}x + \dfrac{1}{8}x = 12$

111. $\dfrac{2}{3}(x+6)$

113. $\dfrac{2}{3}x + 6 = x - 3$

115. $\dfrac{3}{4} \cdot \dfrac{a}{5} = \dfrac{3 \cdot a}{4 \cdot 5} = \dfrac{3a}{20}$

117. $\dfrac{11}{x} + \dfrac{9}{x} = \dfrac{11+9}{x} = \dfrac{20}{x}$

119. $\left(\dfrac{1}{2} - \dfrac{1}{3}\right) \div \dfrac{5}{8} = \left(\dfrac{3}{6} - \dfrac{2}{6}\right) \div \dfrac{5}{8}$

$\qquad = \dfrac{1}{6} \div \dfrac{5}{8}$

$\qquad = \dfrac{1}{6} \cdot \dfrac{8}{5} = \dfrac{8}{30} = \dfrac{\cancel{2} \cdot 4}{\cancel{2} \cdot 15} = \dfrac{4}{15}$

121. $\dfrac{1}{5}(x+2) = \dfrac{1}{2}\left(x - \dfrac{1}{5}\right)$

$\dfrac{1}{5}\left(\dfrac{5}{8} + 2\right) = \dfrac{1}{2}\left(\dfrac{5}{8} - \dfrac{1}{5}\right)$

$\dfrac{1}{5}\left(\dfrac{5}{8} + \dfrac{2}{1}\right) = \dfrac{1}{2}\left(\dfrac{5}{8} - \dfrac{1}{5}\right)$

$\dfrac{1}{5}\left(\dfrac{5}{8} + \dfrac{16}{8}\right) = \dfrac{1}{2}\left(\dfrac{25}{40} - \dfrac{8}{40}\right)$

$\dfrac{1}{5}\left(\dfrac{21}{8}\right) = \dfrac{1}{2}\left(\dfrac{17}{40}\right)$

$\dfrac{21}{40} = \dfrac{17}{80}$

$\dfrac{42}{80} = \dfrac{17}{80}$, false

The given number is not a solution.

123. $C = \dfrac{5}{9}(F - 32)$

$C = \dfrac{5}{9}(68 - 32) = \dfrac{5}{9}(36) = 20$

$68°F$ is equivalent to $20°C$.

125. a. $H = \dfrac{7}{10}(220 - a)$

$\qquad H = \dfrac{7}{10}(220 - 20)$

$\qquad = \dfrac{7}{10}(200)$

$\qquad = 140$

The lower limit of the heart rate for a 20-year-old with this exercise goal is 140 beats per minute.

b. $H = \dfrac{4}{5}(220 - a)$

$\qquad H = \dfrac{4}{5}(220 - 20)$

$\qquad = \dfrac{4}{5}(200)$

$\qquad = 160$

The upper limit of the heart rate for a 20-year-old with this exercise goal is 160 beats per minute.

127. a. $H = \dfrac{9}{10}(220 - a)$

b. $H = \dfrac{9}{10}(220 - a)$

$\qquad H = \dfrac{9}{10}(220 - 40)$

$\qquad = \dfrac{9}{10}(180)$

$\qquad = 162$

The heart rate for a 40-year-old with this exercise goal is 162 beats per minute.

129. 1995 is 15 years after 1980.

$c = 615 - \dfrac{47}{5}n$

$c = 615 - \dfrac{47}{5} \cdot 15$

$\qquad = 615 - 141$

$\qquad = 474$

The model estimates that 474 billion cigarettes were smoked in 1995.
This underestimates the actual total shown in the bar graph by 2 billion.

131. – 149. Answers will vary.

141. makes sense

143. makes sense

8

145. false; Changes to make the statement true will vary. A sample change is: $\frac{1}{2} + \frac{1}{5} = \frac{5}{10} + \frac{2}{10} = \frac{7}{10}$.

147. true

149.

150. 5

151. $2\frac{1}{2}$ or $\frac{5}{2}$

152. −4

1.3 Check Points

1. a. −500

b. −282

2. a.

```
        (a)
 +--+--●--+--+--+--+--+--+--+--+-->
 -5 -4 -3 -2 -1  0  1  2  3  4  5
```

b.

```
            (b)
 +--+--+--+--+--●--+--+--+--+--+-->
 -5 -4 -3 -2 -1  0  1  2  3  4  5
```

c.

```
                      (c)
 +--+--+--+--+--+--+--+--●--+--+-->
 -5 -4 -3 -2 -1  0  1  2  3  4  5
```

3. a.

```
                         (a)
 +--+--+--+--+--+--+--+--+--●--+-->
 -5 -4 -3 -2 -1  0  1  2  3  4  5
```

b.

```
          (b)
 +--+--+--●--+--+--+--+--+--+--+-->
 -5 -4 -3 -2 -1  0  1  2  3  4  5
```

4. a.

$$
\begin{array}{r}
0.375 \\
8\overline{)3.000} \\
\underline{24} \\
60 \\
\underline{56} \\
40 \\
\underline{40} \\
0
\end{array}
$$

$\frac{3}{8} = 0.375$

b.

$$
\begin{array}{r}
0.454... \\
11\overline{)5.000...} \\
\underline{44} \\
60 \\
\underline{55} \\
50 \\
\underline{44} \\
60
\end{array}
$$

$\frac{5}{11} = 0.\overline{45}$

5. a. $\sqrt{9}$

b. $0, \sqrt{9}$

c. $-9, 0, \sqrt{9}$

d. $-9, -1.3, 0, 0.\overline{3}, \sqrt{9}$

e. $\frac{\pi}{2}, \sqrt{10}$

f. $-9, -1.3, 0, 0.\overline{3}, \frac{\pi}{2}, \sqrt{9}, \sqrt{10}$

6. a. $14 > 5$ since 14 is to the right of 5 on the number line.

b. $-5.4 < 2.3$ since -5.4 is to the left of 2.3 on the number line.

c. $-19 < -6$ since -19 is to the left of -6 on the number line.

d. $\frac{1}{4} < \frac{1}{2}$ since $\frac{1}{4}$ is to the left of $\frac{1}{2}$ on the number line.

7. a. $-2 \le 3$ is true because $-2 < 3$ is true.

b. $-2 \ge -2$ is true because $-2 = -2$ is true.

c. $-4 \ge 1$ is false because neither $-4 > 1$ nor $-4 = 1$ is true.

8. a. $|-4| = 4$

b. $|6| = 6$

c. $|-\sqrt{2}| = \sqrt{2}$

1.3 Exercise Set

1. −20

3. 8

5. −3000

7. −4 billion

9. 2 is shown as a dot on the number line.

11. −5 is shown as a dot on the number line.

13. $3\frac{1}{2}$ is shown as a dot on the number line.

15. $\frac{11}{3}$ is shown as a dot on the number line.

17. −1.8 is shown as a dot on the number line.

19. $-\frac{16}{5}$ is shown as a dot on the number line.

21.
$$
\begin{array}{r}
0.75 \\
4\overline{)3.00} \\
\underline{28} \\
20 \\
\underline{20} \\
0
\end{array}
$$

$\frac{3}{4} = 0.75$

23.
$$
\begin{array}{r}
0.35 \\
20\overline{)7.00} \\
\underline{60} \\
100 \\
\underline{100} \\
0
\end{array}
$$

$\frac{7}{20} = 0.35$

25.
$$
\begin{array}{r}
0.875 \\
8\overline{)7.000} \\
\underline{64} \\
60 \\
\underline{56} \\
40 \\
\underline{40} \\
0
\end{array}
$$

$\frac{7}{8} = 0.875$

27.
$$
\begin{array}{r}
0.818... \\
11\overline{)9.000...} \\
\underline{88} \\
20 \\
\underline{11} \\
90 \\
\underline{88} \\
20
\end{array}
$$

$\frac{9}{11} = 0.\overline{81}$

29.
$$
\begin{array}{r}
0.5 \\
2\overline{)1.0} \\
\underline{1.0} \\
0
\end{array}
$$

$-\frac{1}{2} = -0.5$

31.
$$
\begin{array}{r}
0.833... \\
6\overline{)5.000...} \\
\underline{48} \\
20 \\
\underline{18} \\
20 \\
\underline{18} \\
20
\end{array}
$$

$\frac{5}{6} = 0.8\overline{3}$

33. **a.** $\sqrt{100}$ (=10)

    b. $0, \sqrt{100}$

    c. $-9, 0, \sqrt{100}$

    d. $-9, -\dfrac{4}{5}, 0, 0.25, 9.2, \sqrt{100}$

    e. $\sqrt{3}$

    f. $-9, -\dfrac{4}{5}, 0, 0.25, \sqrt{3}, 9.2, \sqrt{100}$

35. **a.** $\sqrt{64}$ (= 8)

    b. $0, \sqrt{64}$

    c. $-11, 0, \sqrt{64}$

    d. $-11, -\dfrac{5}{6}, 0, 0.75, \sqrt{64}$

    e. $\sqrt{5}, \pi$

    f. $-11, -\dfrac{5}{6}, 0, 0.75, \sqrt{5}, \pi, \sqrt{64}$

37. The only whole number that is not a natural number is 0.

39. Answers will vary. As an example, one rational number that is not an integer is $\dfrac{1}{2}$.

41. Answers will vary. As an example, 6 is a number that is an integer, a whole number, and a natural number.

43. Answers will vary. As an example, one number that is an irrational number and a real number is π.

45. $\dfrac{1}{2} < 2$ since $\dfrac{1}{2}$ is to the left of 2 on the number line.

47. $3 > -\dfrac{5}{2}$ since 3 is to the right of $-\dfrac{5}{2} = -2\dfrac{1}{2}$.

49. $-4 > -6$ since -4 is to the right of -6.

51. $-2.5 < 1.5$ since -2.5 is to the left of 1.5.

53. $-\dfrac{3}{4} > -\dfrac{5}{4}$ since $-\dfrac{3}{4}$ is to the right of $-\dfrac{5}{4}$.

55. $-4.5 < 3$ since -4.5 is to the left of 3.

57. $\sqrt{2} < 1.5$ since $\sqrt{2} \approx 1.414$ is to the left of 1.5.

59. $0.\overline{3} > 0.3$ since $0.\overline{3} = 0.333...$ is to the right of 0.3.

61. $-\pi > -3.5$ since $-\pi \approx -3.14$ is to the right of -3.5.

63. $-5 \ge -13$ is true because $-5 > -13$ is true.

65. $-9 \ge -9$ is true because $-9 = -9$ is true.

67. $0 \ge -6$ is true because $0 > -6$ is true.

69. $-17 \ge 6$ is false because neither $-17 > 6$ nor $-17 = 6$ is true.

71. $|6| = 6$ because the distance between 6 and 0 on the number line is 6 units.

73. $|-7| = 7$ because the distance between -7 and 0 on the number line is 7 units.

75. $\left|\dfrac{5}{6}\right| = \dfrac{5}{6}$ because the distance between $\dfrac{5}{6}$ and 0 on the number line is $\dfrac{5}{6}$ units.

77. $\left|-\sqrt{11}\right| = \sqrt{11}$ because the distance between $-\sqrt{11}$ and 0 on the number line is $\sqrt{11}$ units.

79. $|-6| \;\square\; |-3|$

    $6 \;\square\; 3$

    $6 > 3$

    Since $6 > 3$, $|-6| > |-3|$.

81. $\left|\dfrac{3}{5}\right| \;\square\; |-0.6|$

    $|0.6| \;\square\; |-0.6|$

    $0.6 \;\square\; 0.6$

    $0.6 = 0.6$

    Since $0.6 = 0.6$, $\left|\dfrac{3}{5}\right| = |-0.6|$.

83. $\dfrac{30}{40} - \dfrac{3}{4} \; \Box \; \dfrac{14}{15} \cdot \dfrac{15}{14}$

$\dfrac{30}{40} - \dfrac{30}{40} \; \Box \; \dfrac{\cancel{14}}{\cancel{15}} \cdot \dfrac{\cancel{15}}{\cancel{14}}$

$0 \; \Box \; 1$

$0 < 1$

Since $0 < 1$, $\dfrac{30}{40} - \dfrac{3}{4} \; < \; \dfrac{14}{15} \cdot \dfrac{15}{14}$.

85. $\dfrac{8}{13} \div \dfrac{8}{13} \; \Box \; |-1|$

$\dfrac{8}{13} \cdot \dfrac{13}{8} \; \Box \; 1$

$1 \; \Box \; 1$

$1 = 1$

Since $1 = 1$, $\dfrac{8}{13} \div \dfrac{8}{13} = |-1|$.

87. rational numbers

89. integers

91. all real numbers

93. whole numbers

95. a.

b. Rhode Island, Georgia, Louisiana, Florida, Hawaii

97. – 107. Answers will vary

109. does not make sense; Explanations will vary. Sample explanation: The Bismarck's resting place is lower because it is further below sea level.

111. makes sense

113. false; Changes to make the statement true will vary. A sample change is: All whole numbers are integers.

115. false; Changes to make the statement true will vary. A sample change is: Irrational numbers can be negative.

117. false; Changes to make the statement true will vary. A sample change is: All integers are rational numbers.

119. $-\dfrac{1}{2}d$

121. $-\sqrt{12} \approx -3.464$ and should be graphed between -4 and -3.

123. $2 - \sqrt{5} \approx -0.236$ and should be graphed between -1 and 0.

124. $3(x + 5) = 3(4 + 5) = 3(9) = 27$

and

$3x + 15 = 3(4) + 15 = 12 + 15 = 27$

Both expressions have the same value.

125. $3x + 5x = 3(4) + 5(4) = 12 + 20 = 32$

and

$8x = 8(4) = 32$

Both expressions have the same value.

126. $9x - 2x = 9(4) - 2(4) = 36 - 8 = 28$

and

$7x = 7(4) = 28$

Both expressions have the same value.

1.4 Check Points

1. a. 3 terms

b. 6

c. 11

d. $6x$ and $2x$

2. a. $x + 14 = 14 + x$

b. $7y = y7$

3. a. $5x + 17 = 17 + 5x$

b. $5x + 17 = x5 + 17$

4. a. $8 + (12 + x) = (8 + 12) + x$
$$= 20 + x \text{ or } x + 20$$

b. $6(5x) = (6 \cdot 5)x = 30x$

5. $8 + (x + 4) = 8 + (4 + x)$
$$= (8 + 4) + x$$
$$= 12 + x \text{ or } x + 12$$

6. $5(x+3) = 5 \cdot x + 5 \cdot 3$
$= 5x + 15$

7. $6(4y+7) = 6 \cdot 4y + 6 \cdot 7$
$= 24y + 42$

8. a. $7x + 3x = (7+3)x = 10x$

b. $9a - 4a = (9-4)a = 5a$

9. a. $8x + 7 + 10x + 3 = (8x+10x) + (7+3)$
$= 18x + 10$

b. $9x + 6y + 5x + 2y = (9x+5x) + (6y+2y)$
$= 14x + 8y$

10. $7(2x+3) + 11x = 7 \cdot 2x + 7 \cdot 3 + 11x$
$= 14x + 21 + 11x$
$= (14x + 11x) + 21$
$= 25x + 21$

11. $7(4x+3y) + 2(5x+y) = 7 \cdot 4x + 7 \cdot 3y + 2 \cdot 5x + 2 \cdot y$
$= 28x + 21y + 10x + 2y$
$= (28x + 10x) + (21y + 2y)$
$= 38x + 23y$

1.4 Exercise Set

1. $3x + 5$

a. 2 terms
b. 3
c. 5
d. no like terms

3. $x + 2 + 5x$

a. 3 terms
b. 1
c. 2
d. x and $5x$ are like terms.

5. $4y + 1 + 3$

a. 3 terms
b. 4
c. 1
d. no like terms

7. $y + 4 = 4 + y$

9. $5 + 3x = 3x + 5$

11. $4x + 5y = 5y + 4x$

13. $5(x+3) = 5(3+x)$

15. $9x = x \cdot 9$ or $x9$

17. $x + y6 = x + 6y$

19. $7x + 23 = x7 + 23$

21. $5(x+3) = (x+3)5$

23. $7 + (5+x) = (7+5) + x = 12 + x$

25. $7(4x) = (7 \cdot 4)x = 28x$

27. $3(x+5) = 3(x) + 3(5) = 3x + 15$

29. $8(2x+3) = 8(2x) + 8(3) = 16x + 24$

31. $\frac{1}{3}(12+6r) = \frac{1}{3}(12) + \frac{1}{3}(12) + \frac{1}{3}(6r)$
$= 4 + 2r$

33. $5(x+y) = 5x + 5y$

35. $3(x-2) = 3(x) - 3(2) = 3x - 6$

37. $2(4x-5) = 2(4x) - 2(5) = 8x - 10$

39. $\frac{1}{2}(5x-12) = \frac{1}{2}(5x) + \frac{1}{2}(-12)$
$= \frac{5}{2}x - 6$

41. $(2x+7)4 = 2x(4) + 7(4) = 8x + 28$

43. $6(x+3+2y) = 6(x) + 6(3) + 6(2y)$
$= 6x + 18 + 12y$

45. $5(3x-2+4y) = 5(3x) - 5(2) + 5(4y)$
$= 15x - 10 + 20y$

47. $7x + 10x = (7+10)x = 17x$

49. $11a - 3a = (11-3)a = 8a$

51. $3 + (x+11) = (3+11) + x = 14 + x$

53. $5y + 3 + 6y = (5y + 6y) + 3 = 11y + 3$

55. $2x + 5 + 7x - 4 = (2x + 7x) + (5 - 4)$
$= 9x + 1$

57. $11a + 12 + 3a + 2 = (11a + 3a) + (12 + 2)$
$= 14a + 14$

59. $5(3x + 2) - 4 = 15x + 10 - 4 = 15x + 6$

61. $12 + 5(3x - 2) = 12 + 15x - 10$
$= 15x + 12 - 10 = 15x + 2$

63. $7(3a + 2b) + 5(4a + 2b)$
$= 21a + 14b + 20a + 10b$
$= 21a + 20a + 14b + 10b$
$= 41a + 24b$

65. $7 + 2(x + 9)$
$= 7 + (2x + 18)$ Distributive Property
$= 7 + (18 + 2x)$ Commutative Property of Addition
$= (7 + 18) + 2x$ Associative Property of Addition
$= 25 + 2x$
$= 2x + 25$ Commutative Property of Addition

67. $7x + 2x$
$7x + 2x = 9x$

69. $12x - 3x$
$12x - 3x = 9x$

71. $6(4x)$
$6(4x) = 24x$

73. $6(4 + x)$
$6(4 + x) = 24 + 6x$

75. $8 + 5(x - 1)$
$8 + 5(x - 1) = 8 + 5x - 5 = 5x + 3$

77. a. $M = 2(2n + 25) + 0.5(n + 2)$
$= 4n + 50 + 0.5n + 1$
$= 4.5n + 51$

b. $M = 4.5n + 51$
$M = 4.5 \cdot 5 + 51$
$= 22.5 + 51$
$= 73.5$
The percentage of U.S. men who used the Internet in 2005 was 73.5%.
This underestimates the actual percentage shown in the bar graph by 1.5%.

79. – 87. Answers will vary.

89. does not make sense; Explanations will vary. Sample explanation: Subtraction does not have a commutative property.

91. makes sense

93. false; Changes to make the statement true will vary. A sample change is: $(24 \div 6) \div 2 \neq 24 \div (6 \div 2)$.

95. false; Changes to make the statement true will vary. A sample change is: Addition cannot be distributed over multiplication.

97. 60 because $150 - 90 = 60$

98. -40 because $-30 - 10 = -40$

99. -5 because $30 - 35 = -5$

Mid-Chapter Check Point

1. $2 + 10x = 2 + 10(6)$
$= 2 + 60$
$= 62$

2. $10x - 4 = 10\left(\dfrac{3}{5}\right) - 4$
$= 6 - 4$
$= 2$

3. $\dfrac{xy}{2} + 4(y - x) = \dfrac{3 \cdot 10}{2} + 4(10 - 3)$

$\qquad\qquad\quad = \dfrac{30}{2} + 4(7)$

$\qquad\qquad\quad = 15 + 28$

$\qquad\qquad\quad = 43$

4. $\dfrac{1}{4}x - 2$

5. $\dfrac{x}{6} + 5 = 19$

6. $3(x + 2) = 4x - 1$

$\quad 3(6 + 2) = 4 \cdot 6 - 1$

$\qquad 3(8) = 24 - 1$

$\qquad\quad 24 = 23, \text{ false}$

The number is not a solution.

7. $\quad 8y = 12\left(y - \dfrac{1}{2}\right)$

$\quad 8 \cdot \dfrac{3}{4} = 12\left(\dfrac{3}{4} - \dfrac{1}{2}\right)$

$\qquad 6 = 12\left(\dfrac{3}{4} - \dfrac{2}{4}\right)$

$\qquad 6 = 12\left(\dfrac{1}{4}\right)$

$\qquad 6 = 3, \text{ false}$

The number is not a solution.

8. a. $V = 747 - 21n$

$V = 747 - 21 \cdot 10 = 537$

The number of violent crimes in 2000 was 537 per 100,000.

This overestimates the actual number shown in the bar graph by 30 per 100,000.

b. $V = 747 - 21n$

$V = 747 - 21 \cdot 20 = 327$

If trends continue, the number of violent crimes in 2010 will be 327 per 100,000.

9. $\dfrac{7}{10} - \dfrac{8}{15} = \dfrac{7}{10} \cdot \dfrac{3}{3} - \dfrac{8}{15} \cdot \dfrac{2}{2}$

$\qquad\quad = \dfrac{21}{30} - \dfrac{16}{30} = \dfrac{5}{30} = \dfrac{1}{6}$

10. $\dfrac{2}{3} \cdot \dfrac{3}{4} = \dfrac{2}{\cancel{3}} \cdot \dfrac{\cancel{3}}{4} = \dfrac{2}{4} = \dfrac{1}{2}$

11. $\dfrac{5}{22} + \dfrac{5}{33} = \dfrac{5}{22} \cdot \dfrac{3}{3} + \dfrac{5}{33} \cdot \dfrac{2}{2} = \dfrac{15}{66} + \dfrac{10}{66} = \dfrac{25}{66}$

12. $\dfrac{3}{5} \div \dfrac{9}{10} = \dfrac{3}{5} \cdot \dfrac{10}{9} = \dfrac{3}{5} \cdot \dfrac{2 \cdot 5}{3 \cdot 3} = \dfrac{\cancel{3}}{\cancel{5}} \cdot \dfrac{2 \cdot \cancel{5}}{\cancel{3} \cdot 3} = \dfrac{2}{3}$

13. $\dfrac{23}{105} - \dfrac{2}{105} = \dfrac{21}{105} = \dfrac{\cancel{3} \cdot \cancel{7}}{\cancel{3} \cdot 5 \cdot \cancel{7}} = \dfrac{1}{5}$

14. $2\dfrac{7}{9} \div 3 = \dfrac{25}{9} \div \dfrac{3}{1} = \dfrac{25}{9} \cdot \dfrac{1}{3} = \dfrac{25}{27}$

15. $5\dfrac{2}{9} - 3\dfrac{1}{6} = \dfrac{47}{9} - \dfrac{19}{6}$

$\qquad\qquad\quad = \dfrac{47}{9} \cdot \dfrac{2}{2} - \dfrac{19}{6} \cdot \dfrac{3}{3}$

$\qquad\qquad\quad = \dfrac{94}{18} - \dfrac{57}{18} = \dfrac{37}{18} \text{ or } 2\dfrac{1}{18}$

16. $C = \dfrac{5}{9}(F - 32)$

$C = \dfrac{5}{9}(50 - 32) = \dfrac{5}{9}(18) = 10$

$50°F$ is equivalent to $10°C$.

17. $-8000 < -8\dfrac{1}{4}$

18. $\dfrac{1}{11} = 0.\overline{09}$

19. $|-19.3| = 19.3$

20. $-11, \ -\dfrac{3}{7}, \ 0, \ 0.45, \text{ and } \sqrt{25}$ are rational numbers.

21. $5(x + 3) = (x + 3)5$

22. $5(x + 3) = 5(3 + x)$

23. $5(x + 3) = 5x + 15$

24. $7(9x + 3) + \dfrac{1}{3}(6x) = 63x + 21 + 2x$

$\qquad\qquad\qquad\qquad = 65x + 21$

25. $2(3x + 5y) + 4(x + 6y) = 6x + 10y + 4x + 24y$

$\qquad\qquad\qquad\qquad\qquad = 10x + 34y$

1.5 Check Points

1. $4+(-7)=-3$

   Start at 4 and move 7 units to the left.

2. **a.** $-1+(-3)=-4$

   Start at -1 and move 3 units to the left.

   b. $-5+3=-2$

   Start at -5 and move 3 units to the right.

3. **a.** $-10+(-25)=-35$

   b. $-0.3+(-1.2)=-1.5$

   c. $-\dfrac{2}{3}+\left(-\dfrac{1}{6}\right)=-\dfrac{4}{6}+\left(-\dfrac{1}{6}\right)=-\dfrac{5}{6}$

4. **a.** $-15+2=-13$

   b. $-0.4+1.6=1.2$

   c. $-\dfrac{2}{3}+\dfrac{1}{6}=-\dfrac{4}{6}+\dfrac{1}{6}=-\dfrac{3}{6}=-\dfrac{1}{2}$

5. **a.** $-20x+3x=(-20+3)x=-17x$

   b. $3y+(-10z)+(-10y)+16z$
   $=3y+(-10y)+(-10z)+16z$
   $=\big[3+(-10)\big]y+\big[(-10)+16\big]z$
   $=-7y+6z$

   c. $5(2x+3)+(-30x)=10x+15+(-30x)$
   $=10x+(-30x)+15$
   $=\big[10+(-30)\big]x+15$
   $=-20x+15$

6. $2+(-4)+1+(-5)+3=(2+1+3)+\big[(-4)+(-5)\big]$
   $=6+(-9)$
   $=-3$

   At the end of 5 months the water level was down 3 feet.

1.5 Exercise Set

1. $7+(-3)=4$

3. $-2+(-5)=-7$

5. $-6+2=-4$

7. $3+(-3)=0$

9. $-7+0=-7$

11. $30+(-30)=0$

13. $-30+(-30)=-60$

15. $-8+(-10)=-18$

17. $-0.4+(-0.9)=-1.3$

19. $-\dfrac{7}{10}+\left(-\dfrac{3}{10}\right)=-\dfrac{10}{10}=-1$

21. $-9+4=-5$

23. $12+(-8)=4$

25. $6+(-9)=-3$

27. $-3.6+2.1=-1.5$

29. $-3.6+(-2.1)=-5.7$

31. $\dfrac{9}{10}+\left(-\dfrac{3}{5}\right)=\dfrac{9}{10}+\left(-\dfrac{6}{10}\right)=\dfrac{3}{10}$

33. $-\dfrac{5}{8}+\dfrac{3}{4}=-\dfrac{5}{8}+\dfrac{6}{8}=\dfrac{1}{8}$

35. $-\dfrac{3}{7}+\left(-\dfrac{4}{5}\right)=-\dfrac{15}{35}+\left(-\dfrac{28}{35}\right)=-\dfrac{43}{35}$

37. $4+(-7)+(-5)=\left[4+(-7)\right]+(-5)$
$$=-3+(-5)$$
$$=-8$$

39. $85+(-15)+(-20)+12$
$$=\left[85+(-15)\right]+(-20)+12$$
$$=70+(-20)+12$$
$$=\left[70+(-20)\right]+12$$
$$=50+12$$
$$=62$$

41. $17+(-4)+2+3+(-10)$
$$=13+2+3+(-10)$$
$$=15+3+(-10)$$
$$=18+(-10)$$
$$=8$$

43. $-45+\left(-\dfrac{3}{7}\right)+25+\left(-\dfrac{4}{7}\right)$
$$=(-45+25)+\left[-\dfrac{3}{7}+\left(-\dfrac{4}{7}\right)\right]$$
$$=-20+\left(-\dfrac{7}{7}\right)$$
$$=-20+(-1)$$
$$=-21$$

45. $3.5+(-45)+(-8.4)+72$
$$=\left[3.5+(-8.4)\right]+(-45+72)$$
$$=-4.9+27$$
$$=22.1$$

47. $-10x+2x=(-10+2)x=-8x$

49. $25y+(-12y)=\left[25+(-12)\right]y=13y$

51. $-8a+(-15a)=\left[-8+(-15)\right]a$
$$=-23a$$

53. $4y+(-13z)+(-10y)+17z$
$$=4y+(-10y)+(-13z)+17z$$
$$=-6y+4z$$

55. $-7b+10+(-b)+(-6)$
$$=-7b+(-b)+10+(-6)$$
$$=-8b+4$$

57. $7x+(-5y)+(-9x)+19y$
$$=7x+(-9x)+(-5y)+19y$$
$$=-2x+14y$$

59. $8(4y+3)+(-35y)$
$$=32y+24+(-35y)$$
$$=32y+(-35y)+24$$
$$=-3y+24$$

61. $\left|-3+(-5)\right|+\left|2+(-6)\right|=\left|-8\right|+\left|-4\right|$
$$=8+4$$
$$=12$$

63. $-20+\left[-\left|15+(-25)\right|\right]$
$$=-20+\left[-\left|-10\right|\right]$$
$$=-20+\left[-10\right]$$
$$=-30$$

65. $6+\left[2+(-13)\right]\square-3+\left[4+(-8)\right]$
$$6+\left[-11\right]\square-3+\left[-4\right]$$
$$-5\,\square-7$$
$$-5>-7$$

67. $-6x+(-13x)$
$$-6x+(-13x)=-19x$$

69. $\dfrac{-20}{x}+\dfrac{3}{x}$
$$\dfrac{-20}{x}+\dfrac{3}{x}=\dfrac{-17}{x}$$

71. $-56+100=44$
The high temperature was 44°F.

73. $-1312+712=-600$
The elevation of the person is 600 feet below sea level.

75. $-7+15-5=3$

The temperature at 4:00 P.M. was 3°F.

77. $27+4-2+8-12$

$=(27+4+8)+(-2-12)$

$=34-14$

$=25$

The location of the football at the end of the fourth play is at the 25-yard line.

79. a. $1880+(-2293)=-413$

The deficit in 2004 was −$413 billion.

b. $2154+(-2472)=-318$

The deficit in 2005 was −$318 billion.

c. $-413+(-318)=-731$

The combined deficit in 2004 and 2005 was −$731 billion.

81. – 87. Answers will vary.

89. makes sense

91. makes sense

93. true

95. false; Changes to make the statement true will vary. A sample change is: The sum of a positive number and a negative number is sometimes negative.

97. The sum is negative. When finding the sum of numbers with different signs, use the sign of the number with the greater absolute value as the sign of the sum. Since *a* is further from 0 than *c*, we use a negative sign.

99. Though the sum inside the absolute value is negative, the absolute value of this sum is positive.

101. The calculator verifies your results.

102. a. $\sqrt{4}\,(=2)$

b. $0,\sqrt{4}$

c. $-6,0,\sqrt{4}$

d. $-6,0,0.\overline{7},\sqrt{4}$

e. $-\pi,\sqrt{3}$

f. $-6,-\pi,0,0.\overline{7},\sqrt{3},\sqrt{4}$

103. $19\geq-18$ is true because 19 is to the right of −18 on the number line.

104. $16=2(x-1)-x$

$16=2(18-1)-18$

$16=2(17)-18$

$16=34-18$

$16=16,$ true

3 is a solution.

105. $7-10=7+(-10)=-3$

106. $-8-13=-8+(-13)=-21$

107. $-8-(-13)=-8+13=5$

1.6 Check Points

1. a. $3-11=3+(-11)=-8$

b. $4-(-5)=4+5=9$

c. $-7-(-2)=-7+2=-5$

2. a. $-3.4-(-12.6)=-3.4+12.6=9.2$

b. $-\dfrac{3}{5}-\dfrac{1}{3}=-\dfrac{3}{5}+\left(-\dfrac{1}{3}\right)=-\dfrac{9}{15}+\left(-\dfrac{5}{15}\right)=-\dfrac{14}{15}$

c. $5\pi-(-2\pi)=5\pi+2\pi=7\pi$

3. $10-(-12)-4-(-3)-6$

$=10+12+(-4)+3+(-6)$

$=(10+12+3)+\left[(-4)+(-6)\right]$

$=25+(-10)$

$=15$

4. $-6+4a-7ab$ has terms of $-6,\ 4a,$ and $-7ab.$

5. a. $4+2x-9x=4+(2-9)x$

$=4+\left[2+(-9)\right]x$

$=4-7x$

b. $-3x-10y-6x+14y=-3x-6x-10y+14y$

$=(-3-6)x+(-10+14)y$

$=-9x+4y$

6. $8848-(-10,915)=8848+10,915=19,763$

The difference in elevation between the peak of Mount Everest and the Marianas Trench is 19,763 meters.

1.6 Exercise Set

1. **a.** -12
   b. $5 - 12 = 5 + (-12)$

3. **a.** 7
   b. $5 - (-7) = 5 + 7$

5. $14 - 8 = 14 + (-8) = 6$

7. $8 - 14 = 8 + (-14) = -6$

9. $3 - (-20) = 3 + 20 = 23$

11. $-7 - (-18) = -7 + 18 = 11$

13. $-13 - (-2) = -13 + 2 = -11$

15. $-21 - 17 = -21 + (-17) = -38$

17. $-45 - (-45) = -45 + 45 = 0$

19. $23 - 23 = 23 + (-23) = 0$

21. $13 - (-13) = 13 + 13 = 26$

23. $0 - 13 = 0 + (-13) = -13$

25. $0 - (-13) = 0 + 13 = 13$

27. $\dfrac{3}{7} - \dfrac{5}{7} = \dfrac{3}{7} + \left(-\dfrac{5}{7}\right) = -\dfrac{2}{7}$

29. $\dfrac{1}{5} - \left(-\dfrac{3}{5}\right) = \dfrac{1}{5} + \dfrac{3}{5} = \dfrac{4}{5}$

31. $-\dfrac{4}{5} - \dfrac{1}{5} = -\dfrac{4}{5} + \left(-\dfrac{1}{5}\right) = -\dfrac{5}{5} = -1$

33. $-\dfrac{4}{5} - \left(-\dfrac{1}{5}\right) = -\dfrac{4}{5} + \dfrac{1}{5} = -\dfrac{3}{5}$

35. $\dfrac{1}{2} - \left(-\dfrac{1}{4}\right) = \dfrac{1}{2} + \dfrac{1}{4} = \dfrac{2}{4} + \dfrac{1}{4} = \dfrac{3}{4}$

37. $\dfrac{1}{2} - \dfrac{1}{4} = \dfrac{1}{2} + \left(-\dfrac{1}{4}\right) = \dfrac{2}{4} + \left(-\dfrac{1}{4}\right) = \dfrac{1}{4}$

39. $9.8 - 2.2 = 9.8 + (-2.2) = 7.6$

41. $-3.1 - (-1.1) = -3.1 + 1.1 = -2$

43. $1.3 - (-1.3) = 1.3 + 1.3 = 2.6$

45. $-2.06 - (-2.06) = -2.06 + 2.06 = 0$

47. $5\pi - 2\pi = 5\pi + (-2\pi) = 3\pi$

49. $3\pi - (-10\pi) = 3\pi + 10\pi = 13\pi$

51. $13 - 2 - (-8) = 13 + (-2) + 8$
   $\qquad = (13 + 8) + (-2)$
   $\qquad = 21 + (-2)$
   $\qquad = 19$

53. $9 - 8 + 3 - 7 = 9 + (-8) + 3 + (-7)$
   $\qquad = (9 + 3) + \left[(-8) + (-7)\right]$
   $\qquad = 12 + (-15)$
   $\qquad = -3$

55. $-6 - 2 + 3 - 10$
   $\qquad = -6 + (-2) + 3 + (-10)$
   $\qquad = \left[(-6) + (-2) + (-10)\right] + 3$
   $\qquad = -18 + 3$
   $\qquad = -15$

57. $-10 - (-5) + 7 - 2$
   $\qquad = -10 + 5 + 7 + (-2)$
   $\qquad = \left[(-10) + (-2)\right] + (5 + 7)$
   $\qquad = -12 + 12$
   $\qquad = 0$

59. $-23 - 11 - (-7) + (-25)$
   $\qquad = (-23) + (-11) + 7 + (-25)$
   $\qquad = \left[(-23) + (-11) + (-25)\right] + 7$
   $\qquad = -59 + 7$
   $\qquad = -52$

61. $-823 - 146 - 50 - (-832)$

$\quad = -823 + (-146) + (-50) + 832$

$\quad = \left[(-823) + (-146) + (-50)\right] + 832$

$\quad = -1019 + 832$

$\quad = -187$

63. $1 - \dfrac{2}{3} - \left(-\dfrac{5}{6}\right) = 1 + \left(-\dfrac{2}{3}\right) + \dfrac{5}{6}$

$\quad = \left(1 + \dfrac{5}{6}\right) + \left(-\dfrac{2}{3}\right)$

$\quad = \left(\dfrac{6}{6} + \dfrac{5}{6}\right) + \left(-\dfrac{2}{3}\right)$

$\quad = \dfrac{11}{6} + \left(-\dfrac{2}{3} \cdot \dfrac{2}{2}\right)$

$\quad = \dfrac{11}{6} + \left(-\dfrac{4}{6}\right)$

$\quad = \dfrac{7}{6}$ or $1\dfrac{1}{6}$

65. $-0.16 - 5.2 - (-0.87)$

$\quad = -0.16 + (-5.2) + 0.87$

$\quad = \left[(-0.16) + (-5.2)\right] + 0.87$

$\quad = -5.36 + 0.87$

$\quad = -4.49$

67. $-\dfrac{3}{4} - \dfrac{1}{4} - \left(-\dfrac{5}{8}\right) = -\dfrac{3}{4} + \left(-\dfrac{1}{4}\right) + \dfrac{5}{8}$

$\quad = -\dfrac{4}{4} + \dfrac{5}{8}$

$\quad = -\dfrac{8}{8} + \dfrac{5}{8} = -\dfrac{3}{8}$

69. $-3x - 8y = -3x + (-8y)$

The terms are $-3x$ and $-8y$.

71. $12x - 5xy - 4 = 12x + (-5xy) + (-4)$

The terms are $12x$, $-5xy$, and -4.

73. $3x - 9x = 3x + (-9x)$

$\quad = \left[3 + (-9)\right]x = -6x$

75. $4 + 7y - 17y = 4 + 7y + (-17y)$

$\quad = 4 + \left[7 + (-17)\right]y$

$\quad = 4 - 10y$

77. $2a + 5 - 9a = 2a + 5 + (-9a)$

$\quad = 2a + (-9a) + 5$

$\quad = \left[2 + (-9)\right]a + 5$

$\quad = -7a + 5$ or $5 - 7a$

79. $4 - 6b - 8 - 3b$

$\quad = 4 + (-6b) + (-8) + (-3b)$

$\quad = 4 + (-8) + (-6b) + (-3b)$

$\quad = 4 + (-8) + \left[-6 + (-3)\right]b$

$\quad = -4 - 9b$

81. $13 - (-7x) + 4x - (-11)$

$\quad = 13 + 7x + 4x + 11$

$\quad = 13 + 11 + 7x + 4x$

$\quad = 24 + 11x$

83. $-5x - 10y - 3x + 13y$

$\quad = -5x + (-10y) + (-3x) + 13y$

$\quad = -5x + (-3x) + (-10y) + 13y$

$\quad = \left[-5 + (-3)\right]x + (-10 + 13)y$

$\quad = -8x + 3y$ or $3y - 8x$

85. $-\left|-9 - (-6)\right| - (-12) = -\left|-9 + 6\right| + 12$

$\quad = -\left|-3\right| + 12$

$\quad = -3 + 12$

$\quad = 9$

87. $\dfrac{5}{8} - \left(\dfrac{1}{2} - \dfrac{3}{4}\right) = \dfrac{5}{8} - \left(\dfrac{1}{2} \cdot \dfrac{2}{2} - \dfrac{3}{4}\right)$

$\quad = \dfrac{5}{8} - \left(\dfrac{2}{4} + \left(-\dfrac{3}{4}\right)\right)$

$\quad = \dfrac{5}{8} - \left(-\dfrac{1}{4}\right)$

$\quad = \dfrac{5}{8} + \dfrac{1}{4}$

$\quad = \dfrac{5}{8} + \dfrac{1}{4} \cdot \dfrac{2}{2}$

$\quad = \dfrac{5}{8} + \dfrac{2}{8}$

$\quad = \dfrac{7}{8}$

89. $\left|-9-(-3+7)\right|-\left|-17-(-2)\right|$

$=\left|-9-4\right|-\left|-17+2\right|$

$=\left|-9+(-4)\right|-\left|-17+2\right|$

$=\left|-13\right|-\left|-15\right|$

$=13+(-15)$

$=-2$

91. $6x-(-5x)$

$6x-(-5x)=6x+5x=11x$

93. $\dfrac{-5}{x}-\left(\dfrac{-2}{x}\right)$

$\dfrac{-5}{x}-\left(\dfrac{-2}{x}\right)=\dfrac{-5}{x}+\dfrac{2}{x}=\dfrac{-3}{x}$

95. Elevation of Mount Kilimanjaro – elevation of Qattara Depression

$=19,321-(-436)=19,757$

The difference in elevation between the two geographic locations is 19,757 feet.

97. $2-(-19)=2+19=21$

The difference between the average daily low temperature for March and February is 21°F.

99. $-19-(-22)=-19+22=3$

February's average low temperature is 3°F warmer than January's.

101. a. $1.0 billion was exported in 2002.

b. $1.4 billion was imported in 2002.

c. $1.0-1.4=1.0+(-1.4)=-0.4$

The trade deficit was –$0.4 billion in 2002.

103. a. $E=0.04n+0.7$

$E=0.04(8)+0.7$

$=1.02$

$1.02 billion was exported in 2002.

b. $I=0.09n+0.8$

$I=0.09(8)+0.8$

$=1.52$

$1.52 billion was imported in 2002.

c. $1.02-1.52=1.02+(-1.52)=-0.5$

The trade deficit was –$0.5 billion in 2002.

d. $-0.4-(-0.5)=-0.4+0.5=0.1$

The difference in the trade deficit for 2002 found in Exercise 101(c) and the trade deficit given by the models is $0.1 billion.

105. – 109. Answers will vary.

111. makes sense

113. makes sense

115. false; Changes to make the statement true will vary. A sample change is: $7-(-2)=7+2=9$

117. true

119. $a-b=\overbrace{(\text{negative number})}^{a}-\overbrace{(\text{negative number})}^{b}$

$\underbrace{}_{\substack{a \text{ has the greater}\\ \text{absolute value}}}$

$=(\text{negative number})+(\text{positive number})$

$=\text{negative number}$

121. $0-b=0-\overbrace{(\text{negative number})}^{b}$

$=0+(\text{positive number})$

$=\text{positive number}$

123. The calculator verifies your results.

125. $13x+3=3(5x-1)$

$13\cdot 2+3=3(5\cdot 2-1)$

$26+3=3(10-1)$

$29=3(9)$

$29=27, \text{ false}$

The number is not a solution.

126. $5(3x+2y)+6(5y)=15x+10y+30y$

$=15x+40y$

127. Answers will vary. -17 is an example of an integer that is not a natural number.

128. $4(-3)=(-3)+(-3)+(-3)+(-3)=-12$

129. $3(-3)=(-3)+(-3)+(-3)=-9$

130. $2(-3) = -6$
$1(-3) = -3$
$0(-3) = 0$
$-1(-3) = 3$
$-2(-3) = 6$
$-3(-3) = 9$
$-4(-3) = \boxed{12}$

1.7 Check Points

1. a. $8(-5) = -40$

b. $-\dfrac{1}{3} \cdot \dfrac{4}{7} = -\dfrac{4}{21}$

c. $(-12)(-3) = 36$

d. $(-1.1)(-5) = 5.5$

e. $(-543)(0) = 0$

2. a. $(-2)(3)(-1)(4) = 24$

b. $(-1)(-3)(2)(-1)(5) = -30$

3. a. The multiplicative inverse of 7 is $\dfrac{1}{7}$ because
$7 \cdot \dfrac{1}{7} = 1.$

b. The multiplicative inverse of $\dfrac{1}{8}$ is 8 because
$\dfrac{1}{8} \cdot 8 = 1.$

c. The multiplicative inverse of -6 is $-\dfrac{1}{6}$ because
$(-6)\left(-\dfrac{1}{6}\right) = 1.$

d. The multiplicative inverse of $-\dfrac{7}{13}$ is $-\dfrac{13}{7}$
because $\left(-\dfrac{7}{13}\right)\left(-\dfrac{13}{7}\right) = 1.$

4. a. $-28 \div 7 = -28 \cdot \dfrac{1}{7} = -4$

b. $\dfrac{-16}{-2} = -16 \cdot \left(-\dfrac{1}{2}\right) = 8$

5. a. $\dfrac{-32}{-4} = 8$

b. $-\dfrac{2}{3} \div \dfrac{5}{4} = -\dfrac{2}{3} \cdot \dfrac{4}{5} = -\dfrac{8}{15}$

c. $\dfrac{21.9}{-3} = -7.3$

d. $\dfrac{0}{-5} = 0$

6. a. $-4(5x) = (-4 \cdot 5)x = -20x$

b. $9x + x = 9x + 1x = (9+1)x = 10x$

c. $13b - 14b = (13 - 14)b = -1b = -b$

d. $-7(3x - 4) = -7(3x) - 7(-4) = -21x + 28$

e. $-(7y - 6) = -(7y) - (-6) = -7y + 6$

7. $4(3y - 7) - (13y - 2) = 12y - 28 - 13y + 2$
$\qquad\qquad\qquad\qquad = 12y - 13y - 28 + 2$
$\qquad\qquad\qquad\qquad = -1y - 26$
$\qquad\qquad\qquad\qquad = -y - 26$

8. $\quad 2x - 5 = 8x + 7$
$\quad 2(-3) - 5 = 8(-3) + 7$
$\quad -6 - 5 = -24 + 7$
$\quad -11 = -17, \text{ false}$
The number is not a solution.

9. $M = -0.6n + 64.4$
$M = -0.6(25) + 64.4$
$\quad = -15 + 64.4$
$\quad = 49.4$
According to this model, 49.4% of doctorate degrees will be awarded to men in 2014. This overestimates the actual value shown in the bar graph by 0.4%.

1.7 Exercises Set

1. $5(-9) = -(5 \cdot 9) = -45$

3. $(-8)(-3) = +(8 \cdot 3) = 24$

5. $(-3)(7) = -21$

7. $(-19)(-1) = 19$

9. $0(-19) = 0$

11. $\dfrac{1}{2}(-24) = -12$

13. $\left(-\dfrac{3}{4}\right)(-12) = \dfrac{3 \cdot 12}{4 \cdot 1} = 9$

15. $-\dfrac{3}{5} \cdot \left(-\dfrac{4}{7}\right) = \dfrac{3 \cdot 4}{5 \cdot 7} = \dfrac{12}{35}$

17. $-\dfrac{7}{9} \cdot \dfrac{2}{3} = -\dfrac{7 \cdot 2}{9 \cdot 3} = -\dfrac{14}{27}$

19. $3(-1.2) = -3.6$

21. $-0.2(-0.6) = 0.12$

23. $(-5)(-2)(3) = 30$

25. $(-4)(-3)(-1)(6) = -72$

27. $-2(-3)(-4)(-1) = 24$

29. $(-3)(-3)(-3) = 9(-3) = -27$

31. $5(-3)(-1)(2)(3) = 90$

33. $(-8)(-4)(0)(-17)(-6) = 0$

35. The multiplicative inverse of 4 is $\dfrac{1}{4}$.

37. The multiplicative inverse of $\dfrac{1}{5}$ is 5.

39. The multiplicative inverse of -10 is $-\dfrac{1}{10}$.

41. The multiplicative inverse of $-\dfrac{2}{5}$ is $-\dfrac{5}{2}$.

43. a. $-32 \div 4 = -32 \cdot \dfrac{1}{4}$

    b. $-32 \cdot \dfrac{1}{4} = -8$

45. a. $\dfrac{-60}{-5} = -60 \cdot \left(-\dfrac{1}{5}\right)$

    b. $-60 \cdot \left(-\dfrac{1}{5}\right) = 12$

47. $\dfrac{12}{-4} = 12 \cdot \left(-\dfrac{1}{4}\right) = -3$

49. $\dfrac{-21}{3} = -21 \cdot \dfrac{1}{3} = -7$

51. $\dfrac{-90}{-3} = -90 \cdot \left(-\dfrac{1}{3}\right) = 30$

53. $\dfrac{0}{-7} = 0$

55. $\dfrac{-7}{0}$ is undefined.

57. $-15 \div 3 = -15 \cdot \dfrac{1}{3} = -5$

59. $12 \div (-10) = 120 \cdot \left(-\dfrac{1}{10}\right) = -12$

61. $(-180) \div (-30) = -180 \cdot \left(-\dfrac{1}{30}\right) = 6$

63. $0 \div (-4) = 0$

65. $-4 \div 0$ is undefined.

67. $\dfrac{-12.9}{3} = -12.9 \cdot \dfrac{1}{3} = -4.3$

69. $-\dfrac{1}{2} \div \left(-\dfrac{3}{5}\right) = -\dfrac{1}{2} \cdot \left(-\dfrac{5}{3}\right) = \dfrac{5}{6}$

71. $-\dfrac{14}{9} \div \dfrac{7}{8} = -\dfrac{14}{9} \cdot \dfrac{8}{7}$

$\qquad = -\dfrac{112}{63} = \dfrac{\cancel{7} \cdot 16}{\cancel{7} \cdot 9} = -\dfrac{16}{9}$

73. $\dfrac{1}{3} \div \left(-\dfrac{1}{3}\right) = \dfrac{1}{3} \cdot (-3) = -1$

75. $6 \div \left(-\dfrac{2}{5}\right) = 6 \cdot \left(-\dfrac{5}{2}\right) = -\dfrac{30}{2} = -15$

77. $-5(2x) = (-5 \cdot 2)x = -10x$

79. $-4\left(-\dfrac{3}{4}y\right) = \left[-4 \cdot \left(-\dfrac{3}{4}\right)\right]y = 3y$

81. $8x + x = 8x + 1x = (8+1)x = 9x$

83. $-5x + x = -5x + 1x = (-5+1)x = -4x$

85. $6b - 7b = (6-7)b = -1b = -b$

87. $-y + 4y = -1y + 4y = (-1+4)y = 3y$

89. $-4(2x-3) = -4(2x) - 4(-3) = -8x + 12$

91. $-3(-2x+4) = -3(-2x) - 3(4) = 6x - 12$

93. $-(2y-5) = -2y + 5$

95. $4(2y-3) - (7y+2)$

$\qquad = 4(2y) + 4(-3) - 7y - 2$

$\qquad = 8y - 12 + 7y - 2$

$\qquad = 8y + 7y - 12 - 2$

$\qquad = y - 14$

97. $\qquad 4x = 2x - 10$

$\qquad 4(-5) = 2(-5) - 10$

$\qquad -20 = -10 - 10$

$\qquad -20 = -20, \ \text{true}$

The number is a solution.

99. $\qquad -7y + 18 = -10y + 6$

$\qquad -7(-4) + 18 = -10(-4) + 6$

$\qquad 28 + 18 = 40 + 6$

$\qquad 46 = 46, \ \text{true}$

The number is a solution.

101. $\qquad 5(w+3) = 2w - 21$

$\qquad 5(-10+3) = 2(-10) - 21$

$\qquad 5(-7) = -20 - 21$

$\qquad -35 = -41, \ \text{false}$

The number is not a solution.

103. $\qquad 4(6-z) + 7z = 0$

$\qquad 4(6-(-8)) + 7(-8) = 0$

$\qquad 4(6+8) - 56 = 0$

$\qquad 4(14) - 56 = 0$

$\qquad 56 - 56 = 0$

$\qquad 0 = 0, \ \text{true}$

The number is a solution.

105. $\qquad 14 - 2x = -4x + 7$

$\qquad 14 - 2\left(-2\dfrac{1}{2}\right) = -4\left(-2\dfrac{1}{2}\right) + 7$

$\qquad 14 - 2\left(-\dfrac{5}{2}\right) = -4\left(-\dfrac{5}{2}\right) + 7$

$\qquad 14 + 5 = 10 + 7$

$\qquad 19 = 17, \ \text{false}$

The number is not a solution.

107. $\qquad \dfrac{5m-1}{6} = \dfrac{3m-2}{4}$

$\qquad \dfrac{5(-4)-1}{6} = \dfrac{3(-4)-2}{4}$

$\qquad \dfrac{-20-1}{6} = \dfrac{-12-2}{4}$

$\qquad \dfrac{-21}{6} = \dfrac{-14}{4}$

$\qquad \dfrac{-7}{2} = \dfrac{-7}{2}, \ \text{true}$

The number is a solution.

109. $4(-10) + 8 = -40 + 8 = -32$

111. $(-9)(-3) - (-2) = 27 + 2 = 29$

113. $\dfrac{-18}{-15+12} = \dfrac{-18}{-3} = 6$

115. $-6 - \left(\dfrac{12}{-4}\right) = -6 - (-3) = -6 + 3 = -3$

117. $C = \dfrac{5}{9}(F - 32)$

$C = \dfrac{5}{9}(-22 - 32) = \dfrac{5}{9}(-54) = -30$

$-22°F$ is equivalent to $-30°C$.

119. a. According to the line graph, 50% of seniors used alcohol in 2000.

b. $A = -n + 70$

$A = -(20) + 70 = 50$

According to the formula, 50% of seniors used alcohol in 2000.
The model provides the same value as the line graph.

c. According to the line graph, 22% of seniors used marijuana in 2000.

d. $M = -0.5n + 28$

$M = -0.5(20) + 28 = -10 + 28 = 18$

According to the formula, 18% of seniors used marijuana in 2000.
The formula estimates a value that is lower than the value in the line graph.

e. $R = \dfrac{M}{A} = \dfrac{-0.5n + 28}{-n + 70}$

121. a. The ratio is $\dfrac{11}{44} = \dfrac{1}{4}$.

For each $10,000 collected in individual income taxes, $10,000 \cdot \dfrac{1}{4} = \$2500$ is collected from corporate taxes.

b. $\dfrac{1}{4} = 0.25$

c. $D = \dfrac{-0.27n + 23}{44}$

$D = \dfrac{-0.27(45) + 23}{44}$

$= \dfrac{-12.15 + 23}{44}$

$= \dfrac{10.85}{44}$

d. $\dfrac{10.85}{44} \approx 0.25$

This rounded value matches the value in part (b) extremely well.

123. – 129. Answers will vary.

131. makes sense

133. does not make sense; Explanations will vary. Sample explanation: The numerator and denominator of this formula are both positive.

135. false; Changes to make the statement true will vary. A sample change is: If the number is multiplied by 0, which is nonnegative, the result is 0.

137. true

139. $50x$

141. $\dfrac{40}{x + 40}$

143. The calculator verifies your results.

145. Answers will vary.

146. $-6 + (-3) = -9$

147. $-6 - (-3) = -6 + 3 = -3$

148. $-6 \div (-3) = -6\left(-\dfrac{1}{3}\right) = 2$

149. $(-6)^2 = (-6)(-6) = 36$

150. $(-5)^3 = (-5)(-5)(-5) = -125$

151. $(-2)^4 = (-2)(-2)(-2)(-2) = 16$

1.8 Check Points

1. a. $6^2 = 6 \cdot 6 = 36$

b. $(-4)^3 = (-4)(-4)(-4) = -64$

c. $(-1)^4 = (-1)(-1)(-1)(-1) = 1$

d. $-1^4 = -(1 \cdot 1 \cdot 1 \cdot 1) = -1$

2. a. $16x^2 + 5x^2 = (16 + 5)x^2 = 21x^2$

b. $7x^3 + x^3 = 7x^3 + 1x^3 = (7 + 1)x^3 = 8x^3$

c. $10x^2 + 8x^3$ cannot be simplified.

3. $20 + 4 \cdot 3 - 17 = 20 + 12 - 17$
$$= 20 + 12 - 17$$
$$= 15$$

4. $7^2 - 48 \div 4^2 \cdot 5 - 2 = 49 - 48 \div 16 \cdot 5 - 2$
$$= 49 - 3 \cdot 5 - 2$$
$$= 49 - 15 - 2$$
$$= 34 - 2$$
$$= 32$$

5. a. $(3 \cdot 2)^2 = 6^2 = 36$

   b. $3 \cdot 2^2 = 3 \cdot 4 = 12$

6. $\left(-\dfrac{1}{2}\right)^2 - \left(\dfrac{7}{10} - \dfrac{8}{15}\right)^2 (-18) = \left(-\dfrac{1}{2}\right)^2 - \left(\dfrac{1}{6}\right)^2 (-18)$
$$= \frac{1}{4} - \frac{1}{36} \cdot \frac{-18}{1}$$
$$= \frac{1}{4} + \frac{1}{2}$$
$$= \frac{3}{4}$$

7. $4[3(6 - 11) + 5] = 4[3(-5) + 5]$
$$= 4[-15 + 5]$$
$$= 4[-10]$$
$$= -40$$

8. $25 \div 5 + 3[4 + 2(7 - 9)^3] = 25 \div 5 + 3[4 + 2(-2)^3]$
$$= 25 \div 5 + 3[4 + 2(-8)]$$
$$= 25 \div 5 + 3[4 - 16]$$
$$= 25 \div 5 + 3[-12]$$
$$= 5 + (-36)$$
$$= -31$$

9. $\dfrac{5(4 - 9) + 10 \cdot 3}{2^3 - 1} = \dfrac{5(-5) + 10 \cdot 3}{8 - 1}$
$$= \frac{-25 + 30}{7}$$
$$= \frac{5}{7}$$

10. $-x^2 - 4x = -(-5)^2 - 4(-5)$
$$= -25 + 20$$
$$= -5$$

11. $14x^2 + 5 - [7(x^2 - 2) + 4]$
$$= 14x^2 + 5 - [7x^2 - 14 + 4]$$
$$= 14x^2 + 5 - [7x^2 - 10]$$
$$= 14x^2 + 5 - 7x^2 + 10$$
$$= 14x^2 - 7x^2 + 5 + 10$$
$$= 7x^2 + 15$$

12. $P = -0.05x^2 + 3.6x - 15$
$$P = -0.05(20)^2 + 3.6(20) - 15$$
$$= -0.05(400) + 72 - 15$$
$$= -20 + 72 - 15$$
$$= -20 + 72 - 15$$
$$= 37$$
37% of 20-year-olds have been tested for HIV.

13. a. $\overline{C} = \dfrac{30x + 300,000}{x}$
$$\overline{C} = \frac{30(1000) + 300,000}{1000} = \frac{30,000 + 300,000}{1000}$$
$$= \frac{330,000}{1000}$$
$$= 330$$
The average cost is \$330.

   b. $\overline{C} = \dfrac{30x + 300,000}{x}$
$$\overline{C} = \frac{30(10,000) + 300,000}{10,000}$$
$$= \frac{300,000 + 300,000}{10,000}$$
$$= \frac{600,000}{10,000}$$
$$= 60$$
The average cost is \$60.

   c. $\overline{C} = \dfrac{30x + 300,000}{x}$
$$\overline{C} = \frac{30(100,000) + 300,000}{100,000}$$
$$= \frac{3,000,000 + 300,000}{100,000}$$
$$= \frac{3,300,000}{100,000}$$
$$= 33$$
The average cost is \$33.

1.8 Exercise Set

1. $9^2 = 9 \cdot 9 = 81$

3. $4^3 = 4 \cdot 4 \cdot 4 = 64$

5. $(-4)^2 = (-4)(-4) = 16$

7. $(-4)^3 = (-4)(-4)(-4) = -64$

9. $(-5)^4 = (-5)(-5)(-5)(-5) = 625$

11. $-5^4 = -5 \cdot 5 \cdot 5 \cdot 5 = -625$

13. $-10^2 = -10 \cdot 10 = -100$

15. $7x^2 + 12x^2 = (7+12)x^2 = 19x^2$

17. $10x^3 + 5x^3 = (10+5)x^3 = 15x^3$

19. $8x^4 + x^4 = 8x^4 + 1x^4 = (8+1)x^4 = 9x^4$

21. $26x^2 - 27x^2 = 26x^2 + \left(-27x^2\right)$
$$= \left[26 + (-27)\right]x^2$$
$$= -1x^2 = -x^2$$

23. $27x^3 - 26x^3 = 27x^3 + \left(-26x^2\right)$
$$= 1x^3 = x^3$$

25. $5x^2 + 5x^3$ cannot be simplified. The terms $5x^2$ and $5x^3$ are not like terms because they have different variable factors, namely, x^2 and x^3.

27. $16x^2 - 16x^2 = 16x^2 + \left(-16x^2\right)$
$$= \left[16 + (-16)\right]x^2$$
$$= 0x^2 = 0$$

29. $7 + 6 \cdot 3 = 7 + 18 = 25$

31. $45 \div 5 \cdot 3 = 9 + 18 = 27$

33. $6 \cdot 8 \div 4 = 48 \div 4 = 12$

35. $14 - 2 \cdot 6 + 3 = 14 - 12 + 3 = 2 + 3 = 5$

37. $8^2 - 16 \div 2^2 \cdot 4 - 3 = 64 - 16 \div 4 \cdot 4 - 3$
$$= 64 - 4 \cdot 4 - 3$$
$$= 64 - 16 - 3$$
$$= 48 - 3$$
$$= 45$$

39. $3(-2)^2 - 4(-3)^2 = 3 \cdot 4 - 4 \cdot 9$
$$= 12 - 36$$
$$= 12 + (-36)$$
$$= -24$$

41. $(4 \cdot 5)^2 - 4 \cdot 5^2 = 20^2 - 4 \cdot 25$
$$= 400 - 100$$
$$= 300$$

43. $(2-6)^2 - (3-7)^2 = (-4)^2 - (-4)^2$
$$= 16 - 16$$
$$= 0$$

45. $6(3-5)^3 - 2(1-3)^3$
$$= 6(-2)^3 - 2(-2)^3$$
$$= 6(-8) - 2(-8)$$
$$= -48 + 16$$
$$= -32$$

47. $\left[2(6-2)\right]^2 = (2 \cdot 4)^2 = 8^2 = 64$

49. $2\left[5 + 2(9-4)\right] = 2\left[5 + 2(5)\right]$
$$= 2(5+10)$$
$$= 2 \cdot 15 = 30$$

51. $\left[7 + 3\left(2^3 - 1\right)\right] + 21 = \left[7 + 3(8-1)\right] \div 21$
$$= (7 + 3 \cdot 7) \div 21$$
$$= (7 + 21) \div 21$$
$$= 28 \div 21$$
$$= \frac{28}{21} = \frac{\cancel{7} \cdot 4}{\cancel{7} \cdot 3}$$
$$= \frac{4}{3}$$

53. $\dfrac{10+8}{5^2 - 4^2} = \dfrac{18}{25-16} = \dfrac{18}{9} = 2$

55. $\dfrac{37+15 \div (-3)}{2^4} = \dfrac{37+(-5)}{16} = \dfrac{32}{16} = 2$

57. $\dfrac{(-11)(-4)+2(-7)}{7-(-3)} = \dfrac{44+(-14)}{7+3}$

$\qquad\qquad = \dfrac{30}{10} = 3$

59. $4|10-(8-20)| = 4|10-(-12)| = 4|10+12|$

$\qquad\qquad = 4|22| = 4 \cdot 22$

$\qquad\qquad = 88$

61. $8(-10)+|4(-5)| = -80+|-20|$

$\qquad\qquad = -80+20 = -60$

63. $-2^2 + 4\left[16 \div (3-5)\right]$

$\qquad = -4 + 4\left[16 \div (-2)\right]$

$\qquad = -4 + 4(-8) = -4 - 32 = -36$

65. $24 \div \dfrac{3^2}{8-5} - (-6) = 24 \div \dfrac{9}{3} - (-6)$

$\qquad\qquad = 24 \div 3 - (-6)$

$\qquad\qquad = 8 + 6 = 14$

67. $\dfrac{\frac{1}{4}-\frac{1}{2}}{\frac{1}{3}} = \dfrac{\frac{1}{4}-\frac{2}{4}}{\frac{1}{3}} = \dfrac{-\frac{1}{4}}{\frac{1}{3}} = -\dfrac{1}{4} \cdot \dfrac{3}{1} = -\dfrac{3}{4}$

69. $-\dfrac{9}{4}\left(\dfrac{1}{2}\right) + \dfrac{3}{4} \div \dfrac{5}{6} = -\dfrac{9}{4}\left(\dfrac{1}{2}\right) + \dfrac{3}{4} \cdot \dfrac{6}{5}$

$\qquad\qquad = -\dfrac{9}{8} + \dfrac{18}{20}$

$\qquad\qquad = -\dfrac{45}{40} + \dfrac{36}{40} = -\dfrac{9}{40}$

71. $\dfrac{\frac{7}{9}-3}{\frac{5}{6}} \div \dfrac{3}{2} + \dfrac{3}{4} = \dfrac{\frac{7}{9}-\frac{27}{9}}{\frac{5}{6}} \cdot \dfrac{3}{2} + \dfrac{3}{4}$

$\qquad = \dfrac{-\frac{20}{9}}{\frac{5}{6}} \cdot \dfrac{3}{2} + \dfrac{3}{4}$

$\qquad = -\dfrac{20}{9} \cdot \dfrac{6}{5} \cdot \dfrac{2}{3} + \dfrac{3}{4}$

$\qquad = -\dfrac{240}{135} + \dfrac{3}{4}$

$\qquad = -\dfrac{15 \cdot 16}{15 \cdot 9} + \dfrac{3}{4}$

$\qquad = -\dfrac{16}{9} + \dfrac{3}{4}$

$\qquad = -\dfrac{64}{36} + \dfrac{27}{36}$

$\qquad = -\dfrac{37}{36} \quad \text{or} \quad -1\dfrac{1}{36}$

73. $x^2 + 5x; \; x = 3$

$\qquad x^2 + 5x = 3^2 + 5 \cdot 3$

$\qquad\qquad = 9 + 5 \cdot 3 = 9 + 15 = 24$

75. $3x^2 - 8x; \; x = -2$

$\qquad 3x^2 - 8x = 3(-2)^2 - 9(-2)$

$\qquad\qquad = 3 \cdot 4 - 8(-2) = 12 + 16 = 28$

77. $-x^2 - 10x; \; x = -1$

$\qquad -x^2 - 10x = -(-1)^2 - 10(-1)$

$\qquad\qquad = -1 + 10 = 9$

79. $\dfrac{6y - 4y^2}{y^2 - 15}; \; y = 5$

$\qquad \dfrac{6y - 4y^2}{y^2 - 15} = \dfrac{6(5) - 4\left(5^2\right)}{5^2 - 15}$

$\qquad\qquad = \dfrac{6(5) - 4(25)}{25 - 15}$

$\qquad\qquad = \dfrac{30 - 100}{25 - 15} = \dfrac{-70}{10} = -7$

81. $3\left[5(x-2)+1\right] = 3(5x-10+1)$

$\qquad\qquad\qquad = 3(5x-9)$

$\qquad\qquad\qquad = 15x-27$

83. $3\left[6-(y+1)\right] = 3(6-y-1)$

$\qquad\qquad\qquad = 3(5-y)$

$\qquad\qquad\qquad = 15-3y$

85. $7-4\left[3-(4y-5)\right]$

$\quad = 7-4(3-4y+5)$

$\quad = 7-12+16y-20$

$\quad = -25+16y \ \text{ or } \ 16y-25$

87. $2\left(3x^2-5\right)-\left[4\left(2x^2-1\right)+3\right] = 6x^2-10-\left(8x^2-4+3\right)$

$\qquad\qquad\qquad\qquad\qquad = 6x^2-10-\left(8x^2-1\right)$

$\qquad\qquad\qquad\qquad\qquad = 6x^2-10-8x^2-1$

$\qquad\qquad\qquad\qquad\qquad = -2x^2-9$

89. $-10-(-2)^3 = -10-(-8) = -10+8 = -2$

91. $\left[2(7-10)\right]^2 = \left[2(-3)\right]^2 = \left[-6\right]^2 = 36$

93. $x-(5x+8) = x-5x-8 = -4x-8$

95. $5\left(x^3-4\right) = 5x^3-20$

97. $I = -0.09n^2+53n+315$

$\quad I = -0.09(10)^2+53(10)+315 = 836$

In 1990 there were 836 thousand inmates.
This overestimates the value given in the bar graph by 62 thousand.

99. a. According to the line graph, about 92% of people at the college plus level of education used the Internet in 2005.

b. $C = 0.006n^2+3.3n+75$

$\quad C = 0.006(5)^2+3.3(5)+75 = 91.65$

According to the formula, about 91.65% of people at the college plus level of education used the Internet in 2005. This is very close to the value obtained from the line graph.

101. a.

Year	Percentage
2000	34%
2002	45%
2004	52%
2005	62%

b. Substitute the values of *n* into each model.

Year	*n*	Percentage from line graph	Model #1 $H = 0.41n^2 + 2.1n + 17$	Model #2 $H = 0.26n^2 + 3.9n + 34.5$
2000	0	34%	17%	34.5%
2002	2	45%	22.84%	43.34%
2004	4	52%	31.96%	54.26%
2005	5	62%	37.75%	60.5%

Model 2 better describes the data in the line graph.

103. a. $C = \dfrac{200x}{100 - x}$

$C = \dfrac{200(60)}{100 - 60} = 300$

It will cost $300 tens of thousands, or $3,000,000 to remove 60% of the contamination.

b. $C = \dfrac{200x}{100 - x}$

$C = \dfrac{200(90)}{100 - 90} = 1800$

It will cost $1800 tens of thousands, or $18,000,000 to remove 90% of the contamination.

c. The cost of cleanup increases as the percentage of contaminant removed increases.

105. Answers will vary.

107. makes sense

109. makes sense

111. false; Changes to make the statement true will vary. A sample change is: $-3(-3) - 9 = 9 - 9 = 0$

113. true

115. $\dfrac{1}{4} - 6(2+8) \div \left(-\dfrac{1}{3}\right)\left(-\dfrac{1}{9}\right)$

$= \dfrac{1}{4} - 6(10) \div \left(-\dfrac{1}{3}\right)\left(-\dfrac{1}{9}\right)$

$= \dfrac{1}{4} - 60 \div \left(-\dfrac{1}{3}\right)\left(-\dfrac{1}{9}\right)$

$= \dfrac{1}{4} - 60(-3)\left(-\dfrac{1}{9}\right)$

$= \dfrac{1}{4} + 180\left(-\dfrac{1}{9}\right)$

$= \dfrac{1}{4} - 20 = \dfrac{1}{4} - \dfrac{80}{4} = -\dfrac{79}{4}$

117. $\left(2 \cdot 5 - \dfrac{1}{2} \cdot 10\right) \cdot 9 = (10-5) \cdot 9 = 5 \cdot 9 = 45$

118. $-8 - 2 - (-5) + 11$

$= -8 + (-2) + 5 + 11 = \left[(-8) + (-2)\right] + (5+11)$

$= -10 + 16 = 6$

119. $-4(-1)(-3)(2) = -24$

120. Answers will vary. One example is 5.

121. $-\dfrac{1}{2} = x - \dfrac{2}{3}$

$-\dfrac{1}{2} = \dfrac{1}{6} - \dfrac{2}{3}$

$-\dfrac{1}{2} = \dfrac{1}{6} - \dfrac{4}{6}$

$-\dfrac{1}{2} = -\dfrac{3}{6}$

$-\dfrac{1}{2} = -\dfrac{1}{2}$, true

The number is a solution.

122. $5y + 3 - 4y - 8 = 15$

$5(20) + 3 - 4(20) - 8 = 15$

$100 + 3 - 80 - 8 = 15$

$15 = 15$, true

The number is a solution.

123. $4x + 2 = 3(x-6) + 8$

$4(-11) + 2 = 3(-11-6) + 8$

$-44 + 2 = 3(-17) + 8$

$-42 = -51 + 8$

$-42 = -43$, false

The number is not a solution.

Chapter 1 Review

1. $10 + 5x = 10 + 5(6) = 10 + 30 = 40$

2. $8(x-2) + 3x = 8(6-2) + 3(6)$

$= 8(4) + 18$

$= 32 + 18$

$= 50$

3. $\dfrac{40}{x} - \dfrac{y}{5} = \dfrac{40}{8} - \dfrac{10}{5}$

$= \dfrac{200}{40} - \dfrac{80}{40}$

$= \dfrac{120}{40}$

$= 3$

4. $3(2y + x) = 3(2(10) + 8)$

$= 3(20 + 8)$

$= 3(28)$

$= 84$

5. $7x - 6$

6. $\dfrac{x}{5} - 2 = 18$

7. $9 - 2x = 14$

8. $3(x + 7)$

9. $4x + 5 = 13$

$4(3) + 5 = 13$

$12 + 5 = 13$

$17 = 13$, false

The number is not a solution.

10. $2y + 7 = 4y - 5$

$2(6) + 7 = 4(6) - 5$

$12 + 7 = 24 - 5$

$19 = 19$, true

The number is a solution.

11. $3(w + 1) + 11 = 2(w + 8)$

$3(2 + 1) + 11 = 2(2 + 8)$

$3(3) + 11 = 2(10)$

$9 + 11 = 20$

$20 = 20$, true

The number is a solution.

12. According to the line graph, the average number of Latin words that the class remembered after 5 days was about 11.

13. $L = \dfrac{5n+30}{n}$

    $L = \dfrac{5(5)+30}{5} = \dfrac{25+30}{5} = \dfrac{55}{5} = 11$

    According to the mathematical model, the average number of Latin words that the class remembered after 5 days was 11. This is the same value given in the line graph.

14. **a.** $p = 1.7n + 42$

    $p = 1.7(10) + 42 = 17 + 42 = 59$

    59% of sophomores expected to earn a college degree in 1990.
    This underestimates the actual value shown in the bar graph by 1%.

    b. $p = 1.7n + 42$

    $p = 1.7(30) + 42 = 51 + 42 = 93$

    93% of sophomores will expect to earn a college degree in 2010.

15. $3\dfrac{2}{7} = \dfrac{3 \cdot 7 + 2}{7} = \dfrac{21+2}{7} = \dfrac{23}{7}$

16. $5\dfrac{9}{11} = \dfrac{5 \cdot 11 + 9}{11} = \dfrac{55+9}{11} = \dfrac{64}{11}$

17. 17 divided by 9 is 1 with a remainder of 8, so
    $\dfrac{17}{9} = 1\dfrac{8}{9}$.

18. 27 divided by 5 is 5 with a remainder of 2, so
    $\dfrac{27}{5} = 5\dfrac{2}{5}$.

19. Composite
    $60 = 6 \cdot 10 = 2 \cdot 3 \cdot 2 \cdot 5 = 2 \cdot 2 \cdot 3 \cdot 5$

20. Composite
    $63 = 7 \cdot 9 = 7 \cdot 3 \cdot 3 = 3 \cdot 3 \cdot 7$

21. 67 is a prime number.

22. $\dfrac{15}{33} = \dfrac{\cancel{3} \cdot 5}{\cancel{3} \cdot 11} = \dfrac{5}{11}$

23. $\dfrac{40}{75} = \dfrac{\cancel{5} \cdot 8}{\cancel{5} \cdot 15} = \dfrac{8}{15}$

24. $\dfrac{3}{5} \cdot \dfrac{7}{10} = \dfrac{3 \cdot 7}{5 \cdot 10} = \dfrac{21}{50}$

25. $\dfrac{4}{5} \div \dfrac{3}{10} = \dfrac{4}{5} \cdot \dfrac{10}{3} = \dfrac{40}{15} = \dfrac{\cancel{5} \cdot 8}{\cancel{5} \cdot 3} = \dfrac{8}{3}$

26. $1\dfrac{2}{3} \div 6\dfrac{2}{3} = \dfrac{5}{3} \div \dfrac{20}{3}$

    $= \dfrac{5}{\cancel{3}} \cdot \dfrac{\cancel{3}}{20} = \dfrac{5}{20} = \dfrac{1 \cdot \cancel{5}}{4 \cdot \cancel{5}} = \dfrac{1}{4}$

27. $\dfrac{2}{9} + \dfrac{4}{9} = \dfrac{2+4}{9} = \dfrac{6}{9} = \dfrac{2 \cdot \cancel{3}}{3 \cdot \cancel{3}} = \dfrac{2}{3}$

28. $\dfrac{5}{6} + \dfrac{7}{9} = \dfrac{5}{6} \cdot \dfrac{3}{3} + \dfrac{7}{9} \cdot \dfrac{2}{2}$

    $= \dfrac{15}{18} + \dfrac{14}{18} = \dfrac{29}{18}$ or $1\dfrac{11}{18}$

29. $\dfrac{3}{4} - \dfrac{2}{15} = \dfrac{3}{4} \cdot \dfrac{15}{15} - \dfrac{2}{15} \cdot \dfrac{4}{4} = \dfrac{45}{60} - \dfrac{8}{60} = \dfrac{37}{60}$

30. $x - \dfrac{3}{4} = \dfrac{7}{4}$

    $2\dfrac{1}{2} - \dfrac{3}{4} = \dfrac{7}{4}$

    $\dfrac{5}{2} - \dfrac{3}{4} = \dfrac{7}{4}$

    $\dfrac{10}{4} - \dfrac{3}{4} = \dfrac{7}{4}$

    $\dfrac{7}{4} = \dfrac{7}{4}$, true

    The number is a solution.

31. $\dfrac{2}{3}w = \dfrac{1}{15}w + \dfrac{3}{5}$

    $\dfrac{2}{3} \cdot 2 = \dfrac{1}{15} \cdot 2 + \dfrac{3}{5}$

    $\dfrac{4}{3} = \dfrac{2}{15} + \dfrac{3}{5}$

    $\dfrac{4}{3} = \dfrac{2}{15} + \dfrac{9}{15}$

    $\dfrac{4}{3} = \dfrac{11}{15}$, false

    The number is not a solution.

32. $2 - \dfrac{1}{2}x = \dfrac{1}{4}x$

33. $\dfrac{3}{5}(x+6)$

34. $H = \dfrac{4}{5}(220-a)$

$H = \dfrac{4}{5}(220-30) = \dfrac{4}{5}(190) = 152$

The target heart rate of a 30-year-old is 152 beats per minute.

35. -2.5

36. $4\dfrac{3}{4}$

$$
\begin{array}{r}
0.625 \\
8\overline{)5.000} \\
\underline{48} \\
20 \\
\underline{16} \\
40 \\
\underline{40} \\
0
\end{array}
$$

37.

$\dfrac{5}{8} = 0.625$

38.
$$
\begin{array}{r}
0.2727... \\
11\overline{)3.0000...} \\
\underline{22} \\
80 \\
\underline{77} \\
30 \\
\underline{27} \\
30 \\
\underline{22} \\
8 \\
\vdots
\end{array}
$$

$\dfrac{3}{11} = 0.\overline{27}$

39. **a.** $\sqrt{81} \ (=9)$

     b. $0, \sqrt{81}$

     c. $-17, 0, \sqrt{81}$

d. $-17, -\dfrac{9}{13}, 0, 0.75, \sqrt{81}$

e. $\sqrt{2}, \pi$

f. $-17, -\dfrac{9}{13}, 0, 0.75, \sqrt{2}, \pi, \sqrt{81}$

40. Answers will vary. One example of an integer that is not a natural number is -7.

41. Answers will vary. One example of a rational number that is not an integer is $\dfrac{3}{4}$.

42. Answers will vary. One example of a real number that is not a rational number is π.

43. $-93 < 17$; -93 is to the left of 17, so $-93 < 17$.

44. $-2 > -200$; -2 is to the right of -200, so $-2 > -200$.

45. $0 > -\dfrac{1}{3}$; 0 is to the right of $-\dfrac{1}{3}$, so $0 > -\dfrac{1}{3}$.

46.

$-\dfrac{1}{4} < -\dfrac{1}{5}$; $\ -\dfrac{1}{4} = -0.25$ is to the left of

$-\dfrac{1}{5} = -0.2$, so $-\dfrac{1}{4} < -\dfrac{1}{5}$.

47. $-13 \geq -11$ is false because neither $-13 > -11$ nor $-13 = -11$ is true.

48. $-126 \leq -126$ is true because $-126 = -126$.

49. $|-58| = 58$ because the distance between -58 and 0 on the number line is 58.

50. $|2.75| = 2.75$ because the distance between 2.75 and 0 on the number line is 2.75.

51. $7 + 13y = 13y + 7$

52. $9(x+7) = (x+7)9$

53. $6 + (4+y) = (6+4) + y = 10 + y$

54. $7(10x) = (7 \cdot 10)x = 70x$

55. $6(4x - 2 + 5y) = 6(4x) + 6(-2) + 6(5y)$
$$= 24x - 12 + 30y$$

56. $4a+9+3a-7=4a+3a+9-7$
$$=(4+3)a+(9-7)$$
$$=7a+2$$

57. $6(3x+4)+5(2x-1)$
$$=6(3x)+6(4)+5(2x)+5(-1)$$
$$=18x+24+10x-5$$
$$=18x+10x+24-5$$
$$=(18+10)x+\left[24+(-5)\right]$$
$$=28x+19$$

58. $-6+8=+2$ or 2.

Start at -6. Move 8 units to the right because 8 is positive.

59. $8+(-11)=-3$

60. $-\dfrac{3}{4}+\dfrac{1}{5}=-\dfrac{3}{4}\cdot\dfrac{5}{5}+\dfrac{1}{5}\cdot\dfrac{4}{4}$
$$=-\dfrac{15}{20}+\dfrac{4}{20}=-\dfrac{11}{20}$$

61. $7+(-5)+(-13)+4$
$$=\left[7+(-5)\right]+(-13)+4$$
$$=2+(-13)+4$$
$$=\left[2+(-13)\right]+4=-11+4=-7$$

62. $8x+(-6y)+(-12x)+11y$
$$=8x+(-12x)+(-6y)+11y$$
$$=\left[8+(-12)\right]x+(-6+11)y$$
$$=-4x+5y \text{ or } 5y-4x$$

63. $10(3y+4)+(-40y)=30y+40+(-40y)$
$$=30y+(-40y)+40$$
$$=-10y+40$$

64. $-1312+512=-800$

The person's elevation is 800 feet below sea level.

65. $25-3+2+1-4+2$
$$=25+(-3)+2+1+(-4)+2$$
$$=23$$

The reservoir's water level at the end of five months is 23 feet.

66. $9-13=9+(-13)$

67. $-9-(-13)=-9+13=4$

68. $-\dfrac{7}{10}-\dfrac{1}{2}=-\dfrac{7}{10}-\dfrac{1}{2}\cdot\dfrac{5}{5}$
$$=-\dfrac{7}{10}-\dfrac{5}{10}=-\dfrac{12}{10}=-\dfrac{6}{5}$$

69. $-3.6-(-2.1)=-3.6+2.1=-1.5$

70. $-7-(-5)+11-16$
$$=-7+5+11+(-16)$$
$$=\left[(-7)+(-16)\right]+(5+11)$$
$$=-23+16$$
$$=-7$$

71. $-25-4-(-10)+16$
$$=-25+(-4)+10+16$$
$$=\left[(-25)+(-4)\right]+(10+16)$$
$$=-29+26$$
$$=-3$$

72. $3-6a-8-2a=3-8-6a-2a$
$$=\left[3+(-8)\right]+\left[-6a-2a\right]$$
$$=-5+(-6-2)a$$
$$=-5-8a$$

73. $26,000-(-650)=26,500+650$
$$=27,150$$

The difference in elevation is 27,150 feet.

74. $(-7)(-12)=84$

75. $\dfrac{3}{5}\left(-\dfrac{5}{11}\right)=-\dfrac{3\cdot\cancel{5}}{\cancel{5}\cdot11}=-\dfrac{3}{11}$

76. $5(-3)(-2)(-4)=-120$

77. $\dfrac{45}{-5}=45\left(-\dfrac{1}{5}\right)=-9$

78. $-17\div0$ is undefined.

79. $-\dfrac{4}{5}\div\left(-\dfrac{2}{5}\right)=-\dfrac{4}{5}\left(-\dfrac{5}{2}\right)=\dfrac{20}{10}=2$

80. $-4\left(-\dfrac{3}{4}x\right) = \left[-4\left(-\dfrac{3}{4}\right)\right]x = 3x$

81. $-3(2x-1) - (4-5x)$
$= -3(2x) + (-3)(-1) - 4 + 5x$
$= -6x + 3 - 4 + 5x$
$= -6x + 5x + 3 - 4$
$= (-6+5)x + \left[3 + (-4)\right]$
$= -1x - 1$
$= -x - 1$

82. $5x + 16 = -8 - x$
$5(-6) + 16 = -8 - (-6)$
$-30 + 16 = -8 + 6$
$-14 = -2, \text{ false}$
The number is not a solution.

83. $2(x+3) - 18 = 5x$
$2(-4+3) - 18 = 5(-4)$
$2(-1) - 18 = -20$
$-2 - 18 = -20$
$-20 = -20, \text{ true}$
The number is a solution.

84. a. $I = -232n + 3430$
$I = -232(3) + 3430 = -696 + 3430 = 2734$
There were 2734 inmates younger than 18 in 2003.
This underestimates the actual total shown in the bar graph by 7.

b. $I = -232n + 3430$
$I = -232(10) + 3430 = -2320 + 3430 = 1110$
There will be 1110 inmates younger than 18 in 2010.

85. $(-6)^2 = (-6)(-6) = 36$

86. $-6^2 = -6 \cdot 6 = -36$

87. $(-2)^5 = (-2)(-2)(-2)(-2)(-2) = -32$

88. $4x^3 + 2x^3 = (4+2)x^3 = 6x^3$

89. $4x^3 + 4x^2$ cannot be simplified. The terms $4x^3$ and $4x^2$ are not like terms because they have different variable factors.

90. $-40 \div 5 \cdot 2 = -8 \cdot 2 = -16$

91. $-6 + (-2) \cdot 5 = -6 + (-10) = -16$

92. $6 - 5(-3+2) = 6 - 4(-1) = 6 + 4 = 10$

93. $28 \div \left(2 - 4^2\right) = 28 \div (2 - 16)$
$= 28 \div \left[2 + (-16)\right]$
$= 28 \div (-14)$
$= -2$

94. $36 - 24 \div 4 \cdot 3 - 1 = 36 - 6 \cdot 3 - 1$
$= 36 - 18 - 1$
$= 18 - 1$
$= 17$

95. $-8\left[-4 - 5(-3)\right] = -8(-4 + 15)$
$= -8(11) = -88$

96. $\dfrac{6(-10+3)}{2(-15) - 9(-3)} = \dfrac{6(-7)}{-30 + 27}$
$= \dfrac{-42}{-3} = 14$

97. $\left(\dfrac{1}{2} + \dfrac{1}{3}\right) \div \left(\dfrac{1}{4} - \dfrac{3}{8}\right)$
$= \left(\dfrac{3}{6} + \dfrac{2}{6}\right) \div \left(\dfrac{2}{8} - \dfrac{3}{8}\right)$
$= \dfrac{5}{6} \div \left(-\dfrac{1}{8}\right) = \dfrac{5}{6} \cdot \left(-\dfrac{8}{1}\right) = -\dfrac{40}{6} = -\dfrac{20}{3}$

98. $\dfrac{1}{2} - \dfrac{2}{3} \div \dfrac{5}{9} + \dfrac{3}{10}$
$= \dfrac{1}{2} - \dfrac{2}{\cancel{3}_1} \cdot \dfrac{\cancel{9}^3}{5} + \dfrac{3}{10}$
$= \dfrac{1}{2} - \dfrac{6}{5} + \dfrac{3}{10}$
$= \dfrac{5}{10} - \dfrac{12}{10} + \dfrac{3}{10} = -\dfrac{4}{10} = -\dfrac{2}{5}$

99. $x^2 - 2x + 3;\ x = -1$

$$x^2 - 2x + 3 = (-1)^2 - 2(-1) + 3$$
$$= 1 + 2 + 3$$
$$= 6$$

100. $-x^2 - 7x;\ x = -2$

$$-x^2 - 7x = -(-2)^2 - 7(-2)$$
$$= -4 + 14$$
$$= 10$$

101. $4[7(a-1)+2] = 4(7a-7+2)$
$$= 4(7a-5)$$
$$= 4(7a) + 4(-5)$$
$$= 28a - 20$$

102. $-6[4-(y+2)] = -6(4-y-2)$
$$= -6(2-y)$$
$$= -6(2) + (-6)(-y)$$
$$= -12 + 6y \text{ or } 6y - 12$$

103. $V = -1.2n^2 + 10n + 45$

$V = -1.2(5)^2 + 10(5) + 45 = 65$

The number of Americans who volunteered at least once in 2005 was 65%.
This underestimates the actual value shown in the bar graph by 0.4%

Chapter 1 Test

1. $1.4 - (-2.6) = 1.4 + 2.6 = 4$

2.
$$-9 + 3 + (-11) + 6$$
$$= [-9 + (-11)] + (3 + 6)$$
$$= -20 + 9 = -11$$

3. $3(-17) = -51$

4. $\left(-\dfrac{3}{7}\right) \div \left(-\dfrac{15}{7}\right) = \left(-\dfrac{3}{7}\right)\left(-\dfrac{7}{15}\right)$
$$= \dfrac{21}{105} = \dfrac{\cancel{21} \cdot 1}{\cancel{21} \cdot 5} = \dfrac{1}{5}$$

5. $\left(3\dfrac{1}{3}\right)\left(-1\dfrac{3}{4}\right) = \left(\dfrac{10}{3}\right)\left(-\dfrac{7}{4}\right)$
$$= -\dfrac{10 \cdot 7}{3 \cdot 4} = -\dfrac{70}{12}$$
$$= -\dfrac{\cancel{2} \cdot 35}{\cancel{2} \cdot 6}$$
$$= -\dfrac{35}{6} \text{ or } -5\dfrac{5}{6}$$

6. $-50 \div 10 = -50\left(\dfrac{1}{10}\right) = -5$

7. $-6 - (5 - 12) = -6 - (-7) = -6 + 7 = 1$

8. $(-3)(-4) \div (7 - 10)$
$$= (-3)(-4) \div [7 + (-10)]$$
$$= (-3)(-4) \div (-3)$$
$$= 12 \div (-3)$$
$$= -4$$

9. $(6-8)^2 (5-7)^3 = (-2)^2 (-2)^3$
$$= 4(-8) = -32$$

10. $\dfrac{3(-2) - 2(2)}{-2(8-3)} = \dfrac{-6 - 4}{-2(5)}$
$$= \dfrac{-6 + (-4)}{-2(5)} = \dfrac{-10}{-10} = 1$$

11. $11x - (7x - 4) = 11x - 7x + 4$
$$= 11x + (-7x) + 4$$
$$= [11 + (-7)]x + 4$$
$$= 4x + 4$$

12. $5(3x - 4y) - (2x - y)$
$$= 5(3x) - 5(4y) - 2x + y$$
$$= 15x - 20y - 2x + y$$
$$= 15x - 2x - 20y + y$$
$$= 13x - 19y$$

13. $6 - 2[3(x+1) - 5] = 6 - 2[3x + 3 - 5]$
$$= 6 - 2(3x - 2)$$
$$= 6 - 6x + 4$$
$$= 10 - 6x$$

36

14. Rational numbers can be written as the quotient of two integers.

$$-7 = -\frac{7}{1}, -\frac{4}{5} = \frac{-4}{5}, 0 = \frac{0}{1}, 0.25 = \frac{1}{4},$$

$$\sqrt{4} = 2 = \frac{2}{1}, \text{ and } \frac{22}{7} = \frac{22}{7}.$$

Thus, -7, $-\frac{4}{5}$, 0, 0.25, $\sqrt{4}$, and $\frac{22}{7}$ are the rational numbers of the set.

15. $-1 > -100$; -1 is to the right of -100 on the number line, so -1 is greater than -100.

16. $|-12.8| = 12.8$ because the distance between 12.8 and 0 on the number line is 12.8

17. $5(x-7)$; $x = 4$

$$5(x-7) = 5(4-7) = 5(-3) = -15$$

18. $x^2 - 5x$; $x = -10$

$$x^2 - 5x = (-10)^2 - 5(-10)$$
$$= 100 + 50 = 150$$

19. $2(x+3) = 2(3+x)$

20. $-6(4x) = (-6 \cdot 4)x = -24x$

21. $7(5x-1+2y) = 7(5x) - 7(1) + 7(2y)$
$$= 35x - 7 + 14y$$

22. $16,200 - (-830) = 17,030$

The difference in elevations is 17,030 feet.

23. $\frac{1}{5}(x+2) = \frac{1}{10}x + \frac{3}{5}$

$$\frac{1}{5}(3+2) = \frac{1}{10} \cdot 3 + \frac{3}{5}$$

$$\frac{1}{5}(5) = \frac{3}{10} + \frac{3}{5}$$

$$1 = \frac{3}{10} + \frac{6}{10}$$

$$1 = \frac{9}{10}, \text{ false}$$

The number is not a solution.

24. $3(x+2) - 15 = 4x$

$$3(-9+2) - 15 = 4(-9)$$
$$3(-7) - 15 = -36$$
$$-21 - 15 = -36$$
$$-36 = -36, \text{ true}$$

The number is a solution.

25. $\frac{1}{4}x - 5 = 32$

26. $5(x+4) - 7$

27. $V = -n^2 + 8n - 4$

$$V = -(3)^2 + 8(3) - 4 = -9 + 24 - 4 = 11$$

According to the formula, there were 11 million viewers for the opening episode of season 3. This underestimates the actual number shown in the bar graph by 0.3 million.

28. According to the line graph, the target heart rate for a 40-year-old taking a stress test is about 144 beats per minute.

29. $H = \frac{4}{5}(220 - a)$

$$H = \frac{4}{5}(220 - 40) = \frac{4}{5}(180) = 144$$

According to the formula, the target heart rate for a 40-year-old taking a stress test is about 144 beats per minute.
This value is the same as the value estimated from the line graph.

Chapter 2
Linear Equations and Inequalities in One Variable

2.1 Check Points

1.
$$x - 5 = 12$$
$$x - 5 + 5 = 12 + 5$$
$$x + 0 = 17$$
$$x = 17$$
Check:
$$x - 5 = 12$$
$$17 - 5 = 12$$
$$12 = 12$$
The solution set is $\{17\}$.

2.
$$z + 2.8 = 5.09$$
$$z + 2.8 - 2.8 = 5.09 - 2.8$$
$$z + 0 = 2.29$$
$$z = 2.29$$
Check:
$$z + 2.8 = 5.09$$
$$2.29 + 2.8 = 5.09$$
$$5.09 = 5.09$$
The solution set is $\{2.29\}$.

3.
$$-\frac{1}{2} = x - \frac{3}{4}$$
$$-\frac{1}{2} + \frac{3}{4} = x - \frac{3}{4} + \frac{3}{4}$$
$$-\frac{2}{4} + \frac{3}{4} = x$$
$$\frac{1}{4} = x$$
Check:
$$-\frac{1}{2} = x - \frac{3}{4}$$
$$-\frac{1}{2} = \frac{1}{4} - \frac{3}{4}$$
$$-\frac{1}{2} = -\frac{2}{4}$$
$$-\frac{1}{2} = -\frac{1}{2}$$
The solution set is $\left\{\frac{1}{4}\right\}$.

4.
$$8y + 7 - 7y - 10 = 6 + 4$$
$$y - 3 = 10$$
$$y - 3 + 3 = 10 + 3$$
$$y = 13$$
Check:
$$8y + 7 - 7y - 10 = 6 + 4$$
$$8(13) + 7 - 7(13) - 10 = 6 + 4$$
$$104 + 7 - 91 - 10 = 10$$
$$111 - 101 = 10$$
$$10 = 10$$
The solution set is $\{13\}$.

5.
$$7x = 12 + 6x$$
$$7x - 6x = 12 + 6x - 6x$$
$$x = 12$$
Check:
$$7(12) = 12 + 6(12)$$
$$84 = 12 + 72$$
$$84 = 84$$
The solution set is $\{12\}$.

6.
$$3x - 6 = 2x + 5$$
$$3x - 2x - 6 = 2x - 2x + 5$$
$$x - 6 = 5$$
$$x - 6 + 6 = 5 + 6$$
$$x = 11$$
Check:
$$3x - 6 = 2x + 5$$
$$3(11) - 6 = 2(11) + 5$$
$$33 - 6 = 22 + 5$$
$$27 = 27$$
The solution set is $\{11\}$.

7.
$$V + 900 = 60A$$
$$V + 900 = 60(50)$$
$$V + 900 = 3000$$
$$V + 900 - 900 = 3000 - 900$$
$$V = 2100$$
At 50 months, a child will have a vocabulary of 2100 words.

2.1 Exercise Set

1. linear

3. not linear

5. not linear

7. linear

9. not linear

11. $x - 4 = 19$
$x - 4 + 4 = 19 + 4$
$x + 0 = 23$
$x = 23$
Check:
$x - 4 = 19$
$23 - 4 = 19$
$19 = 19$
The solution set is $\{23\}$.

13. $z + 8 = -12$
$z + 8 - 8 = -12 - 8$
$z + 0 = -20$
$z = -20$
Check:
$z + 8 = -12$
$-20 + 8 = -12$
$-12 = -12$
The solution set is $\{-20\}$.

15. $-2 = x + 14$
$-2 - 14 = x + 14 - 14$
$-16 = x$
Check:
$-2 = -16 + 14$
$-2 = -2$
The solution set is $\{-16\}$.

17. $-17 = y - 5$
$-17 + 5 = y - 5 + 5$
$-12 = y$
Check:
$-17 = -12 - 5$
$-17 = -17$
The solution set is $\{-12\}$.

19. $7 + z = 11$
$z = 11 - 7$
$z = 4$
Check:
$7 + 4 = 11$
$11 = 11$
The solution set is $\{4\}$.

21. $-6 + y = -17$
$y = -17 + 6$
$y = -11$
Check:
$-6 - 11 = -17$
$-17 = -17$
The solution set is $\{-11\}$.

23. $x + \dfrac{1}{3} = \dfrac{7}{3}$
$x = \dfrac{7}{3} - \dfrac{1}{3}$
$x = 2$
Check:
$2 + \dfrac{1}{3} = \dfrac{7}{3}$
$\dfrac{6}{3} + \dfrac{1}{3} = \dfrac{7}{3}$
$\dfrac{7}{3} = \dfrac{7}{3}$
The solution set is $\{2\}$.

25. $t + \dfrac{5}{6} = -\dfrac{7}{12}$
$t = -\dfrac{7}{12} - \dfrac{5}{6}$
$t = -\dfrac{7}{12} - \dfrac{10}{12} = -\dfrac{17}{12}$
Check:
$-\dfrac{17}{15} + \dfrac{5}{6} = -\dfrac{7}{12}$
$-\dfrac{17}{12} + \dfrac{10}{12} = -\dfrac{7}{12}$
$-\dfrac{7}{12} = -\dfrac{7}{12}$
The solution set is $\left\{-\dfrac{17}{12}\right\}$.

27. $x - \dfrac{3}{4} = \dfrac{9}{2}$

$x - \dfrac{3}{4} + \dfrac{3}{4} = \dfrac{9}{2} + \dfrac{3}{4}$

$x = \dfrac{21}{4}$

Check:

$\dfrac{21}{4} - \dfrac{3}{4} = \dfrac{9}{2}$

$\dfrac{18}{4} = \dfrac{9}{2}$

$\dfrac{9}{2} = \dfrac{9}{2}$

The solution set is $\left\{ \dfrac{21}{4} \right\}$.

29. $-\dfrac{1}{5} + y = -\dfrac{3}{4}$

$y = -\dfrac{3}{4} + \dfrac{1}{5}$

$y = -\dfrac{15}{20} + \dfrac{4}{20} = -\dfrac{11}{20}$

Check:

$-\dfrac{1}{5} + \left(-\dfrac{11}{20} \right) = -\dfrac{3}{4}$

$-\dfrac{4}{20} - \dfrac{11}{20} = -\dfrac{3}{4}$

$-\dfrac{15}{20} = -\dfrac{3}{4}$

$-\dfrac{3}{4} = -\dfrac{3}{4}$

The solution set is $\left\{ -\dfrac{11}{20} \right\}$.

31. $3.2 + x = 7.5$

$3.2 + x - 3.2 = 7.5 - 3.2$

$x = 4.3$

Check:

$3.2 + 4.3 = 7.5$

$7.5 = 7.5$

The solution set is $\{4.3\}$.

33. $x + \dfrac{3}{4} = -\dfrac{9}{2}$

$x + \dfrac{3}{4} - \dfrac{3}{4} = -\dfrac{9}{2} - \dfrac{3}{4}$

$x = -\dfrac{21}{4}$

Check:

$-\dfrac{21}{4} + \dfrac{3}{4} = -\dfrac{9}{2}$

$-\dfrac{18}{4} = -\dfrac{9}{2}$

$-\dfrac{9}{2} = -\dfrac{9}{2}$

The solution set is $\left\{ -\dfrac{21}{4} \right\}$.

35. $5 = -13 + y$

$5 + 13 = y$

$18 = y$

Check:

$5 = -13 + 18$

$5 = 5$

The solution set is $\{18\}$.

37. $-\dfrac{3}{5} = -\dfrac{3}{2} + s$

$-\dfrac{3}{5} + \dfrac{3}{2} = s$

$-\dfrac{6}{10} + \dfrac{15}{10} = s$

$\dfrac{9}{10} = s$

Check:

$-\dfrac{3}{5} = -\dfrac{3}{2} + \dfrac{9}{10}$

$-\dfrac{6}{10} = -\dfrac{15}{10} + \dfrac{9}{10}$

$-\dfrac{6}{10} = -\dfrac{6}{10}$

The solution set is $\left\{ \dfrac{9}{10} \right\}$.

39. $830 + y = 520$

$\qquad y = 520 - 830$

$\qquad y = -310$

Check:

$830 - 310 = 520$

$\qquad 520 = 520$

The solution set is $\{-310\}$.

41. $r + 3.7 = 8$

$\qquad r = 8 - 3.7$

$\qquad r = 4.3$

Check:

$4.3 + 3.7 = 8$

$\qquad 8 = 8$

The solution set is $\{4.3\}$.

43. $-3.7 + m = -3.7$

$\qquad m = -3.7 + 3.7$

$\qquad m = 0$

Check:

$-3.7 + 0 = -3.7$

$\qquad -3.7 = -3.7$

The solution set is $\{0\}$.

45. $6y + 3 - 5y = 14$

$\qquad y + 3 = 14$

$\qquad y = 14 - 3$

$\qquad y = 11$

Check:

$6(11) + 3 - 5(11) = 14$

$\qquad 66 + 3 - 55 = 14$

$\qquad 14 = 14$

The solution set is $\{11\}$.

47. $7 - 5x + 8 + 2x + 4x - 3 = 2 + 3 \cdot 5$

$\qquad x + 12 = 2 + 15$

$\qquad x = 17 - 12$

$\qquad x = 5$

Check:

$7 - 5(5) + 8 + 2(5) + 4(5) - 3 = 2 + 3 \cdot 5$

$\qquad 7 - 25 + 8 + 10 + 20 - 3 = 2 + 15$

$\qquad 45 - 28 = 17$

$\qquad 17 = 17$

The solution set is $\{5\}$.

49. $7y + 4 = 6y - 9$

$\qquad 7y - 6y + 4 = -9$

$\qquad y = -9 - 4$

$\qquad y = -13$

Check:

$7(-13) + 4 = 6(-13) - 9$

$\qquad -91 + 4 = -78 - 9$

$\qquad -87 = -87$

The solution set is $\{-13\}$.

51. $12 - 6x = 18 - 7x$

$\qquad 12 + x = 18$

$\qquad x = 6$

Check:

$12 - 6(6) = 18 - 7(6)$

$\qquad 12 - 36 = 18 - 42$

$\qquad -24 = -24$

The solution set is $\{6\}$.

53. $4x + 2 = 3(x - 6) + 8$

$\qquad 4x + 2 = 3x - 18 + 8$

$\qquad 4x + 2 = 3x - 10$

$\qquad 4x - 3x + 2 = -10$

$\qquad x + 2 = -10$

$\qquad x = -10 - 2$

$\qquad x = -12$

Check:

$4(-12) + 2 = 3(-12 - 6) + 8$

$\qquad -48 + 2 = 3(-18) + 8$

$\qquad -46 = -54 + 8$

$\qquad -46 = -46$

The solution set is $\{-12\}$.

55. $x - \square = \triangle$

$\qquad x - \square + \square = \triangle + \square$

$\qquad x = \triangle + \square$

57. $2x + \triangle = 3x + \square$

$\qquad \triangle = 3x - 2x + \square$

$\qquad \triangle = x + \square$

$\qquad \triangle - \square = x + \square - \square$

$\qquad \triangle - \square = x$

59. $x - 12 = -2$
$$x = -2 + 12$$
$$x = 10$$
The number is 10.

61. $\dfrac{2}{5}x - 8 = \dfrac{7}{5}x$
$$-8 = \dfrac{7}{5}x - \dfrac{2}{5}x$$
$$-8 = \dfrac{5}{5}x$$
$$-8 = x$$
The number is -8.

63. $S = 1850, \ M = 150$
$$C + M = S$$
$$C + 150 = 1850$$
$$C = 1850 - 150$$
$$C = 1700$$
The cost of the computer is $1700.

65. $C - 4.6x = 25$
$$C - 4.6(15) = 25$$
$$C - 69 = 25$$
$$C - 69 + 69 = 25 + 69$$
$$C = 94$$
According to the formula, 94 channels were received by the average U.S. home in 2005. This underestimates the value given in the bar graph by 2.

67. a. According to the line graph, about 47% of U.S. workers were satisfied with their jobs in 2006.

b. 2006 is 19 years after 1987.
$$S + 0.8x = 62$$
$$S + 0.8(19) = 62$$
$$S + 15.2 = 62$$
$$S + 15.2 - 15.2 = 62 - 15.2$$
$$S = 46.8$$
According to the formula, 46.8% of U.S. workers were satisfied with their jobs in 2006. This matches the line graph very well.

69. – 71. Answers will vary.

73. does not make sense; Explanations will vary. Sample explanation: It does not matter whether the number is added beside or below, as long as it is added to both sides of the equation.

75. makes sense

77. false; Changes to make the statement true will vary. A sample change is: If $y - a = -b$, then $y = a - b$.

79. true

81. Answers will vary. An example is: $x - 100 = -101$

83.
$$6.9825 = 4.2296 + y$$
$$6.9825 - 4.2296 = y$$
$$2.7529 = y$$
The solution set is $\{2.7529\}$.

84. $\dfrac{9}{x} - 4x$

85. $-16 - 8 \div 4 \cdot (-2) = -16 - 2 \cdot (-2)$
$$= -16 + (-2)(-2)$$
$$= -16 + 4$$
$$= -12$$

87. $5 \cdot \dfrac{x}{5} = \dfrac{5}{1} \cdot \dfrac{x}{5} = x$

88. $\dfrac{-7y}{-7} = y$

89. $3x - 14 = -2x + 6$
$$3(4) - 14 = -2(4) + 6$$
$$12 - 14 = -8 + 6$$
$$-2 = -2, \ \text{true}$$
Yes, 4 is a solution of the equation.

2.2 Check Points

1. $\dfrac{x}{3} = 12$

   $3 \cdot \dfrac{x}{3} = 12 \cdot 3$

   $1x = 36$

   $x = 36$

   Check:

   $\dfrac{x}{3} = 12$

   $\dfrac{36}{3} = 12$

   $12 = 12$

   The solution set is $\{36\}$.

2. **a.** $4x = 84$

   $\dfrac{4x}{4} = \dfrac{84}{4}$

   $1x = 21$

   $x = 21$

   The solution set is $\{21\}$.

   b. $-11y = 44$

   $\dfrac{-11y}{-11} = \dfrac{44}{-11}$

   $1x = -4$

   $x = -4$

   The solution set is $\{-4\}$.

   c. $-15.5 = 5z$

   $\dfrac{-15.5}{5} = \dfrac{5z}{5}$

   $-3.1 = 1z$

   $-3.1 = z$

   The solution set is $\{-3.1\}$.

3. **a.** $\dfrac{2}{3}y = 16$

   $\dfrac{3}{2}\left(\dfrac{2}{3}y\right) = \dfrac{3}{2} \cdot 16$

   $1y = 24$

   $y = 24$

   The solution set is $\{24\}$.

b. $28 = -\dfrac{7}{4}x$

   $-\dfrac{4}{7} \cdot 28 = -\dfrac{4}{7}\left(-\dfrac{7}{4}x\right)$

   $-16 = 1x$

   $-16 = x$

   The solution set is $\{-16\}$.

4. **a.** $-x = 5$

   $-1x = 5$

   $(-1)(-1x) = (-1)5$

   $1x = -5$

   $x = -5$

   The solution set is $\{-5\}$.

   b. $-x = -3$

   $-1x = -3$

   $(-1)(-1x) = (-1)(-3)$

   $1x = 3$

   $x = 3$

   The solution set is $\{3\}$.

5. $4x + 3 = 27$

   $4x + 3 - 3 = 27 - 3$

   $4x = 24$

   $\dfrac{4x}{4} = \dfrac{24}{4}$

   $x = 6$

   The solution set is $\{6\}$.

6. $-4y - 15 = 25$

   $-4y - 15 + 15 = 25 + 15$

   $-4y = 40$

   $\dfrac{-4y}{-4} = \dfrac{40}{-4}$

   $y = -10$

   The solution set is $\{-10\}$.

7.
$$2x - 15 = -4x + 21$$
$$2x + 4x - 15 = -4x + 4x + 21$$
$$6x - 15 = 21$$
$$6x - 15 + 15 = 21 + 15$$
$$6x = 36$$
$$\frac{6x}{6} = \frac{36}{6}$$
$$x = 6$$
The solution set is $\{6\}$.

8. a. The bar graph indicates that there were 1.3 million pay phones in 2004. Since 2004 is 4 years after 2000, substitute 4 into the formula for *n*.
$$P = -0.18n + 2.1$$
$$P = -0.18(4) + 2.1$$
$$P = -0.72 + 2.1$$
$$P = 1.38$$
The formula indicates that there were 1.38 million pay phones in 2004.
The formula overestimates by 0.08 million.

b.
$$P = -0.18n + 2.1$$
$$0.3 = -0.18n + 2.1$$
$$0.3 - 2.1 = -0.18n + 2.1 - 2.1$$
$$-1.8 = -0.18n$$
$$\frac{-1.8}{-0.18} = \frac{-0.18n}{-0.18}$$
$$10 = n$$
The formula estimates that there will be 0.3 million pay phones 10 years after 2000, or in 2010.

2.2 Exercise Set

1.
$$\frac{x}{6} = 5$$
$$6 \cdot \frac{x}{6} = 6 \cdot 5$$
$$1x = 30$$
$$x = 30$$
Check:
$$\frac{30}{6} = 5$$
$$5 = 5$$
The solution set is $\{30\}$.

3.
$$\frac{x}{-3} = 11$$
$$-3 \cdot \frac{x}{-3} = -3(11)$$
$$1x = -33$$
$$x = -33$$
Check:
$$\frac{-33}{-3} = 11$$
$$11 = 11$$
The solution set is $\{-33\}$.

5.
$$5y = 35$$
$$\frac{5y}{5} = \frac{35}{5}$$
$$y = 7$$
Check:
$$5(7) = 35$$
$$35 = 35$$
The solution set is $\{7\}$.

7.
$$-7y = 63$$
$$\frac{-7y}{-7} = \frac{63}{-7}$$
$$y = -9$$
Check:
$$-7(-9) = 63$$
$$63 = 63$$
The solution set is $\{-9\}$.

9.
$$-28 = 8z$$
$$\frac{-28}{8} = \frac{8z}{8}$$
$$-\frac{7}{2} = z$$
Check:
$$-28 = 8\left(-\frac{7}{2}\right)$$
$$-28 = -\frac{56}{2}$$
$$-28 = -28$$
The solution set is $\left\{-\frac{7}{2}\right\}$. or $\left\{-3\frac{1}{2}\right\}$.

11. $-18 = -3z$

$$\frac{-18}{-3} = \frac{-3z}{-3}$$

$$6 = z$$

Check:

$$-18 = -3(6)$$

$$-18 = -18$$

The solution set is $\{6\}$.

13. $-8x = 6$

$$\frac{-8x}{-8} = \frac{6}{-8}$$

$$x = -\frac{6}{8} = -\frac{3}{4}$$

Check:

$$-8\left(-\frac{3}{4}\right) = 6$$

$$\frac{24}{4} = 6$$

$$6 = 6$$

The solution set is $\left\{-\frac{3}{4}\right\}$.

15. $17y = 0$

$$\frac{17y}{17} = \frac{0}{17}$$

$$y = 0$$

Check:

$$17(0) = 0$$

$$0 = 0$$

The solution set is $\{0\}$.

17. $\frac{2}{3}y = 12$

$$\frac{3}{2}\left(\frac{2}{3}y\right) = \frac{3}{2}(12)$$

$$1y = \frac{3}{2} \cdot \frac{12}{1} = \frac{36}{2}$$

$$y = 18$$

Check:

$$\frac{2}{3}(18) = 12$$

$$\frac{36}{3} = 12$$

$$12 = 12$$

The solution set is $\{18\}$.

19. $28 = -\frac{7}{2}x$

$$-\frac{2}{7}(28) = -\frac{2}{7}\left(-\frac{7}{2}x\right)$$

$$-\frac{56}{7} = 1x$$

$$-8 = x$$

Check:

$$28 = -\frac{7}{2}(-8)$$

$$28 = \frac{56}{2}$$

$$28 = 28$$

The solution set is $\{-8\}$.

21. $-x = 17$

$$-1x = 17$$

$$-1(-1x) = -1(17)$$

$$x = -17$$

Check:

$$-(-17) = 17$$

$$17 = 17$$

The solution set is $\{-17\}$.

23. $-47 = -y$

$$47 = y$$

Check:

$$-47 = -47$$

The solution set is $\{47\}$.

25. $-\frac{x}{5} = -9$

$$5\left(-\frac{x}{5}\right) = 5(-9)$$

$$-x = -45$$

$$x = 45$$

Check:

$$-\frac{45}{5} = -9$$

$$-9 = -9$$

The solution set is $\{45\}$.

27. $2x - 12x = 50$

$(2 - 12)x = 50$

$-10x = 50$

$\dfrac{-10x}{-10} = \dfrac{50}{-10}$

$x = -5$

Check:

$2(-5) - 12(-5) = 50$

$-10 + 60 = 50$

$50 = 50$

The solution set is $\{-5\}$.

29. $2x + 1 = 11$

$2x + 1 - 1 = 11 - 1$

$2x = 10$

$\dfrac{2x}{2} = \dfrac{10}{2}$

$x = 5$

Check:

$2(5) + 1 = 11$

$10 + 1 = 11$

$11 = 11$

The solution set is $\{5\}$.

31. $2x - 3 = 9$

$2x - 3 + 3 = 9 + 3$

$2x = 12$

$\dfrac{2x}{2} = \dfrac{12}{2}$

$x = 6$

Check:

$2(6) - 3 = 9$

$12 - 3 = 9$

$9 = 9$

The solution set is $\{6\}$.

33. $-2y + 5 = 7$

$-2y + 5 - 5 = 7 - 5$

$-2y = 2$

$\dfrac{-2y}{2} = \dfrac{2}{-2}$

$y = -1$

Check:

$-2(-1) + 5 = 7$

$2 + 5 = 7$

$7 = 7$

The solution set is $\{-1\}$.

35. $-3y - 7 = -1$

$-3y - 7 + 7 = -1 + 7$

$-3y = 6$

$\dfrac{-3y}{-3} = \dfrac{6}{-3}$

$y = -2$

Check:

$-3(-2) - 7 = -1$

$6 - 7 = -1$

$-1 = -1$

The solution set is $\{-2\}$.

37. $12 = 4z + 3$

$12 - 3 = 4z + 3 - 3$

$9 = 4z$

$\dfrac{9}{4} = \dfrac{4z}{4}$

$\dfrac{9}{4} = z$

Check:

$12 = 4\left(\dfrac{9}{4}\right) + 3$

$12 = 9 + 3$

$12 = 12$

The solution set is $\left\{\dfrac{9}{4}\right\}$.

39.
$$-x - 3 = 3$$
$$-x - 3 + 3 = 3 + 3$$
$$-x = 6$$
$$x = -6$$
Check:
$$-(-6) - 3 = 3$$
$$6 - 3 = 3$$
$$3 = 3$$
The solution set is $\{-6\}$.

41.
$$6y = 2y - 12$$
$$6y + 12 = 2y - 12 + 12$$
$$6y + 12 = 2y$$
$$6y + 12 - 6y = 2y - 6y$$
$$12 = -4y$$
$$\frac{12}{-4} = \frac{-4y}{-4}$$
$$-3 = y$$
Check:
$$6(-3) = 2(-3) - 12$$
$$-18 = -6 - 12$$
$$-18 = -18$$
The solution set is $\{-3\}$.

43.
$$3z = -2z - 15$$
$$3z + 2z = -2z - 15 + 2z$$
$$5z = -15$$
$$\frac{5z}{5} = \frac{-15}{3}$$
$$z = -3$$
Check:
$$3(-3) = -2(-3) - 15$$
$$-9 = 6 - 15$$
$$-9 = -9$$
The solution set is $\{-3\}$.

45.
$$-5x = -2x - 12$$
$$-5x + 2x = -2x - 12 + 2x$$
$$-3x = -12$$
$$\frac{-3x}{3} = \frac{-12}{-3}$$
$$x = 4$$
Check:
$$-5(4) = 2(4) - 12$$
$$-20 = -8 - 12$$
$$-20 = -20$$
The solution set is $\{4\}$.

47.
$$8y + 4 = 2y - 5$$
$$8y + 4 - 2y = 2y - 5 - 2y$$
$$6y + 4 = -5$$
$$6y + 4 - 4 = -5 - 4$$
$$6y = -9$$
$$\frac{6y}{6} = \frac{-9}{6}$$
$$y = -\frac{3}{2}$$
Check:
$$8\left(-\frac{3}{2}\right) + 4 = 2\left(-\frac{3}{2}\right) - 5$$
$$-12 + 4 = -3 - 5$$
$$-8 = -8$$
The solution set is $\left\{-\frac{3}{2}\right\}$.

49.
$$6z - 5 = z + 5$$
$$6z - 5 - z = z + 5 - z$$
$$5z - 5 = 5$$
$$5z - 5 + 5 = 5 + 5$$
$$5z = 10$$
$$\frac{5z}{5} = \frac{10}{5}$$
$$z = 2$$
Check:
$$6(2) - 5 = 2 + 5$$
$$12 - 5 = 2 + 5$$
$$7 = 7$$
The solution set is $\{2\}$.

51.
$$6x + 14 = 2x - 2$$
$$6x - 2x + 14 = -2$$
$$4x = -2 - 14$$
$$4x = -16$$
$$x = -4$$
Check:
$$6(-4) + 14 = 2(-4) - 2$$
$$-24 + 14 = -8 - 2$$
$$-10 = -10$$
The solution set is $\{-4\}$.

53.
$$-3y - 1 = 5 - 2y$$
$$-3y + 2y - 1 = 5$$
$$-y = 5 + 1$$
$$-y = 6$$
$$y = -6$$
Check:
$$-3(-6) - 1 = 5 - 2(-6)$$
$$18 - 1 = 5 + 12$$
$$17 = 17$$
The solution set is $\{-6\}$.

55.
$$\frac{x}{\square} = \triangle$$
$$\square \cdot \frac{x}{\square} = \triangle \cdot \square$$
$$x = \triangle \square$$

57.
$$\triangle = -x$$
$$\triangle(-1) = -x(-1)$$
$$-\triangle = x$$

59.
$$6x = 10$$
$$\frac{6x}{6} = \frac{10}{6}$$
$$x = \frac{10}{6} = \frac{5}{3}$$
The number is $\frac{5}{3}$.

61.
$$\frac{x}{-9} = 5$$
$$\frac{x}{-9}(-9) = 5(-9)$$
$$x = -45$$
The number is -45.

63.
$$4x - 8 = 56$$
$$4x - 8 + 8 = 56 + 8$$
$$4x = 64$$
$$\frac{4x}{4} = \frac{64}{4}$$
$$x = 16$$
The number is 16.

65.
$$-3x + 15 = -6$$
$$-3x + 15 - 15 = -6 - 15$$
$$-3x = -21$$
$$\frac{-3x}{-3} = \frac{-21}{-3}$$
$$x = 7$$
The number is 7.

67.
$$M = \frac{n}{5}$$
$$2 = \frac{n}{5}$$
$$5(2) = 5\left(\frac{n}{5}\right)$$
$$10 = n$$
If you are 2 miles away from the lightning flash, it will take 10 seconds for the sound of thunder to reach you.

69.
$$M = \frac{A}{740}$$
$$2.03 = \frac{A}{740}$$
$$740(2.03) = 740 \cdot \frac{A}{740}$$
$$1502.2 = A$$
The speed of the Concorde is 1502.2 miles per hour.

71. a. The bar graph indicates that the debt limit was $30,200 per citizen in 2006.
Since 2006 is 6 years after 2000, substitute 6 into the formula for n.

$D = 1914n + 19{,}371$

$D = 1914(6) + 19{,}371$

$D = 11{,}484 + 19{,}371$

$D = 30{,}855$

The formula indicates that the debt limit was $30,855 per citizen in 2006.
The formula overestimates by $655.

b.

$$D = 1914n + 19{,}371$$

$$40{,}425 = 1914n + 19{,}371$$

$$40{,}425 - 19{,}371 = 1914n + 19{,}371 - 19{,}371$$

$$21054 = 1914n$$

$$\frac{21054}{1914} = \frac{1914n}{1914}$$

$$11 = n$$

The formula estimates that the debt limit will be $40,425 per citizen 11 years after 2000, or in 2011.

73. – 75. Answers will vary.

77. does not make sense; Explanations will vary.
Sample explanation: When you subtract 12 from $12 - 3x$, you should obtain $-3x$, not positive $3x$.

79. does not make sense; Explanations will vary.
Sample explanation: To determine the number of pay phones in 2006, substitute 6 in for n and simplify.

81. false; Changes to make the statement true will vary.
A sample change is: If $3x - 4 = 16$, then $3x = 20$.

83. true

85. Answers will vary. As an example, start with an integer solution, such as 10, and set it equal to x. That is, we have $x = 10$. The solution was obtained by multiplying both sides by $\frac{4}{5}$. To undo this, we multiply both sides of our equation by the reciprocal, $\frac{5}{4}$. This gives, $\frac{5}{4}x = \frac{5}{4}(10)$

$$\frac{5}{4}x = \frac{25}{2}$$

Therefore, an example equation would be

$\frac{5}{4}x = \frac{25}{2}$.

87.

$$-72.8y - 14.6 = -455.43 - 4.98y$$

$$-72.8y - 14.6 + 4.98y =$$
$$-455.43 - 4.98y + 4.98y$$

$$-67.82y - 14.6 = -455.43$$

$$-67.82y - 14.6 + 14.6 = -455.43 + 14.6$$

$$-67.82y = -440.83$$

$$\frac{-67.82y}{-67.82} = \frac{-440.83}{-67.82}$$

$$y = 6.5$$

The solution set is $\{6.5\}$.

88. $(-10)^2 = (-10)(-10) = 100$

89. $-10^2 = -1 \cdot 10^2 = -1(10)(10) = -100$

90. $x^3 - 4x = (-1)^3 - 4(-1)$
$\qquad = -1 + 4$
$\qquad = 3$

91. $13 - 3(x + 2) = 13 - 3x - 6$
$\qquad\qquad\qquad = -3x + 7$

92. $2(x - 3) - 17 = 13 - 3(x + 2)$
$\quad 2(6 - 3) - 17 = 13 - 3(6 + 2)$
$\qquad 2(3) - 17 = 13 - 3(8)$
$\qquad\quad 6 - 17 = 13 - 24$
$\qquad\quad -11 = -11,$ true
Yes, 6 is a solution of the equation.

93. $10\left(\dfrac{x}{5} - \dfrac{39}{5}\right) = 10 \cdot \dfrac{x}{5} - 10 \cdot \dfrac{39}{5}$
$\qquad\qquad\qquad = 2x - 78$

2.3 Check Points

1. Simplify the algebraic expression on each side.
$$-7x + 25 + 3x = 16 - 2x - 3$$
$$-4x + 25 = 13 - 2x$$
Collect variable terms on one side and constant terms on the other side.
$$-4x + 25 = 13 - 2x$$
$$-4x + 25 + 2x = 13 - 2x + 2x$$
$$-2x + 25 = 13$$
$$-2x + 25 - 25 = 13 - 25$$
$$-2x = -12$$
Isolate the variable and solve.
$$\frac{-2x}{-2} = \frac{-12}{-2}$$
$$x = 6$$
The solution set is $\{6\}$.

2. Simplify the algebraic expression on each side.
$$8x = 2(x + 6)$$
$$8x = 2x + 12$$
Collect variable terms on one side and constant terms on the other side.
$$8x - 2x = 2x - 2x + 12$$
$$6x = 12$$
Isolate the variable and solve.
$$\frac{6x}{6} = \frac{12}{6}$$
$$x = 2$$
The solution set is $\{2\}$.

3. Simplify the algebraic expression on each side.
$$4(2x + 1) - 29 = 3(2x - 5)$$
$$8x + 4 - 29 = 6x - 15$$
$$8x - 25 = 6x - 15$$
Collect variable terms on one side and constant terms on the other side.
$$8x - 6x - 25 = 6x - 6x - 15$$
$$2x - 25 = -15$$
$$2x - 25 + 25 = -15 + 25$$
$$2x = 10$$
Isolate the variable and solve.
$$\frac{2x}{2} = \frac{10}{2}$$
$$x = 5$$
The solution set is $\{5\}$.

4. Begin by multiplying both sides of the equation by 12, the least common denominator.
$$\frac{x}{4} = \frac{2x}{3} + \frac{5}{6}$$
$$12 \cdot \frac{x}{4} = 12\left(\frac{2x}{3} + \frac{5}{6}\right)$$
$$12 \cdot \frac{x}{4} = 12 \cdot \frac{2x}{3} + 12 \cdot \frac{5}{6}$$
$$3x = 8x + 10$$
$$3x - 8x = 8x - 8x + 10$$
$$-5x = 10$$
$$\frac{-5x}{-5} = \frac{10}{-5}$$
$$x = -2$$
The solution set is $\{-2\}$.

5.
$$3x + 7 = 3(x + 1)$$
$$3x + 7 = 3x + 3$$
$$3x - 3x + 7 = 3x - 3x + 3$$
$$7 = 3$$
The original equation is equivalent to the false statement $7 = 3$.
The equation has no solution. The solution set is $\{\ \}$.

6. $3(x - 1) + 9 = 8x + 6 - 5x$
$$3x - 3 + 9 = 3x + 6$$
$$3x + 6 = 3x + 6$$
$$3x - 3x + 6 = 3x - 3x + 6$$
$$6 = 6$$
The original equation is equivalent to $6 = 6$, which is true for every value of x.
The equation's solution is all real numbers or $\{x | x \text{ is a real number}\}$.

7.

$$D = \frac{10}{9}x + \frac{53}{9}$$

$$10 = \frac{10}{9}x + \frac{53}{9}$$

$$9 \cdot 10 = 9\left(\frac{10}{9}x + \frac{53}{9}\right)$$

$$90 = 10x + 53$$

$$90 - 53 = 10x + 53 - 53$$

$$37 = 10x$$

$$\frac{37}{10} = \frac{10x}{10}$$

$$3.7 = x$$

$$x = 3.7$$

The formula indicates that if the low-humor group averages a level of depression of 10 in response to a negative life event, the intensity of that event is 3.7. This is shown as the point whose corresponding value on the vertical axis is 10 and whose value on the horizontal axis is 3.7.

2.3 Exercise Set

1. $5x + 3x - 4x = 10 + 2$

$$8x - 4x = 12$$

$$4x = 12$$

$$\frac{4x}{4} = \frac{12}{4}$$

$$x = 3$$

The solution set is $\{3\}$.

3. $4x - 9x + 22 = 3x + 30$

$$-5x + 22 = 3x + 30$$

$$-5x - 3x + 22 = 30$$

$$-8x + 22 = 30$$

$$-8x = 30 - 22$$

$$-8x = 8$$

$$\frac{-8x}{-8} = \frac{8}{-8}$$

$$x = -1$$

The solution set is $\{-1\}$.

5. $3x + 6 - x = 8 + 3x - 6$

$$2x + 6 = 2 + 3x$$

$$2x + 6 - 2 = 2 + 3x - 2$$

$$2x + 4 = 3x$$

$$2x + 4 - 2x = 3x - 2x$$

$$4 = x$$

The solution set is $\{4\}$.

7. $4(x + 1) = 20$

$$4x + 4 = 20$$

$$4x = 20 - 4$$

$$4x = 16$$

$$\frac{4x}{4} = \frac{16}{4}$$

$$x = 4$$

The solution set is $\{4\}$.

9. $7(2x - 1) = 42$

$$14x - 7 = 42$$

$$14x - 7 + 7 = 42 + 7$$

$$14x = 49$$

$$\frac{14x}{14} = \frac{49}{14}$$

$$x = \frac{7}{2}$$

The solution set is $\left\{\frac{7}{2}\right\}$.

11.

$$38 = 30 - 2(x - 1)$$

$$38 = 30 - 2x + 2$$

$$38 = 32 - 2x$$

$$38 - 32 = -2x$$

$$6 = -2x$$

$$\frac{6}{-2} = \frac{-2x}{-2}$$

$$-3 = x$$

The solution set is $\{-3\}$.

13. $2(4z+3)-8=46$

$8z+6-8=46$

$8z-2=46$

$8z-2+2=46+2$

$8z=48$

$\dfrac{8z}{3}=\dfrac{48}{8}$

$z=6$

The solution set is $\{6\}$.

15. $6x-(3x+10)=14$

$6x-3x-10=14$

$3x-10=14$

$3x-10+10=14+10$

$3x=24$

$\dfrac{3x}{3}=\dfrac{24}{3}$

$x=8$

The solution set is $\{8\}$.

17. $5(2x+1)=12x-3$

$10x+5=12x-3$

$10x-10x+5=12x-10x-3$

$5=2x-3$

$5+3=2x-3+3$

$8=2x$

$\dfrac{8}{2}=\dfrac{2x}{2}$

$x=4$

The solution set is $\{4\}$.

19. $3(5-x)=4(2x+1)$

$15-3x=8x+4$

$15-3x-8x=8x+4-8x$

$15-11x=4$

$15-11x-15=4-15$

$-11x=-11$

$\dfrac{-11x}{-11}=\dfrac{-11}{-11}$

$x=1$

The solution set is $\{1\}$.

21. $8(y+2)=2(3y+4)$

$8y+16=6y+8$

$8y+16-16=6y+8-16$

$8y=6y-8$

$8y-6y=6y-8-6y$

$2y=-8$

$y=-4$

The solution set is $\{-4\}$.

23. $3x+3=7x-14-3$

$3x+3=7x-17$

$3x+3-3=7x-17-3$

$3x=7x-20$

$3x-7x=7x-20-7x$

$-4x=-20$

$\dfrac{-4x}{-4}=\dfrac{-20}{-4}$

$x=5$

The solution set is $\{5\}$.

25. $5(2x-8)-2=5(x-3)+3$

$10x-40-2=5x-15+3$

$10x-42=5x-12$

$10x-42+42=5x-12+42$

$10x=5x+30$

$10x=5x+30-5x$

$5x=30$

$\dfrac{5x}{5}=\dfrac{30}{5}$

$x=6$

The solution set is $\{6\}$.

27. $6=-4(1-x)+3(x+1)$

$6=-4+4x+3x+3$

$6=-1+7x$

$6+1=-1+7x+1$

$7=7x$

$\dfrac{7}{7}=\dfrac{7x}{7}$

$1=x$

The solution set is $\{1\}$.

29. $10(z+4)-4(z-2)=3(z-1)+2(z-3)$

$10z+40-4z+8=3z-3+2z-6$

$6z+48=5z-9$

$6z+48-48=5z-9-48$

$6z-5z=5z-57-5z$

$z=-57$

The solution set is $\{-57\}$.

31. $\dfrac{x}{5}-4=-6$

To clear the equation of fractions, multiply both sides by the least common denominator (LCD), which is 5.

$5\left(\dfrac{x}{5}-4\right)=5(-6)$

$5\cdot\dfrac{x}{5}-5\cdot4=-30$

$x-20=-30$

$x-20+20=-30+20$

$x=-10$

The solution set is $\{-10\}$.

33. $\dfrac{2x}{3}-5=7$

To clear the equation of fractions, multiply both sides by the least common denominator (LCD), which is 3.

$3\left(\dfrac{2}{3}x-5\right)=3(7)$

$3\cdot\dfrac{2}{3}x-3\cdot5=21$

$2x-15=21$

$2x-15+15=21+15$

$2x=36$

$\dfrac{2x}{2}=\dfrac{36}{2}$

$x=18$

The solution set is $\{18\}$.

35. $\dfrac{2y}{3}-\dfrac{3}{4}=\dfrac{5}{12}$

To clear the equation of fractions, multiply both sides by the least common denominator (LCD), which is 12.

$12\left(\dfrac{2y}{3}-\dfrac{3}{4}\right)=12\left(\dfrac{5}{12}\right)$

$12\left(\dfrac{2y}{3}\right)-12\left(\dfrac{3}{4}\right)=5$

$8y-9=5$

$8y-9+9=5+9$

$8y=14$

$\dfrac{8y}{8}=\dfrac{14}{8}$

$y=\dfrac{14}{8}=\dfrac{7}{4}$

The solution set is $\left\{\dfrac{7}{4}\right\}$.

37. $\dfrac{x}{3}+\dfrac{x}{2}=\dfrac{5}{6}$

To clear the equation of fractions, multiply both sides by the least common denominator (LCD), which is 6.

$6\left(\dfrac{x}{3}+\dfrac{x}{2}\right)=6\left(\dfrac{5}{6}\right)$

$2x+3x=5$

$5x=5$

$\dfrac{5x}{5}=\dfrac{5}{5}$

$x=1$

The solution set is $\{1\}$.

39. $20 - \dfrac{z}{3} = \dfrac{z}{2}$

To clear the equation of fractions, multiply both sides by the least common denominator (LCD), which is 6.

$$6\left(20 - \dfrac{z}{3}\right) = 6\left(\dfrac{z}{2}\right)$$

$$120 - 2z = 3z$$

$$120 - 2z + 2z = 3z + 2z$$

$$120 = 5z$$

$$\dfrac{120}{5} = \dfrac{5z}{5}$$

$$24 = z$$

The solution set is $\{24\}$.

41. $\dfrac{y}{3} + \dfrac{2}{5} = \dfrac{y}{5} - \dfrac{2}{5}$

To clear the equation of fractions, multiply both sides by the least common denominator (LCD), which is 15.

$$15\left(\dfrac{y}{3} + \dfrac{2}{5}\right) = 15\left(\dfrac{y}{5} + \dfrac{2}{5}\right)$$

$$15\left(\dfrac{y}{3}\right) + 15\left(\dfrac{2}{5}\right) = 15\left(\dfrac{y}{5}\right) + 15\left(-\dfrac{2}{5}\right)$$

$$5y + 6 = 3y - 6$$

$$5y + 6 - 3y = 3y - 6 - 3y$$

$$2y + 6 = -6$$

$$2y + 6 - 6 = -6 - 6$$

$$2y = -12$$

$$\dfrac{2y}{2} = \dfrac{-12}{2}$$

$$y = -6$$

The solution set is $\{-6\}$.

43. $\dfrac{3x}{4} - 3 = \dfrac{x}{2} + 2$

To clear the equation of fractions, multiply both sides by the least common denominator (LCD), which is 8.

$$8\left(\dfrac{3x}{4} - 3\right) = 8\left(\dfrac{x}{2} + 2\right)$$

$$8\left(\dfrac{3x}{4}\right) - 8 \cdot 3 = 8\left(\dfrac{x}{2}\right) + 8 \cdot 2$$

$$6x - 24 = 4x + 16$$

$$6x - 24 - 4x = 4x + 16 - 4x$$

$$2x - 24 = 16$$

$$2x - 24 + 24 = 16 + 24$$

$$2x = 40$$

$$\dfrac{2x}{2} = \dfrac{40}{2}$$

$$x = 20$$

The solution set is $\{20\}$.

45. $\dfrac{x-3}{5} - 1 = \dfrac{x-5}{4}$

To clear the equation of fractions, multiply both sides by the least common denominator (LCD), which is 20.

$$20\left(\dfrac{x-3}{5} - 1\right) = 20\left(\dfrac{x-5}{4}\right)$$

$$4(x-3) - 20 = 5(x-5)$$

$$4x - 12 - 20 = 5x - 25$$

$$4x - 5x - 32 = 5x - 5x - 25$$

$$-x - 32 = -25$$

$$-x - 32 + 32 = -25 + 32$$

$$-x = 7$$

$$-1(-x) = -1(7)$$

$$x = -7$$

The solution set is $\{-7\}$.

47.
$$3x - 7 = 3(x+1)$$

$$3x - 7 = 3x + 3$$

$$3x - 7 - 3x = 3x + 3 - 3x$$

$$-7 = 3$$

The original equation is equivalent to the false statement $-7 = 3$, so the equation is inconsistent and has no solution. The solution set is $\{\ \}$.

49.
$$2(x+4) = 4x+5-2x+3$$
$$2x+8 = 2x+8$$
$$2x-8-2x = 2x+8-2x$$
$$8 = 8$$
The original equation is equivalent to the true statement $8 = 8$, so the equation is an identity and the solution set is all real numbers $\{x|x \text{ is a real number}\}$.

51.
$$7+2(3x-5) = 8-3(2x+1)$$
$$7+6x-10 = 8-6x-3$$
$$6x-3 = 5-6x$$
$$6x+6x-3 = 5-6x+6x$$
$$12x-3 = 5$$
$$12x-3+3 = 5+3$$
$$12x = 8$$
$$\frac{12x}{12} = \frac{8}{12}$$
$$x = \frac{2}{3}$$
The solution set is $\left\{\frac{2}{3}\right\}$.

53.
$$4x+1-5x = 5-(x+4)$$
$$-x+1 = 5-x-4$$
$$-x+1 = 1-x$$
$$-x+1+x = 1-x+x$$
$$1 = 1$$
The original equation is equivalent to the true statement $1 = 1$, so the equation is an identity and the solution set is all real numbers $\{x|x \text{ is a real number}\}$.

55.
$$4(x+2)+1 = 7x-3(x-2)$$
$$4x+8+1 = 7x-3x+6$$
$$4x+9 = 4x+6$$
$$4x-4x+9 = 4x-4x+6$$
$$9 = 6$$
Since $9 = 6$ is a false statement, the original equation is inconsistent and has no solution. The solution set is $\{\ \}$.

57.
$$3-x = 2x+3$$
$$3-x+x = 2x+x+3$$
$$3 = 3x+3$$
$$3-3 = 3x+3-3$$
$$0 = 3x$$
$$\frac{0}{3} = \frac{3x}{3}$$
$$0 = x$$
The solution set is $\{0\}$.

59.
$$\frac{x}{3}+2 = \frac{x}{3}$$
Multiply by the LCD, which is 3.
$$3\left(\frac{x}{3}+2\right) = 3\left(\frac{x}{3}\right)$$
$$x+6 = x$$
$$x-x+6 = x-x$$
$$6 = 0$$
Since $6 = 0$ is a false statement, the original equation has no solution. The solution set is $\{\ \}$.

61.
$$\frac{x}{2}-\frac{x}{4}+4 = x+4$$
Multiply by the LCD, which is 4.
$$4\left(\frac{x}{2}-\frac{x}{4}+4\right) = 4(x+4)$$
$$4\left(\frac{x}{2}\right)-4\left(\frac{x}{4}\right)+16 = 4x+16$$
$$2x-x+16 = 4x+16$$
$$x+16 = 4x+16$$
$$x-x+16 = 4x-x+16$$
$$16 = 3x+16$$
$$16-16 = 3x+16-16$$
$$0 = 3x$$
$$\frac{0}{3} = \frac{3x}{3}$$
$$0 = x$$
The solution set is $\{0\}$.

63. $\dfrac{2}{3}x = 2 - \dfrac{5}{6}x$

Multiply both sides by the LCD which is 6.

$6\left(\dfrac{2}{3}x\right) = 6(2) - 6\left(\dfrac{5}{6}x\right)$

$2(2x) = 12 - 5x$

$4x = 12 - 5x$

$4x + 5x = 12 - 5x + 5x$

$9x = 12$

$\dfrac{9x}{9} = \dfrac{12}{9}$

$x = \dfrac{12}{9} = \dfrac{4}{3}$

The solution set is $\left\{\dfrac{4}{3}\right\}$.

65. $\dfrac{x}{\square} + \triangle = \$$

$\dfrac{x}{\square} + \triangle - \triangle = \$ - \triangle$

$\dfrac{x}{\square} = \$ - \triangle$

$\square\left(\dfrac{x}{\square}\right) = \square(\$ - \triangle)$

$x = \square\$ - \square\triangle$

67. First solve the equation for x.

$\dfrac{x}{5} - 2 = \dfrac{x}{3}$

$\dfrac{x}{5} - \dfrac{x}{5} - 2 = \dfrac{x}{3} - \dfrac{x}{5}$

$-2 = \dfrac{5x}{15} - \dfrac{3x}{15}$

$-2 = \dfrac{2x}{15}$

$15(-2) = 15\left(\dfrac{2x}{15}\right)$

$-30 = 2x$

$\dfrac{-30}{2} = \dfrac{2x}{2}$

$-15 = x$

Now evaluate the expression $x^2 - x$ for $x = -15$.

$x^2 - x = (-15)^2 - (-15)$

$\quad = 225 + 15$

$\quad = 240$

69. $\dfrac{1}{3}x + \dfrac{1}{5}x = 16$

LCD $= 15$

$15\left(\dfrac{1}{3}x\right) + 15\left(\dfrac{1}{5}x\right) = 15(16)$

$5x + 3x = 240$

$8x = 240$

$\dfrac{8x}{8} = \dfrac{240}{8}$

$x = 30$

The number is 30.

71. $\dfrac{3}{4}x - 3 = \dfrac{1}{2}x$

$4\left(\dfrac{3}{4}x\right) - 4(3) = 4\left(\dfrac{1}{2}x\right)$

$3x - 12 = 2x$

$3x - 2x - 12 = 2x - 2x$

$x - 12 = 0$

$x - 12 + 12 = 0 + 12$

$x = 12$

The number is 12.

73. $F = 10(x - 65) + 50$

$250 = 10(x - 65) + 50$

$250 - 50 = 10(x - 65) + 50 - 50$

$200 = 10x - 650$

$200 + 650 = 10x - 650 + 650$

$850 = 10x$

$\dfrac{850}{10} = \dfrac{10x}{10}$

$85 = x$

A person receiving a $250 fine was driving 85 miles per hour.

75.
$$\frac{W}{2} - 3H = 53$$
$$\frac{W}{2} - 3(6) = 53$$
$$\frac{W}{2} - 18 = 53$$
$$\frac{W}{2} - 18 + 18 = 53 + 18$$
$$\frac{W}{2} = 71$$
$$2 \cdot \frac{W}{2} = 2 \cdot 71$$
$$W = 142$$

According to the formula, the healthy weight of a person of height 5'6" is 142 pounds. This is 13 pounds below the upper end of the range shown in the bar graph.

77.
$$p = 15 + \frac{5d}{11}$$
$$201 = 15 + \frac{5d}{11}$$
$$201 - 15 = 15 + \frac{5d}{11} - 15$$
$$186 = \frac{5d}{11}$$
$$11(186) = 11\left(\frac{5d}{11}\right)$$
$$2046 = 5d$$
$$\frac{2046}{5} = d$$
$$409.2 = d$$
He descended to a depth of 409.2 feet below the surface.

79. – 81. Answers will vary.

83. makes sense

85. does not make sense; Explanations will vary. Sample explanation: Though 5 is a solution, the complete solution is all real numbers.

87. false; Changes to make the statement true will vary. A sample change is: The solution of the equation is all real numbers.

89. true

91.
$$f = 0.432h - 10.44$$
$$16 = 0.432h - 10.44$$
$$16 + 10.44 = 0.432h - 10.44 + 10.44$$
$$26.44 = 0.432h$$
$$\frac{26.44}{0.432} = \frac{0.432h}{0.432}$$
$$61.2 \approx h$$
The woman's height was about 61 inches or 5 feet 1 inch, so the partial skeleton could be that of the missing woman.

93.
$$2(3x + 4) = 3x + 2\left[3(x - 1) + 2\right]$$
$$6x + 8 = 3x + 2(3x - 3 + 2)$$
$$6x + 8 = 3x + 2(3x - 1)$$
$$6x + 8 = 3x + 6x - 2$$
$$6x + 8 = 9x - 2$$
$$6x + 8 - 9x = 9x - 2 - 9x$$
$$-3x + 8 = -2$$
$$-3x + 8 - 8 = -2 - 8$$
$$-3x = -10$$
$$\frac{-3x}{-3} = \frac{-10}{3}$$
$$x = \frac{10}{3}$$
The solution set is $\left\{\frac{10}{3}\right\}$.

95.
$$4.8y + 32.5 = 124.8 - 9.4y$$
$$4.8y + 32.5 + 9.4y = 124.8 - 9.4y + 9.4y$$
$$14.2y + 32.5 = 124.8$$
$$14.2y + 32.5 - 32.5 = 124.8 - 32.5$$
$$14.2y = 92.3$$
$$\frac{14.2y}{14.2} = \frac{92.3}{14.2}$$
$$y = 6.5$$
The solution set is $\{6.5\}$.

96. $-24 < -20$ because -24 lies further to the left on a number line.

97. $-\frac{1}{3} < -\frac{1}{5}$ because $-\frac{1}{3}$ lies further to the left on a number line.

98. $-9-11+7-(-3) = -9-11+7+3$
$$= -20+10$$
$$= -10$$

99. a. $T = D + pm$
$$T - D = pm$$

b. $T - D = pm$
$$\frac{T-D}{p} = \frac{pm}{p}$$
$$\frac{T-D}{p} = m$$

100. $4 = 0.25B$
$$\frac{4}{0.25} = \frac{0.25B}{0.25}$$
$$16 = B$$
The solution set is $\{16\}$.

101. $1.3 = P \cdot 26$
$$\frac{1.3}{26} = \frac{P \cdot 26}{26}$$
$$0.05 = P$$
The solution set is $\{0.05\}$.

2.4 Check Points

1. $A = lw$
$$\frac{A}{w} = \frac{lw}{w}$$
$$\frac{A}{w} = l$$

2. $2l + 2w = P$
$$2l + 2w - 2w = P - 2w$$
$$2l = P - 2w$$
$$\frac{2l}{2} = \frac{P-2w}{2}$$
$$l = \frac{P-2w}{2}$$

3. $T = D + pm$
$$T - D = pm$$
$$\frac{T-D}{p} = \frac{pm}{p}$$
$$\frac{T-D}{p} = m$$
$$m = \frac{T-D}{p}$$

4. $\frac{x}{3} - 4y = 5$
$$3\left(\frac{x}{3} - 4y\right) = 3 \cdot 5$$
$$3 \cdot \frac{x}{3} - 3 \cdot 4y = 3 \cdot 5$$
$$x - 12y = 15$$
$$x - 12y + 12y = 15 + 12y$$
$$x = 15 + 12y$$

5. To change a percent to a decimal number, move the decimal point two places to the left and remove the percent sign.

a. $67\% = 0.67$

b. $250\% = 2.50$ or 2.5

6. To change a decimal number to a percent, move the decimal point two places to the right and add a percent sign.
$0.023 = 2.3\%$

7. Use the formula $A = PB$: A is P percent of B.
What is 9% of 50?
$A = 0.09 \cdot 50$
$A = 4.5$

8. Use the formula $A = PB$: A is P percent of B.
9 is 60% of what?
$9 = 0.60 \cdot B$
$$\frac{9}{0.60} = \frac{0.60B}{0.60}$$
$$15 = B$$

9. Use the formula $A = PB$: A is P percent of B.

$\boxed{18}\ \boxed{\text{is}}\ \boxed{\text{what percent}}\ \boxed{\text{of}}\ \boxed{50?}$
$18\ =\quad\ P\quad\ \cdot\ \ 50$

$18 = P \cdot 50$

$\dfrac{18}{50} = \dfrac{50P}{50}$

$0.36 = P$

To change 0.36 to a percent, move the decimal point two places to the right and add a percent sign.
$0.36 = 36\%$

10. Use the formula $A = PB$: A is P percent of B.

Find the price decrease: $\$940 - \$611 = \$329$

$\boxed{\text{The price decrease}}\ \boxed{\text{is}}\ \boxed{\text{what percent}}\ \boxed{\text{of}}\ \boxed{\text{the original price?}}$
$329\quad =\quad P\quad \cdot\quad 940$

$329 = P \cdot 940$

$\dfrac{329}{940} = \dfrac{940P}{940}$

$0.35 = P$

To change 0.35 to a percent, move the decimal point two places to the right and add a percent sign.
$0.35 = 35\%$

11. a.

Year	Tax Paid the Year Before	increase/decrease	Taxes Paid This Year
1	$1200	20% decrease : $0.20 \cdot \$1200 = \$240$	$\$1200 - \$240 = \$960$
2	$960	20% increase : $0.20 \cdot \$960 = \$192$	$\$960 + \$192 = \$1152$

The taxes for year 2 will be $1152.

b. The taxes for year 2 are less than those originally paid.
Find the tax decrease: $\$1200 - \$1152 = \$48$

The tax decrease is what percent of the original tax?
$48\quad =\quad P\quad \cdot\quad 1200$

$48 = P \cdot 1200$

$\dfrac{48}{1200} = \dfrac{1200P}{1200}$

$0.04 = P$

To change 0.04 to a percent, move the decimal point two places to the right and add a percent sign.
$0.04 = 4\%$

The overall tax decrease is 4%.

2.4 Exercise Set

1. $d = rt$ for r

    $$\frac{d}{t} = \frac{rt}{t}$$

    $$\frac{d}{t} = r \text{ or } r = \frac{d}{t}$$

    This is the distance traveled formula:
    distance = rate · time.

3. $I = Prt$ for P

    $$\frac{I}{rt} = \frac{Prt}{rt}$$

    $$\frac{I}{rt} = P \text{ or } P = \frac{I}{rt}$$

    This is the formula for simple interest:
    interest = principal · rate · time.

5. $C = 2\pi r$ for r

    $$\frac{C}{2\pi} = \frac{2\pi r}{2\pi}$$

    $$\frac{C}{2\pi} = r \text{ or } r = \frac{C}{2\pi}$$

    This is the formula for finding the circumference of a circle if you know its radius.

7. $E = mc^2$

    $$\frac{E}{c^2} = \frac{mc^2}{c^2}$$

    $$\frac{E}{c^2} = m \text{ or } m = \frac{E}{c^2}$$

    This is Einstein's formula relating energy, mass, and the speed of light.

9. $y = mx + b$ for m

    $$y - b = mx$$

    $$\frac{y-b}{x} = \frac{mx}{x}$$

    $$\frac{y-b}{x} = m \text{ or } m = \frac{y-b}{x}$$

    This is the slope-intercept formula for the equation of a line.

11. $T = D + pm$ for D

    $$T - pm = D + pm - pm$$

    $$T - pm = D$$

    $$D = T - pm$$

13. $A = \frac{1}{2}bh$ for b

    $$2A = 2\left(\frac{1}{2}bh\right)$$

    $$2A = bh$$

    $$\frac{2A}{h} = \frac{bh}{h}$$

    $$\frac{2A}{h} = b \text{ or } b = \frac{2A}{h}$$

    This is the formula for the area of a triangle: area = $\frac{1}{2}$ · base · height.

15. $M = \frac{n}{5}$ for n

    $$5M = 5\left(\frac{n}{5}\right)$$

    $$5M = n \text{ or } n = 5M$$

17. $\frac{c}{2} + 80 = 2F$ for c

    $$\frac{c}{2} + 80 - 80 = 2F - 80$$

    $$\frac{c}{2} = 2F - 80$$

    $$2\left(\frac{c}{2}\right) = 2(2F - 80)$$

    $$c = 4F - 160$$

19. $A = \frac{1}{2}(a + b)$ for a

    $$2A = 2\left[\frac{1}{2}(a + b)\right]$$

    $$2A = a + b$$

    $$2A - b = a + b - b$$

    $$2A - b = a \text{ or } a = 2A - b$$

    This is the formula for finding the average of two numbers.

21. $S = P + Prt$ for r

$S - P = P + Prt - P$

$S - P = Prt$

$\dfrac{S-P}{Pt} = \dfrac{Prt}{Pt}$

$\dfrac{S-P}{Pt} = r$ or $r = \dfrac{S-P}{Pt}$

This is the formula for finding the sum of principle and interest for simple interest problems.

23. $A = \dfrac{1}{2}h(a+b)$ for b

$2A = 2\left[\dfrac{1}{2}h(a+b)\right]$

$2A = h(a+b)$

$2A = ha + hb$

$2A - ha = ha + hb - ha$

$2A - ha = hb$

$\dfrac{2A - ha}{h} = \dfrac{hb}{h}$

$\dfrac{2A - ha}{h} = b$ or $b = \dfrac{2A}{h} - a$

This is the formula for the area of a trapezoid.

25. $Ax + By = C$ for x

$Ax + By - By = C - By$

$Ax = C - By$

$\dfrac{Ax}{A} = \dfrac{C - By}{A}$

$x = \dfrac{C - By}{A}$

This is the standard form of the equation of a line.

27. To change a percent to a decimal number, move the decimal point two places to the left and remove the percent sign.

$27\% = 0.27$

29. $63.4\% = 0.634$

31. $170\% = 1.7$

33. $3\% = 0.03$

35. $\dfrac{1}{2}\% = 0.5\% = 0.005$

37. To change a decimal number to a percent, move the decimal point two places to the right and add a percent sign.

$0.89 = 89\%$

39. $0.002 = 0.2\%$

41. $4.78 = 478\%$

43. $100 = 10,000\%$

45. $A = PB$; $P = 3\% = 0.03, B = 200$

$A = PB$

$A = 0.03 \cdot 200$

$A = 6$

3% of 200 is 6.

47. $A = PB$; $P = 18\% = 0.18, B = 40$

$A = PB$

$A = 0.18 \cdot 40$

$A = 7.2$

18% of 40 is 7.2.

49. $A = PB$; $A = 3, P = 60\% = 0.6$

$A = PB$

$3 = 0.6 \cdot B$

$\dfrac{3}{0.6} = \dfrac{0.6B}{0.6}$

$5 = B$

3 is 60% of 5.

51. $A = PB$; $A = 40.8, P = 24\% = 0.24$

$A = PB$

$40.8 = 0.24 \cdot B$

$\dfrac{40.8}{0.24} = \dfrac{0.24B}{0.24}$

$170 = B$

24% of 170 is 40.8.

53. $A = PB$; $A = 3$, $B = 15$

$A = PB$

$3 = P \cdot 15$

$\dfrac{3}{15} = \dfrac{P \cdot 15}{15}$

$0.2 = P$

$0.2 = 20\%$

3 is 20% of 15.

55. $A = PB$; $A = 0.3$, $B = 2.5$

$A = PB$

$0.3 = P \cdot 2.5$

$\dfrac{0.3}{2.5} = \dfrac{P - 2.5}{2.5}$

$0.12 = P$

$0.12 = 12\%$

0.3 is 12% of 2.5

57. The increase is $8 - 5 = 3$.

$A = PB$

$3 = P \cdot 5$

$\dfrac{3}{5} = \dfrac{P \cdot 5}{5}$

$0.60 = P$

This is a 60% increase.

59. The decrease is $4 - 1 = 3$.

$A = PB$

$3 = P \cdot 4$

$\dfrac{3}{4} = \dfrac{4P}{4}$

$0.75 = P$

This is a 75% decrease.

61.

$y = (a + b)x$

$\dfrac{y}{(a+b)} = \dfrac{(a+b)x}{(a+b)}$

$\dfrac{y}{a+b} = x$ or $x = \dfrac{y}{a+b}$

63.

$y = (a - b)x + 5$

$y - 5 = (a - b)x + 5 - 5$

$y - 5 = (a - b)x$

$\dfrac{y - 5}{a - b} = \dfrac{(a - b)x}{a - b}$

$\dfrac{y - 5}{a - b} = x$ or $x = \dfrac{y - 5}{a - b}$

65.

$y = cx + dx$

$y = (c + d)x$

$\dfrac{y}{c + d} = \dfrac{(c + d)x}{c + d}$

$\dfrac{y}{c + d} = x$ or $x = \dfrac{y}{c + d}$

67.

$y = Ax - Bx - C$

$y = (A - B)x - C$

$y + C = (A - B)x - C + C$

$y + C = (A - B)x$

$\dfrac{y + C}{A - B} = \dfrac{(A - B)x}{A - B}$

$\dfrac{y + C}{A - B} = x$ or $x = \dfrac{y + C}{A - B}$

69. a. $A = \dfrac{x + y + z}{3}$ for z

$3A = 3\left(\dfrac{x + y + z}{3}\right)$

$3A = x + y + z$

$3A - x - y = x + y + z - x - y$

$3A - x - y = z$

b. $A = 90$, $x = 86$, $y = 88$

$z = 3A - x - y$

$z = 3(90) - 86 - 88 = 96$

You need to get 96% on the third exam to have an average of 90%

71. a. $d = rt$ for t

$\dfrac{d}{r} = \dfrac{rt}{r}$

$\dfrac{d}{r} = t$

b. $t = \dfrac{d}{r}$; $d = 100$, $r = 40$

$t = \dfrac{100}{40} = 2.5$

You would travel for 2.5 $\left(\text{or } 2\dfrac{1}{2}\right)$ hours.

73. $0.34 \cdot 1200 = 408$

408 single women would marry someone other than the perfect mate.

75. This is the equivalent of asking: 175 is 35% of what?

$$A = P \cdot B$$

$$175 = 0.35 \cdot B$$

$$\frac{175}{0.35} = \frac{0.35B}{0.35}$$

$$500 = B$$

Americans throw away 500 billion pounds of trash each year.

77. a. The total number of countries in 1974 was $41 + 48 + 63 = 152$.

$$A = P \cdot B$$

$$41 = P \cdot 152$$

$$\frac{41}{152} = \frac{152B}{152}$$

$$0.27 \approx B$$

About 27% of countries were free in 1974.

b. The total number of countries in 2004 was $89 + 54 + 49 = 192$.

$$A = P \cdot B$$

$$89 = P \cdot 192$$

$$\frac{89}{192} = \frac{192B}{192}$$

$$0.46 \approx B$$

About 46% of countries were free in 2004.

c. The increase is $89 - 41 = 48$.

$$A = P \cdot B$$

$$48 = P \cdot 41$$

$$\frac{48}{41} = \frac{41B}{41}$$

$$1.17 \approx B$$

There was approximately a 117% increase in the number of free countries from 1974 to 2004.

79. $A = PB; \; A = 7500, B = 60,000$

$$A = PB$$

$$7500 = P \cdot 60,000$$

$$\frac{7500}{60,000} = \frac{P \cdot 60,000}{60,000}$$

$$0.125 = P$$

The charity has raised $0.125 = 12.5\%$ of its goal.

81. $A = PB; \; p = 15\% = 0.15, B = 60$

$$A = 0.15 \cdot 60 = 09$$

The tip was $9.

83. a. The sales tax is 6% of $16,800.

$$0.06(16,800) = 1008$$

The sales tax due on the car is $1008.

b. The total cost is the sum of the price of the car and the sales tax.

$$\$16,800 + \$1008 = \$17,808$$

The car's total cost is $17,808.

85. a. The discount is 12% of $860.

$$0.12(860) = 103.20$$

The discount amount is $103.20.

b. The sale price is the regular price minus the discount amount:

$$\$860 - \$103.20 = \$756.80$$

87. The decrease is $\$840 - \$714 = \$126$.

$$A = P \cdot B$$

$$126 = P \cdot 840$$

$$\frac{126}{840} = \frac{P \cdot 840}{840}$$

$$0.15 = P$$

This is a $0.15 = 15\%$ decrease.

89. Investment dollars decreased in year 1 are $0.30 \cdot \$10,000 = \$3000$. This means that $10,000 − $3000 = $7000 remains. Investment dollars increased in year 2 are $0.40 \cdot \$7000 = \$2800$. This means that $7000 + $2800 = $9800 of the original investment remains. This is an overall loss of $200 over the two years.

$$A = P \cdot B$$

$$200 = P \cdot 10,000$$

$$\frac{200}{10,000} = \frac{P \cdot 10,000}{10,000}$$

$$0.02 = P$$

The financial advisor is not using percentages properly. Instead of a 10% gain, this is a $0.02 = 2\%$ loss.

91. – 95. Answers will vary.

97. does not make sense; Explanations will vary. Sample explanation: Sometimes you will solve for one variable in terms of other variables.

99. does not make sense; Explanations will vary. Sample explanation: Since the sale price cannot be negative, the percent decrease cannot be more than 100%.

101. false; Changes to make the statement true will vary.

A sample change is: If $A = lw$, then $w = \dfrac{A}{l}$.

103. true

105.
$$5x + 20 = 8x - 16$$
$$5x + 20 - 8x = 8x - 16 - 8x$$
$$-3x + 20 = -16$$
$$-3x + 20 - 20 = -16 - 20$$
$$-3x = -36$$
$$\frac{-3x}{-3} = \frac{-36}{-3}$$
$$x = 12$$

Check:
$$5(12) + 20 = 8(12) - 16$$
$$60 + 20 = 96 - 16$$
$$80 = 80$$

The solution set is $\{12\}$.

106.
$$5(2y - 3) - 1 = 4(6 + 2y)$$
$$10y - 15 - 1 = 24 + 8y$$
$$10y - 16 = 24 + 8y$$
$$10y - 16 - 8y = 24 + 8y - 8y$$
$$2y - 16 = 24$$
$$2y - 16 + 16 = 24 + 16$$
$$2y = 40$$
$$\frac{2y}{2} = \frac{40}{2}$$
$$y = 20$$

Check:
$$5(2 \cdot 20 - 3) - 1 = 4(6 + 2 \cdot 20)$$
$$5(40 - 3) - 1 = 4(6 + 40)$$
$$5(37) - 1 = 4(46)$$
$$185 - 1 = 184$$
$$184 = 184$$

The solution set is $\{20\}$.

107. $x - 0.3x = 1x - 0.3x = (1 - 0.3)x = 0.7x$

108. $\dfrac{13}{x} - 7x$

109. $8(x + 14)$

110. $9(x - 5)$

Mid-Chapter Check Point

1. Begin by multiplying both sides of the equation by 4, the least common denominator.
$$\frac{x}{2} = 12 - \frac{x}{4}$$
$$4\left(\frac{x}{2}\right) = 4(12) - 4\left(\frac{x}{4}\right)$$
$$2x = 48 - x$$
$$2x + x = 48 - x + x$$
$$3x = 48$$
$$\frac{3x}{3} = \frac{48}{3}$$
$$x = 16$$

The solution set is $\{16\}$.

2.
$$5x - 42 = -57$$
$$5x - 42 + 42 = -57 + 42$$
$$5x = -15$$
$$\frac{5x}{5} = \frac{-15}{5}$$
$$x = -3$$

The solution set is $\{-3\}$.

3.
$$H = \frac{EC}{825}$$
$$H \cdot 825 = \frac{EC}{825} \cdot 825$$
$$825H = EC$$
$$\frac{825H}{E} = \frac{EC}{E}$$
$$\frac{825H}{E} = C$$

4. $A = P \cdot B$
$$A = 0.06 \cdot 140$$
$$A = 8.4$$
8.4 is 6% of 140.

5.
$$\frac{-x}{10} = -3$$
$$10\left(\frac{-x}{10}\right) = 10(-3)$$
$$-x = -30$$
$$-1(-x) = -1(-30)$$
$$x = 30$$

The solution set is $\{30\}$.

6.
$$1-3(y-5)=4(2-3y)$$
$$1-3y+15=8-12y$$
$$-3y+16=8-12y$$
$$-3y+12y+16=8-12y+12y$$
$$9y+16=8$$
$$9y+16-16=8-16$$
$$9y=-8$$
$$\frac{9y}{9}=\frac{-8}{9}$$
$$y=-\frac{8}{9}$$
The solution set is $\left\{-\dfrac{8}{9}\right\}$.

7.
$$S=2\pi rh$$
$$\frac{S}{2\pi h}=\frac{2\pi rh}{2\pi h}$$
$$\frac{S}{2\pi h}=r$$

8.
$$A=P\cdot B$$
$$12=0.30\cdot B$$
$$\frac{12}{0.30}=\frac{0.30\cdot B}{0.30}$$
$$40=B$$
12 is 30% of 40.

9. $\dfrac{3y}{5}+\dfrac{y}{2}=\dfrac{5y}{4}-3$

To clear fractions, multiply both sides by the LCD, 20.
$$20\left(\frac{3y}{5}\right)+20\left(\frac{y}{2}\right)=20\left(\frac{5y}{4}\right)-20(3)$$
$$4(3y)+10y=5(5y)-60$$
$$12y+10y=25y-60$$
$$22y=25y-60$$
$$22y-25y=25y-25y-60$$
$$-3y=-60$$
$$\frac{-3y}{-3}=\frac{-60}{-3}$$
$$y=20$$
The solution set is $\{20\}$.

10.
$$5z+7=6(z-2)-4(2z-3)$$
$$5z+7=6z-12-8z+12$$
$$5z+7=-2z$$
$$5z-5z+7=-2z-5z$$
$$7=-7z$$
$$\frac{7}{-7}=\frac{-7z}{-7}$$
$$-1=z$$
The solution set is $\{-1\}$.

11.
$$Ax-By=C$$
$$Ax-By+By=C+By$$
$$Ax=C+By$$
$$\frac{Ax}{A}=\frac{C+By}{A}$$
$$x=\frac{C+By}{A}\ \text{ or }\ \frac{By+C}{A}$$

12. $6y+7+3y=3(3y-1)$
$$9y+7=9y-3$$
$$9y-9y+7=9y-9y-3$$
$$7=-3$$
Since this is a false statement, there is no solution or $\{\ \}$.

13.
$$10\left(\frac{1}{2}x+3\right)=10\left(\frac{3}{5}x-1\right)$$
$$10\left(\frac{1}{2}x\right)+10(3)=10\left(\frac{3}{5}x\right)-10(1)$$
$$5x+30=6x-10$$
$$5x-5x+30=6x-5x-10$$
$$30=x-10$$
$$30+10=x-10+10$$
$$40=x$$
The solution set is $\{40\}$.

14.
$$A = P \cdot B$$
$$50 = P \cdot 400$$
$$\frac{50}{400} = \frac{P \cdot 400}{400}$$
$$0.125 = P$$
50 is 0.125 = 12.5% of 400.

15.
$$\frac{3(m+2)}{4} = 2m + 3$$
$$4 \cdot \frac{3(m+2)}{4} = 4(2m+3)$$
$$3(m+2) = 4(2m+3)$$
$$3m + 6 = 8m + 12$$
$$3m - 3m + 6 = 8m - 3m + 12$$
$$6 = 5m + 12$$
$$6 - 12 = 5m + 12 - 12$$
$$-6 = 5m$$
$$\frac{-6}{5} = \frac{5m}{5}$$
$$-\frac{6}{5} = m$$
The solution set is $\left\{-\frac{6}{5}\right\}$.

16. The increase is 50 − 40 = 10.
$$A = P \cdot B$$
$$10 = P \cdot 40$$
$$\frac{10}{40} = \frac{P \cdot 40}{40}$$
$$0.25 = P$$
This is a 0.25 = 25% increase.

17.
$$12w - 4 + 8w - 4 = 4(5w - 2)$$
$$20w - 8 = 20w - 8$$
$$20w - 20w - 8 = 20w - 20w - 8$$
$$-8 = -8$$
Since −8 = −8 is a true statement, the solution is all real numbers or $\{x \mid x \text{ is a real number}\}$.

18. a.
$$G = -\frac{1}{2}n + 47$$
$$G = -\frac{1}{2}(10) + 47$$
$$= -5 + 47$$
$$= 42$$
According to the formula, 42% of Americans had guns in their homes in 1990. This underestimates the actual percentage shown in the gar graph by 0.7%

b.
$$G = -\frac{1}{2}n + 47$$
$$30 = -\frac{1}{2}n + 47$$
$$2 \cdot 30 = 2\left(-\frac{1}{2}n + 47\right)$$
$$60 = -n + 94$$
$$60 - 94 = -n + 94 - 94$$
$$-34 = -n$$
$$n = 34$$
According to the formula, 30% of Americans will have guns in their homes 34 years after 1980, or 2014.

2.5 Check Points

1. Let x = the number.
$$6x - 4 = 68$$
$$6x - 4 + 4 = 68 + 4$$
$$6x = 72$$
$$x = 12$$
The number is 12.

2. Let x = the average salary for elementary school teachers.
Let $x + 54{,}890$ = the average salary for lawyers
$$x + (x + 54{,}890) = 142{,}970$$
$$x + x + 54{,}890 = 142{,}970$$
$$2x + 54{,}890 = 142{,}970$$
$$2x + 54{,}890 - 54{,}890 = 142{,}970 - 54{,}890$$
$$2x = 88{,}080$$
$$x = 44{,}040$$
The average salary for elementary school teachers is $44,040 and the average salary for lawyers is $44,040 + $54,890 = $98,930.

3. Let $x =$ the page number of the first facing page.
Let $x + 1 =$ the page number of the second facing page.

$$x + (x + 1) = 145$$
$$x + x + 1 = 145$$
$$2x + 1 = 145$$
$$2x + 1 - 1 = 145 - 1$$
$$2x = 144$$
$$x = 72$$
$$x + 1 = 73$$

The page numbers are 72 and 73.

4. Let $x =$ the number of eighths of a mile traveled.

$$2 + 0.25x = 10$$
$$2 - 2 + 0.25x = 10 - 2$$
$$0.25x = 8$$
$$\frac{0.25x}{0.25} = \frac{8}{0.25}$$
$$x = 32$$

You can go 32 eighths of a mile. That is equivalent to $\frac{32}{8} = 4$ miles.

5. Let $x =$ the width of the swimming pool.
Let $3x =$ the length of the swimming pool.

$$P = 2l + 2w$$
$$320 = 2 \cdot 3x + 2 \cdot x$$
$$320 = 6x + 2x$$
$$320 = 8x$$
$$\frac{320}{8} = \frac{8x}{8}$$
$$40 = x$$
$$x = 40$$
$$3x = 120$$

The pool is 40 feet wide and 120 feet long.

6. Let $x =$ the original price.

Original price	minus	the reduction (40% of original price)	is	the reduced price, $564
x	$-$	$0.4x$	$=$	564

$$x - 0.4x = 564$$
$$0.6x = 564$$
$$\frac{0.6x}{0.6} = \frac{564}{0.6}$$
$$x = 940$$

The original price was $940.

2.5 Exercise Set

1.
$$x + 60 = 410$$
$$x + 60 - 60 = 410 - 60$$
$$x = 350$$
The number is 350.

3.
$$x - 23 = 214$$
$$x - 23 + 23 = 214 + 23$$
$$x = 237$$
The number is 237.

5.
$$7x = 126$$
$$\frac{7x}{7} = \frac{126}{7}$$
$$x = 18$$
The number is 18.

7.
$$\frac{x}{19} = 5$$
$$19\left(\frac{x}{19}\right) = 19(5)$$
$$x = 95$$
The number is 95.

9.
$$4 + 2x = 56$$
$$4 - 4 + 2x = 56 - 4$$
$$2x = 52$$
$$\frac{2x}{2} = \frac{52}{2}$$
$$x = 26$$
The number is 26.

11.
$$5x - 7 = 178$$
$$5x - 7 + 7 = 178 + 7$$
$$5x = 185$$
$$\frac{5x}{5} = \frac{185}{5}$$
$$x = 37$$
The number is 37.

13.
$$x + 5 = 2x$$
$$x + 5 - x = 2x - x$$
$$5 = x$$
The number is 5.

15. $2(x+4) = 36$

$2x + 8 = 36$

$2x = 28$

$x = 14$

The number is 14.

17. $9x = 30 + 3x$

$6x = 30$

$x = 5$

The number is 5.

19. $\dfrac{3x}{5} + 4 = 34$

$\dfrac{3x}{5} = 30$

$3x = 150$

$x = 50$

The number is 50.

21. Let $x =$ the time spent listening to radio.

Let $x + 581 =$ the time spent watching TV.

$x + (x + 581) = 2529$

$x + x + 581 = 2529$

$2x + 581 - 581 = 2529 - 581$

$2x = 1948$

$x = 974$

$x + 581 = 1555$

Americans spent 974 hours listening to radio and 1555 hours watching TV.

23. Let $x =$ the average salary for carpenters.

Let $2x - 7740 =$ the average salary for computer programmers.

$x + (2x - 7740) = 99,000$

$x + 2x - 7740 = 99,000$

$3x - 7740 = 99,000$

$3x - 7740 + 7740 = 99,000 + 7740$

$3x = 106,740$

$x = 35,580$

$2x - 7740 = 63,420$

The average salary for carpenters is \$35,580 and the average salary for computer programmers is \$63,420.

25. Let $x =$ the number of the left-hand page.

Let $x + 1 =$ the number of the right-hand page.

$x + (x + 1) = 629$

$x + x + 1 = 629$

$2x + 1 = 629$

$2x + 1 - 1 = 629 - 1$

$2x = 628$

$\dfrac{2x}{2} = \dfrac{628}{2}$

$x = 314$

The pages are 314 and 315.

27. Let $x =$ the first consecutive odd integer (Babe Ruth).

Let $x + 2 =$ the second consecutive odd integer (Roger Maris).

$x + (x + 2) = 120$

$x + x + 2 = 120$

$2x + 2 = 120$

$2x = 118$

$x = 59$

$x + 2 = 61$

Babe Ruth had 59 home runs and Roger Maris had 61.

29. Let $x =$ the number of miles you can travel in one week for \$320.

$200 + 0.15x = 320$

$200 + 0.15x - 200 = 320 - 200$

$0.15x = 120$

$\dfrac{0.15x}{0.15} = \dfrac{120}{0.15}$

$x = 800$

You can travel 800 miles in one week for \$320. This checks because \$200 + 0.15(\$800) = \$320.

31. Let $x =$ the number of years after 2004.

$960 + 11.40x = 1074$

$960 - 960 + 11.40x = 1074 - 960$

$11.40x = 114$

$\dfrac{11.40x}{11.40} = \dfrac{114}{11.40}$

$x = 10$

Mortgage payments will average \$1074 ten years after 2004, or 2014.

33. Let $x =$ the width of the field.
Let $4x =$ the length of the field.
$$P = 2l + 2w$$
$$500 = 2 \cdot 4x + 2 \cdot x$$
$$500 = 8x + 2x$$
$$500 = 10x$$
$$\frac{500}{10} = \frac{10x}{10}$$
$$50 = x$$
$$x = 50$$
$$4x = 200$$
The field is 50 yards wide and 200 yards long.

35. Let $x =$ the width of a football field.
Let $x + 200 =$ the length of a football field.
$$P = 2l + 2w$$
$$1040 = 2(x + 200) + 2 \cdot x$$
$$1040 = 2x + 400 + 2x$$
$$1040 = 4x + 400$$
$$640 = 4x$$
$$160 = x$$
$$x = 160$$
$$x + 200 = 360$$
A football field is 160 feet wide and 360 feet long.

37. As shown in the diagram,
let $x =$ the height and $3x =$ the length.
To construct the bookcase, 3 heights and 4 lengths are needed.
Since 60 feet of lumber is available,
$$3x + 4(3x) = 60$$
$$3x + 12x = 60$$
$$15x = 60$$
$$x = 4$$
$$3x = 12$$
The bookcase is 12 feet long and 4 feet high.

39. Let $x =$ the price before the reduction.
$$x - 0.20x = 320$$
$$0.80x = 320$$
$$\frac{0.80x}{0.80} = \frac{320}{0.80}$$
$$x = 400$$
The price before the reduction was $400.

41. Let $x =$ the last year's salary.
$$x + 0.08x = 50,220$$
$$1.08x = 50,220$$
$$\frac{1.08x}{1.08} = \frac{50,220}{1.08}$$
$$x = 46,500$$
Last year's salary was $46,500.

43. Let $x =$ the price of the car without tax.
$$x + 0.06x = 23,850$$
$$1.06x = 23,850$$
$$\frac{1.06x}{1.06} = \frac{23,850}{1.06}$$
$$x = 22,500$$
The price of the car without sales tax was $14,500.

45. Let $x =$ the number of hours of labor.
$$63 + 35x = 448$$
$$63 + 35x - 63 = 448 - 63$$
$$35x = 385$$
$$\frac{35x}{35} = \frac{385}{35}$$
$$x = 11$$
It took 11 hours of labor to repair the car.

47. – 59. Answers will vary.

51. does not make sense; Explanations will vary.
Sample explanation: You should practice setting up and solving word problems.

53. makes sense

55. false; Changes to make the statement true will vary.
A sample change is: This should be modeled by $x - 10 = 160$.

57. true

59. Let $x =$ the number of inches over 5 feet.
$$W = 100 + 5x$$
$$135 = 100 + 5x$$
$$135 - 100 = 100 - 100 + 5x$$
$$35 = 5x$$
$$\frac{35}{5} = \frac{5x}{5}$$
$$7 = x$$
The height 5' 7" corresponds to 135 pounds.

61. Let x = the woman's age.
Let $3x$ = the "uncle's" age.
$$3x + 20 = 2(x + 20)$$
$$3x + 20 = 2x + 40$$
$$3x - 2x + 20 = 2x - 2x + 40$$
$$x + 20 = 40$$
$$x + 20 - 20 = 40 - 20$$
$$x = 20$$
The woman is 20 years old and the "uncle" is $3x = 3(20) = 60$ years old.

63. $$\frac{4}{5}x = -16$$
$$\frac{5}{4}\left(\frac{4}{5}x\right) = \frac{5}{4}(-16)$$
$$x = -20$$
Check:
$$\frac{4}{5}(-20) = -16$$
$$\frac{4}{5} \cdot \frac{-20}{1} = -16$$
$$\frac{-80}{5} = -16$$
$$-16 = -16$$
The solution set is $\{-20\}$.

64. $$6(y - 1) + 7 = 9y - y + 1$$
$$6y - 6 + 7 = 9y - y + 1$$
$$6y + 1 = 8y + 1$$
$$6y + 1 - 1 = 8y + 1 - 1$$
$$6y = 8y$$
$$6y - 8y = 8y - 8y$$
$$-2y = 0$$
$$y = 0$$
Check:
$$6(0 - 1) + 7 = 9(0) - 0 + 1$$
$$6 - 10 + 7 = 0 - 0 + 1$$
$$1 = 1$$
The solution set is $\{0\}$.

65. $V = \frac{1}{3}lwh$ for w
$$V = \frac{1}{3}lwh$$
$$3V = 3\left(\frac{1}{3}lwh\right)$$
$$3V = lwh$$
$$\frac{3V}{lh} = \frac{lwh}{lh}$$
$$\frac{3V}{lh} = w \quad \text{or} \quad w = \frac{3V}{lh}$$

66. $$x + 3 < 8$$
$$2 + 3 < 8$$
$$5 < 8, \text{ true}$$
2 is a solution to the inequality.

67. $$4y - 7 \geq 5$$
$$4(6) - 7 \geq 5$$
$$24 - 7 \geq 5$$
$$17 \geq 5, \text{ true}$$
6 is a solution to the inequality.

68. $$2(x - 3) + 5x = 8(x - 1)$$
$$2x - 6 + 5x = 8x - 8$$
$$7x - 6 = 8x - 8$$
$$7x - 8x - 6 = 8x - 8x - 8$$
$$-x - 6 + 6 = -8 + 6$$
$$-x = -2$$
$$x = 2$$
The solution set is $\{2\}$.

2.6 Check Points

1. a.

b.

c.

2. a. $[0, \infty)$

b. $(-\infty, 5)$

3. $x + 6 < 9$

   $x + 6 - 6 < 9 - 6$

   $x < 3$

   The solution set is $(-\infty, 3)$ or $\{x | x < 3\}$.

4. $8x - 2 \geq 7x - 4$

   $8x - 7x - 2 \geq 7x - 7x - 4$

   $x - 2 \geq -4$

   $x - 2 + 2 \geq -4 + 2$

   $x \geq -2$

   The solution set is $[-2, \infty)$ or $\{x | x \geq -2\}$.

5. a. $\dfrac{1}{4}x < 2$

   $4 \cdot \dfrac{1}{4}x < 4 \cdot 2$

   $x < 8$

   The solution set is $(-\infty, 8)$ or $\{x | x < 8\}$.

b. $-6x < 18$

   $\dfrac{-6x}{-6} > \dfrac{18}{-6}$

   $x > -3$

   The solution set is $(-3, \infty)$ or $\{x | x > -3\}$.

6. $5y - 3 \geq 17$

   $5y - 3 + 3 \geq 17 + 3$

   $5y \geq 20$

   $\dfrac{5y}{5} \geq \dfrac{20}{5}$

   $y \geq 4$

   The solution set is $[4, \infty)$ or $\{y | y \geq 4\}$.

7. $6 - 3x \leq 5x - 2$

   $6 - 3x - 5x \leq 5x - 5x - 2$

   $6 - 8x \leq -2$

   $6 - 6 - 8x \leq -2 - 6$

   $-8x \leq -8$

   $\dfrac{-8x}{-8} \geq \dfrac{-8}{-8}$

   $x \geq 1$

   The solution set is $[1, \infty)$ or $\{x | x \geq 1\}$.

8. $2(x - 3) - 1 \leq 3(x + 2) - 14$

   $2x - 6 - 1 \leq 3x + 6 - 14$

   $2x - 7 \leq 3x - 8$

   $2x - 3x - 7 \leq 3x - 3x - 8$

   $-x - 7 \leq -8$

   $-x - 7 + 7 \leq -8 + 7$

   $-x \leq -1$

   $\dfrac{-x}{-1} \geq \dfrac{-1}{-1}$

   $x \geq 1$

   The solution set is $[1, \infty)$ or $\{x | x \geq 1\}$.

9. $4(x + 2) > 4x + 15$

   $4x + 8 > 4x + 15$

   $4x - 4x + 8 > 4x - 4x + 15$

   $8 > 15, \ \text{false}$

   There is no solution or $\{\ \}$.

10. $3(x + 1) \geq 2x + 1 + x$

   $3x + 3 \geq 3x + 1$

   $3x - 3x + 3 \geq 3x - 3x + 1$

   $3 \geq 1, \ \text{true}$

   The solution is $(-\infty, \infty)$ or $\{x | x \text{ is a real number}\}$.

11. Let $x =$ your grade on the final examination.

$$\frac{82+74+78+x+x}{5} \geq 80$$

$$\frac{234+2x}{5} \geq 80$$

$$5\left(\frac{234+2x}{5}\right) \geq 5 \cdot 80$$

$$234+2x \geq 400$$

$$234-234+2x \geq 400-234$$

$$2x \geq 166$$

$$x \geq 83$$

To earn a B you must get at least an 83% on the final examination.

2.6 Exercise Set

1. $x > 5$

3. $x < -2$

5. $x \geq -4$

7. $x \leq 4.5$

9. $-2 < x \leq 6$

11. $-1 < x < 3$

13. $(-\infty, 3]$

15. $\left(\frac{5}{2}, \infty\right)$

17. $(-\infty, 0]$

19. $(-\infty, 4)$

21. $x - 3 > 4$

$$x - 3 + 3 > 4 + 3$$

$$x > 7$$

$(7, \infty)$

23. $x + 4 \leq 10$

$$x + 4 - 4 \leq 10 - 4$$

$$x \leq 6$$

$(-\infty, 6]$

25. $y - 2 < 0$

$$y - 2 + 2 < 0 + 2$$

$$y < 2$$

$(-\infty, 2)$

27. $3x + 4 \leq 2x + 7$

$$3x - 2x \leq 7 - 4$$

$$x \leq 3$$

$(-\infty, 3]$

29. $5x - 9 < 4x + 7$

$$5x - 4x < 7 + 9$$

$$x < 16$$

$(-\infty, 16)$

31. $7x - 7 > 6x - 3$

$$7x - 6x > -3 + 7$$

$$x > 4$$

$(4, \infty)$

33.

$$x - \frac{2}{3} > \frac{1}{2}$$

$$x - \frac{2}{3} + \frac{2}{3} > \frac{1}{2} + \frac{2}{3}$$

$$x > \frac{3}{6} + \frac{4}{6}$$

$$x > \frac{7}{6}$$

$$\left(\frac{7}{6}, \infty\right)$$

35.

$$y + \frac{7}{8} \leq \frac{1}{2}$$

$$y + \frac{7}{8} - \frac{7}{8} \leq \frac{1}{2} - \frac{7}{8}$$

$$y \leq \frac{4}{8} - \frac{7}{8}$$

$$y \leq -\frac{3}{8}$$

$$\left(-\infty, -\frac{3}{8}\right]$$

37.

$$-15y + 13 > 13 - 16y$$

$$-15y + 13 + 16y > 13 - 16y + 16y$$

$$y + 13 > 13$$

$$y + 13 - 13 > 13 - 13$$

$$y > 0$$

$$(0, \infty)$$

39.

$$\frac{1}{2}x < 4$$

$$2\left(\frac{1}{2}x\right) < 2(4)$$

$$1x < 8$$

$$x < 8$$

$$(-\infty, 8)$$

41.

$$\frac{x}{3} > -2$$

$$3\left(\frac{x}{3}\right) > 3(-2)$$

$$x > -6$$

$$(-6, \infty)$$

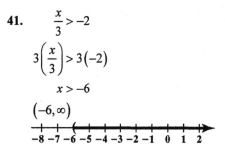

43.

$$4x < 20$$

$$\frac{4x}{4} < 20$$

$$x < 5$$

$$(-\infty, 5)$$

45.

$$3x \geq -21$$

$$\frac{3x}{3} \geq \frac{-21}{3}$$

$$x \geq -7$$

$$[-7, \infty)$$

47.

$$-3x < 15$$

$$\frac{-3x}{-3} > \frac{15}{-3}$$

$$x > -5$$

$$(-5, \infty)$$

49.

$$-3x \geq 15$$

$$\frac{-3x}{-3} \leq \frac{15}{-3}$$

$$x \leq -5$$

$$(-\infty, -5]$$

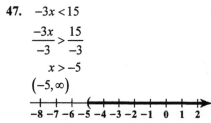

51.

$$-16x > -48$$

$$\frac{-16x}{-16} < \frac{-48}{-16}$$

$$x < 3$$

$$(-\infty, 3)$$

53. $-4y \le \dfrac{1}{2}$

$2(-4y) \le 2\left(\dfrac{1}{2}\right)$

$-8y \le 1$

$\dfrac{-8y}{-8} \ge \dfrac{1}{-8}$

$y \ge -\dfrac{1}{8}$

$\left[-\dfrac{1}{8}, \infty\right)$

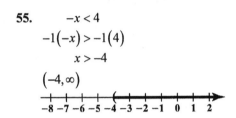

55. $-x < 4$

$-1(-x) > -1(4)$

$x > -4$

$(-4, \infty)$

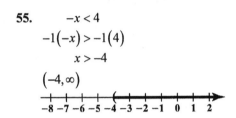

57. $2x - 3 > 7$

$2x - 3 + 3 > 7 + 3$

$2x > 10$

$\dfrac{2x}{2} > \dfrac{10}{2}$

$x > 5$

$(5, \infty)$

59. $3x + 3 < 18$

$3x + 3 - 3 < 18 - 3$

$3x < 15$

$\dfrac{3x}{3} < \dfrac{15}{3}$

$x < 5$

$(-\infty, 5)$

61. $3 - 7x \le 17$

$3 - 7x - 3 \le 17 - 3$

$-7x \le 14$

$\dfrac{-7x}{-7} \ge \dfrac{14}{-7}$

$x \ge -2$

$[-2, \infty)$

63. $-2x - 3 < 3$

$-2x - 3 + 3 < 3 + 3$

$-2x < 6$

$\dfrac{-2x}{-2} > \dfrac{6}{-2}$

$x > -3$

$(-3, \infty)$

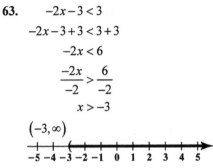

65. $5 - x \le 1$

$5 - x - 5 \le 1 - 5$

$-x \le -4$

$-1(-x) \ge -1(-4)$

$x \ge 4$

$[4, \infty)$

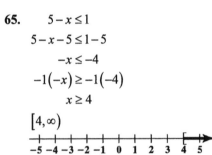

67. $2x - 5 > -x + 6$

$2x - 5 + x > -x + 6 + x$

$3x - 5 > 6$

$3x - 5 + 5 > 6 + 5$

$3x > 11$

$\dfrac{3x}{3} > \dfrac{11}{3}$

$x > \dfrac{11}{3}$

$\left(\dfrac{11}{3}, \infty\right)$

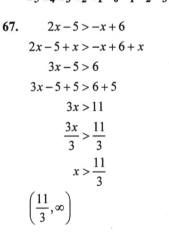

69.
$$2y - 5 < 5y - 11$$
$$2y - 5 - 5y < 5y - 11 - 5y$$
$$-3y - 5 < -11$$
$$-3y - 5 + 5 < -11 + 5$$
$$-3y < -6$$
$$\frac{-3y}{-3} > \frac{-6}{-3}$$
$$y > 2$$
$$(2, \infty)$$

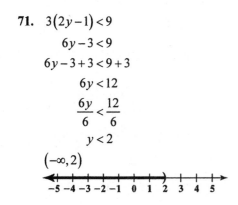

71.
$$3(2y - 1) < 9$$
$$6y - 3 < 9$$
$$6y - 3 + 3 < 9 + 3$$
$$6y < 12$$
$$\frac{6y}{6} < \frac{12}{6}$$
$$y < 2$$
$$(-\infty, 2)$$

73.
$$3(x + 1) - 5 < 2x + 1$$
$$3x + 3 - 5 < 2x + 1$$
$$3x - 2 < 2x + 1$$
$$3x - 2 - 2x < 2x + 1 - 2x$$
$$x - 2 < 1$$
$$x - 2 + 2 < 1 + 2$$
$$x < 3$$
$$(-\infty, 3)$$

75.
$$8x + 3 > 3(2x + 1) - x + 5$$
$$8x + 3 > 6x + 3 - x + 5$$
$$8x + 3 > 5x + 8$$
$$8x + 3 - 5x > 5x + 8 - 5x$$
$$3x + 3 > 8$$
$$3x + 3 - 3 > 8 - 3$$
$$3x > 5$$
$$x > \frac{5}{3}$$
$$\left(\frac{5}{3}, \infty\right)$$

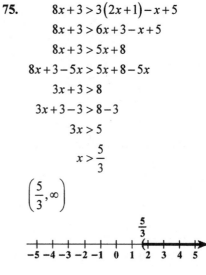

77.
$$\frac{x}{3} - 2 \geq 1$$
$$\frac{x}{3} - 2 + 2 \geq 1 + 2$$
$$\frac{x}{3} \geq 3$$
$$3\left(\frac{x}{3}\right) \geq 3(3)$$
$$x \geq 9$$
$$[9, \infty)$$

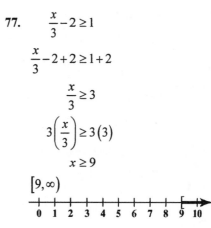

79.
$$1 - \frac{x}{2} - 1 > 4 - 1$$
$$-\frac{x}{2} > 3$$
$$2\left(-\frac{x}{2}\right) > 2(3)$$
$$-x > 6$$
$$-1(-x) < -1(6)$$
$$x < -6$$
$$(-\infty, -6)$$

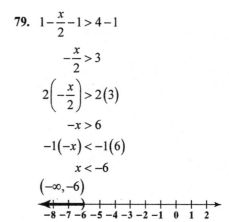

81.
$$4x - 4 < 4(x - 5)$$
$$4x - 4 < 4x - 20$$
$$4x - 4 + 4 < 4x - 20 + 4$$
$$4x < 4x - 16$$
$$4x - 4x < 4x - 16 - 4x$$
$$0 < -16$$

The original inequality is equivalent to the false statement $0 < -16$, so the inequality has no solution. The solution set is $\{\ \}$.

83.
$$x + 3 < x + 7$$
$$x + 3 - x < x + 7 - x$$
$$3 < 7$$

The original inequality is equivalent to the true statement $3 < 7$.
The solution is the set of all real numbers, written $\{x \mid x \text{ is a real number}\}$ or $(-\infty, \infty)$.

85.
$$7x \leq 7(x - 2)$$
$$7x \leq 7x - 14$$
$$7x - 7x \leq 7x - 14 - 7x$$
$$0 \leq -14$$

Since $0 \leq -14$ is a false statement, the original inequality has no solution.
The solution set is $\{\ \}$.

87.
$$2(x + 3) > 2x + 1$$
$$2x + 6 > 2x + 1$$
$$2x + 6 - 2x > 2x + 1 - 2x$$
$$6 > 1$$

Since $6 > 1$ is a true statement, the original inequality is true for all real numbers the solution set is $\{x \mid x \text{ is a real number}\}$ or $(-\infty, \infty)$.

89.
$$5x - 4 \leq 4(x - 1)$$
$$5x - 4 \leq 4x - 4$$
$$5x - 4 + 4 \leq 4x - 4 + 4$$
$$5x \leq 4x$$
$$5x - 4x \leq 4x - 4x$$
$$x \leq 0$$
$$(-\infty, 0]$$

91.
$$3x + a > b$$
$$3x > b - a$$
$$\frac{3x}{3} > \frac{b - a}{3}$$
$$x > \frac{b - a}{3}$$

93.
$$y \leq mx + b$$
$$y - b \leq mx$$
$$\frac{y - b}{m} \geq \frac{mx}{m}$$
$$\frac{y - b}{m} \geq x \text{ or } x \leq \frac{y - b}{m}$$

95. x is between -2 and 2, so $|x| < 2$.

97. x is less than -2 or greater than 2, so $|x| > 2$.

99. Denmark, Netherlands, and Norway

101. Japan and Mexico

103. Netherlands, Norway, Canada, and U.S.

105. $N = 550 - 9x; \ N < 370$
$$550 - 9x < 370$$
$$550 - 9x - 550 < 370 - 550$$
$$-9x < -180$$
$$\frac{-9x}{-9} > \frac{-180}{-9}$$
$$x > 20$$

According to the model, there will be 370 billion cigarettes consumed in $1988 + 20 = 2008$ and less than 370 billion after 2008 (from 2009 onward).

107. a. Let $x =$ your grade on the final exam.
$$\frac{86 + 88 + x}{3} \geq 90$$
$$3\left(\frac{86 + 88 + x}{3}\right) \geq 3(90)$$
$$86 + 88 + x \geq 270$$
$$174 + x \geq 270$$
$$174 + x - 174 \geq 270 - 174$$
$$x \geq 96$$

You must get at least a 96% on the final exam to earn an A in the course.

b. $\dfrac{86+88+x}{3}<80$

$$3\left(\dfrac{86+88+x}{3}\right)<3(80)$$

$$86+88+x<240$$

$$174+x<240$$

$$174+x-174<240-174$$

$$x<66$$

If you get less than a 66 on the final exam, your grade will be below a B.

109. Let x = number of miles driven.

$$80+0.25x\le400$$

$$80+0.25x-80\le400-80$$

$$0.25x\le320$$

$$\dfrac{0.25x}{0.25}\le\dfrac{320}{0.25}$$

$$x\le1280$$

You can drive up to 1280 miles.

111. Let x = number of cement bags.

$$245+95x\le3000$$

$$245+95x-245\le3000-245$$

$$95x\le2755$$

$$\dfrac{95x}{95}\le\dfrac{2755}{95}$$

$$x\le29$$

Up to 29 bags of cement can safely be listed on the elevator in one trip.

113. – 115. Answers will vary.

117. makes sense

119. makes sense

121. false; Changes to make the statement true will vary. A sample change is: The inequality $x-3>0$ is equivalent to $x>3$.

123. false; Changes to make the statement true will vary. A sample change is: The inequality $-4x<-20$ is equivalent to $x>5$.

125. Let x = number of miles driven.
Weekly cost for Basic Rental: $260.
Weekly cost for Continental: $80 + 0.25x$
The cost for Basic Rental is a better deal if $80+0.25x>260$.
Solve this inequality.

$$80+0.25x-80>260-80$$

$$0.25x>180$$

$$\dfrac{0.25x}{0.25}>\dfrac{180}{0.25}$$

$$x>720$$

Basic Car Rental is a better deal if you drive more than 720 miles in a week.

127. $1.45-7.23x>-1.442$

$$1.45-7.23x-1.45>-1.442-1.45$$

$$-7.23x>-2.892$$

$$\dfrac{-7.23x}{-7.23}<\dfrac{-2.892}{-7.23}$$

$$x<0.4$$

$(-\infty,0.4)$

129. $A=PB,\ A=8,\ P=40\%=0.4$

$$A=PB$$

$$8=0.4B$$

$$\dfrac{8}{0.4}=\dfrac{0.4B}{0.4}$$

$$20=B$$

8 is 40% of 20.

130. Let x = the width of the rectangle.
Let $x+5$ = the length of the rectangle.

$$P=2l+2w$$

$$34=2(x+5)+2\cdot x$$

$$34=2x+10+2x$$

$$34=4x+10$$

$$34-10=4x+10-10$$

$$24=4x$$

$$6=x$$

$$x=6$$

$$x+5=11$$

The width is 6 inches and the length is 11 inches.

131.
$$5x + 16 = 3(x + 8)$$
$$5x + 16 = 3x + 24$$
$$5x + 16 - 3x = 3x + 24 - 3x$$
$$2x + 16 = 24$$
$$2x + 16 - 16 = 24 - 16$$
$$2x = 8$$
$$\frac{2x}{2} = \frac{8}{2}$$
$$x = 4$$
Check: $5(4) + 16 = 3(4 + 8)$
$$20 + 16 = 3(12)$$
$$36 = 36, \text{ true}$$
The solution is set is $\{4\}$.

132. $I = Prt$
$$I = (2000)(0.06)(2)$$
$$I = 240$$

133. $0.06x + 0.08(16,000 - x) = 1180$
$$0.06x + 1280 - 0.08x = 1180$$
$$-0.02x + 1280 = 1180$$
$$-0.02x + 1280 - 1280 = 1180 - 1280$$
$$-0.02x = -100$$
$$\frac{-0.02x}{-0.02} = \frac{-100}{-0.02}$$
$$x = 5000$$
The solution is set is $\{5000\}$.

134 $0.18x + 0.45(12 - x) = 0.36(12)$
$$0.18x + 5.4 - 0.45x = 4.32$$
$$-0.27x + 5.4 = 4.32$$
$$-0.27x + 5.4 - 5.4 = 4.32 - 5.4$$
$$-0.27x = -1.08$$
$$\frac{-0.27x}{-0.27} = \frac{-1.08}{-0.27}$$
$$x = 4$$
The solution is set is $\{4\}$.

Chapter 2 Review

1.
$$x - 10 = 22$$
$$x - 10 + 10 = 22 + 10$$
$$x = 32$$
The solution is set is $\{32\}$.

2.
$$-14 = y + 8$$
$$-14 - 8 = y + 8 - 8$$
$$-22 = y$$
The solution is set is $\{-22\}$.

3.
$$7z - 3 = 6z + 9$$
$$7z - 3 - 6z = 6z + 9 - 6z$$
$$z - 3 = 9$$
$$z - 3 + 3 = 9 + 3$$
$$z = 12$$
The solution is set is $\{12\}$.

4.
$$4(x + 3) = 3x - 10$$
$$4x + 12 = 3x - 10$$
$$4x + 12 - 3x = 3x - 10 - 3x$$
$$x + 12 = -10$$
$$x + 12 - 12 = -10 - 12$$
$$x = -22$$
The solution is set is $\{-22\}$.

5. $6x - 3x - 9 + 1 = -5x + 7x - 3$
$$3x - 8 = 2x - 3$$
$$3x - 8 - 2x = 2x - 3 - 2x$$
$$x - 8 = -3$$
$$x - 8 + 8 = -3 + 8$$
$$x = 5$$
The solution is set is $\{5\}$.

6.
$$\frac{x}{8} = 10$$
$$8\left(\frac{x}{8}\right) = 8(10)$$
$$x = 80$$
The solution is set is $\{80\}$.

7. $\dfrac{y}{-8} = 7$

$-8\left(\dfrac{y}{-8}\right) = -8(7)$

$y = -56$

The solution is set is $\{-56\}$.

8. $7z = 77$

$\dfrac{7z}{7} = \dfrac{77}{7}$

$z = 11$

The solution is set is $\{11\}$.

9. $-36 = -9y$

$\dfrac{-36}{-9} = \dfrac{-9y}{-9}$

$4 = y$

The solution is set is $\{4\}$.

10. $\dfrac{3}{5}x = -9$

$\dfrac{5}{3}\left(\dfrac{3}{5}x\right) = \dfrac{5}{3}(-9)$

$1x = -15$

$x = -15$

The solution is set is $\{-15\}$.

11. $30 = -\dfrac{5}{2}y$

$-\dfrac{2}{5}(30) = -\dfrac{2}{5}\left(-\dfrac{5}{2}y\right)$

$-12 = y$

The solution is set is $\{-12\}$.

12. $-x = 25$

$-1(-x) = -1(25)$

$x = -25$

The solution is set is $\{-25\}$.

13. $\dfrac{-x}{10} = -1$

$10\left(\dfrac{-x}{10}\right) = 10(-1)$

$-x = -10$

$-1(-x) = -1(-10)$

$x = 10$

The solution is set is $\{10\}$.

14. $4x + 9 = 33$

$4x + 9 - 9 = 33 - 9$

$4x = 24$

$\dfrac{4x}{4} = \dfrac{24}{4}$

$x = 6$

The solution is set is $\{6\}$.

15. $-3y - 2 = 13$

$-3y - 2 + 2 = 13 + 2$

$-3y = 15$

$\dfrac{-3y}{-3} = \dfrac{15}{-3}$

$y = -5$

The solution is set is $\{-5\}$.

16. $5z + 20 = 3z$

$5z + 20 - 3z = 3z - 3z$

$2z + 20 = 0$

$2z + 20 - 20 = 0 - 20$

$2z = -20$

$\dfrac{2z}{2} = \dfrac{-20}{2}$

$z = -10$

The solution is set is $\{-10\}$.

17. $5x - 3 = x + 5$

$5x - 3 - x = x + 5 - x$

$4x - 3 = 5$

$4x - 3 + 3 = 5 + 3$

$4x = 8$

$\dfrac{4x}{4} = \dfrac{8}{4}$

$x = 2$

The solution is set is $\{2\}$.

18.
$$3 - 2x = 9 - 8x$$
$$3 - 2x + 8x = 9 - 8x + 8x$$
$$3 + 6x = 9$$
$$3 + 6x - 3 = 9 - 3$$
$$6x = 6$$
$$\frac{6x}{6} = \frac{6}{6}$$
$$x = 1$$
The solution is set is $\{1\}$.

19. a. 2005 is 20 years after 1985.
$$I = 12n + 151$$
$$I = 12(20) + 151 = 240 + 151 = 391$$
According to the formula, the U.S. imported 391 million barrels of oil per month in 2005. The formula underestimated the actual value given in the bar graph by 8 million barrels.

b.
$$I = 12n + 151$$
$$511 = 12n + 151$$
$$511 - 151 = 12n + 151 - 151$$
$$360 = 12n$$
$$\frac{360}{12} = \frac{12n}{12}$$
$$30 = n$$
If trends continue, the U.S. will import an average of 511 million barrels of oil per month 30 years after 1985, or 2015.

20.
$$5x + 9 - 7x + 6 = x + 18$$
$$-2x + 15 = x + 18$$
$$-2x + 15 - x = x + 18 - x$$
$$-3x + 15 = 18$$
$$-3x + 15 - 15 = 18 - 15$$
$$-3x = 3$$
$$\frac{-3x}{-3} = \frac{3}{-3}$$
$$x = -1$$
The solution is set is $\{-1\}$.

21.
$$3(x + 4) = 5x - 12$$
$$3x + 12 = 5x - 12$$
$$3x + 12 - 5x = 5x - 12 - 5x$$
$$-2x + 12 = -12$$
$$-2x + 12 - 12 = -12 - 12$$
$$-2x = -24$$
$$\frac{-2x}{-2} = \frac{-24}{-2}$$
$$x = 12$$
The solution is set is $\{12\}$.

22.
$$1 - 2(6 - y) = 3y + 2$$
$$1 - 12 + 2y = 3y + 2$$
$$2y - 11 = 3y + 2$$
$$2y - 11 - 3y = 3y + 2 - 3y$$
$$-y - 11 = 2$$
$$-y - 11 + 11 = 2 + 11$$
$$-y = 13$$
$$y = -13$$
The solution is set is $\{-13\}$.

23.
$$2x - 8 + 3x + 15 = 2x - 2$$
$$5x + 7 = 2x - 2$$
$$5x + 7 - 2x = 2x - 2 - 2x$$
$$3x + 7 = -2$$
$$3x + 7 - 7 = -2 - 7$$
$$3x = -9$$
$$\frac{3x}{3} = \frac{-9}{3}$$
$$x = -3$$
The solution is set is $\{-3\}$.

24.
$$-2(y - 4) - (3y - 2) = -2 - (6y - 2)$$
$$-2y + 8 - 3y + 2 = -2 - 6y + 2$$
$$-5y + 10 = -6y$$
$$-5y + 10 + 6y = -6y + 6y$$
$$10 + y = 0$$
$$10 + y - 10 = 0 - 10$$
$$y = -10$$
The solution is set is $\{-10\}$.

25. $\dfrac{2x}{3} = \dfrac{x}{6} + 1$

To clear fractions, multiply both sides by the LCD, which is 6.

$$6\left(\dfrac{2x}{3}\right) = 6\left(\dfrac{x}{6} + 1\right)$$

$$6\left(\dfrac{2x}{3}\right) = 6\left(\dfrac{x}{6}\right) + 6(1)$$

$$4x = x + 6$$

$$4x - x = x + 6 - x$$

$$3x = 6$$

$$\dfrac{3x}{3} = \dfrac{6}{3}$$

$$x = 2$$

The solution is set is $\{2\}$.

26. $\dfrac{x}{2} - \dfrac{1}{10} = \dfrac{x}{5} + \dfrac{1}{2}$

Multiply both sides by the LCD, which is 10.

$$10\left(\dfrac{x}{2} - \dfrac{1}{10}\right) = 10\left(\dfrac{x}{5} + \dfrac{1}{2}\right)$$

$$10\left(\dfrac{x}{2}\right) - 10\left(\dfrac{1}{10}\right) = 10\left(\dfrac{x}{5}\right) + 10\left(\dfrac{1}{2}\right)$$

$$5x - 1 = 2x + 5$$

$$5x - 1 - 2x = 2x + 5 - 2x$$

$$3x - 1 = 5$$

$$3x - 1 + 1 = 5 + 1$$

$$3x = 6$$

$$\dfrac{3x}{3} = \dfrac{6}{3}$$

$$x = 2$$

The solution is set is $\{2\}$.

27. $3(8x - 1) = 6(5 + 4x)$

$$24x - 3 = 30 + 24x$$

$$24x - 3 - 24x = 30 + 24x - 24x$$

$$-3 = 30$$

Since $-3 = 30$ is a false statement, the original equation is inconsistent and has no solution or $\{\ \}$.

28. $4(2x - 3) + 4 = 8x - 8$

$$8x - 12 + 4 = 8x - 8$$

$$8x - 8 = 8x - 8$$

$$8x - 8 - 8x = 8x - 8 - 8x$$

$$-8 = -8$$

Since $-8 = -8$ is a true statement, so the solution is the set of all real numbers, written $\{x \mid x \text{ is a real number}\}$.

29.

$$H = 0.7(220 - a)$$

$$133 = 0.7(220 - a)$$

$$133 - 154 = 154 - 154 - 0.7a$$

$$-21 = -0.7a$$

$$\dfrac{-21}{-0.7} = \dfrac{-0.7a}{-0.7}$$

$$30 = a$$

If the optimal heart rate is 133 beats per minute, the person is 30 years old.

30. $I = Pr$ for r

$$\dfrac{I}{P} = \dfrac{Pr}{P}$$

$$\dfrac{I}{P} = r \text{ or } r = \dfrac{I}{P}$$

31. $V = \dfrac{1}{3}Bh$ for h

$$3V = 3\left(\dfrac{1}{3}Bh\right)$$

$$3V = Bh$$

$$\dfrac{3V}{B} = \dfrac{Bh}{B}$$

$$\dfrac{3V}{B} = h \text{ or } h = \dfrac{3V}{B}$$

32. $P = 2l + 2w$ for w

$$P - 2l = 2l + 2w - 2l$$

$$P - 2l = 2w$$

$$\dfrac{P - 2l}{2} = \dfrac{2w}{2}$$

$$\dfrac{P - 2l}{2} = w \text{ or } w = \dfrac{P - 2l}{2}$$

33. $A = \dfrac{B+C}{2}$ for B

$$2A = 2\left(\dfrac{B+C}{2}\right)$$

$$2A = B+C$$

$$2A - C = B + C - C$$

$$2A - C = B \ \text{ or } \ B = 2A - C$$

34. $T = D + pm$ for m

$$T - D = D + pm - D$$

$$T - D = pm$$

$$\dfrac{T-D}{p} = \dfrac{pm}{p}$$

$$\dfrac{T-D}{p} = m \ \text{ or } \ m = \dfrac{T-D}{p}$$

35. $65\% = 0.65$

36. $150\% = 1.50$

37. $3\% = 0.03$

38. $0.72 = 72\%$

39. $0.0035 = 0.35\%$

40. $A = PB; \ P = 8\% = 0.08, \ B = 120$

$$A = 0.08 \cdot 120$$

$$A = 9.6$$

8% of 120 is 9.6

41. $A = PB; \ A = 90, \ P = 45\% = 0.45$

$$90 = 0.45B$$

$$\dfrac{90}{0.45} = \dfrac{0.45B}{0.45}$$

$$200 = B$$

90 is 45% of 200.

42. $A = PB; \ A = 36, \ B = 75$

$$36 = P \cdot 75$$

$$\dfrac{36}{75} = \dfrac{P \cdot 75}{75}$$

$$0.48 = P$$

36 is 48% of 75.

43. Increase = Percent $\cdot$ Original
First, find the increase: $12 - 6 = 6$

$$6 = P \cdot 6$$

$$\dfrac{6}{6} = \dfrac{P \cdot 6}{6}$$

$$1 = P$$

The percent increase is 100%.

44. Decrease = Percent $\cdot$ Original
First, find the decrease: $5 - 3 = 2$

$$2 = P \cdot 5$$

$$\dfrac{2}{5} = \dfrac{P \cdot 5}{5}$$

$$0.4 = P$$

The percent decrease is 40%.

45. Increase = Percent $\cdot$ Original
First, find the increase: $45 - 40 = 5$

$$5 = P \cdot 40$$

$$\dfrac{5}{40} = \dfrac{P \cdot 40}{40}$$

$$0.125 = P$$

The percent increase is 12.5%.

46. Investment dollars lost last year were $0.10 \cdot \$10,000 = \$1000$. This means that $\$10,000 - \$1000 = \$9000$ remains. Investment dollars gained this year are $0.10 \cdot \$9000 = \$900$. This means that $\$9000 + \$900 = \$9900$ of the original investment remains. This is an overall loss of $100.
decrease = percent $\cdot$ original

$$100 = P \cdot 10,000$$

$$\dfrac{100}{10,000} = \dfrac{P \cdot 10,000}{10,000}$$

$$0.01 = P$$

The statement is not true. Instead of recouping losses, there is an overall 1% decrease in the portfolio.

47. a. $r = \dfrac{h}{7}$

$$7r = 7\left(\dfrac{h}{7}\right)$$

$$7r = h \ \text{ or } \ h = 7r$$

b. $h = 7r; \ r = 9$

$$h = 7(9) = 63$$

The woman's height is 63 inches or 5 feet, 3 inches.

48.
$$A = P \cdot B$$
$$91 = 0.26 \cdot B$$
$$\frac{91}{0.26} = \frac{0.26 \cdot B}{0.26}$$
$$350 = B$$
The average U.S. household uses 350 gallons of water per day.

49. Let x = the unknown number.
$$6x - 20 = 4x$$
$$6x - 20 - 4x = 4x - 4x$$
$$2x - 20 = 0$$
$$2x - 20 + 20 = 0 + 20$$
$$2x = 20$$
$$x = 10$$
The number is 10.

50. Let x = the average amount spent on cat food.
Let $x + 2$ = the average amount spent on dog food.
$$x + (x + 29) = 405$$
$$x + x + 29 = 405$$
$$2x + 29 = 405$$
$$2x + 29 - 29 = 405 - 29$$
$$2x = 376$$
$$x = 188$$
$$x + 29 = 217$$
$188 was spent on cats and $217 was spent on dogs.

51. Let x = the smaller page number.
Let $x + 1$ = the larger page number.
$$x + (x + 1) = 93$$
$$2x + 1 = 93$$
$$2x = 92$$
$$x = 46$$
The page numbers are 46 and 47.

52. Let x = the percentage of females.
Let $x + 2$ = the percentage of males.
$$x + (x + 2) = 100$$
$$x + x + 2 = 100$$
$$2x + 2 = 100$$
$$2x + 2 - 2 = 100 - 2$$
$$2x = 98$$
$$x = 49$$
$$x + 2 = 51$$
For Americans under 20, 49% are female and 51% are male.

53. Let x = number of years after 2003.
$$612 + 15x = 747$$
$$612 + 15x - 612 = 747 - 612$$
$$15x = 135$$
$$\frac{15x}{15} = \frac{135}{15}$$
$$x = 9$$
According to this model, the average weekly salary will reach $747 in 9 years after 2003, or 2012.

54. Let x = the number of checks written.
$$6 + 0.05x = 6.90$$
$$6 + 0.05x - 6 = 6.90 - 6$$
$$0.05x = 0.90$$
$$\frac{0.05x}{0.05} = \frac{0.90}{0.05}$$
$$x = 18$$

You wrote 18 checks that month.

55. Let x = the width of the field.
Let $3x$ = the length of the field.
$$P = 2l + 2w$$
$$400 = 2 \cdot 3x + 2 \cdot x$$
$$400 = 6x + 2x$$
$$400 = 8x$$
$$\frac{400}{8} = \frac{8x}{8}$$
$$50 = x$$
$$x = 50$$
$$3x = 150$$
The field is 50 yards wide and 150 yards long.

56. Let x = the original price of the table.
$$x - 0.25x = 180$$
$$0.75x = 180$$
$$\frac{0.75x}{0.75} = \frac{180}{0.75}$$
$$x = 240$$
The table's price before the reduction was $240.

57. $x < -1$

58. $-2 < x \leq 4$

59. $\left[\dfrac{3}{2}, \infty\right)$

60. $(-\infty, 0)$

61. $2x - 5 < 3$

$$2x - 5 + 5 < 3 + 5$$
$$2x < 8$$
$$\dfrac{2x}{2} < \dfrac{8}{2}$$
$$x < 4$$

$(-\infty, 4)$

62. $\dfrac{x}{2} > -4$

$$2\left(\dfrac{x}{2}\right) > 2(-4)$$
$$x > -8$$

$(-8, \infty)$

63. $3 - 5x \le 18$

$$3 - 5x - 3 \le 18 - 3$$
$$-5x \le 15$$
$$\dfrac{-5x}{-5} \ge \dfrac{15}{-5}$$
$$x \ge -3$$

$[-3, \infty)$

64. $4x + 6 < 5x$

$$4x + 6 - 5x < 5x - 5x$$
$$-x + 6 < 0$$
$$-x + 6 - 6 < 0 - 6$$
$$-x < -6$$
$$-1(-x) > -1(-6)$$
$$x > 6$$

$(6, \infty)$

65. $6x - 10 \ge 2(x + 3)$

$$6x - 10 \ge 2x + 6$$
$$6x - 10 - 2x \ge 2x + 6 - 2x$$
$$4x - 10 \ge 6$$
$$4x - 10 + 10 \ge 6 + 10$$
$$4x \ge 16$$
$$\dfrac{4x}{4} \ge \dfrac{16}{4}$$
$$x \ge 4$$

$[4, \infty)$

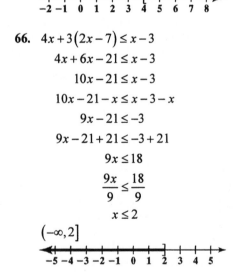

66. $4x + 3(2x - 7) \le x - 3$

$$4x + 6x - 21 \le x - 3$$
$$10x - 21 \le x - 3$$
$$10x - 21 - x \le x - 3 - x$$
$$9x - 21 \le -3$$
$$9x - 21 + 21 \le -3 + 21$$
$$9x \le 18$$
$$\dfrac{9x}{9} \le \dfrac{18}{9}$$
$$x \le 2$$

$(-\infty, 2]$

67. $2(2x+4) > 4(x+2)-6$

$4x+8 > 4x+8-6$

$4x+8 > 4x+2$

$4x+8-4x > 4x+2-4x$

$8 > 2$

Since $8 > 2$ is a true statement, the original inequality is true for all real numbers, and the solution set is $\{x \mid x \text{ is a real number}\}$.

68. $-2(x-4) \le 3x+1-5x$

$-2x+8 \le -2x+1$

$-2x+8+2x \le -2x+1+2x$

$8 \le 1$

Since $8 \le 1$ is a false statement, the original inequality has no solution. The solution set is $\{\ \}$.

69. Let $x =$ the student's score on the third test.

$$\frac{42+74+x}{3} \ge 60$$

$$3\left(\frac{42+74+x}{3}\right) \ge 3(60)$$

$$42+74+x \ge 180$$

$$116+x \ge 180$$

$$116+x-116 \ge 180-116$$

$$x \ge 64$$

The student must score at least 64 on the third test to pass the course.

70. $C = 10+5(x-1); \ C \le 500$

$10+5(x-1) \le 500$

$10+5x-5 \le 500$

$5x+5 \le 500$

$5x+5-5 \le 500-5$

$5x \le 495$

$$\frac{5x}{5} \le \frac{495}{5}$$

$x \le 99$

You can talk no more than 99 minutes.

Chapter 2 Test

1. $4x-5 = 13$

$4x+5+5 = 13+5$

$4x = 18$

$$\frac{4x}{4} = \frac{18}{4} = \frac{9}{2}$$

$$x = \frac{9}{2}$$

The solution set is $\left\{\frac{9}{2}\right\}$.

2. $12x+4 = 7x-21$

$12x+4-7x = 7x-21-7x$

$5x+4 = -21$

$5x+4-4 = -21-4$

$5x = -25$

$$\frac{5x}{5} = \frac{-25}{5}$$

$x = -5$

The solution set is $\{-5\}$.

3. $8-5(x-2) = x+26$

$8-5x+10 = x+26$

$18-5x = x+26$

$18-5x-x = x+26-x$

$18-6x = 26$

$18-6x-18 = 26-18$

$-6x = 8$

$$\frac{-6x}{-6} = \frac{8}{-6}$$

$$x = -\frac{8}{6} = -\frac{4}{3}$$

The solution set is $\left\{-\frac{4}{3}\right\}$.

4.
$$3(2y-4)=9-3(y+1)$$
$$6y-12=9-3y-3$$
$$6y-12=6-3y$$
$$6y-12+3y=6-3y+3y$$
$$9y-12=6$$
$$9y-12+12=6+12$$
$$9y=18$$
$$\frac{9y}{9}=\frac{18}{9}$$
$$y=2$$

The solution set is $\{2\}$.

5.
$$\frac{3}{4}x=-15$$
$$\frac{4}{3}\left(\frac{3}{4}x\right)=\frac{4}{3}(-15)$$
$$x=-20$$

The solution set is $\{-20\}$.

6.
$$\frac{x}{10}+\frac{1}{3}=\frac{x}{5}+\frac{1}{2}$$

Multiply both sides by the LCD, 30.
$$30\left(\frac{x}{10}+\frac{1}{3}\right)=30\left(\frac{x}{5}+\frac{1}{2}\right)$$
$$30\left(\frac{x}{10}\right)+30\left(\frac{1}{3}\right)=30\left(\frac{x}{5}\right)+30\left(\frac{1}{2}\right)$$
$$3x+10=6x+15$$
$$3x+10-6x=6x+15-6x$$
$$-3x+10=15$$
$$-3x+10-10=15-10$$
$$-3x=5$$
$$\frac{-3x}{-3}=\frac{5}{-3}$$
$$x=-\frac{5}{3}$$

The solution set is $\left\{-\frac{5}{3}\right\}$.

7.
$$N=2.4x+180;\ N=324$$
$$2.4x+180=324$$
$$2.4x+180-180=324-180$$
$$2.4x=144$$
$$\frac{2.4x}{2.4}=\frac{144}{2.4}$$
$$x=60$$

The US population is expected to reach 324 million 60 years after 1960, in the year 2020.

8. $V=\pi r^2 h$ for h
$$\frac{V}{\pi r^2}=\frac{\pi r^2 h}{\pi r^2}$$
$$\frac{V}{\pi r^2}=h \text{ or } h=\frac{V}{\pi r^2}$$

9. $l=\dfrac{P-2w}{2}$ for w
$$2l=2\left(\frac{P-2w}{2}\right)$$
$$2l=P-2w$$
$$2l-P=P-2w-P$$
$$2l-P=-2w$$
$$\frac{2l-P}{-2}=\frac{-2w}{-2}$$
$$\frac{2l-P}{-2}=w \text{ or } w=\frac{P-2l}{2}$$

10. $A=PB;\ P=6\%=0.06,\ B=140$
$$A=0.06(140)$$
$$A=8.4$$
6% of 140 is 8.4.

11. $A=PB;\ A=120,\ P=80\%=0.80$
$$120=0.80B$$
$$\frac{120}{0.80}=\frac{0.80B}{0.80}$$
$$150=B$$
120 is 80% of 150.

12. $A=PB;\ A=12,\ B=240$
$$12=P\cdot 240$$
$$\frac{12}{240}=\frac{P\cdot 240}{240}$$
$$0.05=P$$
12 is 5% of 240.

13. Let x = the unknown number.

$$5x - 9 = 306$$
$$5x - 9 + 9 = 306 + 9$$
$$5x = 315$$
$$\frac{5x}{5} = \frac{315}{5}$$
$$x = 63$$

The number is 63.

14. Let x = the number of people, in millions, with an income of \$50,000 - \$74,999.
Let $x + 2.6$ = the number of people, in millions, with an income of \$75,000 or more.

$$x + (x + 2.6) = 14.2$$
$$x + x + 2.6 = 14.2$$
$$2x + 2.6 = 14.2$$
$$2x + 2.6 - 2.6 = 14.2 - 2.6$$
$$2x = 11.6$$
$$x = 5.8$$
$$x + 2.6 = 8.4$$

5.8 million people with an income of \$50,000 - \$74,999 and 8.4 million people with an income of \$75,000 or more had at least one major depressive episode.

15. Let x = number of minutes of long distance calls.

$$15 + 0.05x = 45$$
$$0.05x = 30$$
$$x = \frac{30}{0.05}$$
$$x = 600$$

You can talk long distance for 600 minutes.

16. Let x = the width of the field.
Let $2x$ = the length of the field.

$$P = 2l + 2w$$
$$450 = 2 \cdot 2x + 2 \cdot x$$
$$450 = 4x + 2x$$
$$450 = 6x$$
$$\frac{450}{6} = \frac{6x}{6}$$
$$75 = x$$
$$x = 75$$
$$2x = 150$$

The field is 75 yards wide and 150 yards long.

17. Let x = the book's original price.

$$x - 0.20x = 28$$
$$0.80x = 28$$
$$x = \frac{28}{0.80}$$
$$x = 35$$

The price of the book before the reduction was \$35.

18. $(-2, \infty)$

19. $(-\infty, 3]$

20. $\dfrac{x}{2} < -3$

$$2\left(\frac{x}{2}\right) < 2(-3)$$
$$x < -6$$
$$(-\infty, -6)$$

21. $6 - 9x \geq 33$

$$6 - 9x - 6 \geq 33 - 6$$
$$-9x \geq 27$$
$$\frac{-9x}{-9} \leq \frac{27}{-9}$$
$$x \leq -3$$
$$(-\infty, -3]$$

22. $4x - 2 > 2(x + 6)$

$$4x - 2 > 2x + 12$$
$$4x - 2 - 2x > 2x + 12 - 2x$$
$$2x - 2 > 12$$
$$2x > 14$$
$$x > 7$$
$$(7, \infty)$$

23. Let x = the student's score on the fourth exam.

$$\frac{76+80+72+x}{4} \geq 80$$

$$4\left(\frac{76+80+72+x}{4}\right) \geq 4(80)$$

$$76+80+72+x \geq 320$$

$$228+x \geq 320$$

$$x \geq 92$$

The student must score at least 92 on the fourth exam to have an average of at least 80.

24. Let x = the width of the rectangle.

$$2(20)+2x > 56$$

$$40+2x > 56$$

$$40-40+2x > 56-40$$

$$2x > 16$$

$$x > 8$$

The perimeter is greater than 56 inches when the width is greater than 8 inches.

Cumulative Review (Chapters 1-2)

1. $-8-(12-16) = -8-(-4) = -8+4 = -4$

2. $(-3)(-2)+(-2)(4) = 6+(-8) = -2$

3. $(8-10)^3(7-11)^2 = (-2)^3(-4)^2$
$$= -8(16) = -128$$

4. $2-5\left[x+3(x+7)\right]$
$$= 2-5(x+3x+21)$$
$$= 2-5(4x+21)$$
$$= 2-20x-105$$
$$= -103-20x$$

5. The rational numbers are

$$-4, -\frac{1}{3}, 0, \sqrt{4}\,(=2), \text{ and } 1063.$$

6. $\dfrac{5}{x}-(x+2)$

7. $-10,000 < -2$ since $-10,000$ is to the left of -2 on the number line.

8. $6(4x-1-5y) = 6(4x)-6(1)-6(5y)$
$$= 24x-6-30y$$

9. $T = 5.3n+9.5$
$$T = 5.3(4)+9.5$$
$$T = 21.2+9.5$$
$$T = 30.7$$
According to the formula, 30.7% of consumers looked for trans fats on food labels in 2007. This underestimates the actual value shown in the bar graph by 0.3%

10.
$$T = 5.3n+9.5$$
$$89 = 5.3n+9.5$$
$$89-9.5 = 5.3n+9.5-9.5$$
$$79.5 = 5.3n$$
$$\frac{79.5}{5.3} = \frac{5.3n}{5.3}$$
$$15 = n$$
If trends continue, 89% of consumers will look for trans fats on food labels 15 years after 2003, or 2018.

11. $5-6(x+2) = x-14$
$$5-6x-12 = x-14$$
$$-7-6x = x-14$$
$$-7-6x-x = x-14-x$$
$$-7-7x = -14$$
$$-7-7x+7 = -14+7$$
$$-7x = -7$$
$$\frac{-7x}{-7} = \frac{-7}{-7}$$
$$x = 1$$
The solution set is $\{1\}$.

12. $\dfrac{x}{5} - 2 = \dfrac{x}{3}$

Multiply both sides by the LCD, 15.

$$15\left(\dfrac{x}{5} - 2\right) = 15\left(\dfrac{x}{3}\right)$$

$$15\left(\dfrac{x}{5}\right) - 15(2) = 15\left(\dfrac{x}{3}\right)$$

$$3x - 30 = 5x$$

$$3x - 30 - 3x = 5x - 3x$$

$$-30 = 2x$$

$$\dfrac{-30}{2} = \dfrac{2x}{2}$$

$$-15 = x$$

The solution set is $\{-15\}$.

13. $V = \dfrac{1}{3}Ah$ for A

$$V = \dfrac{1}{3}Ah$$

$$3V = 3\left(\dfrac{1}{3}Ah\right)$$

$$3V = Ah$$

$$\dfrac{3V}{h} = \dfrac{Ah}{h}$$

$$\dfrac{3V}{h} = A \ \text{ or } \ A = \dfrac{3V}{h}$$

14. $A = PB;\ A = 48,\ P = 30\% = 0.30$

$$48 = 0.30B$$

$$\dfrac{48}{0.30} = \dfrac{0.30B}{0.30}$$

$$160 = B$$

48 is 30% of 160.

15. Let $x =$ the width of the parking lot.
Let $2x - 10 =$ the length of the parking lot.

$$P = 2l + 2w$$

$$400 = 2(2x - 10) + 2 \cdot x$$

$$400 = 4x - 20 + 2x$$

$$400 = 6x - 20$$

$$400 + 20 = 6x - 20 + 20$$

$$420 = 6x$$

$$\dfrac{420}{6} = \dfrac{6x}{6}$$

$$70 = x$$

$$x = 70$$

$$2x - 10 = 130$$

The parking lot is 70 yards wide and 130 yards long.

16. Let $x =$ number of gallons of gasoline.

$$0.40x = 30,000$$

$$\dfrac{0.40x}{0.40} = \dfrac{30,000}{0.40}$$

$$x = 75,000$$

75,000 gallons of gasoline must be sold

17. $\left(-\infty, \dfrac{1}{2}\right]$

18.
$$3 - 3x > 12$$

$$3 - 3x - 3 > 12 - 3$$

$$-3x > 9$$

$$\dfrac{-3x}{-3} < \dfrac{9}{-3}$$

$$x < -3$$

$(-\infty, -3)$

19. $5 - 2(3 - x) \leq 2(2x + 5) + 1$

$5 - 6 + 2x \leq 4x + 10 + 1$

$2x - 1 \leq 4x + 11$

$2x - 1 - 4x \leq 4x + 11 - 4x$

$-2x - 1 \leq 11$

$-2x - 1 + 1 \leq 11 + 1$

$-2x \leq 12$

$\dfrac{-2x}{-2} \geq \dfrac{12}{-2}$

$x \geq -6$

$[-6, \infty)$

20. Let x = value of medical supplies sold.

$600 + 0.04x > 2500$

$600 + 0.04x - 600 > 2500 - 600$

$0.04x > 1900$

$\dfrac{0.04x}{0.04} > \dfrac{1900}{0.04}$

$x > 47,500$

You must sell more than $47,500 worth of medical supplies.

Chapter 3
Problem Solving

3.1 Check Points

1. $P = 3000$, $r = 5\% = 0.05$, $t = 1$

   $I = Prt$

   $I = (3000)(0.05)(1)$

   $= 150$

   The interest at the end of one year is \$150.

2.

	Principal $\times$ Rate $=$		Interest
9% Investment	x	0.09	$0.09x$
12% Investment	$25,000 - x$	0.12	$0.12(25,000 - x)$

   The interest for the two investments combined must be \$2550, so the equation is $0.09x + 0.12(25,000 - x) = 2550$.

   Solve for x. $\quad 0.09x + 0.12(25,000 - x) = 2550$

   $$0.09x + 3000 - 0.12x = 2550$$
   $$-0.03x + 3000 = 2550$$
   $$-0.03x + 3000 - 3000 = 2550 - 3000$$
   $$-0.03x = -450$$
   $$\frac{-0.03x}{-0.03} = \frac{-450}{-0.03}$$
   $$x = 15,000$$
   $$25,000 - x = 10,000$$

   \$15,000 should be invested at 9% and \$10,000 should be invested at 12%.

3. The amount of acid that is in the solution $= 0.45(60) = 27$

   There are 27 milliliters of acid in the solution.

4.

	Milliliters $\times$ Percent of Acid $=$		Amount of Acid
10% Acid Solution	x	0.10	$0.10(x)$
60% Acid Solution	$50 - x$	0.60	$0.60(50 - x)$
30% Acid Mixture	50	0.30	$0.30(50)$

   $$0.10(x) + 0.60(50 - x) = 0.30(50)$$
   $$0.10x + 30 - 0.60x = 15$$
   $$-0.50x + 30 = 15$$
   $$-0.50x + 30 - 30 = 15 - 30$$
   $$-0.50x = -15$$
   $$\frac{-0.50x}{-0.50} = \frac{-15}{-0.50}$$
   $$x = 30$$
   $$50 - x = 20$$

   30 milliliters of 10% acid solution should be mixed with 20 milliliters of 60% acid solution to make 50 milliliters of a 30% solution.

5. $d = rt$

$27 = r(3)$

$27 = 3r$

$\dfrac{27}{3} = \dfrac{3r}{3}$

$9 = r$

The average rate is 9 miles per hour.

6.

	Rate ×	Time =	Distance
Faster Car	55	x	$55x$
Slower Car	50	x	$50x$

$55x + 50x = 420$

$105x = 420$

$\dfrac{105x}{105} = \dfrac{420}{105}$

$x = 4$

They will be 420 miles apart after 4 hours.

3.1 Exercise Set

1. $I = Prt; P = 4000, r = 4\% = 0.04, t = 1$

$I = Prt = (4000)(0.04)(1) = 160$

The interest at the end of one year is \$160.

3.

	Principal ×	Rate =	Interest
7% Investment	x	0.07	$0.07x$
8% Investment	$20,000 - x$	0.08	$0.08(20,000 - x)$

The interest for the two investments combined must be \$1520, so the equation is $0.07x + 0.08(20,000 - x) = 1520$.

Solve for x. $0.07x + 0.08(20,000 - x) = 1520$

$0.07x + 1600 - 0.08x = 1520$

$-0.01x + 1600 = 1520$

$-0.10x + 1600 - 1600 = 1520 - 1600$

$-0.01x = -80$

$\dfrac{-0.01x}{-0.01} = \dfrac{80}{-0.01}$

$x = 8000$

$20,000 - x = 12,000$

\$8000 should be invested at 7% and \$12,000 should be invested at 8%.

5.

	Principal	× Rate	=	Interest
8% Loan	x	0.08		$0.08x$
18% Loan	$120,000 - x$	0.18		$0.18(120,000 - x)$

$$0.08x + 0.18(120,000 - x) = 10,000$$
$$0.08x + 21,600 - 0.18x = 10,000$$
$$-0.10x + 21,600 = 10,000$$
$$-0.10x + 21,600 - 21,600 = 10,000 - 21,600$$
$$-0.10x = -11,600$$
$$\frac{-0.10x}{-0.10} = \frac{-11,600}{-0.10}$$
$$x = 116,000$$
$$120,000 - x = 4000$$

$116,000 was loaned at 8% and $4000 was loaned at 18%.

7.

	Principal	× Rate	=	Interest
6% Investment	x	0.06		$0.06x$
9% Investment	$6000 - x$	0.09		$0.09(6000 - x)$

The accounts earned the same amount of interest, so the equation is $0.06x = 0.09(6000 - x)$.

Solve for x. $0.06x = 0.09(6000 - x)$
$$0.06x = 540 - 0.09x$$
$$0.06x + 0.09x = 540$$
$$0.15x = 540$$
$$\frac{0.15x}{0.15} = \frac{540}{0.15}$$
$$x = 3600$$
$$6000 - x = 2400$$

$3600 was invested at 6% and $2400 was invested at 9%.

9.

	Principal	× Rate	=	Interest
15% Investment	x	0.15		$0.15x$
7% Investment	$50,000 - x$	0.07		$0.07(50,000 - x)$

$$0.15x + 0.07(50,000 - x) = 6000$$
$$0.15x + 3500 - 0.07x = 6000$$
$$0.08x = 2500$$
$$\frac{0.08x}{0.08} = \frac{2500}{0.08}$$
$$x = 31,250$$
$$50,000 - x = 18,750$$

$31,250 should be invested at 15% and $18,750 should be invested at 7%.

11. $0.30(20) = 6$
There are 6 milliliters of acid in the solution.

13.

	Number of Liters	×	Percent Fungicide	=	Amount of Fungicide
5% Fungicide Solution	x		0.05		$0.05x$
10% Fungicide Solution	$50 - x$		0.10		$0.10(50 - x)$
8% Fungicide Solution	50		0.08		$0.08(50)$

$$0.05x + 0.10(50 - x) = 0.08(50)$$
$$0.05x + 5 - 0.10x = 4$$
$$-0.05x + 5 = 4$$
$$-0.05x = -1$$
$$\frac{-0.05x}{-0.05} = \frac{-1}{-0.05}$$
$$x = 20$$
$$50 - x = 30$$

20 liters of 5% fungicide solution and 30 liters of 10% fungicide solution should be used.

15.

	Number of Ounces	×	Percent Alcohol	=	Amount of Alcohol
15% Alcohol	x		0.15		$0.15x$
20% Alcohol	4		0.2		$0.2(4)$
17% Alcohol	$x + 4$		0.17		$0.17(x + 4)$

$$0.15x + 0.2(4) = 0.17(x + 4)$$
$$0.15x + 0.8 = 0.17x + 0.68$$
$$0.15x + 0.8 - 0.17x = 0.17x + 0.68 - 0.17x$$
$$-0.02x + 0.8 = 0.68$$
$$-0.02x + 0.8 - 0.8 = 0.68 - 0.8$$
$$-0.02x = -0.12$$
$$-0.02x = -0.12$$
$$\frac{-0.02x}{-0.02} = \frac{-0.12}{-0.02}$$
$$x = 6$$

To make a 17% alcohol solution, 6 ounces of 15% alcohol should be mixed with the 4 ounces of 20% alcohol solution.

17.

	Number of Students	×	Percent Music Majors	=	Music Majors
North Campus	x		0.10		$0.10x$
South Campus	$1000 - x$		0.90		$0.90(1000 - x)$
Merged Campus	1000		0.42		$0.42(1000)$

$$0.10x + 0.90(1000 - x) = 0.42(1000)$$
$$0.10x + 900 - 0.90x = 420$$
$$-0.8x + 900 = 420$$
$$-0.8x = -480$$
$$\frac{-0.8x}{-0.8} = \frac{-420}{-0.8}$$
$$x = 600$$
$$1000 - x = 400$$

There were 600 students at the north campus and 400 students at the south campus.

19.

	Rate	×	Time	=	Distance
Slower Cyclist	10		x		$10x$
Faster Cyclist	12		x		$12x$

After x hours, the cyclists are 66 miles apart, so the equation is $10x + 12x = 66$.
Solve for x. $10x + 12x = 66$

$$22x = 66$$
$$x = 3$$

They will be 66 miles apart after 3 hours.

21.

	Rate	×	Time	=	Distance
Faster Truck	$x + 5$		5		$5(x + 5)$
Slower Truck	x		5		$5x$

$$5(x + 5) + 5x = 600$$
$$5x + 25 + 5x = 600$$
$$10x + 25 = 600$$
$$10x = 575$$
$$x = 57.5$$
$$x + 5 = 62.5$$

The rate of the slower truck is 57.5 miles per hour and the rate of the faster truck is 62.5 miles per hour.

23.

	Rate	×	Time	=	Distance
Car	55		x		$55x$
Bus	45		x		$45x$

The cars traveled a total of 240 miles, so the equation is $55x + 45x = 240$.
Solve for x. $55x + 45x = 240$

$$100x = 240$$
$$x = 2.4$$

The car and bus meet after 2.4 hours or 2 hours and 24 minutes.

25.

	Rate	×	Time	=	Distance
First Part of Trip	50		x		$50x$
Second Part of Trip	40		$5 - x$		$40(5 - x)$

$$50x + 40(5 - x) = 220$$
$$50x + 200 - 40x = 220$$
$$10x + 200 = 220$$
$$10x = 20$$
$$x = 2$$
$$5 - x = 3$$

The bus traveled for 2 hours at 50 miles per hour and for 3 hours at 40 miles per hour.

27.

	Pounds	×	Cost Per Pound	=	Cost
A-Grade Coffee	x		$9.50		$9.50x$
B-Grade Coffee	$20-x$		$7.00		$7.00(20-x)$
Mixture	20		$8.50		$8.50(20)$

$$9.50x + 7.00(20-x) = 20(8.50)$$
$$9.50x + 140 - 7.00x = 170$$
$$2.50x + 140 = 170$$
$$2.50x = 30$$
$$x = 12$$
$$20 - x = 8$$

The mixture should contain 12 pounds of the A-grade coffee and 8 pounds of the B-grade coffee.

29.

	Pounds	×	Cost Per Pound	=	Cost
Cashews	x		$7.40		$7.40x$
Peanuts	6		$2.60		$2.60(6)$
Mixture	$x+6$		$5.80		$5.80(x+6)$

$$7.40x + 2.60(6) = 5.80(x+6)$$
$$7.40x + 15.60 = 5.80x + 34.80$$
$$1.60x + 15.60 = 34.80$$
$$1.60x = 19.20$$
$$x = 12$$

The mixture should contain 12 pounds of cashews.

31.

	Number of Coins	×	Denomination	=	Total Value
Dimes	x		10		$10x$
Quarters	$32-x$		25		$25(32-x)$

$$10x + 25(32-x) = 500$$
$$10x + 800 - 25x = 500$$
$$800 - 15x = 5.00$$
$$-15x = -300$$
$$x = 20$$
$$32 - x = 12$$

There are 20 dimes and 12 quarters.

33.

	Number	×	Denomination	=	Total Value
$5 bills	$x + 25$		5		$5(x+25)$
$10 bills	x		10		$10x$

$$5(x+25)+10x = 200$$
$$5x+125+10x = 200$$
$$15x+125 = 200$$
$$15x = 75$$
$$x = 5$$
$$x+25 = 30$$

There are 5 $10 bills and 30 $5 bills.

35.

	Number of Tickets	×	Cost	=	Total Cost
Adult Tickets	x		$25		$25x$
Children's Tickets	$305 - x$		$5		$5(305 - x)$

$$25x + 5(305 - x) = 6025$$
$$25x + 1525 - 5x = 6025$$
$$20x + 1525 = 6025$$
$$20x = 4500$$
$$x = 225$$
$$305 - x = 80$$

225 adult tickets and 80 children's tickets were sold.

37. – 43. Answers will vary.

45. makes sense

47. does not make sense; Explanations will vary. Sample explanation: The resulting solution must contain between 50% and 60% acid.

49.

	Milliliters	×	Percent Minoxidil	=	Amount of Minoxidil
15% Minoxidil	50		0.15		0.15(50)
Water	x		0		$0(x)$
10% Minoxidil	$x + 50$		0.10		$0.10(x+50)$

$$0.15(50)+0(x) = 0.10(x+50)$$
$$7.50 = 0.10x + 5$$
$$2.50 = 0.10x$$
$$x = 25$$

25 milliliters of water should be mixed with 50 milliliters of 15% minoxidil to make a 10% solution.

51. $3^2 - 5\left[4 - 3(2-6)\right] = 3^2 - 5\left[4 - 3(-4)\right]$
$$= 3^2 - 5(4+12)$$
$$= 3^2 - 5(16)$$
$$= 9 - 80$$
$$= -71$$

52. The integers are -100, 0, and $\sqrt{16} = 4$.

53. $3(x+3) = 5(2x+6)$
$$3x + 9 = 10x + 30$$
$$3x + 9 - 10x = 10x + 30 - 10x$$
$$-7x + 9 - 9 = 30 - 9$$
$$-7x = 21$$
$$\frac{-7x}{-7} = \frac{21}{-7}$$
$$x = -3$$

The solution set is $\{-3\}$.

54. $\dfrac{32}{200} = \dfrac{4 \cdot \cancel{8}}{25 \cdot \cancel{8}} = \dfrac{4}{25}$

55. $\dfrac{-8}{3} = \dfrac{32}{x}$
$$\frac{-8}{3} = \frac{32}{-12}$$
$$\frac{-8}{3} = \frac{-8 \cdot (\cancel{-4})}{3 \cdot (\cancel{-4})}$$
$$\frac{-8}{3} = \frac{-8}{3}$$
Yes, -12 is a solution to the equation.

56. $\dfrac{63}{x} = \dfrac{7}{5}$

3.2 Check Points

1. a. $\dfrac{\text{number of people under age 15}}{\text{number of people over age 65}} = \dfrac{60}{14} = \dfrac{\cancel{2} \cdot 30}{\cancel{2} \cdot 7} = \dfrac{30}{7}$ or 30 to 7

  b. $\dfrac{\text{number of Africans}}{\text{total number of people in global village}} = \dfrac{28}{200} = \dfrac{\cancel{4} \cdot 7}{\cancel{4} \cdot 50} = \dfrac{7}{50}$ or 7 to 50

2. a. $\dfrac{10}{x} = \dfrac{2}{3}$

$10 \cdot 3 = 2x$

$30 = 2x$

$15 = x$

The solution set is $\{15\}$.

b. $\dfrac{-7}{9} = \dfrac{21}{x}$

$-7x = 21 \cdot 9$

$-7x = 189$

$\dfrac{-7x}{-7} = \dfrac{189}{-7}$

$x = -27$

The solution set is $\{-27\}$.

3. Let $x =$ the property tax on the \$420,000 house.

$$\dfrac{\text{Tax on } \$250,000 \text{ house}}{\text{Assessed value } (\$250,000)} = \dfrac{\text{Tax on } \$420,000 \text{ house}}{\text{Assessed value } (\$420,000)}$$

$$\dfrac{\$3500}{\$250,000} = \dfrac{\$x}{\$420,000}$$

$$\dfrac{3500}{250,000} = \dfrac{x}{420,000}$$

$$250,000x = (3500)(420,000)$$

$$250,000x = 1,470,000,000$$

$$\dfrac{250,000x}{250,000} = \dfrac{1,470,000,000}{250,000}$$

$$x = 5880$$

The property tax is \$5880.

4. Let $x =$ the total number of deer in the refuge.

$\dfrac{120}{x} = \dfrac{25}{150}$

$25x = (120)(150)$

$25x = 18,000$

$\dfrac{25x}{25} = \dfrac{18,000}{25}$

$x = 720$

There are about 720 deer in the refuge.

3.2 Exercise Set

1. 24 to 48

$$\frac{24}{48} = \frac{24 \cdot 1}{24 \cdot 2} = \frac{1}{2}$$

3. 48 to 20

$$\frac{48}{20} = \frac{4 \cdot 12}{4 \cdot 5} = \frac{12}{5}$$

5. 27:36

$$\frac{27}{36} = \frac{9 \cdot 3}{9 \cdot 4} = \frac{3}{4}$$

7. 20 men to 10 women

$$\frac{20}{10} = \frac{2}{1} \text{ or } 2:1$$

9. 10 women to 30 students

$$\frac{10}{30} = \frac{1}{3} \text{ or } 1:3$$

11. $\dfrac{20}{x} = \dfrac{5}{3}$

Apply the cross products principle and then solve the resulting equation.

$$5x = 20 \cdot 3$$
$$5x = 60$$
$$x = 12$$

The solution set is $\{12\}$.

13. $\dfrac{x}{3} = \dfrac{5}{2}$

$$2x = 3 \cdot 5$$
$$2x = 15$$
$$x = \frac{15}{2} = 7.5$$

The solution set is $\{7.5\}$.

15. $\dfrac{x}{12} = -\dfrac{3}{4}$

$$4x = 12(-3)$$
$$4x = -36$$
$$x = -9$$

The solution set is $\{-9\}$.

17. $\dfrac{x-2}{12} = \dfrac{8}{3}$

$$3(x-2) = 12(8)$$
$$3x - 6 = 96$$
$$3x = 102$$
$$x = 34$$

The solution set is $\{34\}$.

19. $\dfrac{x}{7} = \dfrac{x+14}{5}$

$$5x = 7(x+14)$$
$$5x = 7x + 98$$
$$-2x = 98$$
$$x = -49$$

The solution set is $\{-49\}$.

21. $\dfrac{x+9}{5} = \dfrac{x-10}{11}$

$$5(x-10) = 11(x+9)$$
$$5x - 50 = 11x + 99$$
$$-50 = 6x + 99$$
$$-149 = 6x$$
$$-\frac{149}{6} = x$$

The solution set is $\left\{-\dfrac{149}{6}\right\}$.

23. $\dfrac{x}{a} = \dfrac{b}{c}$

$$xc = ab$$
$$x = \frac{ab}{c}$$

25. $\dfrac{a+b}{c} = \dfrac{x}{d}$

$$xc = d(a+b)$$
$$x = \frac{d(a+b)}{c} \text{ or } \frac{ad+bd}{c}$$

27.
$$\frac{x+a}{a} = \frac{b+c}{c}$$
$$a(b+c) = c(x+a)$$
$$ab + ac = cx + ca$$
$$ab + ac - ca = cx$$
$$ab = cx$$
$$\frac{ab}{c} = x$$

29. $\dfrac{200}{80} = \dfrac{\cancel{40} \cdot 5}{\cancel{40} \cdot 2} = \dfrac{5}{2}$ or 5:2

31. $\dfrac{2(75)}{200} = \dfrac{150}{200} = \dfrac{\cancel{50} \cdot 3}{\cancel{50} \cdot 4} = \dfrac{3}{4}$ or 3:4

33. Let x = the tax on a property with an assessed value of \$162,500.

$$\frac{\text{Tax on \$62,000 house}}{\text{Assessed value (\$62,000)}} = \frac{\text{Tax on \$162,500 house}}{\text{Assessed value (\$162,500)}}$$
$$\frac{\$720}{\$65,000} = \frac{\$x}{\$162,500}$$
$$\frac{720}{65,000} = \frac{x}{162,500}$$
$$65,000x = (720)(162,500)$$
$$65,000x = 117,000,000$$
$$\frac{65,000x}{65,000} = \frac{117,000,000}{65,000}$$
$$x = 1800$$

The tax on a property assessed at \$162,500 is \$1800.

35. Let x = the total number of fur seal pups in the rookery.

$$\frac{\text{Original \# tagged}}{\text{Total \# fur seal pups}} = \frac{\text{\# tagged in sample}}{\text{\# in sample}}$$
$$\frac{4963}{x} = \frac{218}{900}$$
$$218x = (4963)(900)$$
$$218x = 4,466,700$$
$$\frac{218x}{218} = \frac{4,466,700}{218}$$
$$x \approx 20,489$$

There were approximately 20,489 fur seal pups in the rookery.

37. Let x = the number of people, in billions, suffering from malnutrition (in 2006).

$$\frac{28}{200} = \frac{x}{6.5}$$
$$200x = (28)(6.5)$$
$$200x = 182$$
$$\frac{200x}{200} = \frac{182}{200}$$
$$x \approx 0.9$$

0.9 billion people suffered from malnutrition in 2006.

39. Let x = the height of the critter.

$$\frac{\text{foot length person}}{\text{height of person}} = \frac{\text{foot length critter}}{\text{height of critter}}$$
$$\frac{10 \text{ inches}}{67 \text{ inches}} = \frac{23 \text{ inches}}{x}$$
$$\frac{10}{67} = \frac{23}{x}$$
$$10x = (67)(23)$$
$$10x = 1541$$
$$x = 154.1$$

The height of the critter is 154.1 in.

41. 5 years after installation:
$$\frac{C_{\text{gas}}}{C_{\text{solar}}} = \frac{12,000 + 700x}{30,000 + 150x}$$
$$= \frac{12,000 + 700(5)}{30,000 + 150(5)}$$
$$= \frac{15,500}{30,750} = \frac{62}{123} \text{ or } 62:123$$

40 years after installation:
$$\frac{C_{\text{gas}}}{C_{\text{solar}}} = \frac{12,000 + 700(40)}{30,000 + 150(40)}$$
$$= \frac{40,000}{36,000} = \frac{10}{9} \text{ or } 10:9$$

The ratio of the total cost of gas to solar heating increases over time. Over a short period of time, gas heating is more economical, but over many years, solar heating becomes more economical.

43. – 47. Answers will vary.

49. makes sense

51. does not make sense; Explanations will vary. Sample explanation: Though animals do tend to hide, the capture-recapture method is still dependable because the same ratio is likely to hide each time.

53. true

55. false; Changes to make the statement true will vary. A sample change is: There are 30 men and 40 women. Thus the ratio of women to men is 40:30 (or 4:3).

57.
$$\frac{10+x}{20+x} = \frac{0.600}{1}$$
$$10+x = 0.600(20+x)$$
$$10+x = 12+0.600x$$
$$10+0.4x = 12$$
$$0.4x = 2$$
$$\frac{0.4x}{0.4} = \frac{2}{0.4}$$
$$x = 5$$
A hit must be made the next 5 consecutive times at bat to raise the batting average to 0.600.

59. Let x = actual distance represented by 9.85 inches on a map.
$$\frac{2 \text{ inches}}{13.47 \text{ miles}} = \frac{9.85 \text{ inches}}{x \text{ miles}}$$
$$\frac{2}{13.47} = \frac{9.85}{x}$$
$$2x = (13.47)(9.85)$$
$$2x = 132.6795$$
$$x \approx 66.34$$
The person plans to travel 66.34 miles.

60.
$$-6x+2 \le 2(5-x)$$
$$-6x+2 \le 10-2x$$
$$-6x+2+2x \le 10-2x+2x$$
$$-4x+2 \le 10$$
$$-4x+2-2 \le 10-2$$
$$-4x \le 8$$
$$\frac{-4x}{-4} \ge \frac{8}{-4}$$
$$x \ge -2$$
$$[-2, \infty)$$

61. $A = 112$, $P = 40\% = 0.40$
$$A = PB$$
$$112 = 0.40 \cdot B$$
$$\frac{112}{0.40} = \frac{0.40B}{0.40}$$
$$280 = B$$
112 is 40% of 280.

62.
$$9-2\left[4(x-3)+7\right]$$
$$= 9-2(4x-12+7)$$
$$= 9-2(4x-5)$$
$$= 9-8x+10$$
$$= 19-8x$$

63.
$$A = \frac{1}{2}bh$$
$$30 = \frac{1}{2}(12)h$$
$$\frac{30}{6} = \frac{6h}{6}$$
$$5 = h$$

64. $A = \frac{1}{2}h(a+b)$
$$A = \frac{1}{2} \cdot 7 \cdot (10+16) = \frac{1}{2} \cdot 7 \cdot (26) = 91$$

65.
$$x = 4(90-x)-40$$
$$x = 360-4x-40$$
$$x = 320-4x$$
$$x+4x = 320-4x+4x$$
$$5x = 320$$
$$\frac{5x}{5} = \frac{320}{5}$$
$$x = 64$$
The solution set is $\{64\}$.

Mid-Chapter Check Point

1. Let x = the number of days it will take to type the manuscript.

$$\frac{600}{21} = \frac{230}{x}$$

$$600x = 21 \cdot 230$$

$$600x = 4830$$

$$x = 8.05$$

It will take 8.05 days to type the manuscript.

2.

	Number of Liters	× Percent Alcohol	= Amount of Alcohol
30% Alcohol	x	0.30	$0.30x$
70% Alcohol	$12 - x$	0.70	$0.70(12 - x)$
60% Alcohol	12	0.60	$0.60(12)$

$$0.30x + 0.70(12 - x) = 0.60(12)$$

$$0.30x + 8.4 - 0.70x = 7.2$$

$$8.4 - 0.40x = 7.2$$

$$-0.40x = -1.2$$

$$x = 3$$

$$12 - x = 9$$

3 liters of 30% alcohol solution must be mixed with 9 liters of 70% alcohol solution.

3. $\dfrac{4x}{9} = \dfrac{5}{-15}$

$$-60x = 45$$

$$x = -\frac{45}{60}$$

$$x = -\frac{3}{4}$$

The solution set is $\left\{ -\dfrac{3}{4} \right\}$.

4.

	Principal	× Rate	= Interest
8% Investment	x	0.08	$0.08x$
9% Investment	$25,000 - x$	0.09	$0.09(25,000 - x)$

$$0.08x + 0.09(25,000 - x) = 2135$$

$$0.08x + 2250 - 0.09x = 2135$$

$$2250 - 0.01x = 2135$$

$$-0.01x = -115$$

$$x = 11,500$$

$$25,000 - x = 13,500$$

She invested $11,500 at 8% and $13,500 at 9%.

5. $\dfrac{\text{number of men}}{\text{number of students}} = \dfrac{25}{60} = \dfrac{5}{12}$; 5:12 or 5 to 12

6.

	Rate	× Time	= Distance
Slower Plane	x	5	$5x$
Faster Plane	$x+100$	5	$5(x+100)$

$$5x + 5(x+100) = 4250$$
$$5x + 5x + 500 = 4250$$
$$10x + 500 = 4250$$
$$10x = 3750$$
$$x = 375$$
$$x + 100 = 475$$

The slow plane is traveling at 375 miles per hour and the fast plane is traveling at 475 miles per hour.

7. Let $x =$ the total number of elk at the refuge.

$$\frac{\text{Original number of tagged elk}}{\text{Total number of elk}} = \frac{\text{Number of tagged elk in sample}}{\text{Total number of elk in sample}}$$

$$\frac{40}{x} = \frac{4}{80}$$
$$4x = 40 \cdot 80$$
$$4x = 3200$$
$$x = 800$$

There are approximately 800 elk at the refuge.

8.

	Number of Quarts	× Percent Milk Fat	= Amount of Milk Fat
$\frac{1}{2}$% Milk Fat	x	0.005	$0.005x$
2% Milk Fat	4	0.02	$0.02(4)$
1% Milk Fat	$x+4$	0.01	$0.01(x+4)$

$$0.005x + 0.02(4) = 0.01(x+4)$$
$$0.005x + 0.08 = 0.01x + 0.04$$
$$0.08 = 0.005x + 0.04$$
$$0.04 = 0.005x$$
$$8 = x$$

8 quarts of the $\frac{1}{2}$% milk fat should be added.

9. $\dfrac{2}{x+1} = \dfrac{3}{2x+3}$

$$2(2x+3) = 3(x+1)$$
$$4x + 6 = 3x + 3$$
$$x + 6 = 3$$
$$x = -3$$

The solution set is $\{-3\}$.

10.

	Principal	×	Rate	=	Interest
4% Gain	x		0.04		$0.04x$
3% Loss	$4000 - x$		0.03		$0.03(4000 - x)$

$$0.04x - 0.03(4000 - x) = 55$$
$$0.04x - 120 + 0.03x = 55$$
$$0.07x - 120 = 55$$
$$0.07x = 175$$
$$x = 2500$$
$$4000 - x = 1500$$

She earned 4% on $2500 and lost 3% on $1500.

11.

	Rate	×	Time	=	Distance
Plane	450		x		$450x$
Car	50		$x - 2$		$50(x - 2)$

$$450x + 50(x - 2) = 1900$$
$$450x + 50x - 100 = 1900$$
$$500x - 100 = 1900$$
$$500x = 2000$$
$$x = 4$$
$$x - 2 = 2$$

You travel 4 hours by plane and 2 hours by car.

12. Let x = the distance that the spring stretches with an 80 pound weight.

$$\frac{\text{weight}_{(60)}}{\text{distance}_{(60)}} = \frac{\text{weight}_{(80)}}{\text{distance}_{(80)}}$$

$$\frac{60}{4} = \frac{80}{x}$$
$$60x = 4 \cdot 80$$
$$60x = 320$$
$$x = \frac{320}{60} = \frac{16}{3} = 5\frac{1}{3}$$

An 80-pound weight will stretch the spring $5\frac{1}{3}$ inches.

3.3 Check Points

1. $A = 24, b = 4$

   $A = \dfrac{1}{2}bh$

   $24 = \dfrac{1}{2} \cdot 4 \cdot h$

   $24 = 2h$

   $12 = h$

   The height of the sail is 12 ft.

2. Use the formulas for the area and circumference of a circle. The radius is 20 ft.

   $A = \pi r^2$

   $A = \pi (20)^2$

   $ = 400\pi$

   $ \approx 1256 \text{ or } 1257$

   The area is 400π ft^2 or approximately 1256 ft^2 or 1257 ft^2.

   $C = 2\pi r$

   $C = 2\pi (20)$

   $ = 40\pi$

   $ \approx 126$

   The circumference is 40π ft or approximately 126 ft.

3. The radius of the large pizza is 9 inches, and the radius of the medium pizza is 7 inches.

   large pizza: $A = \pi r^2 = \pi(9 \text{ in.})^2 = 81\pi \text{ in.}^2 \approx 254 \text{ in.}^2$

   medium pizza: $A = \pi r^2 = \pi(7 \text{ in.})^2 = 49\pi \text{ in.}^2 \approx 154 \text{ in.}^2$

   For each pizza, find the price per inch by dividing the price by the area.

   Price per square inch for the large pizza $= \dfrac{\$20.00}{81\pi \text{ in.}^2} \approx \dfrac{\$20.00}{254 \text{ in.}^2} \approx \dfrac{\$0.08}{\text{in.}^2}$

   Price per square inch for the medium pizza $= \dfrac{\$14.00}{49\pi \text{ in.}^2} \approx \dfrac{\$14.00}{154 \text{ in.}^2} \approx \dfrac{\$0.09}{\text{in.}^2}$.

   The large pizza is the better buy.

4. Smaller cylinder: $r = 3$ in., $h = 5$ in.

   $V = \pi r^2 h$

   $V = \pi (3)^2 \cdot 5$

   $ = 45\pi$

   The volume of the smaller cylinder is 45π in.^{3}.

   Larger cylinder: $r = 3$ in., $h = 10$ in.

   $V = \pi r^2 h$

   $V = \pi (3)^2 \cdot 10$

   $ = 90\pi$

   The volume of the smaller cylinder is 90π in.^{3}.

   The ratio of the volumes of the two cylinders is $\dfrac{V_{\text{larger}}}{V_{\text{smaller}}} = \dfrac{90\pi \text{ in.}^3}{45\pi \text{ in.}^3} = \dfrac{2}{1}$.

   So, the volume of the larger cylinder is 2 times the volume of the smaller cylinder.

5. Use the formula for the volume of a sphere. The radius is 4.5 in.

$$V = \frac{4}{3}\pi r^3$$

$$V = \frac{4}{3}\pi (4.5)^3$$

$$= 121.5\pi$$

$$\approx 382$$

The volume is approximately 382 in.^{3}. Thus the 350 cubic inches will not be enough to fill the ball.

6. Let $3x$ = the measure of the first angle.
Let x = the measure of the second angle.
Let $x - 20$ = the measure of the third angle.

$$3x + x + (x - 20) = 180$$
$$5x - 20 = 180$$
$$5x = 200$$
$$x = 40$$
$$3x = 120$$
$$x - 20 = 20$$

The three angle measures are 120°, 40°, and 20°.

7. *Step 1* Let x = the measure of the angle.

Step 2 Let $90 - x$ = the measure of its complement.

Step 3 The angle's measure is twice that of its complement, so the equation is $x = 2 \cdot (90 - x)$.

Step 4 Solve this equation
$$x = 2 \cdot (90 - x)$$
$$x = 180 - 2x$$
$$x + 2x = 180 - 2x + 2x$$
$$3x = 180$$
$$x = 60$$
The measure of the angle is 60°.

Step 5 The complement of the angle is $90° - 60° = 30°$, and 60° is indeed twice 30°.

3.3 Exercise Set

1. Use the formulas for the perimeter and area of a rectangle. The length is 6 m and the width is 3 m.

$$P = 2l + 2w$$
$$= 2(6) + 2(3) = 12 + 6 = 18$$
$$A = lw = 6 \cdot 3 = 18$$

The perimeter is 18 meters, and the area is 18 square meters.

3. Use the formula for the area of a triangle. The base is 14 in and the height is 8 in.

$$A = \frac{1}{2}bh = \frac{1}{2}(14)(8) = 56$$

The area is 56 square inches.

5. Use the formula for the area of a trapezoid. The bases are 16 m and 10 m and the height is 7 m.

$$A = \frac{1}{2}h(a+b)$$
$$= \frac{1}{2}(7)(16+10) = \frac{1}{2} \cdot 7 \cdot 26 = 91$$

The area is 91 square meters.

7. $A = 1250,\ w = 25$

$$A = lw$$
$$1250 = l \cdot 25$$
$$50 = l$$

The length of the swimming pool is 50 feet.

9. $A = 20, b = 5$

$$A = \frac{1}{2}bh$$
$$20 = \frac{1}{2} \cdot 5 \cdot h$$
$$20 = \frac{5}{2}h$$
$$\frac{2}{5}(20) = \frac{2}{5}\left(\frac{5}{2}h\right)$$
$$8 = h$$

The height of the triangle is 8 feet.

11. $P = 188,\ w = 44$

$$188 = 2l + 2(44)$$
$$188 = 2l + 88$$
$$100 = 2l$$
$$50 = l$$

The length of the rectangle is 50 cm.

13. Use the formulas for the area and circumference of a circle. The radius is 4 cm.

$$A = \pi r^2$$
$$A = \pi(4)^2$$
$$= 16\pi$$
$$\approx 50$$

The area is 16π cm^2 or approximately 50 cm^2.

$$C = 2\pi r$$
$$C = 2\pi(4)$$
$$= 8\pi$$
$$\approx 25$$

The circumference is 8π cm or approximately 25 cm.

15. Since the diameter is 12 yd, the radius is $\frac{12}{2} = 6$ yd.

$$A = \pi r^2$$
$$A = \pi(6)^2$$
$$= 36\pi$$
$$\approx 113$$

The area is 36π yd^2 or approximately 113 yd^2.

$$C = 2\pi r$$
$$C = 2\pi \cdot 6$$
$$= 12\pi$$
$$\approx 38$$

The circumference is 12π yd or approximately 38 yd.

17.

$$C = 2\pi r$$
$$14\pi = 2\pi r$$
$$\frac{14\pi}{2\pi} = \frac{2\pi r}{2\pi}$$
$$7 = r$$

The radius is 7 in. and the diameter is 2(7 in) = 14 in.

19. Use the formula for the volume of a rectangular solid. The length and width are each 3 inches and the height is 4 inches.

$$V = lwh$$
$$V = 3 \cdot 3 \cdot 4$$
$$= 36$$

The volume is 36 in.^{3}.

21. Use the formula for the volume of a cylinder. The radius is 5 cm and the height is 6 cm.

$$V = \pi r^2 h$$
$$V = \pi(5)^2 6$$
$$= \pi(25)6$$
$$= 150\pi$$
$$\approx 471$$

The volume of the cylinder is 150π cm^3 or approximately 471 cm^3.

23. Use the formula for the volume of a sphere. The diameter is 18 cm, so the radius is 9 cm.

$$V = \frac{4}{3}\pi r^3$$

$$V = \frac{4}{3}\pi (9)^3$$

$$= 972\pi$$

$$\approx 3052$$

The volume is 972π cm^3 or approximately 3052 cm^3.

25. Use the formula for the volume of a cone. The radius is 4 m and the height is 9 m.

$$V = \frac{1}{3}\pi r^2 h$$

$$V = \frac{1}{3}\pi (4)^2 \cdot 9$$

$$= 48\pi$$

$$\approx 151$$

The volume is 48π m^3 or approximately 151 m^3.

27.
$$\frac{V}{\pi r^2} = \frac{\pi r^2 h}{\pi r^2}$$

$$\frac{V}{\pi r^2} = h$$

29. Smaller cylinder: $r = 3$ in, $h = 4$ in.
$$V = \pi r^2 h = \pi (3)^2 \cdot 4 = 36\pi$$

The volume of the smaller cylinder is $36\pi\ in^3$.

Larger cylinder: $r = 3(3\text{ in}) = 9$ in, $h = 4$ in.
$$V = \pi r^2 h = \pi (9)^2 \cdot 4 = 324\pi$$

The volume of the larger cylinder is 324π in.^{3}.
The ratio of the volumes of the two cylinders is

$$\frac{V_{larger}}{V_{smaller}} = \frac{324\pi}{36\pi} = \frac{9}{1}.$$

So, the volume of the larger cylinder is 9 times the volume of the smaller cylinder.

31. The sum of the measures of the three angles of any triangle is $180°$.
$$x + x + (x+30) = 180$$
$$3x + 30 = 180$$
$$3x = 150$$
$$x = 50$$
$$x + 30 = 80$$
The three angle measures are $50°, 50°,$ and $80°$.

33.
$$4x + (3x+4) + (2x+5) = 180$$
$$9x + 9 = 180$$
$$9x = 171$$
$$x = 19$$
$$3x + 4 = 61$$
$$2x + 5 = 43$$
The three angle measures are $76°,\ 61°,$ and $43°$.

35. Let $x = $ the measure of the smallest angle.
Let $2x = $ the measure of the second angle.
Let $x + 20 = $ the measure of the third angle.
$$x + 2x + (x+20) = 180$$
$$4x + 20 = 180$$
$$4x = 160$$
$$x = 40$$
$$2x = 80$$
$$x + 20 = 60$$
The three angle measures are $40°, 80°,$ and $60°$.

37. If the measure of an angle is $58°$, the measure of its complement is $90° - 58° = 32°$.

39. If the measure of an angle is $88°$, the measure of its complement is $2°$.

41. If the measure of an angle is $132°$, the measure of its supplement is $180° - 132° = 48°$.

43. If the measure of an angle is $90°$, the measure of its supplement is $180° - 90° = 90°$.

45. *Step 1* Let $x = $ the measure of the angle.

Step 2 Let $90 - x = $ the measure of its complement.

Step 3 The angle's measure is $60°$ more than that of its complement, so the equation is
$$x = (90 - x) + 60.$$

Step 4 Solve this equation
$$x = 90 - x + 60$$
$$x = 150 - x$$
$$2x = 150$$
$$x = 75$$
The measure of the angle is $75°$.

Step 5 The complement of the angle is $90° - 75° = 15°$, and $75°$ is $60°$ more than $15°$.

47. *Step 1* Let x = the measure of the angle.

Step 2 Then $180 - x$ = the measure of its supplement.

Step 3 The angle's measure is three times that of its supplement, so the equation is $x = 3(180 - x)$.

Step 4 Solve this equation
$$x = 3(180 - x)$$
$$x = 540 - 3x$$
$$4x = 540$$
$$x = 135$$
The measure of the angle is $135°$.

Step 5 The measure of its supplement is $180° - 135° = 45°$, and $135° = 3(45°)$, so the proposed solution checks.

49. *Step 1* Let x = the measure of the angle.

Step 2 Let $180 - x$ = the measure of its supplement, and, $90 - x$ = the measure of its complement.

Step 3 The measure of the angle's supplement is $10°$ more than three times that of its complement, so the equation is $180 - x = 3(90 - x) + 10$.

Step 4 Solve this equation
$$180 - x = 3(90 - x) + 10$$
$$180 - x = 270 - 3x + 10$$
$$180 - x = 280 - 3x$$
$$2x = 100$$
$$x = 50$$
The measure of the angle is $50°$.

Step 5 The measure of its supplement is $130°$ and the measure of its complement is $40°$. Since $130° = 3(40°) + 10°$, the proposed solution checks.

51. Divide the shape into two rectangles.

$A_{\text{entire figure}} = A_{\text{bottom rectangle}} + A_{\text{side rectangle}}$

$A_{\text{entire figure}} = 3 \cdot 8 + 4(9 + 3)$

$\phantom{A_{\text{entire figure}}} = 24 + 4(12)$

$\phantom{A_{\text{entire figure}}} = 24 + 48$

$\phantom{A_{\text{entire figure}}} = 72$

The area of the figure is 72 square meters.

53. Divide the shape into a rectangle and a triangle.

$A_{\text{entire figure}} = A_{\text{rectangle}} + A_{\text{triangle}}$

$A_{\text{entire figure}} = lw + \dfrac{1}{2} bh$

$\phantom{A_{\text{entire figure}}} = 10(6) + \dfrac{1}{2}(3)(10 - 3)$

$\phantom{A_{\text{entire figure}}} = 60 + \dfrac{1}{2}(3)(7)$

$\phantom{A_{\text{entire figure}}} = 60 + 10.5 = 70.5$

The area of the figure is 70.5 cm^2.

55. Subtract the volume of the three hollow portions from the volume of the whole rectangular solid.

$V_{\text{cement block}} = V_{\text{rectangular solid}} - 3 \cdot V_{\text{hollow}}$

$\phantom{V_{\text{cement block}}} = LWH - 3 \cdot lwh$

$\phantom{V_{\text{cement block}}} = (8)(8)(16) - 3 \cdot (4)(6)(8)$

$\phantom{V_{\text{cement block}}} = 1024 - 576$

$\phantom{V_{\text{cement block}}} = 448$

The volume of the cement block is 448 cubic inches.

57. The area of the office is $(20 \text{ ft})(16 \text{ ft}) = 320 \text{ ft}^2$. Use a proportion to determine how much of the yearly electric bill is deductible.

    Let x = the amount of the electric bill that is deductible.

    $$\frac{320}{2200} = \frac{x}{4800}$$

    $$2200x = (320)(4800)$$

    $$2200x = 1,536,000$$

    $$\frac{2200x}{2200} = \frac{1,546,000}{2200}$$

    $$x \approx 698.18$$

    $698.18 of the yearly electric bill is deductible.

59. The radius of the large pizza is $\frac{1}{2} \cdot 14 = 7$ inches, and the radius of the medium pizza is $\frac{1}{2} \cdot 7$ inches $= 3.5$ inches.

    large pizza:

    $$A = \pi r^2 = \pi (7 \text{ in.})^2$$

    $$= 49\pi \text{ in.}^2 \approx 154 \text{ in.}^2$$

    medium pizza:

    $$A = \pi r^2 = \pi (3.5 \text{ in.})^2$$

    $$= 12.25 \text{ in.}^2 \approx 38.465 \text{ in.}^2$$

    For each pizza, find the price per inch by dividing the price by the area.

    Price per square inch for the large pizza $= \dfrac{\$12.00}{154 \text{ in.}^2} \approx \dfrac{\$0.08}{\text{in.}^2}$ and the price per square inch for the medium pizza

    $= \dfrac{\$5.00}{28.465 \text{ in.}^2} \approx \dfrac{\$0.13}{\text{in.}^2}$.

    The large pizza is the better buy.

61. The area of the larger circle is $A = \pi r^2 = \pi \cdot 50^2 = 2500\pi \text{ ft}^2$.

    The area of the smaller circle is $A = \pi r^2 = \pi \cdot 40^2 = 1600\pi \text{ ft}^2$.

    The area of the circular road is the difference between the area of the larger circle and the area of the smaller circle.

    $A = 2500\pi \text{ ft}^2 - 1600\pi \text{ ft}^2 = 900\pi \text{ ft}^2$

    The cost to pave the circular road is $\$0.80(900\pi) \approx \$2262$.

63. To find the perimeter of the entire window, first find the perimeter of the lower rectangular portion. This is the bottom and two sides of the window, which is 3 ft + 6 ft + 6 ft = 15 ft. Next, find the perimeter or circumference of the semicircular portion of the window. The radius of the semicircle is $\frac{1}{2} \cdot 3$ ft $= 1.5$ ft, so the circumference is

    $\frac{1}{2} \cdot 2\pi r \approx 3.14(1.5) = 4.7$ ft.

    So, approximately 15 ft + 4.7 ft = 19.7 ft of stripping would be needed to frame the window.

65. First, find the volume of water when the reservoir was full.

    $V = lwh = 50 \cdot 0 \cdot 20 = 30,000$

    The volume was 30,000 yd^3.

    Next, find the volume when the height of the water was 6 yards.

    $V = 50 \cdot 30 \cdot 6 = 9000$

    The volume was 9000 yd^3. The amount of water used in the three-month period was 30,000 yd^3 – 9000 yd^3 = 21,000 yd^3.

67. For the first can, the diameter is 6 in. so the radius is 3 in. and $V = \pi r^2 h = \pi(3)^2 \cdot 5 = 45\pi \approx 141.3$.

The volume of the first can is 141.3 in^3. For the second can, the diameter is 5 in., so the radius is 2.5 in. and $V = \pi r^2 h = \pi(2.5)^2 \cdot 6 = 37.5\pi \approx 117.75$.

The volume of the second can is 117.75 in^2. Since the cans are the same price, the can with the greater volume is the better buy. Choose the can with the diameter of 6 inches and height of 5 inches.

69. Find the volume of a cylinder with radius 3 feet and height 2 feet 4 inches.

$$2 \text{ ft } 4 \text{ in} = 2\frac{1}{3} \text{ feet} = \frac{7}{3} \text{ feet}$$

$$V = \pi r^2 h$$

$$= \pi(3)^2 \left(\frac{7}{3}\right) = \pi \cdot 9 \cdot \frac{7}{3} = 21\pi \approx 65.94$$

The volume of the tank is approximately 65.94 ft^3. This is a little over 1 ft^3 smaller than 67 ft^3 so it is too small to hold 500 gallons of water. Yes, you should be able to win your case.

71. – 77. Answers will vary.

79. does not make sense; Explanations will vary. Sample explanation: Though the heights of the books are proportional to the data, the widths are also changing. This cause the larger values to be visually exaggerated.

81. does not make sense; Explanations will vary. Sample explanation: If the radius is doubled, the area is multiplied by 4.

$$A_{\text{radius } x} = \pi r^2 \qquad A_{\text{radius } 2x} = \pi r^2$$
$$= \pi(x)^2 \qquad\qquad = \pi(2x)^2$$
$$= \pi x^2 \qquad\qquad = 4\pi x^2$$

83. true

85. false; Changes to make the statement true will vary. A sample change is: 90° does not have a complement.

87. Area of smaller deck $= (8 \text{ ft})(10) = 80 \text{ ft}^2$.

Area of larger deck $= (12 \text{ ft})(15) = 180 \text{ ft}^2$.

Find the ratio of the areas.

$$\frac{A_{\text{larger}}}{A_{\text{smaller}}} = \frac{180 \text{ } ft^2}{80 \text{ } ft^2} = \frac{2.25}{1} \text{ or } 2.25:1$$

The cost will increase 2.25 times.

89. Let x = the radius of the original sphere.
Let $2x$ = the radius of the larger sphere.
Find the ratio of the volumes of the two spheres.

$$\frac{A_{\text{larger}}}{A_{\text{original}}} = \frac{\frac{4}{3}\pi(2x)^3}{\frac{4}{3}\pi x^3} = \frac{8x^3}{x^3} = \frac{8}{1} \text{ or } 8:1$$

If the radius of a sphere is doubled, the volume increases 8 times.

91. The angles marked $2x$ and $2x + 40$ in the figure are supplementary, so their sum is $180°$.

$$2x + (2x + 40) = 180$$
$$2x + 2x + 40 = 180$$
$$4x + 40 = 180$$
$$4x = 10$$
$$x = 35$$

The angle of inclination is $35°$.

92. $P = 2s + b$ for s

$$P - b = 2s$$
$$\frac{P - b}{2} = \frac{2s}{2}$$
$$\frac{P - b}{2} = s \ \text{ or } \ s = \frac{P - b}{2}$$

93. $\dfrac{x}{2} + 7 = 13 - \dfrac{x}{4}$

Multiply both sides by the LCD, 4.

$$4\left(\frac{x}{2} + 7\right) = 4\left(13 - \frac{x}{4}\right)$$
$$2x + 28 = 52 - x$$
$$2x + 28 + x = 52 - x + x$$
$$3x + 28 = 52$$
$$3x + 28 - 28 = 52 - 28$$
$$3x = 24$$
$$\frac{3x}{3} = \frac{24}{3}$$
$$x = 8$$

The solution set is $\{8\}$.

94. $\left[3\left(12 \div 2^2 - 3\right)^2\right]^2$

$$= \left[3\left(12 \div 4 - 3\right)^2\right]^2$$
$$= \left[3(3 - 3)^2\right]^2 = \left(3 \cdot 0^2\right)^2 = 0^2 = 0$$

95. $x - 4y = 14$

$$2 - 4(-3) = 14$$
$$2 + 12 = 14$$
$$14 = 14, \ \text{true}$$

Yes, the values make it a true statement.

96. $x - 4y = 14$

$12 - 4(1) = 14$

$12 - 4 = 14$

$8 = 14,$ false

No, the values make it a false statement.

97. $y = \dfrac{2}{3}x + 1$

$y = \dfrac{2}{3}(-6) + 1$

$y = -4 + 1$

$y = -3$

Chapter 3 Review

1.

	Principal	×	Rate	=	Interest
8% Investment	x		0.08		0.08x
10% Investment	$10,000 - x$		0.10		$0.10(10,000 - x)$

The interest for the two investments combined must be \$940, so the equation is $0.08x + 0.10(10,000 - x) = 940$.

$0.08x + 0.10(10,000 - x) = 940$

$0.08x + 1000 - 0.10x = 940$

$-0.02x + 1000 = 940$

$-0.02x + 1000 - 1000 = 940 - 1000$

$-0.02x = -60$

$\dfrac{-0.02x}{-0.02} = \dfrac{-60}{-0.02}$

$x = 3000$

$10,000 - x = 7000$

\$3000 was invested at 8% and \$7000 was invested at 10%.

2.

	Principal	×	Rate	=	Interest
10% Investment	x		0.10		$0.10x$
12% Investment	$x + 6000$		0.12		$0.12(x + 6000)$

$0.10x + 0.12(x + 6000) = 2480$

$0.10x + 0.12x + 720 = 2480$

$0.22x + 720 = 2480$

$0.22x + 720 - 720 = 2480 - 720$

$0.22x = 1760$

$\dfrac{0.22x}{0.22} = \dfrac{1760}{0.22}$

$x = 8000$

$x + 6000 = 14,000$

\$8000 was invested at 10% and \$14,000 was invested at 12%.

3.

	Gallons $\times$	Percent Salt $=$	Amount of Salt
75% Saltwater Solution	x	0.75	$0.75x$
50% Saltwater Solution	$10-x$	0.50	$0.50(10-x)$
60% Saltwater Solution	10	0.60	$0.60(10)$

$$0.75x + 0.50(10-x) = 0.60(10)$$
$$0.75x + 5 - 0.50x = 6$$
$$0.25x + 5 = 6$$
$$0.25x = 1$$
$$\frac{0.25x}{0.25} = \frac{1}{0.25}$$
$$x = 4$$
$$10 - x = 6$$

To obtain 10 gallons of a 60% saltwater solution, 4 gallons of a 75% saltwater solution and 6 gallons of a 50% saltwater solution must be used.

4. In a mixture of two alloys, the percentage of copper will fall between the percentages of the two alloys being combined. Since 70% is greater than both 30% and 50%, it is not possible to obtain an alloy that is 70% copper.

5.

	Number of Students $\times$	Percent of Men $=$	Men
North Campus	x	0.05	$0.05x$
South Campus	$150-x$	0.80	$0.80(150-x)$
Merged Campus	150	0.50	$0.50(150)$

$$0.05x + 0.80(150-x) = 0.5(150)$$
$$0.05x + 120 - 0.80x = 75$$
$$-0.75x + 120 = 75$$
$$-0.75x = -45$$
$$\frac{-0.75x}{-0.75} = \frac{-45}{-0.75}$$
$$x = 60$$
$$150 - x = 90$$

Before the merger, there were 60 students in the department at the north campus and 90 students at south campus.

6.

	Rate $\times$	Time $=$	Distance
Slower Train	60	x	$60x$
Faster Train	80	x	$80x$

$$60x + 80x = 420$$
$$140x = 420$$
$$\frac{140x}{140} = \frac{420}{140}$$
$$x = 3$$

They will be 420 miles apart after 3 hours.

7.

	Rate	× Time	= Distance
Slower Bus	x	3	$3x$
Faster Bus	$x+10$	3	$3(x+10)$

$$3x + 3(x+10) = 210$$
$$3x + 3x + 30 = 210$$
$$6x + 30 = 210$$
$$6x = 180$$
$$x = 30$$
$$x + 10 = 40$$

The rate of the slower bus is 30 miles per hour and the rate of the faster bus is 40 miles per hour.

8.

	Number of Bills	× Denomination	= Total Value
\$5 bills	x	5	$5x$
\$10 bills	$15-x$	10	$10(15-x)$

$$5x + 10(15-x) = 120$$
$$5x + 150 - 10x = 120$$
$$150 - 5x = 120$$
$$-5x = -30$$
$$x = 6$$
$$15 - x = 9$$

There were 6 \$5 bills and 9 \$10 bills.

9. There is exactly enough information to solve the problem.

10. There is not enough information to solve the problem. Either the total quantity of the 15% solution, or the relationship between the quantities of the 12% and 20% solutions is needed.

11. There is exactly enough information to solve the problem.

12. There are 10 women and a total of 25 students in the class. The ratio of the number of women to the number of students in the class is $\dfrac{10}{25} = \dfrac{2}{5}$; $2:5$ or 2 to 5.

13. $\dfrac{42\%}{58\%} = \dfrac{42}{58} = \dfrac{2 \cdot 21}{2 \cdot 29} = \dfrac{21}{29}$ or 21:29 or 21 to 29.

14. $\dfrac{68\%}{32\%} = \dfrac{68}{32} = \dfrac{4 \cdot 17}{4 \cdot 8} = \dfrac{17}{8}$ or 17:8 or 17 to 8.

15. $\dfrac{3}{x} = \dfrac{15}{25}$

$$15x = 3 \cdot 25$$
$$15x = 75$$
$$\dfrac{15x}{15} = \dfrac{75}{15}$$
$$x = 5$$

The solution set is $\{5\}$.

16. $\dfrac{-7}{5} = \dfrac{91}{x}$

$-7x = 5 \cdot 91$

$-7x = 455$

$\dfrac{-7x}{-7} = \dfrac{455}{-7}$

$x = -65$

The solution set is $\{-65\}$.

17. $\dfrac{x+2}{3} = \dfrac{4}{5}$

$5(x+2) = 3 \cdot 4$

$5x + 10 = 12$

$5x = 2$

$x = \dfrac{2}{5}$

The solution set is $\left\{\dfrac{2}{5}\right\}$.

18. $\dfrac{5}{x+7} = \dfrac{3}{x+3}$

$5(x+3) = 3(x+7)$

$5x + 15 = 3x + 21$

$5x + 15 - 3x = 3x + 21 - 3x$

$2x + 15 = 21$

$2x + 15 - 15 = 21 - 15$

$2x = 6$

$x = 3$

The solution set is $\{3\}$.

19. Let x = number of teachers needed for 5400 students.

$\dfrac{3}{50} = \dfrac{x}{5400}$

$50x = 3 \cdot 5400$

$50x = 16,200$

$\dfrac{50x}{50} = \dfrac{16,200}{50}$

$x = 324$

For an enrollment of 5400 students, 324 teachers are needed.

20. Let x = number of trout in the lake.

$$\frac{\text{Original Number Tagged Deer}}{\text{Total Number of Deer}} = \frac{\text{Number Tagged Deer in Sample}}{\text{Total Number Deer in Sample}}$$

$$\frac{112}{x} = \frac{32}{82}$$

$$32x = 112 \cdot 82$$

$$32x = 9184$$

$$\frac{32x}{32} = \frac{9184}{32}$$

$$x = 287$$

There are 287 trout in the lake.

21. Let x = monthly sales if \$96,000 is spent on advertising.

$$\frac{12,000 \text{ skates}}{\$60,000} = \frac{x \text{ skates}}{\$96,000}$$

$$\frac{12,000}{60,000} = \frac{x}{96,000}$$

$$\frac{1}{5} = \frac{x}{96,000}$$

$$5x = 96,000$$

$$x = 19,200$$

If \$96,000 is spent on advertising, they will sell 19,200 pairs of skates.

22. Find the area of a rectangle with length 6.5 ft and width 5 ft.

$A = lw = (6.5)(5) = 32.5$

The area is 32.5 ft^2.

23. Find the area of a triangle with base 20 cm and height 5 cm.

$A = \dfrac{1}{2}bh = \dfrac{1}{2}(20)(5) = 50$

The area is 50 cm^2.

24. Find the area of a trapezoid with bases 22 yd and 5 yd and height 10 yd.

$$A = \frac{1}{2}h(a+b)$$

$$= \frac{1}{2}(10)(22+5)$$

$$= \frac{1}{2} \cdot 10 \cdot 27 = 135$$

The area is 135 yd^2.

25. Notice that the height of the middle rectangle is $64 - 12 - 12 = 40$ m.

Using $A = lw$ we must find the sum of areas of the middle rectangle and the two side rectangles.

$A = (40)(75) + 2 \cdot (64)(36)$

$\quad = 3000 + 2 \cdot 2304$

$\quad = 3000 + 4608$

$\quad = 7608$

The area is 7608 m^2.

26. Since the diameter is 20 m, the radius is $\dfrac{20}{2} = 10$ m.

$C = 2\pi = 2\pi(10) = 20\pi \approx 63$

$A = \pi r^2 = \pi(10)^2 = 100\pi \approx 314$

The circumference is 20π m or approximately 63 m; the area is 100π m^2 or approximately 314 m^2.

27. $A = 42, b = 14$

$A = \dfrac{1}{2}bh$

$42 = \dfrac{1}{2} \cdot 14 \cdot h$

$42 = 7h$

$\;6 = h$

The height of the sail is 6 ft.

28. Area of floor:

$A = bh = (12 \text{ ft})(15 \text{ ft}) = 180 \text{ ft}^2$

Area of base of stove:

$A = bh = (3 \text{ ft})(4 \text{ ft}) = 12 \text{ ft}^2$

Area of bottom of refrigerator:

$A = bh = (3 \text{ ft})(4 \text{ ft}) = 12 \text{ ft}^2$

The area to be covered with floor tile is $180 \text{ ft}^2 - 12 \text{ ft}^2 - 12 \text{ ft}^2 = 156 \text{ ft}^2$.

29. First, find the area of a trapezoid with bases 80 ft and 100 ft and height 60 ft.

$A = \dfrac{1}{2}h(a + b)$

$\quad = \dfrac{1}{2}(60)(80 + 100) = 5400$

The area of the yard is 5400 ft^2. The cost is $0.35(5400) = \$1890$.

30. The radius of the medium pizza is $\frac{1}{2} \cdot 14$ inches $= 7$ inches, and the radius of each small pizza is

$\frac{1}{2} \cdot 8$ inches $= 4$ inches.

Medium pizza:

$A = \pi r^2 = \pi (7 \text{ in.})^2$

$\quad = 49\pi \text{ in.}^2 \approx 154 \text{ in.}^2$

Small pizza:

$A = \pi r^2 = \pi (4 \text{ in.})^2$

$\quad = 16\pi \text{ in.}^2 \approx 50 \text{ in.}^2$

The area of one medium pizza is approximately 154 in.^{2} and the area of two small pizzas is approximately $2(50) = 100$ in.^{2}. Since the price of one medium pizza is the same as the price of two small pizzas and the medium pizza has the greater area, the medium pizza is the better buy. (Because the prices are the same, it is not necessary to find price per square inch in this case.)

31. Find the volume of a rectangular solid with length 5 cm, width 3 cm, and height 4 cm.

$A = lwh = 5 \cdot 3 \cdot 4 = 60$

The volume is 60 cm^3.

32. Find the volume of a cylinder with radius 4 yd and height 8 yd.

$V = \pi r^2 h$

$\quad = \pi (4)^2 \cdot 8 = 128\pi \approx 402$

The volume is 128π yd$^3 \approx 402$ yd^3.

33. Find the volume of a sphere with radius 6 m.

$V = \frac{4}{3}\pi r^3$

$\quad = \frac{4}{3}\pi (6)^3 = \frac{4}{3} \cdot \pi \cdot 216$

$\quad = 288\pi \approx 905$

The volume is 288π m$^3 \approx 905$ m^3.

34. Find the volume of each box.

$V = lwh = (8\text{m})(4\text{m})(3\text{m}) = 96\text{m}^3$

The space required for 50 containers is $50(96 \text{ m}^3) = 4800 \text{ m}^3$.

35. Since the diameter of the fish tank 6 ft, the radius is 3 ft.

$V = \pi r^2 h = \pi (3)^2 \cdot 3 = 27\pi \approx 84.82$

The volume of the tank is approximately 85 ft^3. Divide by 5 to determine how many fish can be put in the tank.

$\frac{84.82}{5} \approx 16.96$

There is enough water in the tank for 16 fish. Round down to 16, since 0.96 of a fish cannot be purchased.

36. The sum of the measures of the angles of any triangle is $180°$, so $x + 3x + 2x = 180$.

$x + 3x + 2x = 180$

$\qquad 6x = 180$

$\qquad x = 30$

If $x = 30$, then $3x = 90$ and $2x = 60$, so the angles measure $30°$, $60°$, and $90°$.

37. Let x = the measure of the second angle.
Let $2x + 15$ = the measure of the first angle.
Let $x + 25$ = the measure of the third angle.
$$x + (2x + 15) + (x + 25) = 180$$
$$4x + 40 = 180$$
$$4x = 140$$
$$x = 35$$
If $x = 35$, then $2x + 15 = 2(35) + 15 = 85$ and $x + 25 = 35 + 25 = 60$. The angles measure $85°$, $35°$, and $60°$.

38. If the measure of an angle is $57°$, the measure of its complement is $90° - 57° = 33°$

39. If the measure of an angle is $75°$, the measure of its supplement is $180° - 75° = 105°$.

40. Let x = the measure of the angle.
Let $90 - x$ = the measure of its complement.
$$x = (90 - x) + 25$$
$$x = 115 - x$$
$$2x = 115$$
$$x = 57.5$$
The measure of the angle is $57.5°$.

41. Let x = the measure of the angle.
Let $180 - x$ = the measure of its supplement.
$$180 - x = 4x - 45$$
$$180 - 5x = -45$$
$$-5x = -225$$
$$x = 45$$
If $x = 45$, then $180 - x = 135$. The measure of the angle is $45°$ and the measure of its supplement is $135°$.

Chapter 3 Test

1.

	Principal	× Rate =	Interest
9% Investment	x	0.09	$0.09x$
6% Investment	$6000 - x$	0.06	$0.06(6000 - x)$

$$0.09x + 0.06(6000 - x) = 480$$
$$0.09x + 360 - 0.06x = 480$$
$$0.03x + 360 = 480$$
$$0.03x = 120$$
$$\frac{0.03x}{0.03} = \frac{120}{0.03}$$
$$x = 4000$$
$$6000 - x = 2000$$

$4000 was invested at 9% at $2000 was invested at 6%.

2.

	Milliliters	×	Percent of Acid	=	Amount of Acid
50% Acid Solution	x		0.50		$0.50x$
80% Acid Solution	$100 - x$		0.80		$0.80(100 - x)$
68% Acid Mixture	100		0.68		$0.68(100)$

$$0.50x + 0.80(100 - x) = 0.68(100)$$
$$0.50x + 80 - 0.80x = 68$$
$$-0.30x = -12$$
$$\frac{-0.30x}{-0.30} = \frac{-12}{-0.30}$$
$$x = 40$$
$$100 - x = 60$$

40 milliliters of 50% acid solution and 60 milliliters of 80% acid solution must be used.

3.

	Rate	×	Time	=	Distance
Fast Car	45		x		$45x$
Slow Car	35		x		$35x$

$$45x + 35x = 400$$
$$80x = 400$$
$$x = 5$$

The two cars will meet after 5 hours.

4. $\dfrac{\text{men}}{\text{students}} = \dfrac{20}{20 + 15} = \dfrac{20}{35} = \dfrac{4}{7}$;

4 : 7 or 4 to 7

5. $\dfrac{-5}{8} = \dfrac{x}{12}$

$$8x = -60$$
$$x = \frac{-60}{8} = -\frac{15}{2}$$

The solution set is $\left\{ -\dfrac{15}{2} \right\}$.

6. Let x = number of tule elk in the park.

$$\frac{200}{x} = \frac{5}{150}$$
$$5x = 30,000$$
$$x = 6000$$

There are 6000 tule elk in the park.

7. Let x = pressure on object 330 feet below the surface.

$$\frac{25 \text{ pounds per square inch}}{60 \text{ feet}} = \frac{x \text{ pounds per square inch}}{330 \text{ feet}}$$

$$\frac{25}{60} = \frac{x}{330}$$

$$60x = 25 \cdot 330$$

$$60x = 8250$$

$$x = 137.5$$

The pressure 330 feet below the surface is 137.5 pounds per square inch.

8. Find the area of a triangle with base 47 meters and height 22 meters.

$$A = \frac{1}{2}bh = \frac{1}{2}(47)(22) = 517$$

The area of the triangle is 517 m^2.

9. Find the area of a trapezoid with height 15 in, lower base 40 in and upper base 30 in.

$$A = \frac{1}{2}h(a+b)$$

$$= \frac{1}{2}(15)(40+30)$$

$$= \frac{1}{2} \cdot 15 \cdot 70 = 525$$

The area is 525 in^2.

10. Notice that the height of the side rectangle is $6 + 3 = 9$ ft.

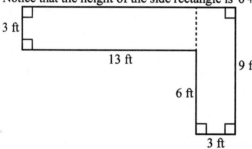

Using $A = lw$ we must find the sum of areas of the upper rectangle and the side rectangle.

$$A = (3)(13) + (3)(9)$$

$$= 39 + 27$$

$$= 66$$

The area is 66 ft^2.

11. Find the volume of a rectangular solid with length 3 in, width 2 in, and height 3 in.

$V = lwh = 3 \cdot 2 \cdot 3 = 18$

The volume is 18 in^3.

12. Find the volume of a cylinder with radius 5 cm and height 7 cm.

$$V = \pi r^2 h$$

$$= \pi(5)^2 \cdot 7 = \pi \cdot 25 \cdot 7$$

$$= 175\pi \approx 550$$

The volume is 175π cm^3 or approximately 550 cm^3.

13. The area of the floor is $A = (40 \text{ ft})(50 \text{ ft}) = 2000 \text{ ft}^2$.

The area of each tile is $A = (2 \text{ ft})(2 \text{ ft}) = 4 \text{ ft}^2$.

The number of tiles needed is $\dfrac{2000 \text{ ft}^2}{4 \text{ ft}^2} = 500$.

Since there are 10 tiles in a package, the number of packages needed is $\dfrac{500}{10} = 50$.

Since each package costs \$13, the cost for enough tiles to cover the floor is $50(\$13) = \$650$.

14. $A = 56, b = 8$

$$A = \frac{1}{2}bh$$
$$56 = \frac{1}{2} \cdot 8 \cdot h$$
$$56 = 4h$$
$$14 = h$$

The height of the sail is 14 feet.

15. Let x = the measure of the second angle.
Let $3x$ = the measure of the first angle.
Let $x - 30$ = the measure of the third angle.
$$x + 3x + (x - 30) = 180$$
$$5x - 30 = 180$$
$$5x = 210$$
$$x = 42$$

The measure of the first angle: $3x = 3(42°) = 126°$.
The measure of the second angle: $x = 42°$.
The measure of the third angle: $x - 30 = 42° - 30° = 12°$.

16. Let x = the measure of the angle.
Let $90 - x$ = the measure of its complement.
$$x = (90 - x) + 16$$
$$x = 106 - x$$
$$2x = 106$$
$$x = 53$$

The measure of the angle is $53°$.

Cumulative Review (Chapters 1-3)

1. $\dfrac{-9(3-6)}{(-12)(3)+(-3-5)(8-4)}$

   $= \dfrac{-9(-3)}{-36+(-8)(4)}$

   $= \dfrac{27}{-36-32} = \dfrac{27}{-68} = -\dfrac{27}{68}$

2. $8-3\big[2(x-1)+5\big]$

   $= 8-3(2x-2+5)$

   $= 8-3(2x+3)$

   $= 8-6x-9$

   $= -1-6x$

3. The integers are $-3, 0,$ and $\sqrt{9}=3.$

4. $x^2-10x; x=-3$

   $x^2-10x=(-3)^2-10(-3)$

   $\quad\quad = 9+30 = 39$

5. -2000 is to the left of -3 on the number line, so $-2000 < -3.$

6. $-4+(-11)+21 = -15+21 = 6$

   The temperature at noon was $6\,^\circ$F.

7. $10(2x-1) = 8(2x+1)+14$

   $20x-10 = 16x+8+14$

   $20x-10 = 16x+22$

   $4x-10 = 22$

   $4x = 32$

   $x = 8$

   The solution set is $\{8\}.$

8. $\dfrac{x}{5}+\dfrac{2x}{3} = x+\dfrac{1}{15}$

   $15\left(\dfrac{x}{5}+\dfrac{2x}{3}\right) = 15\left(x+\dfrac{1}{15}\right)$

   $3x+10x = 15x+1$

   $13x = 15x+1$

   $-2x = 1$

   $\dfrac{-2x}{-2} = \dfrac{1}{-2}$

   $x = -\dfrac{1}{2}$

   The solution set is $\left\{-\dfrac{1}{2}\right\}.$

9. $A = \dfrac{m+n}{2}$

   $2 \cdot A = 2 \cdot \dfrac{m+n}{2}$

   $2A = m+n$

   $2A-n = m$

   $m = 2A-n$

10. $C = 2.2a+589$

    $C = 2.2(20)+589 = 633$

    The average credit score of a 20-year-old is 633.

11. $C = 2.2a+589$

    $699 = 2.2a+589$

    $110 = 2.2a$

    $\dfrac{110}{2.2} = \dfrac{2.2a}{2.2}$

    $50 = a$

    An average credit score of 699 corresponds to an age of 50.

12. $A = 144, P = 60\% = 0.6$

    $A = PB$

    $144 = 0.60 \cdot B$

    $\dfrac{144}{0.60} = \dfrac{0.60 \cdot B}{0.60}$

    $240 = B$

    144 is 60% of 240.

13. Let x = the width of the field.
Let $2x + 14$ = the length of the field.
$$2x + 2(2x + 14) = 346$$
$$2x + 4x + 28 = 346$$
$$6x = 318$$
$$x = 53$$
$$2x + 14 = 120$$
The width is 53 meters and the length is 120 meters.

14. Let x = the person's weight before the weight loss.
$$x - 0.10x = 180$$
$$0.90x = 180$$
$$\frac{0.90x}{0.90} = \frac{180}{0.90}$$
$$x = 200$$
The person's weight was 200 pounds.

15.
$$5x - 5 \le -5$$
$$5x + 5 + 5 \le -5 + 5$$
$$5x \le 0$$
$$\frac{5x}{5} \le \frac{0}{5}$$
$$x \le 0$$
$$(-\infty, 0]$$

16.
$$-5x + 9 > -2x + 6$$
$$-5x + 9 + 2x > -2x + 6 + 2x$$
$$-3x + 9 > 6$$
$$-3x + 9 - 9 > 6 - 9$$
$$-3x > -3$$
$$\frac{-3x}{-3} < \frac{-3}{-3}$$
$$x < 1$$
$$(-\infty, 1)$$

17.

	Rate	×	Time	=	Distance
Slow Runner	6		x		$6x$
Fast Runner	8		x		$8x$

$$6x + 8x = 21$$
$$14x = 21$$
$$\frac{14x}{14} = \frac{21}{14}$$
$$x = 1\frac{1}{2}$$

They will be 21 miles apart in $1\frac{1}{2}$ hours.

18. $$\frac{-5}{20} = \frac{x}{21}$$
$$20x = (-5)(21)$$
$$20x = -105$$
$$\frac{20x}{20} = \frac{-105}{20}$$
$$x = -\frac{21}{4}$$
The solution set is $\left\{-\frac{21}{4}\right\}$.

19. Let x = Buchanan's age.
Let $x + 4$ = Reagan's age.
$$x + (x + 4) = 134$$
$$2x + 4 = 134$$
$$2x = 130$$
$$x = 65$$
$$x + 4 = 69$$
Buchanan was 65 years old and Reagan was 69 years old.

20. Use the formula increase = percent · original. The increase is $13 - 4 = 9$.
$$9 = P \cdot 4$$
$$\frac{9}{4} = \frac{P \cdot 4}{4}$$
$$2.25 = P$$
9 is 225% of 4. This means that the PBS audience increased by 225%. John Tesh did not report the percent increase correctly.

Chapter 4
Linear Equations and Inequalities in Two Variables

4.1 Check Points

1.

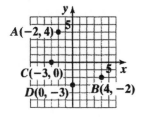

2. $E(-4,-2)$ $F(-2,0)$ $G(6,0)$

3. a. $x - 3y = 9$
$$3 - 3(-2) = 9$$
$$3 + 6 = 9$$
$$9 = 9, \text{ true}$$
$(3,-2)$ is a solution.

b. $x - 3y = 9$
$$-2 - 3(3) = 9$$
$$-2 - 9 = 9$$
$$-11 = 9, \text{ false}$$
$(-2,3)$ is not a solution.

4.

x	$y = 3x + 2$	(x, y)
-2	$y = 3(-2) + 2 = -4$	$(-2,-4)$
-1	$y = 3(-1) + 2 = -1$	$(-1,-1)$
0	$y = 3(0) + 2 = 2$	$(0,2)$
1	$y = 3(1) + 2 = 5$	$(1,5)$
2	$y = 3(2) + 2 = 8$	$(2,8)$

5.

x	$y = 2x$	(x, y)
-2	$y = 2(-2) = -4$	$(-2,-4)$
-1	$y = 2(-1) = -2$	$(-1,-2)$
0	$y = 2(0) = 0$	$(0,0)$
1	$y = 2(1) = 2$	$(1,2)$
2	$y = 2(2) = 4$	$(2,4)$

6.

x	$y = 2x - 2$	(x, y)
-2	$y = 2(-2) - 2 = -6$	$(-2,-6)$
-1	$y = 2(-1) - 2 = -4$	$(-1,-4)$
0	$y = 2(0) - 2 = -2$	$(0,-2)$
1	$y = 2(1) - 2 = 0$	$(1,0)$
2	$y = 2(2) - 2 = 2$	$(2,2)$

7.

x	$y = \frac{1}{2}x + 2$	(x, y)
-4	$y = \frac{1}{2}(-4) + 2 = 0$	$(-4,0)$
-2	$y = \frac{1}{2}(-2) + 2 = 1$	$(-2,1)$
0	$y = \frac{1}{2}(0) + 2 = 2$	$(0,2)$
2	$y = \frac{1}{2}(2) + 2 = 3$	$(2,3)$
4	$y = \frac{1}{2}(4) + 2 = 4$	$(4,4)$

8. a.

n	$D = 1.4n + 1$	(n, D)
0	$D = 1.4(0) + 1 = 1$	$(0, 1)$
5	$D = 1.4(5) + 1 = 8$	$(5, 8)$
10	$D = 1.4(10) + 1 = 15$	$(10, 15)$
15	$D = 1.4(15) + 1 = 22$	$(15, 22)$

b. Graph formula:

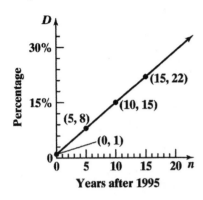

c. According to the graph, about 29% of consumers will pay primarily with debit cards in 2015.

d. $D = 1.4n + 1$

$D = 1.4(20) + 1$

$\quad = 29$

According to the formula, about 29% of consumers will pay primarily with debit cards in 2015.

4.1 Exercise Set

1. Quadrant I

3. Quadrant II

5. Quadrant III

7. Quadrant IV

9. – 23. All points for Exercises 10 through 24 are graphed on the same set of axes and labeled by the problem number accordingly.

25. $A\,(5, 2)$

27. $C\,(-6, 5)$

29. $E(-2, -3)$

31. $G(5, -3)$

33. The y-coordinates are positive in Quadrants I and II.

35. The x- and y-coordinates have the same sign in Quadrants I and III.

37. $y = 3x$

$y = 3x$
$3 = 3(2)$
$3 = 6$, false
$(2,3)$ is not a solution.

$y = 3x$
$2 = 3(3)$
$2 = 9$, false
$(3,2)$ is not a solution.

$y = 3x$
$-12 = 3(-4)$
$-12 = -12$, true
$(-4,-12)$ is a solution.

39. $y = -4x$

$-20 = -4(-5)$
$-20 = 20$, false
$(-5,-20)$ is not a solution.

$y = -4x$
$0 = -4(0)$
$0 = 0$, true
$(0,0)$ is a solution.

$y = -4x$
$-36 = -4(9)$
$-36 = -36$, true
$(9,-36)$ is a solution.

41. $y = 2x + 6$

$6 = 2(0) + 6$
$6 = 6$, true
$(0,6)$ is a solution.

$y = 2x + 6$
$0 = 2(-3) + 6$
$0 = 0$, true
$(-3,0)$ is a solution.

$y = 2x + 6$
$-2 = 2(2) + 6$
$-2 = 10$, false
$(2,-2)$ is not a solution.

43. $3x + 5y = 15$

$3(-5) + 5(6) = 15$
$-15 + 30 = 15$
$15 = 15$, true
$(-5,6)$ is a solution.

$3x + 5y = 15$
$3(0) + 5(5) = 15$
$0 + 25 = 15$
$25 = 15$, false
$(0,5)$ is not a solution.

$3x + 5y = 15$
$3(10) + 5(-3) = 15$
$30 - 15 = 15$
$15 = 15$, true
$(10,-3)$ is a solution.

45. $x + 3y = 0$

$0 + 3(0) = 0$
$0 = 0$, true
$(0,0)$ is a solution.

$x + 3y = 0$
$1 + 3\left(\dfrac{1}{3}\right) = 0$
$1 + 1 = 0$
$2 = 0$, false
$\left(1,\dfrac{1}{3}\right)$ is not a solution.

$x + 3y = 0$
$2 + 3\left(-\dfrac{2}{3}\right) = 0$
$2 - 2 = 0$
$0 = 0$, true
$\left(2,-\dfrac{2}{3}\right)$ is a solution.

47. $x - 4 = 0$

$\quad 4 - 4 = 0$

$\qquad 0 = 0$, true

$(4, 7)$ is a solution.

$x - 4 = 0$

$\quad 3 - 4 = 0$

$\qquad -1 = 0$, false

$(3, 4)$ is not a solution.

$x - 4 = 0$

$\quad 0 - 4 = 0$

$\qquad -4 = 0$, false

$(0, -4)$ is not a solution.

49.

x	$y = 12x$	(x, y)
-2	$y = 12(-2) = -24$	$(-2, -24)$
-1	$y = 12(-1) = -12$	$(-1, -12)$
0	$y = 12(0) = 0$	$(0, 0)$
1	$y = 12(1) = 12$	$(1, 12)$
2	$y = 12(2) = 24$	$(2, 24)$

51.

x	$y = -10x$	(x, y)
-2	$y = -10(-2) = 20$	$(-2, 20)$
-1	$y = -10(-1) = 10$	$(-1, 10)$
0	$y = -10(0) = 0$	$(0, 0)$
1	$y = -10(1) = -10$	$(1, -10)$
2	$y = -10(2) = -20$	$(2, -20)$

53.

x	$y = 8x - 5$	(x, y)
-2	$y = 8(-2) - 5 = -21$	$(-2, -21)$
-1	$y = 8(-1) - 5 = -13$	$(-1, -13)$
0	$y = 8(0) - 5 = -5$	$(0, -5)$
1	$y = 8(1) - 5 = 3$	$(1, 3)$
2	$y = 8(2) - 5 = 11$	$(2, 11)$

55.

x	$y = -3x + 7$	(x, y)
-2	$y = -3(-2) + 7 = 13$	$(-2, 13)$
-1	$y = -3(-1) + 7 = 10$	$(-1, 10)$
0	$y = -3(0) + 7 = 7$	$(0, 7)$
1	$y = -3(1) + 7 = 4$	$(1, 4)$
2	$y = -3(2) + 7 = 1$	$(2, 1)$

57.

x	$y = x$	(x, y)
-2	$y = -2$	$(-2, -2)$
-1	$y = -1$	$(-1, -1)$
0	$y = 0$	$(0, 0)$
1	$y = 1$	$(1, 1)$
2	$y = 2$	$(2, 2)$

59.

x	$y = x - 1$	(x, y)
-2	$y = -2 - 1 = -3$	$(-2, -3)$
-1	$y = -1 - 1 = -2$	$(-1, -2)$
0	$y = 0 - 1 = -1$	$(0, -1)$
1	$y = 1 - 1 = 0$	$(1, 0)$
2	$y = 2 - 1 = 1$	$(2, 1)$

61.

x	$y = 2x + 1$	(x, y)
-2	$y = 2(-2) + 1 = -3$	$(-2, -3)$
-1	$y = 2(-1) + 1 = -1$	$(-1, -1)$
0	$y = 2(0) + 1 = 1$	$(0, 1)$
1	$y = 2(1) + 1 = 3$	$(1, 3)$
2	$y = 2(2) + 1 = 5$	$(2, 5)$

130

63.

x	$y=-x+2$	(x,y)
-2	$y=-(-2)+2=4$	$(-2,4)$
-1	$y=-(-1)+2=3$	$(-1,3)$
0	$y=-0+2=2$	$(0,2)$
1	$y=-1+2=1$	$(1,1)$
2	$y=-2+2=0$	$(2,0)$

65.

x	$y=-3x-1$	(x,y)
-2	$y=-3(-2)-1=5$	$(-2,5)$
-1	$y=-3(-1)-1=2$	$(-1,2)$
0	$y=-3(0)-1=-1$	$(0,-1)$
1	$y=-3(1)-1=-4$	$(1,-4)$
2	$y=-3(2)-1=-7$	$(2,-7)$

67.

x	$y=\frac{1}{2}x$	(x,y)
-4	$y=\frac{1}{2}(-4)=-2$	$(-4,-2)$
-2	$y=\frac{1}{2}(-2)=-1$	$(-2,-1)$
0	$y=\frac{1}{2}(0)=0$	$(0,0)$
2	$y=\frac{1}{2}(2)=1$	$(2,1)$
4	$y=\frac{1}{2}(4)=2$	$(4,2)$

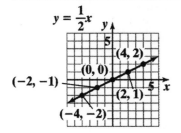

69.

x	$y=-\frac{1}{4}x$	(x,y)
-8	$y=-\frac{1}{4}(-8)=2$	$(-8,2)$
-4	$y=-\frac{1}{4}(-4)=1$	$(-4,1)$
0	$y=-\frac{1}{4}(0)=0$	$(0,0)$
4	$y=-\frac{1}{4}(4)=-1$	$(4,-1)$
8	$y=-\frac{1}{4}(8)=-2$	$(8,-2)$

71.

x	$y=\frac{1}{3}x+1$	(x,y)
-6	$y=\frac{1}{3}(-6)+1=-1$	$(-6,-1)$
-3	$y=\frac{1}{3}(-3)+1=0$	$(-3,0)$
0	$y=\frac{1}{3}(0)+1=1$	$(0,-1)$
3	$y=\frac{1}{3}(3)+1=2$	$(3,2)$
6	$y=\frac{1}{3}(6)+1=3$	$(6,3)$

73.

x	$y = -\frac{3}{2}x + 1$	(x, y)
-4	$y = -\frac{3}{2}(-4) + 1 = 7$	$(-4, 7)$
-2	$y = -\frac{3}{2}(-2) + 1 = 4$	$(-2, 4)$
0	$y = -\frac{3}{2}(0) + 1 = 1$	$(0, 1)$
2	$y = -\frac{3}{2}(2) + 1 = -2$	$(2, -2)$
4	$y = -\frac{3}{2}(4) + 1 = -5$	$(4, -5)$

77.

x	$y = x + \frac{1}{2}$	(x, y)
-4	$y = -4 + \frac{1}{2} = -3.5$	$(-4, -3.5)$
-2	$y = -2 + \frac{1}{2} = -1.5$	$(-2, -1.5)$
0	$y = 0 + \frac{1}{2} = 0.5$	$(0, 0.5)$
2	$y = 2 + \frac{1}{2} = 2.5$	$(2, 2.5)$
4	$y = 4 + \frac{1}{2} = 4.5$	$(4, 4.5)$

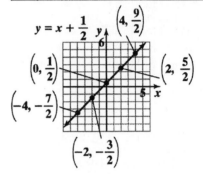

75.

x	$y = -\frac{5}{2}x - 1$	(x, y)
-4	$y = -\frac{5}{2}(-4) - 1 = 9$	$(-4, 9)$
-2	$y = -\frac{5}{2}(-2) - 1 = 4$	$(-2, 4)$
0	$y = -\frac{5}{2}(0) - 1 = -1$	$(0, -1)$
2	$y = -\frac{5}{2}(2) - 1 = -6$	$(2, -6)$
4	$y = -\frac{5}{2}(4) - 1 = -11$	$(4, -11)$

79.

x	$y = 0x + 4$	(x, y)
-6	$y = 0(-6) + 4 = 4$	$(-6, 4)$
-3	$y = 0(-3) + 4 = 4$	$(-3, 4)$
0	$y = 0(0) + 4 = 4$	$(0, 4)$
3	$y = 0(3) + 4 = 4$	$(3, 4)$
6	$y = 0(6) + 4 = 4$	$(6, 4)$

81. $y = x + 3$

132

83. $y = 2x + 5$

85. a. $8x + 6y = 14.50$

    b. $8x + 6(0.75) = 14.50$

        $8x + 4.50 = 14.50$

             $8x = 10.00$

               $x = 1.25$

    One pen costs $1.25.

87. The coordinates of point *A* are (2,7). When the football is 2 yards from the quarterback, its height is 7 feet.

89. The coordinates of point *C* are approximately (6, 9.25).

91. The football's maximum height is 12 feet. It reaches this height when it is 15 yards from the quarterback.

93. a.

n	$C = 1.3n + 28$	(n, C)
0	$C = 1.3(0) + 28 = 28$	$(0, 28)$
10	$C = 1.3(10) + 28 = 41$	$(10, 41)$
20	$C = 1.3(20) + 28 = 54$	$(20, 54)$
30	$C = 1.3(30) + 28 = 67$	$(30, 67)$
40	$C = 1.3(40) + 28 = 80$	$(40, 80)$

    b. Graph formula:

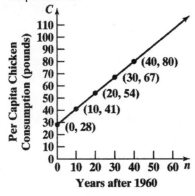

c. According to the graph, per capita chicken consumption will be about 99 pounds in 2015.

d. $C = 1.3n + 28$

    $C = 1.3(55) + 28$

      $= 99.5$

According to the formula, per capita chicken consumption will be about 99.5 pounds in 2015.

95. – 101. Answers will vary.

103. makes sense

105. does not make sense; Explanations will vary. Sample explanation: These points do not lie along a line.

107. false; Changes to make the statement true will vary. A sample change is: The lines are not parallel as they both contain the point $(-1, -2)$.

109. false; Changes to make the statement true will vary. A sample change is: The point $(4, 3)$ satisfies the equation.

111. a. $\left(1, \frac{1}{2}\right)$, $(2, 1)$, $\left(3, \frac{3}{2}\right)$, $(4, 2)$

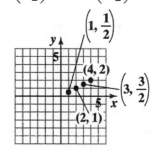

    b. In order for the resulting graph to be a mirror-image reflection about the *y*-axis of the graph in part (a), the sign of each *x*-coordinate should be changed: $\left(-1, \frac{1}{2}\right)$, $(-2, 1)$, $\left(-3, \frac{3}{2}\right)$, $(-4, 2)$

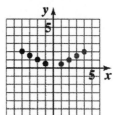

c. In order for the resulting graph to be a mirror-image reflection about the *x*-axis of the graph in part (a), the sign of each *y*-coordinate should be changed: $\left(1,-\dfrac{1}{2}\right)$, $(2,-1)$, $\left(3,-\dfrac{3}{2}\right)$, $(4,-2)$

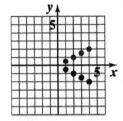

d. In order for the resulting graph to be a straight-line extension of the graph in part (a), the signs of both coordinates of each ordered pair should be changed:

$\left(-1,-\dfrac{1}{2}\right)$, $(-2,-1)$, $\left(-3,-\dfrac{3}{2}\right)$, $(-4,-2)$

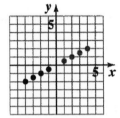

113. Answers will vary depending upon the points chosen. One example is shown here.

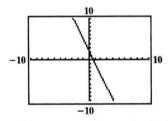

115. Answers will vary depending upon the points chosen. One example is shown here.

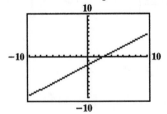

117.
$$3x+5 = 4(2x-3)+7$$
$$3x+5 = 8x-12+7$$
$$3x+5 = 8x-5$$
$$3x+5-8x = 8x-5-8x$$
$$-5x+5 = -5$$
$$-5x+5-5 = -5-5$$
$$-5x = -10$$
$$\frac{-5x}{-5} = \frac{-10}{-5}$$
$$x = 2$$
The solution set is $\{2\}$.

118. $3(1-2\cdot5)-(-28) = 3(1-10)+28$
$$= 3(-9)+28$$
$$= -27+28 = 1$$

119. $V = \dfrac{1}{3}Ah$ for h

$$V = \frac{1}{3}Ah$$
$$3V = 3\left(\frac{1}{3}Ah\right)$$
$$3V = Ah$$
$$\frac{3V}{A} = \frac{Ah}{A}$$
$$\frac{3V}{A} = h \text{ or } h = \frac{3V}{A}$$

120.
$$3x-4y = 24$$
$$3x-4(0) = 24$$
$$3x = 24$$
$$x = 8$$
The equation is satisfied by the ordered pair $(8,0)$.

121.
$$3x-4y = 24$$
$$3(0)-4y = 24$$
$$-4y = 24$$
$$y = -6$$
The equation is satisfied by the ordered pair $(0,-6)$.

122. $x+2y = 0$
$$0+2y = 0$$
$$2y = 0$$
$$y = 0$$
The equation is satisfied by the ordered pair $(0,0)$.

4.2 Check Points

1. **a.** The graph crosses the x-axis at $(-3,0)$. Thus, the x-intercept is -3.
    The graph crosses the y-axis at $(0,5)$. Thus, the y-intercept is 5.

    b. The graph does not cross the x-axis. Thus, there is no x-intercept.
    The graph crosses the y-axis at $(0,4)$. Thus, the y-intercept is 4.

    c. The graph crosses the x-axis at $(0,0)$. Thus, the x-intercept is 0.
    The graph crosses the y-axis at $(0,0)$. Thus, the y-intercept is 0.

2. To find the x-intercept, let $y = 0$ and solve for x.
    $$4x - 3y = 12$$
    $$4x - 3(0) = 12$$
    $$4x = 12$$
    $$x = 3$$
    The x-intercept is 3.

3. To find the y-intercept, let $x = 0$ and solve for y.
    $$4x - 3y = 12$$
    $$4(0) - 3y = 12$$
    $$-3y = 12$$
    $$y = -4$$
    The y-intercept is -4.

4. Find the x-intercept. Let $y = 0$ and solve for x.
    $$2x + 3y = 6$$
    $$2x + 3(0) = 6$$
    $$2x = 6$$
    $$x = 3$$
    The x-intercept is 3.
    Find the y- intercept. Let $x = 0$ and solve for y.
    $$2x + 3y = 6$$
    $$2(0) + 3y = 6$$
    $$3y = 6$$
    $$y = 2$$
    The y-intercept is 2.
    Find a checkpoint. For example, let $x = 1$ and solve for y.

$$2x + 3y = 6$$
$$2(1) + 3y = 6$$
$$2 + 3y = 6$$
$$3y = 4$$
$$y = \frac{4}{3} \text{ or } 1\frac{1}{3}$$

5. Find the x-intercept. Let $y = 0$ and solve for x.
    $$x - 2y = 4$$
    $$x - 2(0) = 4$$
    $$x = 4$$
    The x-intercept is 4.
    Find the y- intercept. Let $x = 0$ and solve for y.
    $$x - 2y = 4$$
    $$0 - 2y = 4$$
    $$-2y = 4$$
    $$y = -2$$
    The y-intercept is -2.
    Find a checkpoint. For example, let $x = 2$ and solve for y.
    $$x - 2y = 4$$
    $$2 - 2y = 4$$
    $$-2y = 2$$
    $$y = -1$$

6. Because the constant on the right is 0, the graph passes through the origin. The x- and y-intercepts are both 0.

Thus we will need to find two more points.

Let $y = -1$ and solve for x.

$$x + 3y = 0$$
$$x + 3(-1) = 0$$
$$x - 3 = 0$$
$$x = 3$$

Let $y = 1$ and solve for x.

$$x + 3y = 0$$
$$x + 3(1) = 0$$
$$x + 3 = 0$$
$$x = -3$$

Use these three solutions of $(0,0)$, $(3,-1)$, and $(-3,1)$.

7. As demonstrated in the table below, all ordered pairs that are solutions of $y = 3$ have a value of y that is always 3.

x	$y = 3$	(x, y)
-2	3	$(-2, 3)$
0	3	$(0, 3)$
1	3	$(1, 3)$

Thus the line is horizontal.

8. As demonstrated in the table below, all ordered pairs that are solutions of $x = -2$ have a value of x that is always -2.

$x = -2$	y	(x, y)
-2	-3	$(-2, -3)$
-2	0	$(-2, 0)$
-2	2	$(-2, 2)$

Thus the line is vertical.

4.2 Exercise Set

1. a. The graph crosses the x-axis at $(3,0)$.
Thus, the x-intercept is 3.

b. The graph crosses the y-axis at $(0,4)$.
Thus, the y-intercept is 4.

3. a. The graph crosses the x-axis at $(-4,0)$.
Thus, the x-intercept is -4.

b. The graph crosses the y-axis at $(0,-2)$.
Thus, the y-intercept is -2.

5. a. The graph crosses the x-axis at $(0,0)$ (the origin).
Thus, the x-intercept is 0.

b. The graph also crosses the y-axis at $(0,0)$.
Thus, the y-intercept is 0.

7. a. The graph does not cross the x-axis.
Thus, there is no x-intercept.

b. The graph crosses the y-axis at $(0,-2)$.
Thus the y-intercept is -2.

9. To find the *x*-intercept, let *y* = 0 and solve for *x*.
$$2x + 5y = 20$$
$$2x + 5(0) = 20$$
$$2x = 20$$
$$x = 10$$
The *x*-intercept is 10.

To find the *y*-intercept, let *x* = 0 and solve for *y*.
$$2x + 5y = 20$$
$$2(0) + 5y = 20$$
$$5y = 20$$
$$y = 4$$
The *y*-intercept is 4.

11. To find the *x*-intercept, let *y* = 0 and solve for *x*.
$$2x - 3y = 15$$
$$2x - 3(0) = 15$$
$$2x = 15$$
$$x = \frac{15}{2}$$
The *x*-intercept is $\frac{15}{2}$.

To find the *y*-intercept, let *x* = 0 and solve for *y*.
$$2x - 3y = 15$$
$$2(0) - 3y = 15$$
$$-3y = 15$$
$$y = -5$$
The *y*-intercept is −5.

13. To find the *x*-intercept, let *y* = 0 and solve for *x*.
$$-x + 3y = -8$$
$$-x + 3(0) = -8$$
$$-x = -8$$
$$x = 8$$
The *x*-intercept is 8.

To find the *y*-intercept, let *x* = 0 and solve for *y*.
$$-x + 3y = -8$$
$$-0 + 3y = -8$$
$$3y = -8$$
$$y = -\frac{8}{3}$$
The *y*-intercept is $-\frac{8}{3}$.

15. To find the *x*-intercept, let *y* = 0 and solve for *x*.
$$7x - 9y = 0$$
$$7x - 9(0) = 0$$
$$7x = 0$$
$$x = 0$$
The *x*-intercept is 0.

To find the *y*-intercept, let *x* = 0 and solve for *y*.
$$7x - 9y = 0$$
$$7(0) - 9y = 0$$
$$-9y = 0$$
$$y = 0$$
The *y*-intercept is 0.

17. To find the *x*-intercept, let *y* = 0 and solve for *x*.
$$2x = 3y - 11$$
$$2x = 3(0) - 11$$
$$2x = -11$$
$$x = -\frac{11}{2}$$
The *x*-intercept is $-\frac{11}{2}$.

To find the *y*-intercept, let *x* = 0 and solve for *y*.
$$2x = 3y - 11$$
$$2(0) = 3y - 11$$
$$0 = 3y - 11$$
$$11 = 3y$$
$$\frac{11}{3} = y$$
The *y*-intercept is $\frac{11}{3}$.

19. $x + y = 5$
x-intercept: 5
y-intercept: 5
checkpoint: (2,3)
Draw a line through (5,0), (0,5), and (2,3).

In Exercises 21-39, checkpoints will vary.

21. $x + 3y = 6$

x-intercept: 6
y-intercept: 2
checkpoint: (3,1)
Draw a line through (6,0), (0,2), and (3,1).

23. $6x - 9y = 18$

x-intercept: 3
y-intercept: −2
checkpoint: $\left(1, -\dfrac{4}{3}\right)$

Draw a line through (3,0), (0,−2), and $\left(1, -\dfrac{4}{3}\right)$.

25. $-x + 4y = 6$

x-intercept: −6

y-intercept: $\dfrac{3}{2}$

checkpoint: (2,2)

Draw a line through (−6,0), $\left(0, \dfrac{3}{2}\right)$, and (2,2).

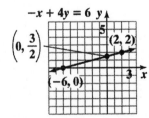

27. $2x - y = 7$

x-intercept: $\dfrac{7}{2}$

y-intercept: −7
checkpoint: (1,−5)

Draw a line through $\left(\dfrac{7}{2}, 0\right)$, (0,7), and (1,−5).

29. $3x = 5y - 15$

x-intercept: −5
y-intercept: 3

checkpoint: $\left(-\dfrac{10}{3}, 1\right)$

Draw a line through (−5,0), (0,3), and $\left(-\dfrac{10}{3}, 1\right)$.

31. $25y = 100 - 50x$

x-intercept: 2
y-intercept: 4
checkpoint: (1, 2)
Draw a line through (2,0), (0,4), and (1, 2).

33. $2x - 8y = 12$

x-intercept: 6

y-intercept: $-\dfrac{3}{2}$

checkpoint: $(2, -1)$

Draw a line through $(6, 0)$, $\left(0, -\dfrac{3}{2}\right)$, and $(2, -1)$.

35. $x + 2y = 0$

x-intercept: 0
y-intercept: 0
Since the line goes through the origin, find two
additional points.
checkpoint: $(2, -1)$
checkpoint: $(4, -2)$
Draw a line through $(0,0)$, $(2, -1)$, and $(4, -2)$.

37. $y - 3x = 0$

x-intercept: 0
y-intercept: 0
Since the line goes through the origin, find two
additional points.
checkpoint: $(1, 3)$
checkpoint: $(2, 6)$
Draw a line through $(0,0)$, $(1, 3)$, and $(2, 6)$.

39. $2x - 3y = -11$

x-intercept: $-\dfrac{11}{2}$

y-intercept: $\dfrac{11}{3}$

checkpoint: $(-1, 3)$

Draw a line through $\left(-\dfrac{11}{2}, 0\right)$, $\left(0, \dfrac{11}{3}\right)$ and

$(-1, 3)$.

41. The equation for this horizontal line is $y = 3$.

43. The equation for this vertical line is $x = -3$.

45. The equation for this horizontal line, which is the x-axis is $y = 0$.

47. $y = 4$

All ordered pairs that are solutions will have a value
of y that is 4. Any value can be used for x. Three
ordered pairs that are solutions are $(-2,4)$, $(0,4)$, and
$(3,4)$.
Plot these points and draw the line through them.
The graph is a horizontal line.

49. $y = -2$

Three ordered pairs are $(-3,-2)$, $(0,-2)$, and $(4,-2)$.
The graph is a horizontal line.

51. $x = 2$

All ordered pairs that are solutions will have a value of x that is 2. Any value can be used for y. Three ordered pairs that are solutions are $(2, -3)$, $(2,0)$, and $(2,2)$.

The graph is a vertical line.

53. $x + 1 = 0$

$x = -1$

Three ordered pairs are $(-1,-3)$, $(-1,0)$, and $(-1,3)$. The graph is a vertical line.

55. $y - 3.5 = 0$

$y = 3.5$

Three ordered pairs are $(-2, 3.5)$, $(0, 3.5)$, and $(3.5, 3.5)$. The graph is a horizontal line.

57. $x = 0$

Three ordered pairs are $(0,-2)$, $(0,0)$, and $(0,4)$. The graph is a vertical line, the y-axis.

59. $3y = 9$

$y = 3$

Three ordered pairs are $(-3,3)$, $(0,3)$, and $(3,3)$. The graph is a horizontal line.

61. $12 - 3x = 0$

$-3x = -12$

$x = 4$

Three ordered pairs are $(4,-2)$, $(4,1)$, and $(4,3)$. The graph is a vertical line.

63. Using intercepts, we see that $3x + 2y = -6$ corresponds to Exercise 4.

x-intercept: $3x + 2y = -6$

$$3x + 2(0) = -6$$
$$3x = -6$$
$$x = -2$$

y-intercept: $3x + 2y = -6$

$$3(0) + 2y = -6$$
$$2y = -6$$
$$y = -3$$

65. Since $y = -2$ is a horizontal line at -2, it corresponds to Exercise 7.

67. Using intercepts, we see that $4x + 3y = 12$ corresponds to Exercise 1.

x-intercept: $4x + 3y = 12$

$$4x + 3(0) = 12$$
$$4x = 12$$
$$x = 3$$

y-intercept: $4x + 3y = 12$

$$4(0) + 3y = 12$$
$$3y = 12$$
$$y = 4$$

69. a. Let $x + 5 + 5 = x + 10 =$ the length.

Let $y + 8 =$ width.

Using the formula for the perimeter of a rectangle, we have $2l + 2w = P$

$$2(x + 10) + 2(y + 8) = 58$$
$$2x + 20 + 2y + 16 = 58$$
$$2x + 2y + 36 = 58$$
$$2x + 2y = 22$$
$$x + y = 11$$

b. x and y must be non-negative because they are dimensions.

71. The eagle's height is decreasing from 3 seconds to 12 seconds.

73. The y-intercept is 45. This means that the eagle's height was 45 meters at the beginning of the observation.

75. Five x-intercepts of the graph are 12, 13, 14, 15, and 16. During these times (12-16 minutes), the eagle was on the ground.

77. a.
$$y = -5000x + 45,000$$
$$0 = -5000x + 45,000$$
$$5000x = 45,000$$
$$x = 9$$
After 9 years, the car is worth nothing.

b. $y = -5000x + 45,000$

$$y = -5000(0) + 45,000$$
$$y = 45,000$$
The new car is worth \$45,000.

c. x and y must be non-negative because they represent time and the car's value.

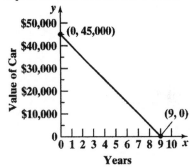

d. According to the graph, the car's value will be about \$20,000 after five years. Estimates will vary.

79. – 85. Answers will vary.

87. makes sense

89. makes sense

91. Since the x-intercept is 5, $y = 0$ when $x = 5$.

$$\boxed{?}x + \boxed{}y = 10$$
$$\boxed{?}(5) + \boxed{}(0) = 10$$
$$\boxed{?}(5) = 10$$
$$\boxed{?} = 2$$

So, the coefficient of x is 2.

Similarly, since the y-intercept is 2, $x = 0$ when $y = 2$.

$$2x + \boxed{?}y = 10$$
$$2(0) + \boxed{?}(2) = 10$$
$$\boxed{?}(2) = 10$$
$$\boxed{?} = 5$$

So, the coefficient of y is 5.

The equation of the line is $2x + 5y = 10$.

141

93. Answers will vary.

95.
$$3x - y = 9$$
$$-y = -3x + 9$$
$$(-1)(-y) = -1(3x + 9)$$
$$y = 3x - 9$$

The y-intercept is -9.
The x-intercept is 3.

97. $4x - 2y = -40$
$$-2y = -4x - 40$$
$$\frac{-2y}{-2} = \frac{-4x - 40}{-2}$$
$$y = 2x + 20$$

The y-intercept is 20.
The x-intercept is -10.

98. $|-13.4| = 13.4$

99. $7x - (3x - 5) = 7x - 3x + 5 = 4x + 5$

100. $8(x - 2) - 2(x - 3) \le 8x$
$$8x - 16 - 2x + 6 \le 8x$$
$$6x - 10 \le 8x$$
$$6x - 8x - 10 \le 8x - 8x$$
$$-2x - 10 \le 0$$
$$-2x \le 10$$
$$\frac{-2x}{-2} \ge \frac{10}{-2}$$
$$x \ge -5$$
The solution set is $[-5, \infty)$.

101. $\dfrac{y_2 - y_1}{x_2 - x_1} = \dfrac{13 - 3}{6 - 1} = \dfrac{10}{5} = 2$

102. $\dfrac{y_2 - y_1}{x_2 - x_1} = \dfrac{-4 - (-2)}{6 - 4} = \dfrac{-2}{2} = -1$

103. $\dfrac{y_2 - y_1}{x_2 - x_1} = \dfrac{4 - 4}{5 - 3} = \dfrac{0}{2} = 0$

4.3 Check Points

1. a. Let $(x_1, y_1) = (-3, 4)$ and $(x_2, y_2) = (-4, -2)$.
$$m = \frac{\text{Change in } y}{\text{Change in } x} = \frac{y_2 - y_1}{x_2 - x_1} = \frac{-2 - 4}{-4 - (-3)} = \frac{-6}{-1} = 6$$

The slope is 6. Since the slope is positive, the line rises from left to right.

b. Let $(x_1, y_1) = (4, -2)$ and $(x_2, y_2) = (-1, 5)$.
$$m = \frac{\text{Change in } y}{\text{Change in } x} = \frac{y_2 - y_1}{x_2 - x_1} = \frac{5 - (-2)}{-1 - 4} = \frac{7}{-5} = -\frac{7}{5}$$

The slope is $-\dfrac{7}{5}$. Since the slope is negative, the line falls from left to right.

2. a. Let $(x_1, y_1) = (6, 5)$ and $(x_2, y_2) = (2, 5)$.
$$m = \frac{\text{Change in } y}{\text{Change in } x} = \frac{y_2 - y_1}{x_2 - x_1} = \frac{5 - 5}{2 - 6} = \frac{0}{-4} = 0$$
Since the slope is 0, the line is horizontal.

b. Let $(x_1, y_1) = (1, 6)$ and $(x_2, y_2) = (1, 4)$.
$$m = \frac{\text{Change in } y}{\text{Change in } x} = \frac{y_2 - y_1}{x_2 - x_1} = \frac{4 - 6}{1 - 1} = \frac{-2}{0}$$
Because division by 0 is undefined the slope is undefined. Since the slope is undefined, the line is vertical.

3. Line through (4,2) and (6,6):
$$m = \frac{\text{Change in } y}{\text{Change in } x} = \frac{6 - 2}{6 - 4} = \frac{4}{2} = 2$$
Line through (0,–2) and (1,0):
$$m = \frac{\text{Change in } y}{\text{Change in } x} = \frac{0 - (-2)}{1 - 0} = \frac{2}{1} = 2$$
Since their slopes are equal, the lines are parallel.

4. Line through $(-1,4)$ and $(3,2)$:
$$m = \frac{\text{Change in } y}{\text{Change in } x} = \frac{2-4}{3-(-1)} = \frac{-2}{4} = -\frac{1}{2}$$
Line through $(-2,-1)$ and $(2,7)$:
$$m = \frac{\text{Change in } y}{\text{Change in } x} = \frac{7-(-1)}{2-(-2)} = \frac{8}{4} = 2$$

Since the product of their slopes is $-\frac{1}{2}(2) = -1$, the
lines are perpendicular.

5. Let
$(x_1, y_1) = (1990, 9.0)$ and $(x_2, y_2) = (2005, 12.7)$.
$$m = \frac{\text{Change in } y}{\text{Change in } x} = \frac{y_2 - y_1}{x_2 - x_1}$$
$$= \frac{12.7 - 9.0}{2005 - 1990} = \frac{3.7}{15} \approx 0.25$$
The number of men living alone increased at a rate
of 0.25 million per year. The rate of change is 0.25
million men per year.

4.3 Exercise Set

1. Let $(x_1, y_1) = (4, 7)$ and $(x_2, y_2) = (8, 10)$.
$$m = \frac{\text{Change in } y}{\text{Change in } x} = \frac{y_2 - y_1}{x_2 - x_1} = \frac{10-7}{8-4} = \frac{3}{4}$$
Since the slope is positive, the line rises from left to
right.

3. Let $(x_1, y_1) = (-2, 1)$ and $(x_2, y_2) = (2, 2)$.
$$m = \frac{\text{Change in } y}{\text{Change in } x} = \frac{y_2 - y_1}{x_2 - x_1} = \frac{2-1}{2-(-2)} = \frac{1}{4}$$
Since the slope is positive, the line rises from left to
right.

5. Let $(x_1, y_1) = (4, -2)$ and $(x_2, y_2) = (3, -2)$.
$$m = \frac{\text{Change in } y}{\text{Change in } x} = \frac{y_2 - y_1}{x_2 - x_1} = \frac{-2-(-2)}{3-4} = \frac{0}{-1} = 0$$
Since the slope is zero, the line is horizontal.

7. Let $(x_1, y_1) = (-2, 4)$ and $(x_2, y_2) = (-1, -1)$.
$$m = \frac{\text{Change in } y}{\text{Change in } x} = \frac{y_2 - y_1}{x_2 - x_1} = \frac{-1-4}{-1-(-2)} = \frac{-5}{1} = -5$$
Since the slope is negative, the line falls from left to
right.

9. Let $(x_1, y_1) = (5, 3)$ and $(x_2, y_2) = (5, -2)$.
$$m = \frac{\text{Change in } y}{\text{Change in } x} = \frac{y_2 - y_1}{x_2 - x_1} = \frac{-2-3}{5-5} = \frac{-5}{0}$$
Since the slope is undefined, the line is vertical.

11. Line through $(-2,2)$ and $(2,4)$:
$$m = \frac{4-2}{2-(-2)} = \frac{2}{4} = \frac{1}{2}$$

13. Line through $(-3,4)$ and $(3,2)$:
$$m = \frac{2-4}{3-(-3)} = \frac{-2}{6} = -\frac{1}{3}$$

15. Line through $(-2,1)$, $(0,0)$, and $(2,-1)$
Use any two of these points to find the slope.
$$m = \frac{0-1}{0-(-2)} = \frac{-1}{2} = -\frac{1}{2}$$

17. Line through $(0,2)$ and $(3,0)$:
$$m = \frac{0-2}{3-0} = -\frac{2}{3}$$

19. Line through $(-2,1)$ and $(4,1)$:
$$m = \frac{1-1}{4-(-2)} = \frac{0}{6} = 0$$
(Since the line is horizontal, it is not necessary to do
this computation. The slope of every horizontal line
is 0.)

21. Line through $(-3,4)$ and $(-3,-2)$:
$$m = \frac{-2-4}{-3-(-3)} = \frac{-6}{0}; \text{ undefined}$$
(Since the line is vertical, it is not necessary to do
this computation. The slope of every vertical line is
undefined.)

23. Line through $(-2,0)$ and $(0,6)$:
$$m = \frac{6-0}{0-(-2)} = 3$$
Line through $(1,8)$ and $(0,5)$:
$$m = \frac{5-8}{0-1} = \frac{-3}{-1} = 3$$
Since their slopes are equal, the lines are parallel.

25. Line through $(0,3)$ and $(1,5)$:

$$m = \frac{5-3}{1-0} = \frac{2}{1} = 2$$

Line through $(-1,7)$ and $(1,10)$:

$$m = \frac{10-7}{1-(-1)} = \frac{3}{2}$$

Since their slopes are not equal, the lines are not parallel.

27. Line through $(1,5)$ and $(0,3)$:

$$m = \frac{3-5}{0-1} = 2$$

Line through $(-2,8)$ and $(2,6)$:

$$m = \frac{6-8}{2-(-2)} = -\frac{1}{2}$$

Since the product of their slopes is $2\left(-\frac{1}{2}\right) = -1$,

the lines are perpendicular.

29. Line through $(-1,-6)$ and $(2,9)$:

$$m = \frac{9-(-6)}{2-(-1)} = 5$$

Line through $(-15,-1)$ and $(5,3)$:

$$m = \frac{3-(-1)}{5-(-15)} = \frac{1}{5}$$

Since the product of their slopes is $5\left(\frac{1}{5}\right) = 1 \neq -1$,

the lines are not perpendicular.

31. Line through $(-2,-5)$ and $(3,10)$:

$$m = \frac{10-(-5)}{3-(-2)} = 3$$

Line through $(-1,-9)$ and $(4,6)$:

$$m = \frac{6-(-9)}{4-(-1)} = 3$$

Since their slopes are equal the lines are parallel.

33. Line through $(-4,-12)$ and $(0,-4)$:

$$m = \frac{-4-(-12)}{0-(-4)} = 2$$

Line through $(0,-5)$ and $(2,-4)$:

$$m = \frac{-4-(-5)}{2-0} = \frac{1}{2}$$

Since their slopes are not equal, nor are the slopes negative reciprocals, the lines are neither parallel nor perpendicular.

35. Line through $(-5,-1)$ and $(0,2)$:

$$m = \frac{2-(-1)}{0-(-5)} = \frac{3}{5}$$

Line through $(-6,9)$ and $(3,-6)$:

$$m = \frac{-6-9}{3-(-6)} = -\frac{5}{3}$$

Since the product of their slopes is $\frac{3}{5}\left(-\frac{5}{3}\right) = -1$,

the lines are perpendicular.

37.

39. $m = \dfrac{y_2 - y_1}{x_2 - x_1} = \dfrac{-3-1}{-3-0} = \dfrac{-4}{-3} = \dfrac{4}{3}$

$m = \dfrac{y_2 - y_1}{x_2 - x_1} = \dfrac{-1-1}{5-0} = \dfrac{-2}{5} = -\dfrac{2}{5}$

$m = \dfrac{y_2 - y_1}{x_2 - x_1} = \dfrac{-5-(-1)}{2-5} = \dfrac{-4}{-3} = \dfrac{4}{3}$

$m = \dfrac{y_2 - y_1}{x_2 - x_1} = \dfrac{-3-(-5)}{-3-2} = \dfrac{2}{-5} = -\dfrac{2}{5}$

Slopes of opposite sides are equal, so the figure is a parallelogram.

41. First find the slope of the line passing through (2, 3) and (−2, 1).

$$m = \frac{y_2 - y_1}{x_2 - x_1} = \frac{3-1}{2-(-2)} = \frac{2}{4} = \frac{1}{2}$$

Now, use the slope formula, the slope and the points (5, y) and (1, 0) to find y.

$$\frac{1}{2} = \frac{y-0}{5-1}$$

$$\frac{1}{2} = \frac{y}{4}$$

$$4\left(\frac{1}{2}\right) = 4\left(\frac{y}{4}\right)$$

$$2 = y$$

43. Find the slope of the line passing through $(-1, y)$ and $(1, 0)$.

$$m = \frac{y_2 - y_1}{x_2 - x_1} = \frac{0-y}{1-(-1)} = \frac{-y}{2}$$

Find the slope of the line passing through $(2, 3)$ and $(-2, 1)$.

$$m = \frac{y_2 - y_1}{x_2 - x_1} = \frac{1-3}{-2-2} = \frac{1}{2}$$

Since the lines are perpendicular, the product of their slopes is −1..

$$\left(\frac{-y}{2}\right)\left(\frac{1}{2}\right) = -1$$

$$\frac{-y}{4} = -1$$

$$\frac{y}{4} = 1$$

$$y = 4$$

45. a. $m = \dfrac{\text{Change in } y}{\text{Change in } x} = \dfrac{42-26}{180-80} = \dfrac{16}{100} = 0.16$

b. For each minute of brisk walking, the percentage of patients with depression in remission increased by 0.16%. The rate of change is 0.16% per minute of brisk walking.

47. $m = \dfrac{\text{Change in } y}{\text{Change in } x} = \dfrac{6}{18} = \dfrac{1}{3}$

The pitch of the roof is $\dfrac{1}{3}$.

49. The grade of an access ramp is

$$\frac{1 \text{ foot}}{12 \text{ feet}} = \frac{1}{12} \approx 0.083 = 8.3\%.$$

51. – 55. Answers will vary.

57. does not make sense; Explanations will vary. Sample explanation: Either point can be considered (x_1, y_1) or (x_2, y_2).

59. makes sense

61. false; Changes to make the statement true will vary. A sample change is: Slope is rise divided by run.

63. false; Changes to make the statement true will vary. A sample change is: A line with slope 3 can not be parallel to a line with slope −3.

65. The positive slopes are m_1 and m_2, and of these, the line with slope m_1 is the steeper one so has the larger slope. The negative slopes are m_2 and m_4, and of these, the line with slope m_4 is the steeper one, so has the slope with the largest absolute value, which is the smaller slope. Therefore, in decreasing size, the slopes are m_1, m_3, m_2 and m_4.

67. $y = 2x + 4$

Two points on the graph are $(-2.5, -1)$, and $(1.5, 7)$.

$$m = \frac{7-(-1)}{1.5-(-2.5)} = \frac{8}{4} = 2$$

69. $y = -\dfrac{1}{2}x - 5$

Two points on the graph are $(-2, -4)$ and $(3, -6.5)$.

$$m = \frac{-6.5-(-4)}{3-(-2)} = \frac{-2.5}{5} = -0.5 \text{ or } -\frac{1}{2}$$

71. The slope is always the coefficient of x.

72. Let x = length of shorter piece (in inches).
Let $2x$ = length of longer piece.
$$x + 2x = 36$$
$$3x = 36$$
$$x = 12$$
The pieces are 12 inches and 24 inches.

73. $-10 + 16 \div 2(-4) = -10 + 8(-4)$
$$= -10 - 32$$
$$= -10 + (-32) = -42$$

74. $2x - 3 \le 5$
$$2x \le 8$$
$$x \le 4$$
$$(-\infty, 4]$$

75. $(0 \overset{\text{1 unit right}}{+1}, -3 \overset{\text{4 units up}}{+4}) = (1,1)$

76. $(0 \overset{\text{3 units right}}{+3}, 1 \overset{\text{2 units down}}{-2}) = (3,-1)$

77. $2x + 5y = 0$
$$2x - 2x + 5y = 0 - 2x$$
$$5y = -2x$$
$$y = \frac{-2x}{5}$$
$$y = -\frac{2}{5}x$$

4.4 Check Points

1. a. $y = 5x - 3$
The slope is the x-coefficient, which is $m = 5$.
The y-intercept is the constant term, which is -3.

b. $y = \frac{2}{3}x + 4$
The slope is the x-coefficient, which is $m = \frac{2}{3}$.
The y-intercept is the constant term, which is 4.

c. $7x + y = 6 \rightarrow y = -7x + 6$
The slope is the x-coefficient, which is $m = -7$.
The y-intercept is the constant term, which is 6.

2. $y = 3x - 2$
The y-intercept is -2, so plot the point $(0, -2)$.

The slope is $m = 3$ or $m = \frac{3}{1}$. Find another point by going up 3 units and to the right 1 unit.
Use a straightedge to draw a line through the two points.

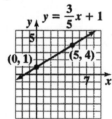

3. $y = \frac{3}{5}x + 1$
The y-intercept is 1, so plot the point $(0,1)$.

The slope is $m = \frac{3}{5}$. Find another point by going up 3 units and to the right 5 units.
Use a straightedge to draw a line through the two points.

4. $3x + 4y = 0$
$$4y = -3x$$
$$y = -\frac{3}{4}x$$
The y-intercept is 0, so plot the point $(0,0)$.

The slope is $m = \frac{-3}{4}$. Find another point by going down 3 units and to the right 4 units.
Use a straightedge to draw a line through the two points.

5. a. The *y*-intercept is 3.9 and the slope is

$$m = \frac{\text{Change in } y}{\text{Change in } x} = \frac{7.7 - 3.9}{30 - 0} = \frac{3.8}{30} \approx 0.13$$

The equation is $y = 0.13x + 3.9$.

b. $y = 0.13x + 3.9 = 0.13(40) + 3.9 = 9.1$

The model projects that 9.1% of Hispanics will be divorced in 2010.

4.4 Exercise Set

1. $y = 3x + 2$

The slope is the *x*-coefficient, which is 3. The *y*-intercept is the constant term, which is 2.

3. $y = 3x - 5$

$y = 3x + (-5)$

$m = 3;\ y-\text{intercept} = -5$

5. $y = -\dfrac{1}{2}x + 5$

$m = -\dfrac{1}{2};\ y\text{-intercept} = 5$

7. $y = 7x$

$y = 7x + 0$

$m = 7;\ y\text{-intercept} = 0$

9. $y = 10$

$y = 0x + 10$

$m = 0;\ y\text{-intercept} = 10$

11. $y = 4 - x$

$y = -x + 4 = -1x + 4$

$m = -1;\ y\text{-intercept} = 4$

13. $-5x + y = 7$

$-5x + y + 5x = 5x + 7$

$y = 5x + 7$

$m = 5;\ y\text{-intercept} = 7$

15. $x + y = 6$

$y = -x + 6 = -1x + 6$

$m = -1;\ y\text{-intercept} = 6$

17. $6x + y = 0$

$y = -6x = -6x + 0$

$m = -6;\ y\text{-intercept} = 0$

19. $3y = 6x$

$y = 2x$

$m = 2;\ y\text{-intercept} = 0$

21. $2x + 7y = 0$

$7y = -2x$

$y = -\dfrac{2}{7}x$

$m = -\dfrac{2}{7};\ y\text{-intercept} = 0$

23. $3x + 2y = 3$

$2y = -3x + 3$

$y = -\dfrac{3}{2}x + \dfrac{3}{2}$

$m = -\dfrac{3}{2};\ y\text{-intercept} = \dfrac{3}{2}$

25. $3x - 4y = 12$

$-4y = -3x + 12$

$y = \dfrac{3}{4}x - 3$

$m = \dfrac{3}{4};\ y\text{-intercept} = -3$

27. $y = 2x + 4$

Step 1. Plot (0,4) on the *y*-axis.

Step 2. $m = \dfrac{2}{1} = \dfrac{\text{rise}}{\text{run}}$

Start at (0,4). Using the slope, move 2 units *up* (the rise) and 1 unit to the *right* (the run) to reach the point (1,6).

Step 3. Draw a line through (0,4) and (1,6).

$y = 2x + 4$

29. $y = -3x + 5$

Slope = $-3 = \dfrac{-3}{1}$; y-intercept = 5.

Plot (0,5) on the y-axis. From this point, move 3 units *down* (because -3 is negative) and 1 unit to the *right* to reach the point (1,2). Draw a line through (0,5) and (1,2).

31. $y = \dfrac{1}{2}x + 1$

Slope = $\dfrac{1}{2}$; y-intercept = 1

Plot (0,1). From this point, move 1 unit *up* and 2 units to the *right* to reach the point (2,2). Draw a line through (0,1) and (2,2).

33. $y = \dfrac{2}{3}x - 5$

Slope = $\dfrac{2}{3}$; y-intercept = -5

Plot (0,-5). From this point move 2 units *up* and 3 units to the *right* to reach the point (3,-3). Draw a line through (0,-5) and (3,-3).

35. $y = -\dfrac{3}{4}x + 2$

Slope = $-\dfrac{3}{4} = \dfrac{-3}{4}$; y-intercept = 2

Plot (0,2). From this point move 3 units *down* and 4 units to the *right* to reach the point (4,-1). Draw a line through (0,2) and (4,-1)

37. $y = -\dfrac{5}{3}x$

Slope = $-\dfrac{5}{3} = \dfrac{-5}{3}$; y-intercept = 0

Plot (0,0). From this point, move 5 units *down* and 3 units to the *right* to reach the point (3,-5). Draw a line through (0,0) and (3,-5).

39. a. $3x + y = 0$

$\qquad y = -3x$

b. $m = -3$; y-intercept = 0

c. Plot (0,0). Since $m = -3 = -\dfrac{3}{1}$, move 3 units *down* and 1 units to the *right* to reach the point (1,-3). Draw a line through (0,0) and (1,-3).

41. a. $3y = 4x$

$$y = \frac{4}{3}x$$

b. $m = \frac{4}{3}$; y-intercept = 0

c. Plot (0,0). Move 4 units *up* and 3 units to the *right* to reach the point (3,4).
Draw a line through (0,0) and (3,4).

$y = \frac{4}{3}x$

43. a. $2x + y = 3$

$$y = -2x + 3$$

b. $m = -2$; y-intercept = 3

c. Plot (0,3). Since $m = -2 = -\frac{2}{1}$, move 2 units *down* and 1 units to the *right* to reach the point (1,1).
Draw a line through (0,3) and (1,1).

$y = -2x + 3$

45. a. $7x + 2y = 14$

$$2y = -7x + 14$$

$$\frac{2y}{2} = \frac{-7x + 14}{2}$$

$$y = -\frac{7}{2}x + 7$$

b. $m = -\frac{7}{2}$; y-intercept = 7

c. Plot (0,7). Since $m = -\frac{7}{2} = -\frac{7}{2}$, move 7 units *down* and 2 units to the *right* to reach the point (2,0).
Draw a line through (0,7) and (2,0).

$y = -\frac{7}{2}x + 7$

47. $y = 3x + 1$:

$m = 3$; y-intercept $= 1$

$y = 3x - 3$:

$m = 3$; y-intercept $= -3$

The lines are parallel because their slopes are equal.

49. $y = -3x + 2$:

$m = -3$; y-intercept $= 2$

$y = 3x + 2$:

$m = 3$; y-intercept $= 2$

The lines are not parallel because their slopes are not equal.
The lines are not perpendicular because the product of their slopes is not -1.

51. $y = x + 3$

$m = 1$; y-intercept $= 3$

$y = -x + 1$

$m = -1$; y-intercept $= 1$

The lines are perpendicular because the product of their slopes is -1.

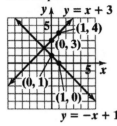

53. $x - 2y = 2 \rightarrow y = \dfrac{1}{2}x - 1$

$2x - 4y = 3 \rightarrow y = \dfrac{1}{2}x - \dfrac{3}{4}$

The lines are parallel because their slopes are equal.

55. $2x - y = -1 \rightarrow y = 2x + 1$

$x + 2y = -6 \rightarrow y = -\dfrac{1}{2}x - 3$

The lines are perpendicular because the product of their slopes is $2\left(-\dfrac{1}{2}\right) = -1$.

57. Find the slope of the parallel line. $3x + y = 6$

$$y = -3x + 6$$

The slope is -3. We are given that the y-intercept is 5, so using slope-intercept form, we have $y = -3x + 5$.

59. The slope of the line $y = 5x - 1$ is 5. The negative reciprocal of 5 is $-\dfrac{1}{5}$.

We are given that the y-intercept is 6, so using the slope-intercept form, we have $y = -\dfrac{1}{5}x + 6$.

61. Find the y-intercept of the line.

$16y = 8x + 32$

$$\dfrac{16}{16}y = \dfrac{8}{16}x + \dfrac{32}{16}$$

$$y = \dfrac{1}{2}x + 2$$

The y-intercept is 2.

Find the slope of the parallel line.

$3x + 3y = 9$

$$3y = -3x + 9$$

$$y = -x + 3$$

The slope is -1. Using slope-intercept form, we have $y = -x + 2$.

63. If the line rises from left to right, it has a positive slope. It passes through the origin, $(0, 0)$ and a second point with equal x- and y-coordinates. The point $(2, 2)$ is one example.

Use the two points to find the slope.

$$m = \dfrac{0 - 2}{0 - 2} = \dfrac{-2}{-2} = 1$$

The slope is 1. The y-intercept is 0. Using slope-intercept form, we have $y = 1x + 0$ or $y = x$.

65. a. The y-intercept is 68 and the slope is
$$m = \frac{\text{Change in } y}{\text{Change in } x} = \frac{51-68}{47-0} = \frac{-17}{47} \approx -0.36$$
The equation is $y = -0.36x + 68$.

b. $y = -0.36x + 68 = -0.36(100) + 68 = 32$
The model projects that 32% of the U.S. population will be white in 2103.

67. – 69. Answers will vary.

71. does not make sense; Explanations will vary. Sample explanation: The slope can be determined if the equation is solved for y.

73. does not make sense; Explanations will vary. Sample explanation: Under these circumstances, you can either find a different point to plot or change the scale on your graph paper.

75. false; Changes to make the statement true will vary. A sample change is: Vertical lines cannot be expressed in slope-intercept form.

77. false; Changes to make the statement true will vary. A sample change is: By solving the equation for y, you can determine that the y-intercept is $\frac{7}{2}$.

79. $\frac{x}{2} + 7 = 13 - \frac{x}{4}$
Multiply by the LCD, which is 4.
$$4\left(\frac{x}{2} + 7\right) = 4\left(13 - \frac{x}{4}\right)$$
$$2x + 28 = 52 - x$$
$$3x + 28 = 52$$
$$3x = 24$$
$$x = 8$$
The solution is $\{8\}$.

80. $3\left(12 \div 2^2 - 3\right)^2$
$$= 3\left(12 \div 4 - 3\right)^2$$
$$= 3\left(3 - 3\right)^2$$
$$= 3 \cdot 0^2 = 3 \cdot 0 = 0$$

81. $A = 14$, $P = 25\% = 0.25$
$$A = PB$$
$$14 = 0.25 \cdot B$$
$$\frac{14}{0.25} = \frac{0.25B}{0.25}$$
$$56 = B$$
14 is 25% of 56.

82. $y - 3 = 4(x + 1)$
$$y - 3 = 4x + 4$$
$$y = 4x + 7$$

83. $y + 3 = -\frac{3}{2}(x - 4)$
$$y + 3 = -\frac{3}{2}x + 6$$
$$y = -\frac{3}{2}x + 3$$

84. $y - 30.0 = 0.265(x - 10)$
$$y - 30.0 = 0.265x - 2.65$$
$$y = 0.265x + 27.35$$

Mid-Chapter Check Point

1. **a.** The *x*-intercept is 4.

   b. The *y*-intercept is 2.

   c. The points (4, 0) and (0, 2) lie on the line.
   $$m = \frac{2-0}{0-4} = \frac{2}{-4} = -\frac{1}{2}$$

2. **a.** The *x*-intercept is −5.

   b. There is no *y*-intercept.

   c. It is a vertical line, so the slope is undefined.

3. **a.** The *x*-intercept is 0.

   b. The *y*-intercept is 0.

   c. The points (0, 0) and (5, 3) lie on the line.
   $$m = \frac{3-0}{5-0} = \frac{3}{5}$$

4. $y = -2x$

5. $y = -2$

6. $x + y = -2$
   $$y = -x - 2$$

7. $y = \frac{1}{3}x - 2$

8. $x = 3.5$

9. $4x - 2y = 8$
   $$-2y = -4x + 8$$
   $$\frac{-2y}{-2} = \frac{-4x}{-2} + \frac{8}{-2}$$
   $$y = 2x - 4$$

10. $y = 3x + 2$

11. $3x + y = 0$
    $$y = -3x$$

12. $y = -x + 4$

13. $y = x - 4$

14. $5y = -3x$

$$y = -\frac{3}{5}x$$

15. $5y = 20$

$$y = 4$$

16. $5x - 2y = 10$

$$-2y = -5x + 10$$

$$y = \frac{5}{2}x - 5$$

The slope is $\frac{5}{2}$ and the y-intercept is -5.

17. Line through $(-5,-3)$ and $(0,-4)$:
$$m = \frac{\text{Change in } y}{\text{Change in } x} = \frac{-4-(-3)}{0-(-5)} = \frac{-1}{5} = -\frac{1}{5}$$
Line through $(-2,-8)$ and $(1,7)$:
$$m = \frac{\text{Change in } y}{\text{Change in } x} = \frac{7-(-8)}{1-(-2)} = \frac{15}{3} = 5$$

Since the product of their slopes is $-\frac{1}{5}(5) = -1$, the lines are perpendicular.

18. Line through $(-4,1)$ and $(2,7)$:
$$m = \frac{\text{Change in } y}{\text{Change in } x} = \frac{7-1}{2-(-4)} = \frac{6}{6} = 1$$
Line through $(-5,13)$ and $(4,-5)$:
$$m = \frac{\text{Change in } y}{\text{Change in } x} = \frac{-5-13}{4-(-5)} = \frac{-18}{9} = -2$$
Since their slopes are not equal, the lines are not parallel.
Since the product of their slopes is
$1(-2) = -2 \neq -1$, the lines are not perpendicular.

19. Line through $(2,-4)$ and $(7,0)$:
$$m = \frac{\text{Change in } y}{\text{Change in } x} = \frac{0-(-4)}{7-2} = \frac{4}{5}$$
Line through $(-4,2)$ and $(1,6)$:
$$m = \frac{\text{Change in } y}{\text{Change in } x} = \frac{6-2}{1-(-4)} = \frac{4}{5}$$
Since their slopes are equal, the lines are parallel.

20. a. The y-intercept is 1098 and the slope is
$$m = \frac{\text{Change in } y}{\text{Change in } x} = \frac{2277-1098}{9-0} = \frac{1179}{9} = 131$$
The equation is $y = 131x + 1098$.

  b. The average annual household gasoline bill increased at an average of $131 per year.

  c. 2013 is 16 years after 1997.
  $y = 131x + 1098 = 131(16) + 1098 = 3194$
  The model projects that in 2013 the average annual household gasoline bill will be $3194.

4.5 Check Points

1. Begin with the point-slope equation of a line.

   $$y - y_1 = m(x - x_1)$$
   $$y - (-5) = 6(x - 2)$$
   $$y + 5 = 6(x - 2)$$

   Now solve this equation for y to write the equation in slope-intercept form.

   $$y + 5 = 6(x - 2)$$
   $$y + 5 = 6x - 12$$
   $$y = 6x - 17$$

2. **a.** Begin by finding the slope:

   $$m = \frac{-6 - (-1)}{-1 - (-2)} = \frac{-5}{1} = -5$$

   Using the slope and either point, find the point-slope equation of a line.

   $$y - y_1 = m(x - x_1) \qquad \text{or} \qquad y - y_1 = m(x - x_1)$$
   $$y - (-1) = -5(x - (-2)) \qquad\qquad y - (-6) = -5(x - (-1))$$
   $$y + 1 = -5(x + 2) \qquad\qquad\quad y + 6 = -5(x + 1)$$

   b. Solve the above equation for y:

   $$y + 1 = -5(x + 2) \quad \text{or} \quad y + 6 = -5(x + 1)$$
   $$y + 1 = -5x - 10 \qquad\qquad y + 6 = -5x - 5$$
   $$y = -5x - 11 \qquad\qquad\quad y = -5x - 11$$

3. Find slope: $m = \dfrac{32.8 - 30.0}{20 - 10} = \dfrac{2.8}{10} = 0.28$

   Use the point-slope form to write the equation. Then solve for y to obtain slope-intercept form.

   $$y - y_1 = m(x - x_1)$$
   $$y - 30.0 = 0.28(x - 10)$$
   $$y - 30.0 = 0.28x - 2.8$$
   $$y = 0.28x + 27.2$$

   Because 2020 is 50 years after 1970, substitute 50 for x and compute y.

   $$y = 0.28x + 27.2 = 0.28(50) + 27.2 = 14 + 27.2 = 41.2$$

   The model predicts that 41.2 will be the median age in 2020.

4.5 Exercise Set

1. Begin with the point-slope equation of a line.

   $$y - y_1 = m(x - x_1)$$
   $$y - 5 = 3(x - 2)$$

   Now solve this equation for y to write the equation in slope-intercept form.

   $$y - 5 = 3x - 6$$
   $$y = 3x - 1$$

3. Begin with the point-slope equation of a line.

   $$y - y_1 = m(x - x_1)$$
   $$y - 6 = 5(x - (-2))$$
   $$y - 6 = 5(x + 2)$$

   Now solve this equation for y to write the equation in slope-intercept form.

   $$y - 6 = 5(x + 2)$$
   $$y - 6 = 5x + 10$$
   $$y = 5x + 16$$

5. Begin with the point-slope equation of a line.

   $$y - y_1 = m(x - x_1)$$
   $$y - (-2) = -8(x - (-3))$$
   $$y + 2 = -8(x + 3)$$

   Now solve this equation for y to write the equation in slope-intercept form.

   $$y + 2 = -8(x + 3)$$
   $$y + 2 = -8x - 24$$
   $$y = -8x - 26$$

7. Begin with the point-slope equation of a line.

   $$y - y_1 = m(x - x_1)$$
   $$y - 0 = -12(x - (-8))$$
   $$y = -12(x + 8)$$
   $$y = -12x - 96$$

   Now solve this equation for y to write the equation in slope-intercept form.

   $$y = -12(x + 8)$$
   $$y = -12x - 96$$

9. Begin with the point-slope equation of a line.

$$y - y_1 = m(x - x_1)$$

$$y - (-2) = -1\left(x - \left(-\frac{1}{2}\right)\right)$$

$$y + 2 = -1\left(x + \frac{1}{2}\right)$$

Now solve this equation for y to write the equation in slope-intercept form.

$$y + 2 = -1\left(x + \frac{1}{2}\right)$$

$$y + 2 = -x - \frac{1}{2}$$

$$y = -x - \frac{5}{2}$$

11. Begin with the point-slope equation of a line.

$$y - y_1 = m(x - x_1)$$

$$y - 0 = \frac{1}{2}(x - 0)$$

Now solve this equation for y to write the equation in slope-intercept form.

$$y - 0 = \frac{1}{2}(x - 0)$$

$$y = \frac{1}{2}x$$

13. Begin with the point-slope equation of a line.

$$y - y_1 = m(x - x_1)$$

$$y - (-2) = -\frac{2}{3}(x - 6)$$

$$y + 2 = -\frac{2}{3}(x - 6)$$

Now solve this equation for y to write the equation in slope-intercept form.

$$y + 2 = -\frac{2}{3}(x - 6)$$

$$y + 2 = -\frac{2}{3}x + 4$$

$$y = -\frac{2}{3}x + 2$$

15. slope $= \dfrac{10 - 2}{5 - 1} = \dfrac{8}{4} = 2$

Using the slope and either point, find the point-slope equation of a line.

$$y - y_1 = m(x - x_1)$$

$$y - 2 = 2(x - 1) \text{ or } y - 10 = 2(x - 5)$$

Now solve this equation for y to write the equation in slope-intercept form.

$$y - 2 = 2(x - 1)$$

$$y - 2 = 2x - 2$$

$$y = 2x$$

17. slope $= \dfrac{3 - 0}{0 + 3} = \dfrac{3}{3} = 1$

Using the slope and either point, find the point-slope equation of a line.

$$y - y_1 = m(x - x_1)$$

$$y - 0 = 1(x + 3) \text{ or } y - 3 = 1(x - 0)$$

Now solve this equation for y to write the equation in slope-intercept form.

$$y - 0 = 1(x + 3)$$

$$y = x + 3$$

19. slope $= \dfrac{4 + 1}{2 + 3} = \dfrac{5}{5} = 1$

Using the slope and either point, find the point-slope equation of a line.

$$y - y_1 = m(x - x_1)$$

$$y - (-1) = 1(x - (-3))$$

$$y + 1 = 1(x + 3) \text{ or } y - 4 = 1(x - 2)$$

Now solve this equation for y to write the equation in slope-intercept form.

$$y + 1 = 1(x + 3)$$

$$y + 1 = x + 3$$

$$y = x + 2$$

21. slope $= \dfrac{4-(-1)}{3-(-4)} = \dfrac{5}{7}$

Using the slope and either point, find the point-slope equation of a line.

$y - y_1 = m(x - x_1)$

$y - 4 = \dfrac{5}{7}(x-3)$ or $y+1 = \dfrac{5}{7}(x+4)$

Now solve this equation for y to write the equation in slope-intercept form.

$y - 4 = \dfrac{5}{7}(x-3)$

$y - 4 = \dfrac{5}{7}x - \dfrac{15}{7}$

$y = \dfrac{5}{7}x + \dfrac{13}{7}$

23. slope $= \dfrac{-1+1}{4+3} = \dfrac{0}{7} = 0$

Using the slope and either point, find the point-slope equation of a line.

$y - y_1 = m(x - x_1)$

$y - (-1) = 0(x - (-3))$

$y + 1 = 0(x+3)$ or $y+1 = 0(x-4)$

Now solve this equation for y to write the equation in slope-intercept form.

$y + 1 = 0(x+3)$

$y + 1 = 0$

$y = -1$

25. Use the points $(2,4)$ and $(-2,0)$ to find the slope.

slope $= \dfrac{0+4}{-2-2} = \dfrac{-4}{-4} = 1$

Find the point-slope equation of a line.

$y - y_1 = m(x - x_1)$

$y - 4 = 1(x-2)$

Now solve this equation for y to write the equation in slope-intercept form.

$y - 4 = 1(x-2)$

$y - 4 = x - 2$

$y = x + 2$

27. Use the points $\left(-\dfrac{1}{2}, 0\right)$ and $(0,4)$ to find the slope.

slope $= \dfrac{4-0}{0+\dfrac{1}{2}} = \dfrac{4}{\dfrac{1}{2}} = 8$

Find the point-slope equation of a line.

$y - y_1 = m(x - x_1)$

$y - 0 = 8\left(x - \left(-\dfrac{1}{2}\right)\right)$

$y - 0 = 8\left(x + \dfrac{1}{2}\right)$ or $y - 4 = 8(x-0)$

Now solve this equation for y to write the equation in slope-intercept form.

$y - 4 = 8(x-0)$

$y - 4 = 8x$

$y = 8x + 4$

29. The slope of the line is 4 since the line is parallel to a line with a slope of 4.

Use point-slope form to find the equation of the line.

$y - y_1 = m(x - x_1)$

$y - 2 = 4(x - (-3))$

$y - 2 = 4(x+3)$

$y - 2 = 4x + 12$

$y = 4x + 14$

31. Solve $3x + y = 6$ for y to obtain the slope.

$3x + y = 6$

$y = -3x + 6$

The slope of the line is -3 since the line is parallel to a line with a slope of -3.

Use point-slope form to find the equation of the line.

$y - y_1 = m(x - x_1)$

$y - (-5) = -3(x - (-1))$

$y + 5 = -3(x+1)$

$y + 5 = -3x - 3$

$y = -3x - 8$

33. Solve $x - 2y = 3$ for y to obtain the slope.

$x - 2y = 3$

$-2y = -x + 3$

$y = \dfrac{1}{2}x - \dfrac{3}{2}$

The slope of the line is -2 since the line is parallel to a line with a slope of $\dfrac{1}{2}$.

Use point-slope form to find the equation of the line.

$y - y_1 = m(x - x_1)$

$y - (-7) = -2(x - 4)$

$y + 7 = -2x + 8$

$y = -2x + 1$

35. Through (2, 4) and same y-intercept as $x - 4y = 8$. Solve the equation to obtain the y-intercept.

$x - 4y = 8$

$-4y = -x + 8$

$y = \dfrac{1}{4}x - 2$

Now, use the two points to find the slope.

$m = \dfrac{4 - (-2)}{2 - 0} = \dfrac{6}{2} = 3$

Now use the slope and one of the points to find the equation of the line.

$y - 4 = 3(x - 2)$

$y - 4 = 3x - 6$

$y = 3x - 2$

37. x-intercept at -4 and parallel to the line containing (3, 1) and (2, 6)

First, find the slope of the line going through the points (3, 1) and (2, 6).

$m = \dfrac{6 - 1}{2 - 3} = \dfrac{5}{-1} = -5$

The slope of the line is -5. Since this line is parallel to the line we are writing the equation for, its slope is also -5. Since the x-intercept is -4, the line goes through the point $(-4, 0)$. Use the point and the slope to find the equation of the line.

$y - 0 = -5(x - (-4))$

$y = -5(x + 4)$

$y = -5x - 20$

39. a. Find slope: $m = \dfrac{71.4 - 64.6}{15 - 5} = \dfrac{6.8}{10} = 0.68$

$y - y_1 = m(x - x_1)$

$y - 64.6 = 0.68(x - 5)$

$y - 64.6 = 0.68x - 3.4$

$y = 0.68x + 61.2$

b. $y = 0.68x + 61.2 = 0.68(35) + 61.2 = 85$

According to the model, women will earn 85% of men in 2015.

41. a. Scatter plot:

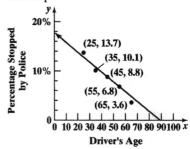

b. Find slope: $m = \dfrac{6.8 - 8.8}{55 - 45} = \dfrac{-2}{10} = -0.2$

$y - y_1 = m(x - x_1)$

$y - 8.8 = -0.2(x - 45)$

$y - 8.8 = -0.2x + 9$

$y = -0.2x + 17.8$

c. $y = -0.2x + 17.8 = -0.2(35) + 17.8 = 10.8$

According to the model, 10.8% of 35-year-old drivers are stopped by police.

This overestimates the actual percentage shown in the bar graph by 0.7%.

43. – 45. Answers will vary.

47. does not make sense; Explanations will vary. Sample explanation: Typically, we go from point-slope form to slope-intercept form. It is not common to go from slope-intercept form to point-slope form.

49. makes sense

51. false; Changes to make the statement true will vary. A sample change is: This line passes through $(-3, -4)$.

53. false; Changes to make the statement true will vary. A sample change is: Solving this line for y shows that its slope is -3.

55. Answers will vary.

57. Let x = the number of sheets of paper.
$$4 + 2x \le 29$$
$$2x \le 25$$
$$x \le \frac{25}{2} \text{ or } 12\frac{1}{2}$$
Since the number of sheets of paper must be a whole number, at most 12 sheets of paper can be put in the envelope.

58. The only natural numbers in the given set are 1 and $\sqrt{4} \, (=2)$

59. $3x - 5y = 15$
x-intercept:
$$3x - 5(0) = 15$$
$$3x = 15$$
$$x = 5$$
y-intercept:
$$3(0) - 5y = 15$$
$$-5y = 15$$
$$y = -3$$

60. $\qquad 2x - 3y \ge 6$
$$2(3) - 3(-1) \ge 6$$
$$6 + 4 \ge 6$$
$$10 \ge 6, \text{ true}$$
Yes, the values make the inequality a true statement.

61. $\qquad 2x - 3y \ge 6$
$$2(0) - 3(0) \ge 6$$
$$0 \ge 6, \text{ false}$$
No, the values make the inequality a false statement.

62. $y \le \dfrac{2}{3} x$
$$1 \le \frac{2}{3}(1)$$
$$1 \le \frac{2}{3}, \text{ false}$$
No, the values make the inequality a false statement.

4.6 Check Points

1. a. $\qquad 5x + 4y \le 20$
$$5(0) + 4(0) \le 20$$
$$0 \le 20, \text{ true}$$
$(0, 0)$ is a solution.

b. $\qquad 5x + 4y \le 20$
$$5(6) + 4(2) \le 20$$
$$30 + 8 \le 20$$
$$38 \le 20, \text{ false}$$
$(6, 2)$ is not a solution.

2. $2x - 4y < 8$

Step 1. Replace $<$ with $=$ and graph the linear equation $2x - 4y = 8$ The x-intercept is 4 and the y-intercept is –2, so the line passes through $(4, 0)$ and $(0, -2)$. Draw a dashed line because the inequality contains a $<$ symbol.

Step 2. Use $(0, 0)$ as a test point.
$$2x - 4y < 8$$
$$2(0) - 4(0) < 8$$
$$0 < 8, \text{ true}$$

Step 3. The test point $(0, 0)$ is part of the solution set, so shade the half-plane containing $(0, 0)$.

3. $y \geq \dfrac{1}{2}x$

Step 1. Replace $\geq$ with $=$ and graph the linear

equation $y = \dfrac{1}{2}x$ The line passes through the

origin so we must find an additional point. For example, using the slope we get the point $(2,1)$. Draw a solid line because the inequality contains a $\geq$ symbol.

Step 2. We cannot use $(0,0)$ as a test point because the line passes through it.

$$\text{Use } (0,10) \text{ as a test point} \quad y \geq \dfrac{1}{2}x$$

$$10 \geq \dfrac{1}{2}(0)$$

$$10 \geq 0, \text{ true}$$

Step 3. The test point $(0,10)$ is part of the solution set, so shade the half-plane containing $(0,10)$.

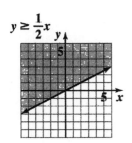

4. a. $y > 1$

Graph the horizontal line, $y = 1$, with a dashed line and shade the half-plane above the line.

b. $x \leq -2$

Graph the vertical line, $x = -2$, with a solid line and shade the half-plane to the left of the line.

5. a. The coordinates of B are $(60,20)$. A region that has an average annual temperature of $60°F$ and an average annual precipitation of 20 inches is a grassland.

b.
$$5T - 7P \geq 70$$
$$5(60) - 7(20) \geq 70$$
$$300 - 140 \geq 70$$
$$160 \geq 70, \text{ true}$$

$$3T - 35P \leq -140$$
$$3(60) - 35(20) \leq -140$$
$$180 - 700 \leq -140$$
$$-520 \leq -140, \text{ true}$$

4.6 Exercise Set

1. $x + y > 4$

$(2,2)$: $2 + 2 > 4$; $4 > 4$, false

$(2,2)$ is not a solution.

$(3,2)$: $3 + 2 > 4$; $5 > 4$, true

$(3,2)$ is a solution.

$(-3,8)$: $-3 + 8 > 4$; $5 > 4$, true

$(-3,8)$ is a solution.

3. $2x + y \geq 5$

$(4,0)$: $8 + 0 \geq 5$, true

$(4,0)$ is a solution.

$(1,3)$: $2 + 3 \geq 5$, true

$(1,3)$ is a solution.

$(0,0)$: $0 + 0 \geq 5$, false

$(0,0)$ is not a solution.

5. $y \geq -2x + 4$

$(4,0)$: $0 \geq -8 + 4$, true

$(4,0)$ is a solution.

$(1,3)$: $3 \geq -2 + 4 = 2$, true

$(1,3)$ is a solution.

$(-2,-4)$: $-4 \geq 4 + 4 = 8$, false

$(-2,-4)$ is not a solution.

7. $y > -2x + 1$

$(2,3)$: $3 > -4 + 1 = -3$, true

$(2,3)$ is a solution.

$(0,0)$: $0 > 0 + 1 = 1$, false

$(0,0)$ is not a solution.

$(0,5)$: $5 > 0 + 1 = 1$, true

$(0,5)$ is a solution.

9. $x + y \geq 3$

Step 1. Replace $\geq$ with $=$ and graph the linear equation $x + y = 3$. The x-intercept is 4 and the y-intercept is 3, so the line passes through $(3,0)$ and $(0,3)$. Draw a solid line because the inequality contains a $\geq$ symbol.

Step 2. Use $(0,0)$ as a test point. $x + y \geq 3$

$$0 + 0 \geq 3$$
$$0 \geq 3, \text{ false}$$

Step 3. The test point $(0,0)$ is not part of the solution set, so shade the half-plane *not* containing $(0,0)$.

11. $x - y < 5$

Graph the equation $x - y = 5$, which passes through the points $(3,0)$ and $(0, -5)$. Draw a dashed line because the inequality contains a $<$ symbol. Use $(0,0)$ as a test point. Since $0 - 0 < 5$ is a true statement, shade the half-plane containing $(0,0)$.

13. $x + 2y > 4$

Graph the equation $x + 2y = 4$ as a dashed line through $(4,0)$ and $(0,2)$. Use $(0,0)$ as a test point. Since $0 + 2(0) > 4$ is false, shade the half-plane *not* containing $(0,0)$.

15. $3x - y \leq 6$

Graph the equation $3x - y = 6$ as a solid line through $(2,0)$ and $(0, -6)$. Use $(0,0)$ as a test point. Since $3(0) - \leq 6$ is true, shade the half-plane containing $(0,0)$.

17. $3x - 2y \leq 8$

Graph the equation $3x - 2y = 8$ as a solid line through $\left(\dfrac{8}{3}, 0\right)$ and $(0, -4)$. Use $(0,0)$ as a test point. Since $3(0) - 2(0) \leq 8$ is true, shade the half-plane containing $(0,0)$.

19. $4x + 3y > 15$

Graph $4x + 3y = 15$ as a dashed line through

$\left(\dfrac{15}{4}, 0\right)$ and $(0, 5)$.

Use $(0,0)$ as a test point. Since $4(0) + 3(0) > 15$ is false, shade the half-plane not containing $(0,0)$.

21. $5x - y < -7$

Graph the equation $5x - y = -7$ as a dashed line

through $\left(-\dfrac{7}{5}, 0\right)$ and $(0, 7)$. Use $(0,0)$ as a test

point. Since $5(0) - 0 < -7$ is false, shade the half-plane *not* containing $(0,0)$.

23. $y \le \dfrac{1}{3}x$

Graph the equation $y = \dfrac{1}{3}x$ as a solid line through

$(0,0)$ and $(3,1)$. Because $(0,0)$ lies on the line, it cannot be used as a test point. Instead use a point

not on the line, such as $(0,6)$. Since $6 \le \dfrac{1}{2}(0)$ is

false, shade the half-plane *not* containing $(0,6)$.

25. $y > 2x$

Graph the equation $y = 2x$ as a dashed line through the origin with slope 2. Use $(3,3)$ as a test point. Since $3 > 2(3)$ is false, shade the half-plane *not* containing $(3,3)$.

27. $y > 3x + 2$

Graph $y = 3x + 2$ as a dashed line using the slope and y-intercept. Use $(0,0)$ as a test point. Since $0 > 3(0) + 2$ is false, shade the half-plane *not* containing $(0,0)$.

29. $y < \dfrac{3}{4}x - 3$

Graph $y = \dfrac{3}{4}x - 3$ as a dashed line using the slope

and y-intercept. (Plot $(0, -3)$ and move 3 units up and 4 units to the right to the point $(4,0)$.) Use $(0,0)$

as a test point. Since $0 < \dfrac{3}{4}(0) - 3$ is false, shade

the half-plane *not* containing $(0,0)$.

31. $x \le 1$

Graph the vertical line $x = 1$ as a solid line. Use (0,0) as a test point. Since $0 \le 1$ is true, shade the half-plane containing (0,0), which is the half-plane to the *left* of the line.

33. $y > 1$

Graph the horizontal line $y = 1$ as a dashed line.

Use (0,0) as a test point. Since $0 > 1$ is false, shade the half-plane *not* containing (0,0), which is the half-plane *above* the line.

35. $x \ge 0$

Graph the vertical line $x = 0$ (the *y*-axis) as a solid line. Since (0,0) is on the line, choose a different test point, such as (3,3). Since $3 > 0$ is true, shade the half-plane containing (3,3), which is the half-plane to the *right* of the *y*-axis.

37. $x + y \ge 2$

Rewrite: $y \ge -x + 2$

39. $5x - 2y \le 10$

Rewrite: $y \ge \dfrac{5}{2}x - 5$

41. $y \ge \dfrac{1}{2}x$

43. $y \le -1$

45. a. $20x + 10y \le 80,000$

Graph the line $20x + 10y = 80,000$ as a solid line, using the *x*-intercept 4000 and the *y*-intercept 8000. Use (1000,1000) as a test point. Since $20(1000) + 10(1000) = 30,000 \le 80,000$ is true, shade the half-plane containing (1000,1000). Draw the graph in quadrant I only.

b. Answers will vary. One example is (1000, 2000) since

$20(1000) + 10(2000) = 20,000 + 20,000$

$= 40,000 < 80,000$.

This indicates that the plane can carry 1000 bottles of water and 2000 medical kits.

47. a. $50x + 150y > 2000$

    b. Graph $50x + 150y = 2000$ as a dashed line, using the *x*-intercept 40 and *y*-intercept $\dfrac{2000}{150} \approx 13.3$. Use $(10,20)$ as a test point. Since $50(10) + 150(20) = 3500 > 2000$ is true, shade the half-plane containing $(10,20)$. Draw the graph in quadrant I only.

    c. Answers will vary. One example is $(20,15)$ since $50(20) + 150(150) = 3200 > 2000$. This indicates that the elevator cannot carry 20 children and 15 adults.

49. a. $BMI = \dfrac{703W}{H^2}; W = 200, H = 72$

    The man's $BMI = \dfrac{703(200)}{72^2} \approx 27.1$

    b. Locate the point $(20,27.1)$ on the graph for males. The point falls in the "Overweight" region, so the man is overweight.

51. – 57. Answers will vary.

59. does not make sense; Explanations will vary. Sample explanation: This inequality is satisfied by the points above the line

61. makes sense

63. false; Changes to make the statement true will vary. A sample change is: This inequality is satisfied by the points in the half-plane above the line.

65. true

67. The *x*-intercept of the line is 2 and the *y*-intercept is 4, so the equation of the line is $2x + y = 4$, which can be written in slope-intercept form as $y = -2x + 4$. The line is solid, so the inequality symbol must be either $\geq$ or $\leq$. Choose a test point in the shaded region, for example $(0,0)$. Since $2(0) + 0 = 0 < 4$, the inequality symbol must be $\leq$. Therefore, the inequality is $2x + y \leq 4$ or $y \leq -2x + 4$.

69. $y \geq x - 2$

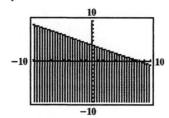

71. $y \leq -\dfrac{1}{2}x + 4$

72. $V = lwh$

$$\dfrac{V}{lw} = \dfrac{lwh}{lw}$$

$$\dfrac{V}{lw} = h \text{ or } h = \dfrac{V}{lw}$$

73. $\dfrac{2}{3} \div \left(-\dfrac{5}{4}\right) = \dfrac{2}{3} \cdot \left(-\dfrac{4}{5}\right) = -\dfrac{8}{15}$

74. $x^2 - 4 = (-3)^2 - 4 = 9 - 4 = 5$

75.
$$x + 2y = 2$$
$$4 + 2(-1) = 2$$
$$4 - 2 = 2$$
$$2 = 2, \text{ true}$$

$$x - 2y = 6$$
$$4 - 2(-1) = 6$$
$$4 + 2 = 6$$
$$6 = 6, \text{ true}$$

Yes, the values are a solution of both equations.

76. $x + 2y = 2$

$-4 + 2(3) = 2$

$-4 + 6 = 2$

$2 = 2,$ true

$x - 2y = 6$

$-4 - 2(3) = 6$

$-4 - 6 = 6$

$-10 = 6,$ false

No, the values are not a solution of both equations.

77. Graph $2x + 3y = 6$ by finding intercepts.

Find the x-intercept.

$2x + 3y = 6$

$2x + 3(0) = 6$

$2x = 6$

$x = 3$

Find the y-intercept.

$2x + 3y = 6$

$2(0) + 3y = 6$

$3y = 6$

$y = 2$

Graph $2x + y = -2$ by finding intercepts.

Find the x-intercept.

$2x + y = -2$

$2x + 0 = -2$

$2x = -2$

$x = -1$

Find the y-intercept.

$2x + y = -2$

$2(0) + y = -2$

$y = -2$

The point of intersection is $(-3, 4)$.

Chapter 4 Review

1. Quadrant IV

2. Quadrant IV

3. Quadrant I

4. Quadrant II

5. $A(5, 6)$ $B(-3, 0)$ $C(-5, 2)$

$D(-4, -2)$ $E(0, -5)$ $F(3, -1)$

6. $y = 3x + 6$

$3 = 3(-3) + 6$

$3 = -6 + 9$

$3 = -3$, false

$(-3, 3)$ is not a solution.

$y = 3x + 6$

$6 = 3(0) + 6$

$6 = 6$, true

$(0, 6)$ is a solution.

$y = 3x + 6$

$9 = 3(1) + 6$

$9 = 9$, true

$(1, 9)$ is a solution.

7. $3x - y = 12$

$3(0) - 4 = 12$

$-4 = 12$, false

$(0, 4)$ is not a solution.

$3x - y = 12$

$3(4) - 0 = 12$

$12 = 12$, true

$(4, 0)$ is a solution.

$3x - y = 12$

$3(-1) - 15 = 12$

$-3 - 15 = 12$

$-18 = 12$, false

$(-1, 15)$ is not a solution.

8. a.

x	$y = 2x - 3$	(x, y)
-2	$y = 2(-2) - 3 = -7$	$(-2, -7)$
-1	$y = 2(-1) - 3 = -5$	$(-1, -5)$
0	$y = 2(0) - 3 = -3$	$(0, -3)$
1	$y = 2(1) - 3 = -1$	$(1, -1)$
2	$y = 2(2) - 3 = 1$	$(2, 1)$

b. $y = 2x - 3$

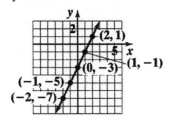

9. a.

x	$y = \frac{1}{2}x + 1$	(x, y)
-2	$y = \frac{1}{2}(-2) + 1 = 0$	$(-2, 0)$
-1	$y = \frac{1}{2}(-1) + 1 = \frac{1}{2}$	$\left(-1, \frac{1}{2}\right)$
0	$y = \frac{1}{2}(0) + 1 = 1$	$(0, 1)$
1	$y = \frac{1}{2}(1) + 1 = \frac{3}{2}$	$\left(1, \frac{3}{2}\right)$
2	$y = \frac{1}{2}(2) + 1 = 2$	$(2, 2)$

b. $y = \dfrac{1}{2}x + 1$

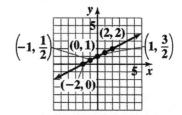

10. a. The graph crosses the x-axis at $(-2, 0)$, so the x-intercept is -2.

b. The graph crosses the y-axis at $(0, -4)$, so the y-intercept is -4.

11. a. The graph does not cross the x-axis, so there is no x-intercept.

b. The graph crosses the y-axis at $(0, 2)$, so the y-intercept is 2.

12. a. The graph crosses the x-axis at $(0, 0)$ (the origin), so the x-intercept is 0.

b. The graph also crosses the y-axis at $(0, 0)$, so the y-intercept is 0.

13. Find the *x*-intercept. Let $y = 0$ and solve for *x*.

$$2x + y = 4$$
$$2x + 0 = 4$$
$$2x = 4$$
$$x = 2$$

The *x*-intercept is 2.

Find the *y*- intercept. Let $x = 0$ and solve for *y*.

$$2x + y = 4$$
$$2(0) + y = 4$$
$$y = 4$$

The *y*-intercept is 4.

Find a checkpoint. For example, let $x = 1$ and solve for *y*.

$$2x + y = 4$$
$$2(1) + y = 4$$
$$2 + y = 4$$
$$y = 2$$

The checkpoint is (1,2).

Draw the line through these three points.

14. Find the *x*-intercept. Let $y = 0$ and solve for *x*.

$$3x - 2y = 12$$
$$3x - 2(0) = 12$$
$$3x = 12$$
$$x = 4$$

The *x*-intercept is 4.

Find the *y*- intercept. Let $x = 0$ and solve for *y*.

$$3x - 2y = 12$$
$$3(0) - 2y = 12$$
$$-2y = 12$$
$$y = -6$$

The *y*-intercept is –6.

Find a checkpoint. For example, let $x = 2$ and solve for *y*.

$$3x - 2y = 12$$
$$3(2) - 2y = 12$$
$$6 - 2y = 12$$
$$-2y = 6$$
$$y = -3$$

The checkpoint is (2,–3).

Draw the line through these three points.

15. Find the *x*-intercept. Let $y = 0$ and solve for *x*.

$$3x = 6 - 2y$$
$$3x = 6 - 2(0)$$
$$3x = 6$$
$$x = 2$$

The *x*-intercept is 2.

Find the *y*- intercept. Let $x = 0$ and solve for *y*.

$$3x = 6 - 2y$$
$$3(0) = 6 - 2y$$
$$0 = 6 - 2y$$
$$2y = 6$$
$$y = 3$$

The *y*-intercept is 3.

Find a checkpoint. For example, let $x = 4$ and solve for *y*.

$$3x = 6 - 2y$$
$$3(4) = 6 - 2y$$
$$12 = 6 - 2y$$
$$6 = -2y$$
$$-3 = y$$

The checkpoint is (4,–3).

Draw the line through these three points.

16. Because the constant on the right is 0, the graph passes through the origin. The x- and y-intercepts are both 0.
Thus we will need to find two more points.
Let $x = 1$ and solve for y.

$$3x - y = 0$$
$$3(1) - y = 0$$
$$3 - y = 0$$
$$3 = y$$

This gives the point (1,3).
Let $x = -1$ and solve for y.

$$3x - y = 0$$
$$3(-1) - y = 0$$
$$-3 - y = 0$$
$$-3 = y$$

This gives the point (−1,−3).
Draw the line through these three points.

17. $x = 3$
Three ordered pairs are (3, −2), (3,0), and (3,2). The graph is a vertical line.

18. $y = -5$
Three ordered pairs are (−2, −5), (0, −5), and (2, −5). The graph is a horizontal line.

19. $y + 3 = 5$
$$y = 2$$
Three ordered pairs are (−2,2), (0,2), and (2,2). The graph is a horizontal line.

20. $2x = -8$
$$x = -4$$
Three ordered pairs (−4, −2), (−4,0), and (−4,2). The graph is a vertical line.

21. a. The minimum temperature occurred at 5 P.M. and was −4°F.

b. The maximum temperature occurred at 8 P.M. and was at 16°F.

c. The x-intercepts are 4 and 6. This indicates that 4 P.M. and 6 P.M., the temperature was 0°F.

d. The y-intercept is 12. This indicates that at noon the temperature was 12°F.

e. This indicates that the temperature stayed the same, at 12°F, from 9 P.M. until midnight.

22. $m = \dfrac{y_2 - y_1}{x_2 - x_1} = \dfrac{1 - 2}{5 - 3} = -\dfrac{1}{2}$

The slope is $-\dfrac{1}{2}$. Since the slope is negative, the line falls from left to right.

23. $m = \dfrac{-4 - 2}{-3 - (-1)} = \dfrac{-6}{-2} = 3$

Since the slope is positive, the line rises from left to right.

24. $m = \dfrac{4 - 4}{6 - (-3)} = \dfrac{0}{9} = 0$

Since the slope is 0, the line is horizontal.

25. $m = \dfrac{-3-3}{5-5} = \dfrac{-6}{0}$; undefined

Since the slope is undefined, the line is vertical.

26. $m = \dfrac{1-(-2)}{2-(-3)} = \dfrac{3}{5}$

27. The line is vertical, so its slope is undefined.

28. $m = \dfrac{-3-(-1)}{2-(-4)} = \dfrac{-2}{6} = -\dfrac{1}{3}$

29. The line is horizontal, so its slope is 0.

30. Line through $(-1, -3)$ and $(2, -8)$:

$m = \dfrac{-8-(-3)}{2-(-1)} = \dfrac{-5}{3} = -\dfrac{5}{3}$

Line through $(8, -7)$ and $(9, 10)$:

$m = \dfrac{10-(-7)}{9-8} = \dfrac{17}{1} = 17$

Since their slopes are not equal, the lines are not parallel.

Since the product of their slopes is not -1, the lines are not perpendicular.

31. Line through $(0, -4)$ and $(5, -1)$:

$m = \dfrac{-1-(-4)}{5-0} = \dfrac{3}{5}$

Line through $(-6, 8)$ and $(3, -7)$:

$m = \dfrac{-7-8}{3-(-6)} = \dfrac{-15}{9} = \dfrac{-5}{3}$

Since the product of their slopes is

$\dfrac{3}{5}\left(-\dfrac{5}{3}\right) = -1$, the lines are perpendicular.

32. Line through $(5, 4)$ and $(9, 7)$:

$m = \dfrac{7-4}{9-5} = \dfrac{3}{4}$

Line through $(-6, 0)$ and $(-2, 3)$:

$m = \dfrac{3-0}{-2-(-6)} = \dfrac{3}{4}$

Since their slopes are equal, the lines are parallel.

33. a. $m = \dfrac{47-7}{2005-1965} = \dfrac{40}{40} = 1$

b. For each year from 1965 through 2005, the percentage of female medical school graduates increased by 1%. The rate of change was 1% per year.

34. $y = 5x - 7$

$y = 5x + (-7)$

The slope is the *x*-coefficient, which is 5. The *y*-intercept is the constant term, which is -7.

35. $y = 6 - 4x$

$y = -4x + 6$

$m = -4$; *y*-intercept $= 6$

36. $y = 3$

$m = 0$; *y*-intercept $= 3$

37. $2x + 3y = 6$

$3y = -2x + 6$

$y = \dfrac{-2x + 6}{3}$

$y = -\dfrac{2}{3}x + 2$

$m = -\dfrac{2}{3}$; *y*-intercept $= 2$

38. $y = 2x - 4$

slope $= 2 = \dfrac{2}{1}$; *y*-intercept $= -4$

Plot $(0, -4)$ on the *y*-axis. From this point, move 2 units *up* (because 2 is positive) and 1 unit to the *right* to reach the point $(1, -2)$. Draw a line through $(0, -4)$ and $(1, -2)$.

39. $y = \dfrac{1}{2}x - 1$

slope $= \dfrac{1}{2}$; *y*-intercept $= -1$

Plot $(0, -1)$. From the point, move 1 unit *up* and 2 units to the *right* to reach the point $(2, 0)$. Draw a line through $(0, -1)$ and $(2, 0)$.

40. $y = -\dfrac{2}{3}x + 5$

slope $= -\dfrac{2}{3} = \dfrac{-2}{3}$; y-intercept $= 5$

Plot $(0,5)$. Move 2 units *down* (because -2 is negative) and 3 units to the *right* to reach the point $(3,3)$. Draw a line through $(0,5)$ and $(3,3)$.

$y = -\dfrac{2}{3}x + 5$

41. $y - 2x = 0$

$y = 2x$

slope $= 2 = \dfrac{2}{1}$; y-intercept $= 0$

Plot $(0,0)$ (the origin). Move 2 units *up* and 1 unit to the *right* to reach the point $(1,2)$. Draw a line through $(0,0)$ and $(1,2)$.

$y = 2x$

42. $\dfrac{1}{3}x + y = 2$

$y = -\dfrac{1}{3}x + 2$

slope $= -\dfrac{1}{3} = \dfrac{-1}{3}$; y-intercept $= 2$

Plot $(0,2)$. Move 1 unit *down* and 3 units to the *right* to reach the point $(3,1)$. Draw line through $(0,2)$ and $(3,1)$.

$y = -\dfrac{1}{3}x + 2$

43. $y = -\dfrac{1}{2}x + 4$

slope $= -\dfrac{1}{2} = \dfrac{-1}{2}$

y-intercept $= 4$

$y = -\dfrac{1}{2}x - 1$

slope $= -\dfrac{1}{2} = \dfrac{-1}{2}$

y-intercept $= -1$

Graph each line using its slope and y-intercept.

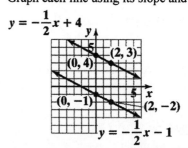

$y = -\dfrac{1}{2}x + 4$

$y = -\dfrac{1}{2}x - 1$

Yes, they are parallel since both lines have a slope of $-\dfrac{1}{2}$ and different y-intercepts.

44. a. $m = \dfrac{51.1 - 12.6}{10 - 0} = \dfrac{38.5}{10} = 3.85$

The y-intercept is 12.6 as shown in the graph.

$y = mx + b$

$y = 3.85x + 12.6$

b. $y = 3.85x + 12.6$

$y = 3.85(20) + 12.6 = 89.6$

The model predicts that 89.6% of tax returns will be e-filed in 2015.

45. Slope $= 6$, passing through $(-4,7)$

point-slope form:

$y - y_1 = m(x - x_1)$

$y - 7 = 6\left[x - (-4)\right]$

$y - 7 = 6(x + 4)$

slope-intercept form:

$y - 7 = 6(x + 4)$

$y - 7 = 6x + 24$

$y = 6x + 31$

46. Passing through $(3,4)$ and $(2,1)$
First, find the slope.
$$m = \frac{1-4}{2-3} = \frac{-3}{-1} = 3$$
Next, use the slope and one of the points to write the equation of the line in point-slope form.
$$y - y_1 = m(x - x_1)$$
$$y - 4 = 3(x - 3)$$
Solve for y to obtain slope-intercept form.
$$y - 4 = 3x - 9$$
$$y = 3x - 5$$

47. a. First, find the slope.
$$m = \frac{5.3 - 3.7}{40 - 20} = \frac{1.6}{20} = 0.08$$
Next, use the slope and one of the points to write the equation of the line in point-slope form.
$$y - y_1 = m(x - x_1)$$
$$y - 3.7 = 0.08(x - 20)$$
Solve for y to obtain slope-intercept form.
$$y - 3.7 = 0.08(x - 20)$$
$$y - 3.7 = 0.08x - 1.6$$
$$y = 0.08x + 2.1$$

b. $y = 0.08x + 2.1$
$$y = 0.08(75) + 2.1 = 8.1$$
The model projects a world population of 8.1 billion in 2025.

48. $3x - 4y > 7$
$$3(0) - 4(0) > 7$$
$$0 - 0 > 7$$
$$0 > 7, \text{ false}$$
$(0,0)$ is not a solution.

$$3x - 4y > 7$$
$$3(3) - 4(-6) > 7$$
$$9 + 24 > 7$$
$$33 > 7, \text{ true}$$
$(3,-6)$ is a solution.

$$3x - 4y > 7$$
$$3(-2) - 4(-5) > 7$$
$$-6 + 20 > 7$$
$$14 > 7, \text{ true}$$
$(-2,-5)$ is a solution.

$$3x - 4y > 7$$
$$3(-3) - 4(4) > 7$$
$$-9 - 16 > 7$$
$$-25 > 7, \text{ false}$$
$(-3,4)$ is not a solution.

49. $x - 2y > 6$
Graph the equation $x - 2y = 6$ as a dashed line through $(6,0)$ and $(0, -3)$. Use $(0,0)$ as a test point. Since $0 - 2(0) > 6$ is false, shade the half-plane *not* containing $(0,0)$.

50. $4x - 6y \le 12$
Graph the equation $4x - 6y = 12$ as a solid line through $(3,0)$ and $(0, -2)$. Use $(0,0)$ as a test point. Since $4(0) - 6(0) \le 12$ is true, shade the half-plane containing $(0,0)$.

51. $y > 3x + 2$

Graph $y = 3x + 2$ as a dashed line using the slope and y-intercept. Use $(0,0)$ as a test point. Since $0 > 3(0) + 2$ is false, shade the half-plane *not* containing $(0,0)$.

52. $y \le \frac{1}{3}x - 1$

Graph $y = \frac{1}{3}x - 1$ as a solid line using slope and y-intercept. Use $(0,0)$ as a test point. Since $0 \le \frac{1}{3}(0) - 1$ is false, shade the half-plane *not* containing $(0,0)$.

53. $y < -\frac{1}{2}x$

Graph $y = -\frac{1}{2}x$ as a solid line using the slope and y-intercept. Since the line passes through the origin, a point other than $(0,0)$ must be chosen as the test point, for example $(4,4)$. Since $4 \le -\frac{1}{2}(4)$ is false, shade the half-plane not containing $(4,4)$.

54. $x < 4$

Graph the vertical line $x = 4$ as a dashed line. Use $(0,0)$ as a test point. Since $0 < 4$ is true, shade the half-plane containing $(0,0)$, which is the half-plane to the *left* of the line.

55. $y \ge -2$

Graph the horizontal line $y = -2$ as a solid line. Use $(0,0)$ as a test point. Since $0 \ge -2$ is true, shade the half-plane containing $(0,0)$, which is the half-plane *above* the line.

56. $x + 2y \le 0$

Graph $x + 2y = 0$ as a solid line through $(0,0)$ and $(2, -1)$. Since the line goes through the origin, choose another point as the test point, for example $(1,1)$.

Since $1 + 2(1) \le 0$ is false, shade the half-plane *not* containing $(1,1)$.

Chapter 4 Test

1.
$$4x - 2y = 10$$
$$4(0) - 2(-5) = 10$$
$$0 + 10 = 10$$
$$10 = 10, \text{ true}$$
$(0, -5)$ is a solution.

$$4x - 2y = 10$$
$$4(-2) - 2(1) = 10$$
$$-8 - 2 = 10$$
$$-10 = 10, \text{ false}$$
$(-2, 1)$ is not a solution.

$$4x - 2y = 10$$
$$4(4) - 2(3) = 10$$
$$16 - 6 = 10$$
$$10 = 10, \text{ true}$$
$(4, 3)$ is a solution.

2.

x	$y = 3x + 1$	(x, y)
-2	$y = 3(-2) + 1 = -5$	$(-2, -5)$
-1	$y = 3(-1) + 1 = -2$	$(-1, -2)$
0	$y = 3(0) + 1 = 1$	$(0, 1)$
1	$y = 3(1) + 1 = 4$	$(1, 4)$
2	$y = 3(2) + 1 = 7$	$(2, 7)$

3. a. The graph crosses the *x*-axis at (2,0), so the *x*-intercept is 2.

b. The graph crosses the *y*-axis at (0, −3), so the *y*-intercept is −3.

4. Find the *x*-intercept. Let $y = 0$ and solve for *x*.
$$4x - 2y = -8$$
$$4x - 2(0) = -8$$
$$4x = -8$$
$$x = -2$$
The *x*-intercept is −2.
Find the *y*-intercept. Let $x = 0$ and solve for *y*.
$$4x - 2y = -8$$
$$4(0) - 2y = -8$$
$$-2y = -8$$
$$y = 4$$
The *y*-intercept is 4.
Find a checkpoint. For example, let $x = -1$ and solve for *y*.
$$4x - 2y = -8$$
$$4(-1) - 2y = -8$$
$$-4 - 2y = -8$$
$$-2y = -4$$
$$y = 2$$
The checkpoint is (−1, 2).
Draw the line through these three points.

5. $y = 4$
The graph is a horizontal line.

6. $m = \dfrac{-2 - 4}{-5 - (-3)} = \dfrac{-6}{-2} = 3$

The slope is 3. Since the slope is positive, the line rises from left to right.

7. $m = \dfrac{3 - (-1)}{6 - 6} = \dfrac{4}{0}$; undefined

Since the slope is undefined, the line is vertical.

8. Use the points $(-1, -2)$ and $(1,1)$.

$$m = \frac{1-(-2)}{1-(-1)} = \frac{3}{2}$$

9. Line through $(-2,10)$ and $(0,2)$:

$$m = \frac{2-10}{0-(-2)} = \frac{-8}{2} = -4$$

Line through $(-8,-7)$ and $(24,1)$:

$$m = \frac{1-(-7)}{24-(-8)} = \frac{8}{32} = \frac{1}{4}$$

Since the product of their slopes is $-4\left(\dfrac{1}{4}\right) = -1$, the

lines are perpendicular.

10. Line through $(2,4)$ and $(6,1)$:

$$m = \frac{1-4}{6-2} = \frac{-3}{4} = -\frac{3}{4}$$

Line through $(-3,1)$ and $(1, -2)$:

$$m = \frac{-2-1}{1-(-3)} = \frac{-3}{4} = -\frac{3}{4}$$

Since the slopes are equal, the lines are parallel.

11. $y = -x + 10$

$y = -1x + 10$

The slope is the coefficient of x, which is -1. The y-intercept is the constant term, which is 10.

12. $2x + y = 6$

$y = -2x + 6$

$m = -2$; y-intercept = 6

13. $y = \dfrac{2}{3}x - 1$

slope = $\dfrac{2}{3}$; y-intercept = -1

Plot $(0, -1)$. From this point, move 2 units *up* and 3 units to the *right* to reach the point $(3,1)$.
Draw a line through $(0, -1)$ and $(3,1)$.

$y = \dfrac{2}{3}x - 1$

14. $y = -2x + 3$

slope $= -2 = \dfrac{-2}{1}$; y-intercept = 3

Plot $(0,3)$. Move 2 units *down* and 1 unit to the right to reach the point $(1,1)$. Draw a line through $(0,3)$ and $(1,1)$.

$y = -2x + 3$

15. point-slope form:

$y - y_1 = m(x - x_1)$

$y - 4 = -2\left[x - (-1)\right]$

$y - 4 = -2(x + 1)$

slope-intercept form:

$y - 4 = -2(x + 1)$

$y - 4 = -2x - 2$

$y = -2x + 2$

16. Passing through $(2,1)$ and $(-1, -8)$
First, find the slope.

$$m = \frac{-8-1}{-1-2} = \frac{-9}{-3} = 3$$

Next, use the slope and one of the points to write the equation of the line in point-slope form.

$y - y_1 = m(x - x_1)$

$y - 1 = 3(x - 2)$

Solve for y to obtain slope-intercept form.

$y - 1 = 3(x - 2)$

$y - 1 = 3x - 6$

$y = 3x - 5$

17. $3x - 2y < 6$

Graph the line $3x - 2y = 6$ as a dashed line through $(2,0)$ and $(0, -3)$. Use $(0,0)$ as a test point. Since $3(0) - 2(0) < 6$ is true, shade the half-plane containing $(0,0)$.

$3x - 2y < 6$

18. $y \geq 2x - 2$

Graph the line $y = 2x - 2$ as a solid line using the slope and y-intercept. Use (0,0) as a test point. Since $0 \geq 2(0) - 2$ is true, shade the half-plane containing (0,0).

$y \geq 2x - 2$

19. $x > -1$

Graph the vertical line $x = -1$ as a dashed line. Use (0,0) as a test point. Since $0 > -1$ is true, shade the half-plane containing (0,0), which is the half-plane to the *right* of the line.

$x > -1$

20. a. $m = \dfrac{1616 - 886}{2006 - 2002} = \dfrac{730}{4} = 182.5$

b. For the period shown, corporate profits increased each year by approximately $\underline{\$182.5}$ $\underline{\text{billion}}$. The rate of change was $\underline{\$182.5 \text{ billion}}$ per $\underline{\text{year}}$.

Cumulative Review (Chapters 1-4)

1. $\dfrac{10 - (-6)}{3^2 - (4 - 3)} = \dfrac{10 + 6}{9 - 1} = \dfrac{16}{8} = 2$

2. $6 - 2\big[3(x - 1) + 4\big]$

$= 6 - 2(3x - 3 + 4) = 6 - 2(3x + 1)$

$= 6 - 6x - 2 = 4 - 6x$

3. The only irrational number in the given set is $\sqrt{5}$.

4. $6(2x - 1) - 6 = 11x + 7$

$12x - 6 - 6 = 11x + 7$

$12x - 12 = 11x + 7$

$x - 12 = 7$

$x = 19$

The solution set is $\{19\}$.

5. $x - \dfrac{3}{4} = \dfrac{1}{2}$

$x - \dfrac{3}{4} + \dfrac{3}{4} = \dfrac{1}{2} + \dfrac{3}{4}$

$x = \dfrac{2}{4} + \dfrac{3}{4} = \dfrac{5}{4}$

The solution set is $\left\{\dfrac{5}{4}\right\}$.

6. $y = mx + b$

$y - b = mx + b - b$

$y - b = mx$

$\dfrac{y - b}{m} = \dfrac{mx}{m}$

$\dfrac{y - b}{m} = x$ or $x = \dfrac{y - b}{m}$

7. $A = 120; P = 15\% = 0.15$

$A = PB$

$120 = 0.15 \cdot B$

$\dfrac{120}{0.15} = \dfrac{0.15B}{0.15}$

$800 = B$

120 is 15% of 800.

8. $y = 4.5x - 46.7$

$133.3 = 4.5x - 46.7$

$133.3 + 46.7 = 4.5x - 46.7 + 46.7$

$180 = 4.5x$

$\dfrac{180}{4.5} = \dfrac{4.5x}{4.5}$

$40 = x$

The car is traveling 40 miles per hour.

9.
$$2 - 6x \geq 2(5 - x)$$
$$2 - 6x \geq 10 - 2x$$
$$2 - 6x + 2x \geq 10 - 2x + 2x$$
$$2 - 4x \geq 10$$
$$2 - 4x - 2 \geq 10 - 2$$
$$-4x \geq 8$$
$$\frac{-4x}{-4} \leq \frac{8}{-4}$$
$$x \leq -2$$
$$(-\infty, -2]$$

10.
$$6(2 - x) > 12$$
$$12 - 6x > 12$$
$$12 - 6x - 12 > 12 - 12$$
$$-6x > 0$$
$$\frac{-6x}{-6} < \frac{0}{-6}$$
$$x < 0$$
$$(-\infty, 0)$$

11. Let x = the number of hours the plumber worked.
$$18 + 35x = 228$$
$$35x = 210$$
$$x = 6$$
The plumber worked 6 hours.

12.

	Liters	× Percent of Acid	= Amount of Acid
40% Acid Solution	x	0.40	$0.40(x)$
70% Acid Solution	$12 - x$	0.70	$0.70(12 - x)$
50% Acid Mixture	12	0.50	$0.50(12)$

$$0.40x + 0.70(12 - x) = 0.50(12)$$
$$0.40x + 8.4 - 0.70x = 6$$
$$-0.30x + 8.4 = 6$$
$$-0.30x + 8.4 - 8.4 = 6 - 8.4$$
$$-0.30x = -2.4$$
$$x = 8$$

To obtain 12 liters of a 50% acid solution, 8 liters of a 40% solution and $12 - 8 = 4$ liters of a 70% solution should be used.

13.

	Rate	×	Time	=	Distance
Slower Car	40		x		$40x$
Faster Car	60		x		$60x$

$$40x + 60x = 350$$
$$100x = 350$$
$$x = 3.5$$

The cars will be 350 miles apart after 3.5 hours.

14. Let x = the measure of the first angle.
Let $x + 20$ = the measure of the second angle.
Let $2x$ = the measure of third angle.

$$x + (x + 20) + 2x = 180$$
$$4x + 20 = 180$$
$$4x = 160$$
$$x = 40$$

The angles measure $x = 40°$, $x + 20 = 60°$, and $2x = 80°$.

15.
$$\frac{45}{2} = \frac{360}{x}$$
$$45x = 2 \cdot 360$$
$$45x = 720$$
$$\frac{45x}{45} = \frac{720}{45}$$
$$x = 16$$

The solution set is $\{16\}$.

16. *x*-intercept:
$$2x - y = 4$$
$$2x - 0 = 4$$
$$2x = 4$$
$$x = 2$$

y-intercept :
$$2x - y = 4$$
$$2(0) - y = 4$$
$$-y = 4$$
$$y = -4$$

checkpoint:
$$2x - y = 4$$
$$2(1) - y = 4$$
$$2 - y = 4$$
$$-y = 2$$
$$y = -2$$

Draw a line through (2,0), (0, −4), and (1,−2.)

17. $x = -5$
The graph is a vertical line.

18. $y = -4x + 3$

slope $= -4 = \dfrac{-4}{1}$; *y*-intercept = 3

Plot (0,3). Move 4 units *down* and 1 unit to the *right* to reach the point
$(1, -1)$. Draw a line through (0,3) and (1, −1).

19. $3x - 2y < -6$

Graph the equation $3x - 2y = -6$ as a dashed line through $(-2,0)$ and $(0,3)$.

Use $(0,0)$ as a test point. Since $3(0) - 2(0) < -6$ is false, shade the half-plane not containing $(0,0)$.

20. $y \geq -1$

Graph the horizontal line $y = -1$ as a solid line. Use $(0,0)$ as a test point. Since $0 \geq -1$ is true, shade the half-plane containing $(0,0)$.

Chapter 5
Systems of Linear Equations and Inequalities

1. **a.** To determine if $(1,2)$ is a solution to the system, replace x with 1 and y with 2 in both equations.
$$2x - 3y = -4$$
$$2(1) - 3(2) = -4$$
$$2 - 6 = -4$$
$$-4 = -4, \text{ true}$$
$$2x + y = 4$$
$$2(1) + 2 = 4$$
$$2 + 2 = 4$$
$$4 = 4, \text{ true}$$
The ordered pair satisfies both equations, so it is a solution to the system.

   b. To determine if $(7,6)$ is a solution to the system, replace x with 7 and y with 6 in both equations.
$$2x - 3y = -4$$
$$2(7) - 3(6) = -4$$
$$14 - 18 = -4$$
$$-4 = -4, \text{ true}$$
$$2x + y = 4$$
$$2(7) + 6 = 4$$
$$14 + 6 = 4$$
$$20 = 4, \text{ false}$$
The ordered pair does not satisfy both equations, so it is not a solution to the system.

2. Graph $2x + y = 6$ by using intercepts.
x-intercept (Set $y = 0$.)
$$2x + y = 6$$
$$2x + 0 = 6$$
$$2x = 6$$
$$x = 3$$
y-intercept (Set $x = 0$.)
$$2x + y = 6$$
$$2(0) + y = 6$$
$$0 + y = 6$$
$$y = 6$$
Graph $2x - y = -2$ by using intercepts.
x-intercept (Set $y = 0$.)
$$2x - y = -2$$
$$2x - 0 = -2$$
$$2x = -2$$
$$x = -1$$

y-intercept (Set $x = 0$.)
$$2x - y = -2$$
$$2(0) - y = -2$$
$$-y = -2$$
$$y = 2$$

The lines intersect at $(1,4)$.
The solution set is $\{(1,4)\}$.

3. Graph $y = -x + 6$ by using the y-intercept of 6 and the slope of -1.
Graph $y = 3x - 6$ by using the y-intercept of -6 and the slope of 3.

The lines intersect at $(3,3)$.
The solution set is $\{(3,3)\}$.

4. Graph $y = 3x - 2$ by using the y-intercept of -2 and the slope of 3.
Graph $y = 3x + 1$ by using the y-intercept of 1 and the slope of 3.

Because both equations have the same slope, 3, but different y-intercepts, the lines are parallel. Thus, the system is inconsistent and has no solution. The solution set is the empty set, $\{\ \}$.

5. Graph $x + y = 3$ by using intercepts.

x-intercept (Set $y = 0.$)

$$x + y = 3$$
$$x + 0 = 3$$
$$x = 3$$

y-intercept (Set $x = 0.$)

$$x + y = 3$$
$$0 + y = 3$$
$$y = 3$$

Graph $2x + 2y = 6$ by using intercepts.

x-intercept (Set $y = 0.$)

$$2x + 2y = 6$$
$$2x + 2(0) = 6$$
$$2x = 6$$
$$x = 3$$

y-intercept (Set $x = 0.$)

$$2x + 2y = 6$$
$$2(0) + 2y = 6$$
$$2y = 6$$
$$y = 3$$

Both lines have the same x-intercept and the same y-intercept. Thus, the graphs of the two equations in the system are the same line.

Any ordered pair that is a solution to one equation is a solution to the other, and, consequently, a solution of the system. The system has an infinite number of solutions, namely all points that are solutions of either line.

The solution set is $\{(x, y) | x + y = 3\}$.

6. a. Graph $y = 2x$ by using the y-intercept of 0 and the slope of 2.

Graph $y = x + 10$ by using the y-intercept of 10 and the slope of 1.

The solution is the ordered pair (10,20).

b. If the bridge is used 10 times in a month, the total monthly cost without the coupon book is the same as the monthly cost with the coupon book, namely $20.

5.1 Exercise Set

1. To determine if $(2, -3)$ is a solution to the system, replace x with 2 and y with -3 in both equations.

$$2x + 3y = -5$$
$$2(2) + 3(-3) = -5$$
$$4 + (-9) = -5$$
$$-5 = -5, \text{ true}$$

$$7x - 3y = 23$$
$$7(2) - 3(-3) = 23$$
$$14 + 9 = 23$$
$$23 = 23, \text{ true}$$

The ordered pair satisfies both equations, so it is a solution to the system.

3.
$$x + 3y = 1$$
$$\frac{2}{3} + 3\left(\frac{1}{9}\right) = 1$$
$$\frac{2}{3} + \frac{1}{3} = 1$$
$$1 = 1, \text{ true}$$

$$4x + 3y = 3$$
$$4\left(\frac{2}{3}\right) + 3\left(\frac{1}{9}\right) = 3$$
$$\frac{8}{3} + \frac{1}{3} = 3$$
$$\frac{9}{3} = 3$$
$$3 = 3, \text{ true}$$

The ordered pair satisfies both equations, so it is a solution to the system.

5.

$$5x + 3y = 2$$
$$5(-5) + 3(9) = 2$$
$$-25 + 27 = 2$$
$$2 = 2, \text{ true}$$

$$x + 4y = 14$$
$$-5 + 4(9) = 14$$
$$-5 + 36 = 14$$
$$31 = 14, \text{ false}$$

The ordered pair does not satisfy both equations, so it is not a solution to the system.

7.

$$x - 2y = 500$$
$$1400 - 2(450) = 500$$
$$1400 - 900 = 500$$
$$500 = 500, \text{ true}$$

$$0.03x + 0.02y = 51$$
$$0.03(1400) + 0.02(450) = 51$$
$$42 + 9 = 51$$
$$51 = 51, \text{ true}$$

The ordered pair satisfies both equations, so the ordered pair is a solution to the system.

9.

$$5x - 4y = 20$$
$$5(8) - 4(5) = 20$$
$$40 - 20 = 20$$
$$20 = 20, \text{ true}$$

$$3y = 2x + 1$$
$$3(5) = 2(8) + 1$$
$$15 = 16 + 1$$
$$15 = 17, \text{ false}$$

The ordered pair does not satisfy both equations, so it is not a solution to the system.

11. Graph both equations on the same axes.
$x + y = 6$:

x-intercept = 6; y-intercept = 6
$x - y = 2$:

x-intercept = 2; y-intercept = -2

The solution set is $\{(4, 2)\}$.

13. Graph both equations on the same axes.
$x + y = 1$:

x-intercept = 1; y-intercept = 1
$y - x = 3$:

x-intercept = -3; y-intercept = 3

The solution set is $\{(-1, 2)\}$.

15. Graph both equations.
$2x - 3y = 6$:

x-intercept = 3; y-intercept = -2
$4x + 3y = 12$:

x-intercept = 3; y-intercept = 4

The solution set is $\{(3, 0)\}$.

17. Graph both equations.

$4x + y = 4$:

x-intercept = 1: y-intercept = 4

$3x - y = 3$:

x-intercept = 1: y-intercept = −3

The solution set is $\{(1,0)\}$.

19. Graph both equations.

$y = x + 5$:

Slope = 1; y-intercept = 5

$y = -x + 3$:

Slope = −1; y-intercept = 3

The solution set is $\{(-1,4)\}$.

21. Graph both equations.

$y = 2x$:

slope = 2; y-intercept = 0

$y = -x + 6$:

slope = −1; y-intercept = 6

The solution set is $\{(2,4)\}$.

23. Graph both equations.

$y = -2x + 3$:

slope = −2; y-intercept = 3

$y = -x + 1$:

slope = −1; y-intercept = 1

The solution set is $\{(2,-1)\}$.

25. Graph both equations.

$y = 2x - 1$:

Slope = 2; y-intercept = −1

$y = 2x + 1$:

Slope = 2; y-intercept = 1

The lines are parallel, so the solution set is $\{\ \}$.

27. Graph each equation.

$x + y = 4$:

x-intercept = 4; y-intercept = 4

$x = -2$:

vertical line with x-intercept −2

The solution set is $\{(-2,6)\}$.

29. Graph each equation.

$x - 2y = 4$:

x-intercept = 4; y-intercept = -2

$2x - 4y = 8$:

x-intercept = 4; y-intercept = -2

The graph of the two equations are the same line. (Note that they have the same slope and same y-intercept.) Because the lines coincide, the system has an infinite number of solutions. The solution set is $\{(x,y)|x-2y=4\}$ or $\{(x,y)|2x-4y=8\}$.

31. Graph both lines.

$y = 2x - 1$:

slope = 2; y-intercept = -1

$x - 2y = -4$:

x-intercept = -4; y-intercept = 2

The solution set is $\{(2,3)\}$.

33. Graph both lines.

$x + y = 5$:

x-intercept = 5; y-intercept = 5

$2x + 2y = 12$:

x-intercept = 6; y-intercept = 6

The lines are parallel, so the solution set is $\{\ \}$.

35. $x - y = 0$

$y = x$

Because the lines coincide, the system has an infinite number of solutions. The solution set is $\{(x,y)|x-y=0\}$ or $\{(x,y)|y=x\}$.

37. $x = 2$

$y = 4$

The solution set is $\{(2,4)\}$.

39. $x = 2$

$x = -1$

The two vertical lines are parallel, so the solution set is $\{\ \}$.

41. $y = 0$

$y = 4$

The two horizontal lines are parallel, so the solution set is $\{\ \}$.

43. $y = \frac{1}{2}x - 3$:

slope = $\frac{1}{2}$, y-intercept = -3

$y = \frac{1}{2}x - 5$:

slope = $\frac{1}{2}$, y-intercept = -5

Since the slopes are the same, but the y-intercepts are different, the lines are parallel and there is no solution.

45. $y = -\frac{1}{2}x + 4$

slope = $-\frac{1}{2}$, y-intercept = 4

$3x - y = -4$

$-y = -3x - 4$

$y = 3x + 4$

slope = 3, y-intercept = 4
Since the lines have different slopes, there will be one solution.

47. $3x - y = 6$

$-y = -3x + 6$

$y = 3x - 6$

slope = 3, y-intercept = -6

$x = \frac{y}{3} + 2$

$3x = y + 6$

$3x - 6 = y$

$y = 3x - 6$

slope = 3, y-intercept = -6
Since the lines have the same slopes and y-intercepts, the graphs will coincide and there are an infinite number of solutions.

49. $3x + y = 0$

$y = -3x$

slope = -3, y-intercept = 0
$y = -3x + 1$

slope = -3, y-intercept = 1
Since the slopes are the same, but the y-intercepts are different, the lines are parallel and there is no solution.

51. a. The x-coordinate of the intersection point is 40. Both companies charge the same for 40 miles driven.

b. The y-coordinate of the intersection point is about 55.

c. $y = 0.35x + 40$

$y = 0.35(40) + 40 = 54$

$y = 0.45x + 36$

$y = 0.45(40) + 36 = 54$

Both companies charge $54 for 40 miles driven.

53. a. The solution is the ordered pair (5,20).

b. Nonmembers and members pay the same amount per month for taking 5 classes, namely $20.

55. – 61. Answers will vary.

63. does not make sense; Explanations will vary. Sample explanation: Some linear systems have no solutions or one solution.

65. makes sense

67. false; Changes to make the statement true will vary. A sample change is: The system's lines could have different slopes.

69. false; Changes to make the statement true will vary. A sample change is: The two lines of a linear system that has one solution must have different slopes.

71. Answers will vary.

73. $y = 2x + 2$

$y = -2x + 6$

The solution set is $\{(1,4)\}$.

75. $x + 2y = 2$

$x - y = 2$

In order to enter the equations into a graphing calculator, each of them must be solved for y.

$x + 2y = 2$

$2y = -x + 2$

$\dfrac{2y}{2} = \dfrac{-x+2}{2}$

$y = -\dfrac{1}{2}x + 1$

$x - y = 2$

$-y = -x + 2$

$y = x - 2$

 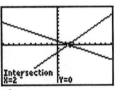

The solution set is $\{(2,0)\}$.

77. $3x - y = 5$

$-5x + 2y = -10$

Solve each equation for y.

$3x - y = 5$

$-y = -3x + 5$

$y = 3x - 5$

$-5x + 2y = -10$

$2y = 5x - 10$

$y = \dfrac{5}{2}x - 5$

The solution set is $\{(0,-5)\}$.

79. $y = \dfrac{1}{3}x + \dfrac{2}{3}$

$y = \dfrac{5}{7}x - 2$

The solution set is $\{(7,3)\}$.

81. $-3 + (-9) = -3 - 9 = -12$

82. $-3 - (-9) = -3 + 9 = 6$

83. $-3(-9) = 27$

84. $4x - 3(-x - 1) = 24$

$4x + 3x + 3 = 24$

$7x + 3 = 24$

$7x = 21$

$x = 3$

The solution set is $\{3\}$.

85. $5(2y - 3) - 4y = 9$

$10y - 15 - 4y = 9$

$6y - 15 = 9$

$6y = 24$

$y = 4$

The solution set is $\{4\}$.

86. $(5x - 1) + 1 = 5x + 5$

$5x - 1 + 1 = 5x + 5$

$5x = 5x + 5$

$0 = 5$

The solution set is $\{\ \}$.

5.2 Check Points

1.
$$y = 5x - 13$$
$$2x + 3y = 12$$
Substitute $5x - 13$ for y in the second equation.
$$2x + 3(5x - 13) = 12$$
$$2x + 15x - 39 = 12$$
$$17x - 39 = 12$$
$$17x = 51$$
$$x = 3$$
Back substitute 3 for x into the first equation.
$$y = 5x - 13$$
$$y = 5(3) - 13 = 2$$
The solution set is $\{(3, 2)\}$.

2. $3x + 2y = -1$
$\quad x - y = 3$
Solve the second equation for x.
$$x - y = 3$$
$$x = y + 3$$
Substitute $y + 3$ for x in the first equation.
$$3x + 2y = -1$$
$$3(y + 3) + 2y = -1$$
$$3y + 9 + 2y = -1$$
$$5y + 9 = -1$$
$$5y = -10$$
$$y = -2$$
Back substitute –2 for y into $x = y + 3$.
$$x = y + 3$$
$$x = -2 + 3 = 1$$
The solution set is $\{(1, -2)\}$.

3. $3x + y = -5$
$\quad y = -3x + 3$
Substitute $-3x + 3$ for y in the first equation.
$$3x + y = -5$$
$$3x + \overbrace{(-3x + 3)}^{y} = -5$$
$$3x - 3x + 3 = -5$$
$$3 = -5, \text{ false}$$
The false statement indicates that the system is inconsistent and has no solution.
The solution set is $\{\ \}$.

4.
$$y = 3x - 4$$
$$9x - 3y = 12$$
Substitute $3x - 4$ for y in the second equation.
$$9x - 3y = 12$$
$$9x - 3\overbrace{(3x - 4)}^{y} = 12$$
$$9x - 3(3x - 4) = 12$$
$$9x - 9x + 12 = 12$$
$$12 = 12, \text{ true}$$
The true statement indicates that the system contains dependent equations and has infinitely many solutions.
The solution set is $\{(x, y) | y = 3x - 4\}$.

5. a. $p = -30x + 1800$
$\quad p = 30x$
Substitute $30x$ for p in the first equation.
$$p = -30x + 1800$$
$$\overbrace{30x}^{p} = -30x + 1800$$
$$60x = 1800$$
$$x = 30$$
Back-substitute to find p.
$$p = 30x$$
$$p = 30(30) = 900$$
The solution set is $\{(30, 900)\}$.

Equilibrium quantity: 30,000
Equilibrium price: $900

b. When rents are $\underline{\$900}$ per month, consumers will demand $\underline{30,000}$ apartments and suppliers will offer $\underline{30,000}$ apartments for rent.

5.2 Exercise Set

1. $x + y = 4$
$\quad y = 3x$
Substitute $3x$ for y in the first equation.
$$x + y = 4$$
$$x + (3x) = 4$$
Solve this equation for x.
$$4x = 4$$
$$x = 1$$
Back substitute 1 for x into the second equation.
$$y = 3x$$
$$y = 3(1) = 3$$
The solution set is $\{(1, 3)\}$.

3. $x + 3y = 8$

   $y = 2x - 9$

   Substitute $2x - 9$ for y in the first equation and solve for x.

   $$x + 3y = 8$$
   $$x + 3(2x - 9) = 8$$
   $$x + 6x - 27 = 8$$
   $$7x - 27 = 8$$
   $$7x = 35$$
   $$x = 5$$

   Back-substitute 5 for x into the second equation and solve for y.

   $$y = 2x - 9$$
   $$y = 2(5) - 9 = 1$$

   The solution set is $\{5, 1\}$.

5. $x + 3y = 5$

   $4x + 5y = 13$

   Solve the first equation for x.

   $$x + 3y = 5$$
   $$x = 5 - 3y$$

   Substitute $5 - 3y$ for x in the second equation and solve for y.

   $$4x + 5y = 13$$
   $$4(5 - 3y) + 5y = 13$$
   $$20 - 12y + 5y = 13$$
   $$20 - 7y = 13$$
   $$-7y = -7$$
   $$y = 1$$

   Back-substitute 1 for y in the equation $x = 5 - 3y$ and solve for x.

   $$x = 5 - 3y$$
   $$x = 5 - 3(1) = 2$$

   The solution set is $\{(2, 1)\}$.

7. $2x - y = -5$

   $x + 5y = 14$

   Solve the second equation for x.

   $$x + 5y = 14$$
   $$x = 14 - 5y$$

   Substitute $14 - 5y$ for x in the first equation.

   $$2(14 - 5y) - y = -5$$
   $$28 - 10y - y = -5$$
   $$28 - 11y = -5$$
   $$-11y = -33$$
   $$y = 3$$

   Back-substitute.

   $$x = 14 - 5y$$
   $$x = 14 - 5(3) = 14 - 15 = -1$$

   The solution set is $\{(-1, 3)\}$.

9. $2x - y = 3$

   $5x - 2y = 10$

   Solve the first equation for y.

   $$2x - y = 3$$
   $$-y = -2x + 3$$
   $$y = 2x - 3$$

   Substitute $2x - 3$ for y in the second equation.

   $$5x - 2(2x - 3) = 10$$
   $$5x - 4x + 6 = 10$$
   $$x + 6 = 10$$
   $$x = 4$$

   Back-substitute.

   $$y = 2x - 3$$
   $$y = 2(4) - 3 = 8 - 3 = 5$$

   The solution set is $\{(4, 5)\}$.

11. $-3x + y = -1$

$x - 2y = 4$

Solve the second equation for x.

$x - 2y = 4$

$x = 2y + 4$

Substitute $2y + 4$ for x in the first equation.

$-3x + y = -1$

$-3(2y + 4) + y = -1$

$-6y - 12 + y = -1$

$-5y - 12 = -1$

$-5y = 11$

$y = -\dfrac{11}{5}$

Back-substitute.

$x = 2y + 4$

$x = 2\left(-\dfrac{11}{5}\right) + 4$

$x = -\dfrac{22}{5} + 4$

$x = -\dfrac{22}{5} + \dfrac{20}{5}$

$x = -\dfrac{2}{5}$

The solution set is $\left\{\left(-\dfrac{2}{5}, -\dfrac{11}{5}\right)\right\}$.

13. $x = 9 - 2y$

$x + 2y = 13$

The first equation is already solved for x.

Substitute $9 - 2y$ for x in the second equation.

$x + 2y = 13$

$(9 - 2y) + 2y = 13$

$9 = 13,$ false

The false statement $9 = 13$ indicates that the system is inconsistent and has no solution.

The solution set is $\{\ \}$.

15. $y = 3x - 5$

$21x - 35 = 7y$

Substitute $3x-5$ for y in the second equation.

$21x - 35 = 7y$

$21x - 35 = 7(3x - 5)$

$21x - 35 = 21x - 35$

$-35 = -35,$ true

The true statement $-35 = -35$ indicates that the system contains dependent equations and has an infinite number of solutions.

The solution set is $\{(x, y) | y = 3x - 5\}$.

17. $5x + 2y = 0$

$x - 3y = 0$

Solve the second equation for x.

$x - 3y = 0$

$x = 3y$

Substitute $3y$ for x in the first equation.

$5x + 2y = 0$

$5(3y) + 2y = 0$

$15y + 2y = 0$

$17y = 0$

$y = 0$

Back-substitute to find x.

$x = 3y$

$x = 3(0) = 0$

The solution set is $\{(0, 0)\}$.

19. $2x - y = 6$

$3x + 2y = 5$

Solve the first equation for y.

$2x - y = 6$

$-y = -2x + 6$

$y = 2x - 6$

Substitute $2x - 6$ for y in the second equation.

$3x + 2y = 5$

$3x + 2(2x - 6) = 5$

$3x + 4x - 12 = 5$

$7x - 12 = 5$

$7x = 17$

$x = \dfrac{17}{7}$

Back-substitute to find y.

$y = 2x - 6 = 2\left(\dfrac{17}{7}\right) - 6 = -\dfrac{8}{7}$

The solution set is $\left\{\left(\dfrac{17}{7}, -\dfrac{8}{7}\right)\right\}$.

21. $2(x - 1) - y = -3$

$y = 2x + 3$

Substitute $2x + 3$ for y in the first equation.

$2(x - 1) - (2x + 3) = -3$

$2x - 2 - 2x - 3 = -3$

$-5 = -3, \text{ false}$

The false statement $-5 = -5$ indicates that the system has no solution.

The solution set is $\{\ \}$.

23. $x = 2y + 9$

$x = 7y + 10$

Substitute $7y + 10$ for x in the first equation.

$x = 2y + 9$

$7y + 10 = 2y + 9$

$5y + 10 = 9$

$5y = -1$

$y = -\dfrac{1}{5}$

Back-substitute to find x.

$x = 2y + 9 = 2\left(-\dfrac{1}{5}\right) + 9$

$= -\dfrac{2}{5} + 9 = -\dfrac{2}{5} + \dfrac{45}{5} = \dfrac{43}{5}$

The solution set is $\left\{\left(\dfrac{43}{5}, -\dfrac{1}{5}\right)\right\}$.

25. $4x - y = 100$

$0.05x - 0.06y = -32$

Solve the first equation for y.

$4x - y = 100$

$-y = -4x + 100$

$y = 4x - 100$

Substitute $4x - 100$ for y in the second equation.

$0.05x - 0.06y = -32$

$0.05x - 0.06(4x - 100) = -32$

$0.05x - 0.24x + 6 = -32$

$-0.19x + 6 = -32$

$-0.19x = -38$

$x = 200$

Back-substitute to find y.

$y = 4x - 100$

$= 4(200) - 100$

$= 800 - 100 = 700$

$\left(-\dfrac{44}{3}, -\dfrac{7}{3}\right)$

The solution set is $\{(200, 700)\}$.

27. $y = \dfrac{1}{3}x + \dfrac{2}{3}$

$y = \dfrac{5}{7}x - 2$

First, clear both equations of fractions. Multiply the first equation by the LCD, 3.

$$3y = 3\left(\dfrac{1}{3}x + \dfrac{2}{3}\right)$$

$$3y = 3x + 2$$

Multiply the second equation by the LCD, 7.

$$7y = 7\left(\dfrac{5}{7}x - 2\right)$$

$$7y = 5x - 14$$

Now solve the new system

$3y = x + 2$

$7y = 5x - 14$

Solve the first of these equations for x.

$3y = x + 2$

$3y - 2 = x$

Substitute $3y - 2$ for x in the second equation of the new system.

$7y = 5x - 14$

$7y = 5(3y - 2) - 14$

$7y = 15y - 10 - 14$

$7y = 15y - 24$

$-8y = -24$

$y = 3$

Back-substitute to find x.

$x = 3y - 2$

$x = 3(3) - 2 = 9 - 2 = 7$

The solution set is $\{(7, 3)\}$.

29. $\dfrac{x}{6} - \dfrac{y}{2} = \dfrac{1}{3}$

$x + 2y = -3$

Clear the first equation of fractions by multiplying 6.

$$6\left(\dfrac{x}{6} - \dfrac{y}{2}\right) = 6\left(\dfrac{1}{3}\right)$$

$$x - 3y = 2$$

Solve this equation for x.

$x = 3y + 2$

Substitute $3y + 2$ for x in the second equation of the system.

$(3y + 2) + 2y = -3$

$5y + 2 = -3$

$5y = -5$

$y = -1$

Back-substitute to find x.

$x = 3y + 2 = 3(-1) + 2 = -1$

The solution set is $\{(-1, -1)\}$.

31. $2x - 3y = 8 - 2x$

$3x + 4y = x + 3y + 14$

Simplify the first equation.

$2x - 3y = 8 - 2x$

$2x - 3y + 2x = 8 - 2x + 2x$

$4x - 3y = 8$

Simplify the second equation.

$3x + 4y = x + 3y + 14$

$3x + 4y - x - 3y = x + 3y + 14 - x - 3y$

$2x + y = 14$

Solve the last equation for y.

$2x + y = 14$

$y = 14 - 2x$

Substitute $14 - 2x$ for y in the equation $4x - 3y = 8$.

$4x - 3y = 8$

$4x - 3(14 - 2x) = 8$

$4x - 42 + 6x = 8$

$10x - 42 = 8$

$10x = 50$

$x = 5$

Back-substitute to find y.

$y = 14 - 2x$

$y = 14 - 2(5) = 4$

The solution set is $\{(5, 4)\}$.

33. $x + y = 81$

$x = y + 41$

Substitute $y + 41$ for x in the first equation.

$x + y = 81$

$(y + 41) + y = 81$

$y + 41 + y = 81$

$2y + 41 = 81$

$2y = 40$

$y = 20$

Back-substitute.

$x = y + 41 = 20 + 41 = 61$

The numbers are 20 and 61.

35. $x - y = 5$

$\qquad 4x = 6y$

Solve the first equation for x.

$x - y = 5$

$\qquad x = y + 5$

Substitute $y + 5$ for x in the second equation.

$\qquad 4x = 6y$

$4(y + 5) = 6y$

$\quad 4y + 20 = 6y$

$\qquad 20 = 2y$

$\qquad 10 = y$

Back-substitute.

$x = y + 5 = 10 + 5 = 15$

The numbers are 10 and 15.

37. $x - y = 1$

$\quad x + 2y = 7$

Solve the first equation for x.

$x - y = 1$

$\qquad x = y + 1$

Substitute $y + 1$ for x in the second equation.

$\qquad x + 2y = 7$

$(y + 1) + 2y = 7$

$\quad y + 1 + 2y = 7$

$\qquad 3y + 1 = 7$

$\qquad\quad 3y = 6$

$\qquad\quad y = 2$

Back-substitute.

$x = y + 1 = 2 + 1 = 3$

The numbers are 2 and 3.

39. $0.7x - 0.1y = 0.6$

$\quad 0.8x - 0.3y = -0.8$

Multiply both sides of both equations by 10.

$7x - y = 6$

$8x - 3y = -8$

Solve the first equation for y.

$7x - y = 6$

$\quad 7x = 6 + y$

$7x - 6 = y$

Substitute $7x - 6$ for y in the second equation.

$8x - 3y = -8$

$8x - 3(7x - 6) = -8$

$\quad 8x - 21x + 18 = -8$

$\qquad -13x + 18 = -8$

$\qquad\quad -13x = -26$

$\qquad\qquad x = 2$

Back-substitute.

$y = 7x - 6 = 7(2) - 6 = 14 - 6 = 8$

The solution set is $\{(2,8)\}$.

41. a. Substitute $0.375x + 3$ for p in the first equation.

$$p = -0.325x + 5.8$$

$$\overbrace{0.375x + 3}^{p} = -0.325x + 5.8$$

$$0.375x + 3 = -0.325x + 5.8$$

$$0.375x + 0.325x + 3 = -0.325x + 0.325x + 5.8$$

$$0.7x + 3 = 5.8$$

$$0.7x + 3 - 3 = 5.8 - 3$$

$$0.7x = 2.8$$

$$\frac{0.7x}{0.7} = \frac{2.8}{0.7}$$

$$x = 4$$

Back-substitute to find p.

$p = -0.325x + 5.8$

$p = -0.325(4) + 5.8 = 4.5$

The ordered pair is (4,4.5).
Equilibrium number of workers: 4 million
Equilibrium hourly wage: $4.50

b. If workers are paid $4.50 per hour, there will be 4 million available workers and 4 million workers will be hired. In this state of market equilibrium, there is no unemployment.

c. $\qquad p = -0.325x + 5.8$

$\quad 5.15 = -0.325x + 5.8$

$\quad 0.65 = -0.325x$

$$\frac{-0.65}{-0.325} = \frac{-0.325x}{-0.325}$$

$\qquad 2 = x$

At $5.15 per hour, 2 million workers will be hired.

d. $p = 0.375x + 3$

$5.15 = 0.375x + 3$

$2.15 = 0.375x$

$\dfrac{2.15}{0.375} = \dfrac{0.375x}{0.375}$

$x \approx 5.7$

At \$5.15 per hour, there will be about 5.7 million available workers.

e. $5.7 - 2 = 3.7$

At \$5.15 per hour, there will be about 3.7 million more people looking for work than employers are willing to hire.

43. – 47.   Answers will vary.

49. does not make sense; Explanations will vary. Sample explanation: Solving for x in the second equation will allow us to avoid fractions.

51. does not make sense; Explanations will vary. Sample explanation: Equilibrium is the point at which demand is equal to supply.

53. true

55. false; Changes to make the statement true will vary. A sample change is: Replace y in the second equation with $2x - 5$.

57. $y = mx + 3$

$5x - 2y = 7$

Start by writing the second equation in slope-intercept form.

$5x - 2y = 7$

$-2y = -5x + 7$

$y = \dfrac{5}{2}x - \dfrac{7}{2}$

The system will be inconsistent if the graphs of the two equations have the same slope and different y-intercepts. The y-intercepts are different. Therefore, the system will be inconsistent if $m = \dfrac{5}{2}$.

58. $4x + 6y = 12$

x-intercept:

$4x + 6y = 12$

$4x + 6(0) = 12$

$4x = 12$

$x = 3$

y-intercept:

$4x + 6y = 12$

$4(0) + 6y = 12$

$6y = 12$

$y = 2$

Checkpoint:

$4x + 6y = 12$

$4(-3) + 6y = 12$

$-12 + 6y = 12$

$6y = 24$

$y = 4$

Draw a line through (3,0), (0, 2), and (−3, 4).

59. $4(x + 1) = 25 + 3(x - 3)$

$4x + 4 = 25 + 3x - 9$

$x + 4 = 16$

$x = 12$

The solution set is $\{12\}$.

60. The integers in the given set are −73, 0, and $\dfrac{3}{1} = 3$.

61.
$$3x + 2y = 48$$
$$3x + 2(12) = 48$$
$$3x + 24 = 48$$
$$3x = 24$$
$$x = 8$$

$$9x - 8y = -24$$
$$9x - 8(12) = -24$$
$$9x - 96 = -24$$
$$9x = 72$$
$$x = 8$$

The same value of x is obtained in both equations, so (8,12) is the solution.

62. $-14y = -168$
$$\frac{-14y}{-14} = \frac{-168}{-14}$$
$$y = 12$$
The solution set is $\{12\}$.

63.
$$x - 5y = 3$$
$$-4(x - 5y) = -4(3)$$
$$-4x + 20y = -12$$

5.3 Check Points

1. $x + y = 5$
$x - y = 9$
Add the equations to eliminate the *y*-terms.
$x + y = 5$
$\underline{x - y = 9}$
$2x \quad = 14$
Now solve for *x*.
$2x = 14$
$x = 7$
Back-substitute into either of the original equations to solve for *y*.
$x + y = 5$
$7 + y = 5$
$y = -2$
The solution set is $\{(7, -2)\}$.

2. $4x - y = 22$
$3x + 4y = 26$
Multiply each term of the first equation by 4 and add the equations to eliminate *y*.
$16x - 4y = 88$
$\underline{3x + 4y = 26}$
$19x \quad = 114$
$x = 6$
Back-substitute into either of the original equations to solve for *y*.
$4x - y = 22$
$4(6) - y = 22$
$24 - y = 22$
$-y = -2$
$y = 2$
The solution set is $\{(6, 2)\}$.

3. $4x + 5y = 3$
$2x - 3y = 7$
Multiply each term of the second equation by −2 and add the equations to eliminate *x*.
$4x + 5y = 3$
$\underline{-4x + 6y = -14}$
$11y = -11$
$y = -1$
Back-substitute into either of the original equations to solve for *x*.
$2x - 3y = 7$
$2x - 3(-1) = 7$
$2x + 3 = 7$
$2x = 4$
$x = 2$
The solution set is $\{(2, -1)\}$.

4. $2x = 9 + 3y$

$4y = 8 - 3x$

Rewrite each equation in the form $Ax + By = C$.

$2x - 3y = 9$

$3x + 4y = 8$

Multiply the top equation by 4 and multiply the bottom equation by 3.

$8x - 12y = 36$

$\underline{9x + 12y = 24}$

$17x \quad\;\; = 60$

$x = \dfrac{60}{17}$

Back-substitution of $\dfrac{60}{17}$ to find y would cause cumbersome arithmetic.

Instead, use the system that is in the form $Ax + By = C$ to eliminate x and find y.

$2x - 3y = 9$

$3x + 4y = 8$

Multiply the top equation by -3 and multiply the bottom equation by 2.

$-6x + 9y = -27$

$\underline{6x + 8y = \;16}$

$17y = -11$

$y = \dfrac{-11}{17}$

The solution set is $\left\{\left(\dfrac{60}{17}, -\dfrac{11}{17}\right)\right\}$.

5. $x + 2y = 4$

$3x + 6y = 13$

Multiply the first equation by -3.

$-3x - 6y = -12$

$\underline{3x + 6y = \;13}$

$0 = \;1, \;$ false

The false statement indicates that the system is inconsistent and has no solution.

The solution set is $\{\ \}$.

6. $x - 5y = 7$

$3x - 15y = 21$

Multiply the first equation by -3.

$-3x + 15y = -21$

$\underline{3x - 15y = \;21}$

$0 = \;\; 0, \;$ true

The true statement indicates that the system has infinitely many solutions.

The solution set is $\left\{(x, y) \big| x - 5y = 7\right\}$ or $\left\{(x, y) \big| 3x - 15y = 21\right\}$.

5.3 Exercise Set

1. $x + y = -3$

$x - y = 11$

Add the equations to eliminate the y-terms.

$x + y = -3$

$\underline{x - y = 11}$

$2x \quad\;\; = 8$

Now solve for x.

$2x = 8$

$x = 4$

Back-substitute into either of the original equations to solve for y.

$x + y = -3$

$4 + y = -3$

$y = -7$

The solution set is $\left\{(4, -7)\right\}$.

3. $2x + 3y = 6$

$\underline{2x - 3y = 6}$

$4x = 12$

$x = 3$

Back-substitute into either of the original equations to solve for y.

$2x + 3y = 6$

$2(3) + 3y = 6$

$3y = 0$

$y = 0$

The solution set is $\left\{(3, 0)\right\}$.

5. $x + 2y = 7$

$\underline{-x + 3y = 18}$

$\quad 5y = 25$

$\quad\ y = 5$

Back-substitute into either of the original equations to solve for x.

$x + 2y = 7$

$x + 2(5) = 7$

$\quad x + 10 = 7$

$\qquad x = -3$

The solution set is $\{(-3, 5)\}$.

7. $5x - y = 14$

$\underline{-5x + 2y = -13}$

$\qquad y = 1$

Back-substitute into either of the original equations to solve for x.

$5x - (1) = 14$

$\quad 5x = 15$

$\qquad x = 3$

The solution set is $\{(3, 1)\}$.

9. $3x + y = 7$

$2x - 5y = -1$

Multiply each term of the first equation by 5 and add the equations to eliminate y.

$15x + 5y = 35$

$\underline{\ 2x - 5y = -1}$

$17x \quad\ = 34$

$\quad x \quad\ = 2$

Back-substitute into either of the original equations to solve for y.

$3x + y = 7$

$3(2) + y = 7$

$\quad 6 + y = 7$

$\qquad y = 1$

The solution set is $\{(2, 1)\}$.

11. $x + 3y = 4$

$4x + 5y = 2$

Multiply each term of the first equation by -4 and add the equations to eliminate x.

$-4x - 12y = -16$

$\underline{\ 4x + 5y = \quad 2}$

$\quad -7y = -14$

$\qquad y = \quad 2$

Back-substitute into either of the original equations to solve for x.

$x + 3y = 4$

$x + 3(2) = 4$

$\quad x + 6 = 4$

$\qquad x = -2$

The solution set is $\{(-2, 2)\}$.

13. $-3x + 7y = 14$

$\quad 2x - y = -13$

Multiply each term of the second equation by 7 and add the equations to eliminate y.

$-3x + 7y = 14$

$\underline{14x - 7y = -91}$

$11x \qquad = -77$

$\quad x \qquad = -7$

Back-substitute into either of the original equations to solve for y.

$2x - y = -13$

$2(-7) - y = -13$

$\quad -14 - y = -13$

$\qquad -y = 1$

$\qquad y = -1$

The solution set is $\{(-7, -1)\}$.

15. $3x - 14y = 6$

$5x + 7y = 10$

Multiply each term of the second equation by 2 and add the equations to eliminate y.

$3x - 14y = 6$

$\underline{10x + 14y = 20}$

$13x \qquad = 26$

$\quad x \qquad = 2$

Back-substitute into either of the original equations to solve for y.

$5x + 7y = 10$

$5(2) + 7y = 10$

$\quad 10 + 7y = 10$

$\qquad 7y = 0$

$\qquad y = 0$

The solution set is $\{(2, 0)\}$.

17. $3x - 4y = 11$

$2x + 3y = -4$

Multiply the first equation by 3, and the second equation by 4.

$9x - 12y = 33$

$\underline{8x + 12y = -16}$

$17x = 17$

$x = 1$

Back-substitute into either of the original equations to solve for y.

$2x + 3y = -4$

$2(1) + 3y = -4$

$3y = -6$

$y = -2$

The solution set is $\{(1, -2)\}$.

19. $3x + 2y = -1$

$-2x + 7y = 9$

Multiply the first equation by 2 and the second equation by 3.

$6x + 4y = -2$

$\underline{-6x + 21y = 27}$

$25y = 25$

$y = 1$

Back-substitute into either of the original equations to solve for x.

$3x + 2(1) = -1$

$3x = -3$

$x = -1$

The solution set is $\{(-1, 1)\}$.

21. $3x = 2y + 7$

$5x = 2y + 13$

Rewrite each equation in the form $Ax + By = C$.

$3x - 2y = 7$

$5x - 2y = 13$

Multiply the first equation by -1 and add the equations to eliminate y.

$-3x + 2y = -7$

$\underline{5x - 2y = 13}$

$2x = 6$

$x = 3$

Back-substitute into either of the original equations to solve for y.

$3x = 2y + 7$

$3(3) = 2y + 7$

$2 = 2y$

$1 = y$

The solution set is $\{(3, 1)\}$.

23. $2x = 3y - 4$

$-6x + 12y = 6$

Rewrite the first equation in the form $Ax + By = C$.

$2x - 3y = -4$

Multiply the first equation by 3 and add to eliminate x.

$6x - 9y = -12$

$\underline{-6x + 12y = 6}$

$3y = -6$

$y = -2$

Back-substitute into either of the original equations to solve for x.

$2x = 3(-2) - 4$

$2x = -6 - 4$

$2x = -10$

$x = -5$

The solution set is $\{(-5, -2)\}$.

25. $2x - y = 3$

$4x + 4y = -1$

Multiply the first equation by 4 and add to eliminate y.

$8x - 4y = 12$

$\underline{4x + 4y = -1}$

$12x = 11$

$x = \dfrac{11}{12}$

Instead of back-substituting $\dfrac{11}{12}$ and working with fractions, go back to the original system. Multiply the first equation by -2 and add the equations to eliminate x.

$-4x + 2y = -6$

$\underline{4x + 4y = -1}$

$6y = -7$

$y = -\dfrac{7}{6}$

The solution set is $\left\{\left(\dfrac{11}{12}, -\dfrac{7}{6}\right)\right\}$.

27. $4x = 5 + 2y$

$2x + 3y = 4$

Rewrite the first equation in the form $Ax + By = C$, and multiply the second equation by -2.

$4x - 2y = 5$

$\underline{-4x - 6y = -8}$

$-8y = -3$

$$y = \frac{3}{8}$$

Instead of back-substituting $\dfrac{3}{8}$ and working with fractions, go back to the original system. Use the rewritten form of the first equation, and multiply by -3. Solve by addition.

$-12x + 6y = -15$

$\underline{-4x - 6y = -8}$

$-16x = -23$

$$x = \frac{23}{16}$$

The solution set is $\left\{\left(\dfrac{23}{16}, \dfrac{3}{8}\right)\right\}$.

29. $3x - y = 1$

$3x - y = 2$

Multiply the first equation by -1.

$-3x + y = -1$

$\underline{3x - y = 2}$

$0 = 1$, false

The false statement indicates that the system is inconsistent and has no solution.

The solution set is $\{\ \}$.

31. $x + 3y = 2$

$3x + 9y = 6$

Multiply the first equation by -3.

$-3x - 9y = -6$

$\underline{3x + 9y = 6}$

$0 = 0$, true

The true statement indicates that the system has infinitely many solutions.

The solution set is $\{(x, y) \mid x + 3y = 2\}$ or $\{(x, y) \mid 3x + 9y = 6\}$.

33. $7x - 3y = 4$

$-14x + 6y = -7$

Multiply the first equation by 2.

$14x - 6y = 8$

$\underline{-14x + 6y = -7}$

$0 = 1$, false

The false statement indicates that the system is inconsistent and has no solution.

The solution set is $\{\ \}$.

35. $5x + y = 2$

$3x + y = 1$

Multiply the second equation by -1.

$5x + y = 2$

$\underline{-3x - y = -1}$

$2x = 1$

$$x = \frac{1}{2}$$

Back-substitute $\dfrac{1}{2}$ for x and solve for y.

$$3\left(\frac{1}{2}\right) + y = 1$$

$$y = -\frac{1}{2}$$

The solution set is $\left\{\left(\dfrac{1}{2}, -\dfrac{1}{2}\right)\right\}$.

37. $x = 5 - 3y$

$2x + 6y = 10$

Rewrite the first equation in the form $Ax + By = C$, and multiply the second equation by -2.

$-2x - 6y = -10$

$\underline{2x + 6y = 10}$

$0 = 0$, true

The true statement indicates that the system has infinitely many solutions.

The solution set is $\{(x, y) \mid x = 5 - 3y\}$ or $\{(x, y) \mid 2x + 6y = 10\}$.

39. $4(3x - y) = 0$

　　$3(x + 3) = 10y$

Rewrite both equations.

$12x - 4y = 0$

$3x - 10y = -9$

Multiply the second equation by -4 and add the equations to eliminate x.

　　$12x - 4y = 0$

$\underline{-12x + 40y = 36}$

　　　$36y = 36$

　　　　$y = 1$

Back-substitute 1 for y in one of the original equations and solve for x.

　　$12x - 4y = 0$

$12x - 4(1) = 0$

　　　$12x = 4$

　　　　$x = \dfrac{1}{3}$

The solution set is $\left\{\left(\dfrac{1}{3}, 1\right)\right\}$.

41.　$x + y = 11$

$\dfrac{x}{5} + \dfrac{y}{7} = 1$

Multiply the second equation by the LCD, 35, to clear fractions.

$35\left(\dfrac{x}{5} + \dfrac{y}{7}\right) = 35(1)$

　　$7x + 5y = 35$

Now solve the system.

　　$x + y = 11$

$7x + 5y = 35$

Multiply the top equation by -5 and add the result to the second equation.

$-5x - 5y = -55$

$\underline{7x + 5y = 35}$

　　$2x = -20$

　　　$x = -10$

Back-substitute to find y.

$-10 + y = 11$

　　　$y = 21$

The solution set is $\{(-10, 21)\}$.

43.　$\dfrac{4}{5}x - y = -1$

$\dfrac{2}{5}x + y = 1$

Multiply both equations by 5 to clear fractions.

$4x - 5y = -5$

$\underline{2x + 5y = 5}$

　$6x = 0$

　　$x = 0$

Back-substitute 0 for x and solve for y.

$\dfrac{2}{5}(0) + y = 1$

　　　$y = 1$

The solution set is $\{(0, 1)\}$.

45.　$3x - 2y = 8$

　　　$x = -2y$

The substitution method is a good choice because the second equation is already solved for x. Substitute $-2y$ for x in the first equation

　　$3x - 2y = 8$

$3(-2y) - 2y = 8$

　$-6y - 2y = 8$

　　　$-8y = 8$

　　　　$y = -1$

Back-substitute -1 for y in the second equation.

$x = -2y = -2(-1) = 2$

The solution set is $\{(2, -1)\}$.

47.　$3x + 2y = -3$

　　$2x - 5y = 17$

The addition method is a good choice because both equations are written in the form $Ax + By = C$.

Multiply the first equation by 2 and the second equation by -3.

　$6x + 4y = -6$

$\underline{-6x + 15y = -51}$

　　$19y = -57$

　　　$y = -3$

Back-substitute -3 for y and solve for x.

$3x + 2(-3) = -3$

　　$3x - 6 = -3$

　　　$3x = 3$

　　　　$x = 1$

The solution set is $\{(1, -3)\}$.

49. $3x - 2y = 6$

$\qquad y = 3$

The substitution method is a good choice because the second equation is already solved for y. Substitute 3 for y in the first equation.

$3x - 2y = 6$

$3x - 2(3) = 6$

$3x - 6 = 6$

$3x = 12$

$x = 4$

It is not necessary to back-substitute to find the value of y because $y = 3$ is one of the equations of the given system.

The solution set is $\{(4, 3)\}$.

51. $y = 2x + 1$

$\quad y = 2x - 3$

The substitution method is a good choice, because both equations are already solved for y. Substitute $2x + 1$ for y in the second equation.

$y = 2x - 3$

$2x + 1 = 2x - 3$

$2x + 1 - 2x = 2x - 3 - 2x$

$1 = -3$, false

The false statement indicates that the system has no solution.

The solution set is $\{\ \}$.

53. $\quad 2(x + 2y) = 6$

$\quad 3(x + 2y - 3) = 0$

The addition method is a good choice since the equations can easily be simplified to give equations of the form $Ax + By = C$.

$2x + 4y = 6 \qquad\qquad 3x + 6y - 9 = 0$

$\qquad\qquad\qquad\qquad\qquad 3x + 6y = 9$

Solve the resulting system.

$2x + 4y = 6$

$3x + 6y = 9$

Multiply the first equation by -3 and the second by 2 and solve by addition.

$-6x - 12y = -18$

$\underline{6x + 12y = \ 18}$

$\qquad\qquad 0 = 0, \text{ true}$

The true statement indicates that the system has infinitely many solutions.

The solution set is $\{(x, y) | 2(x + 2y) = 6\}$ or

$\{(x, y) | 3(x + 2y - 3) = 0\}$.

55. $\quad 3y = 2x$

$\quad 2x + 9y = 24$

The substitution method is a good choice because the first equation can easily be solved for one of the variables. Solve this equation for y.

$3y = 2x$

$y = \dfrac{2}{3}x$

Substitute $\dfrac{2}{3}x$ for y in the second equation.

$2x + 9y = 24$

$2x + 9\left(\dfrac{2}{3}x\right) = 24$

$2x + 6x = 24$

$8x = 24$

$x = 3$

Back-substitute 3 for x in the equation, $y = \dfrac{2}{3}x$.

$y = \dfrac{2}{3}x = \dfrac{2}{3}(3) = 2$

The solution set is $\{(3, 2)\}$.

57.
$$\frac{3x}{5} + \frac{4y}{5} = 1$$
$$\frac{x}{4} - \frac{3y}{8} = -1$$

Multiply the first equation by 5 and the second equation by 8 to clear fractions.

$$\frac{3x}{5} + \frac{4y}{5} = 1 \qquad \frac{x}{4} - \frac{3y}{8} = -1$$

$$3x + 4y = 5 \qquad 2x - 3y = -8$$

The addition method is a good choice since both equations are of the form $Ax + By = C$.

$$3x + 4y = 5$$
$$2x - 3y = -8$$

Multiply the first equation by 3 and the second equation by 4.

$$\begin{array}{rcl} 9x + 12y &=& 15 \\ 8x - 12y &=& -32 \\ \hline 17x &=& -17 \\ x &=& -1 \end{array}$$

Back-substitute -1 for x in the equation and solve for y.

$$3x + 4y = 5$$
$$3(-1) + 4y = 5$$
$$-3 + 4y = 5$$
$$4y = 8$$
$$y = 2$$

The solution set is $\{(-1, 2)\}$.

59.
$$5(x+1) = 7(y+1) - 7$$
$$6(x+1) + 5 = 5(y+1)$$

Simplify both equations.

$$5(x+1) = 7(y+1) - 7$$
$$5x + 5 = 7y + 7 - 7$$
$$5x + 5 = 7y$$
$$5x - 7y + 5 = 0$$
$$5x - 7y = -5$$

$$6(x+1) + 5 = 5(y+1)$$
$$6x + 6 + 5 = 5y + 5$$
$$6x + 11 = 5y + 5$$
$$6x - 5y + 11 = 5$$
$$6x - 5y = -6$$

Solve the rewritten system.

$$5x - 7y = -5$$
$$6x - 5y = -6$$

Multiply the first equation by -6 and the second equation by 5, and solve by addition.

$$\begin{array}{rcl} -30x + 42y &=& 30 \\ 30x - 25y &=& -30 \\ \hline 17y &=& 0 \\ y &=& 0 \end{array}$$

Back-substitute 0 for y to find x.

$$5x - 7y = -5$$
$$5x - 7(0) = -5$$
$$5x - 0 = -5$$
$$5x = -5$$
$$x = -1$$

The solution set is $\{(-1, 0)\}$.

61.
$$0.4x + y = 2.2$$
$$0.5x - 1.2y = 0.3$$

Multiply the first equation by 1.2 and solve by addition.

$$\begin{array}{rcl} 0.48x + 1.2y &=& 2.64 \\ 0.50x - 1.2y &=& 0.30 \\ \hline 0.98x &=& 2.94 \\ x &=& 3 \end{array}$$

Back-substitute 3 for x to find y.

$$0.4x + y = 2.2$$
$$0.4(3) + y = 2.2$$
$$1.2 + y = 2.2$$
$$y = 1$$

The solution set is $\{(3, 1)\}$.

63.
$$\frac{x}{2} = \frac{y+8}{3}$$
$$\frac{x+2}{2} = \frac{y+11}{3}$$

Simplify the first equation.
$$\frac{x}{2} = \frac{y+8}{3}$$
$$3x = 2(y+8)$$
$$3x = 2y+16$$
$$3x - 2y = 16$$

Simplify the second equation.
$$\frac{x+2}{2} = \frac{y+11}{3}$$
$$3(x+2) = 2(y+11)$$
$$3x+6 = 2y+22$$
$$3x - 2y + 6 = 22$$
$$3x - 2y = 16$$

When simplified, the equations are the same. This means that the system is dependent and there are an infinite number of solutions.

The solution set is $\left\{ (x,y) \middle| \frac{x}{2} = \frac{y+8}{3} \right\}$ or

$\left\{ (x,y) \middle| \frac{x+2}{2} = \frac{y+11}{3} \right\}$.

65.
$$x + 2y = 50$$
$$-x + 2y = 24$$

Add the equations.
$$x + 2y = 50$$
$$-x + 2y = 24$$
$$\overline{4y = 74}$$
$$y = 18.5$$

Back-substitute 18.5 for y and solve for x.
$$x + 2y = 50$$
$$x + 2(18.5) = 50$$
$$x + 37 = 50$$
$$x = 13$$

The solution is (13, 18.5). This means that 13 years after 1996, or 2009, the percentage who will be pro-life and pro-choice will be the same at 18.5%.

67. – 71. Answers will vary.

73. does not make sense; Explanations will vary. Sample explanation: The addition method does not involve graphing.

75. does not make sense; Explanations will vary. Sample explanation: When one of equations has a variable on one side by itself, it is typically best to use the substitution method.

77. false; Changes to make the statement true will vary. A sample change is: If $(2,-2)$ satisfies $Ax + 2y = 2$ and $2x + By = 10$, then A and B can be found by substitution.
Find A.
$$Ax + 2y = 2$$
$$A(2) + 2(-2) = 2$$
$$2A - 4 = 2$$
$$2A = 6$$
$$A = 3$$
Find B.
$$2x + By = 10$$
$$2(2) + B(-2) = 10$$
$$4 - 2B = 10$$
$$-2B = 6$$
$$B = -3$$

79. false; Changes to make the statement true will vary. A sample change is: After these multiplications, the coefficients of x will be the same. Thus, adding them will not eliminate them.

81.
$$Ax - 3y = 16$$
$$A(5) - 3(-2) = 16$$
$$5A + 6 = 16$$
$$5A = 10$$
$$A = 2$$

$$3x + By = 7$$
$$3(5) + B(-2) = 7$$
$$15 - 2B = 7$$
$$-2B = -8$$
$$B = 4$$

82. Let x = the unknown number.
$$5x = x + 40$$
$$4x = 40$$
$$x = 10$$
The number is 10.

83. Because the x-coordinate is negative and the y-coordinate is positive, $\left(-\frac{3}{2}, 15 \right)$ is located in quadrant II.

84. $29,700 + 150x = 5000 + 1100x$
$29,700 - 950x = 5000$
$\qquad -950x = -24,700$
$\qquad\qquad x = 26$
The solution set is $\{26\}$.

85. a. $x + y = 28$
$\qquad x - y = 6$

b. $x + y = 28$
$\qquad \underline{x - y = 6}$
$\qquad 2x \quad\;\; = 34$
$\qquad\qquad x = 17$
Substitute 17 for x to find y.
$\qquad x + y = 28$
$\qquad 17 + y = 28$
$\qquad\qquad y = 11$
The numbers are 17 and 11.

86. $3x + 2y$

87. a. $\$20 + \$0.05(200) = \$30$

b. $y = 20 + 0.05x$

Mid-Chapter Check Point

1. $3x + 2y = 6$
$\quad 2x - \;y = 4$

The lines intersect at (2, 0).
The solution set is $\{(2,0)\}$.

2. $y = 2x - 1$
$\quad y = 3x - 2$

The lines intersect at (1, 1).
The solution set is $\{(1,1)\}$.

3. $\qquad y = 2x - 1$
$\quad 6x - 3y = 12$

Since the lines are parallel, the system is inconsistent and there is no solution.
The solution set is $\{\ \}$.

4. $5x - 3y = 1$
$\qquad y = 3x - 7$
Substitute $3x - 7$ for y in the first equation and solve for x.
$\qquad 5x - 3y = 1$
$\qquad 5x - 3(3x - 7) = 1$
$\qquad 5x - 9x + 21 = 1$
$\qquad\quad -4x + 21 = 1$
$\qquad\qquad\quad -4x = -20$
$\qquad\qquad\qquad x = 5$
Back-substitute to find y.
$y = 3x - 7 = 3(5) - 7 = 15 - 7 = 8$
The solution set is $\{(5,8)\}$.

5. $6x + 5y = 7$
$\quad 3x - 7y = 13$
Multiply the second equation by -2 and add to eliminate x.
$\qquad 6x + \;5y = \quad 7$
$\qquad \underline{-6x + 14y = -26}$
$\qquad\qquad 19y = -19$
$\qquad\qquad\;\; y = \;-1$
Back-substitute -1 for y and solve for x.
$\qquad 6x + 5y = 7$
$\qquad 6x + 5(-1) = 7$
$\qquad\quad 6x - 5 = 7$
$\qquad\qquad 6x = 12$
$\qquad\qquad\;\; x = 2$
The solution set is $\{(2,-1)\}$.

6. $x = \dfrac{y}{3} - 1$

$6x + y = 21$

Substitute $\dfrac{y}{3} - 1$ for x in the second equation and solve for y.

$$6x + y = 21$$

$$6\left(\dfrac{y}{3} - 1\right) + y = 21$$

$$2y - 6 + y = 21$$

$$3y - 6 = 21$$

$$3y = 27$$

$$y = 9$$

Back-substitute to find x.

$$x = \dfrac{y}{3} - 1 = \dfrac{9}{3} - 1 = 3 - 1 = 2$$

The solution set is $\{(2, 9)\}$.

7. $3x - 4y = 6$

$5x - 6y = 8$

Multiply the first equation by -5, the second equation by 3 and add to eliminate x.

$$-15x + 20y = -30$$

$$\underline{15x - 18y = 24}$$

$$2y = -6$$

$$y = -3$$

Back-substitute -3 for y and solve for x.

$$3x - 4y = 6$$

$$3x - 4(-3) = 6$$

$$3x + 12 = 6$$

$$3x = -6$$

$$x = -2$$

The solution set is $\{(-2, -3)\}$.

8. $3x - 2y = 32$

$\dfrac{x}{5} + 3y = -1$

Multiply the second equation by 5 to clear the fraction.

$$5\left(\dfrac{x}{5} + 3y\right) = 5(-1)$$

$$x + 15y = -5$$

The system is as follows.

$$3x - 2y = 32$$

$$x + 15y = -5$$

Multiply the second equation by -3 and solve by addition.

$$3x - 2y = 32$$

$$\underline{-3x - 45y = 15}$$

$$-47y = 47$$

$$y = -1$$

Back-substitute -1 for y and solve for x.

$$x + 15y = -5$$

$$x + 15(-1) = -5$$

$$x - 15 = -5$$

$$x = 10$$

The solution set is $\{(10, -1)\}$.

9. $x - y = 3$

$2x = 4 + 2y$

Solve the first equation for x.

$$x - y = 3$$

$$x = y + 3$$

Substitute $y + 3$ for x in the second equation and solve for y.

$$2x = 4 + 2y$$

$$2(y + 3) = 4 + 2y$$

$$2y + 6 = 4 + 2y$$

$$6 = 4$$

Notice that y has also been eliminated. The false statement $6 = 4$ indicates that the system is inconsistent and has no solution. The solution set is $\{\ \}$.

10. $x = 2(y - 5)$

$4x + 40 = y - 7$

Substitute $2(y - 5)$ for x in the second equation and solve for y.

$$4x + 40 = y - 7$$

$$4(2(y - 5)) + 40 = y - 7$$

$$4(2y - 10) + 40 = y - 7$$

$$8y - 40 + 40 = y - 7$$

$$8y = y - 7$$

$$7y = -7$$

$$y = -1$$

Back-substitute -1 for y and solve for x.

$$x = 2(y - 5)$$

$$= 2(-1 - 5) = 2(-6) = -12$$

The solution set is $\{(-12, -1)\}$.

11.　$y = 3x - 2$

$y = 2x - 9$

Substitute $3x - 2$ for y in the second equation and solve for x.

$y = 2x - 9$

$3x - 2 = 2x - 9$

$x - 2 = -9$

$x = -7$

Back-substitute -7 for x and solve for y.

$y = 3(-7) - 2 = -21 - 2 = -23$

The solution set is $\{(-7, -23)\}$.

12.　$2x - 3y = 4$

$3x + 4y = 0$

Multiply the first equation by 4, the second equation by 3 and add to eliminate y.

$8x - 12y = 16$

$\underline{9x + 12y = 0}$

$17x \quad\quad = 16$

$x \quad\quad = \dfrac{16}{17}$

Back-substitution of $\dfrac{16}{17}$ to find y would cause cumbersome arithmetic.

Instead, use the addition to eliminate x and find y.

$2x - 3y = 4$

$3x + 4y = 0$

Multiply the top equation by -3 and multiply the bottom equation by 2.

$-6x + 9y = -12$

$\underline{6x + 8y = 0}$

$17y = -12$

$y = \dfrac{-12}{17}$

The solution set is $\left\{\left(\dfrac{16}{17}, -\dfrac{12}{17}\right)\right\}$.

13.　$y - 2x = 7$

$4x = 2y - 14$

Solve the first equation for y.

$y - 2x = 7$

$y = 2x + 7$

Substitute $2x + 7$ for y and solve for x.

$4x = 2y - 14$

$4x = 2(2x + 7) - 14$

$4x = 4x + 14 - 14$

$0 = 14 - 14$

$0 = 0$

Notice that x has also been eliminated. The true statement $0 = 0$ indicates that the system is dependent and has infinitely many solutions. The solution set is

$\{(x, y) \mid y - 2x = 7\}$　or　$\{(x, y) \mid 4x = 2y - 14\}$.

14.　$4(x + 3) = 3y + 7$

$2(y - 5) = x + 5$

First, rewrite both equations in the form $Ax + By = C$.

$4(x + 3) = 3y + 7$

$4x + 12 = 3y + 7$

$4x - 3y + 12 = 7$

$4x - 3y = -5$

$2(y - 5) = x + 5$

$2y - 10 = x + 5$

$-x + 2y - 10 = 5$

$-x + 2y = 15$

The system is as follows.

$4x - 3y = -5$

$-x + 2y = 15$

Multiply the second equation by 4 and add to eliminate x.

$4x - 3y = -5$

$\underline{-4x + 8y = 60}$

$5y = 55$

$y = 11$

Back-substitute 11 for y and solve for x.

$-x + 2y = 15$

$-x + 2(11) = 15$

$-x + 22 = 15$

$-x = -7$

$x = 7$

The solution set is $\{(7, 11)\}$.

15. $\dfrac{x}{2} - \dfrac{y}{5} = 1$

$y - \dfrac{x}{3} = 8$

Multiply the first equation by 10 and the second equation by 3 to clear fractions.

$10\left(\dfrac{x}{2}\right) - 10\left(\dfrac{y}{5}\right) = 10(1)$

$5x - 2y = 10$

$3y - 3\left(\dfrac{x}{3}\right) = 3(8)$

$3y - x = 24$

$-x + 3y = 24$

The system is as follows.

$5x - 2y = 10$

$-x + 3y = 24$

Multiply the second equation by 5 and solve by addition.

$5x - 2y = 10$

$\underline{-5x + 15y = 120}$

$13y = 130$

$y = 10$

Back-substitute and solve for x.

$-x + 3y = 24$

$-x + 3(10) = 24$

$-x + 30 = 24$

$-x = -6$

$x = 6$

The solution set is $\{(6, 10)\}$.

5.4 Check Points

1. Let x = average time per day women spend socializing.
Let y = average time per day men spend socializing.

$x + y = 138$

$\underline{x - y = \quad 8}$

$2x = 146$

$x = 73$

Back-substitute 73 for x to find y.

$x + y = 138$

$73 + y = 138$

$y = 65$

Men average 65 minutes per day socializing and women average 73 minutes.

2. Let x = the number of calories in a Quarter Pounder.
Let y = the number of calories in a Whopper with cheese.

$2x + 3y = 2607$

$x + y = 1000 + 9$

Solve the second equation for x.

$x + y = 1000 + 9$

$x = -y + 1009$

Substitute $-y + 1009$ for x to find y.

$2x + 3y = 2607$

$\overset{x}{\overbrace{2(-y + 1009)}} + 3y = 2607$

$2(-y + 1009) + 3y = 2607$

$-2y + 2018 + 3y = 2607$

$y + 2018 = 2607$

$y = 589$

Back substitute to find x.

$x = -y + 1009 = -589 + 1009 = 420$

There are 420 calories in a Quarter Pounder and 589 calories in a Whopper with cheese.

3. Let x = the length of the lot.
Let y = the width of the lot.
Use the formula for the perimeter of a rectangle to write the first equation.

$P = 2l + 2w$

$360 = 2x + 2y$

Use the other information in the problem to write the second equation.

$20x + 8 \cdot 2y = 3280$

The two equations form the system.

$2x + 2y = 360$

$20x + 16y = 3280$

Multiply the first equation by -8 and add the result to the second equation.

$-16x - 16y = -2880$

$\underline{20x + 16y = \quad 3280}$

$4x = 400$

$x = 100$

Back-substitute to find y.

$2x + 2y = 360$

$2(100) + 2y = 360$

$200 + 2y = 360$

$2y = 160$

$y = 80$

The length is 100 feet and the width is 80 feet.

4. Let x = the number of years the heating system is used.

Let y = the total cost of the heating system.

$y = 5000 + 1100x$

$y = 12,000 + 700x$

Solve by the substitution method.

$$y = 12,000 + 700x$$

$$\overbrace{\hspace{2cm}}^{y}$$

$$5000 + 1100x = 12,000 + 700x$$

$$5000 + 1100x = 12,000 + 700x$$

$$5000 + 400x = 12,000$$

$$400x = 7000$$

$$x = 17.5$$

Back-substitute to find y.

$y = 5000 + 1100(17.5)$

$y = 24,250$

After 17.5 years, the total costs for the two systems will be the same, namely \$24,250.

5.4 Exercise Set

1. Let x = one number.

Let y = the other number.

$$x + y = 17$$

$$\underline{x - y = -3}$$

$$2x \quad\;\; = 14$$

$$x \quad\;\; = \;\; 7$$

Back-substitute 7 for x to find y.

$x + y = 17$

$7 + y = 17$

$y = 10$

The numbers are 7 and 10.

3. Let x = one number.

Let y = the other number.

$$3x - \;\; y = -1$$

$$x + 2y = 23$$

Solve the second equation for x.

$x + 2y = 23$

$$x = -2y + 23$$

Substitute $-2y + 23$ for x to find y.

$$3x - y = -1$$

$$3(-2y + 23) - y = -1$$

$$-6y + 69 - y = -1$$

$$-7y + 69 = -1$$

$$-7y = -70$$

$$y = 10$$

Back substitute 10 for y to find x.

$x = -2y + 23 = -2(10) + 23 = 3$

The numbers are 3 and 10.

5. Let x = the average number of minutes 20- to 24-year-old women spend grooming.

Let y = the average number of minutes 20- to 24-year-old men spend grooming.

$x + y = 86$

$x - y = 12$

Add the equations to eliminate y.

$$x + y = 86$$

$$\underline{x - y = 12}$$

$$2x \quad\;\; = 98$$

$$x = 49$$

Back-substitute to find y.

$x + y = 86$

$49 + y = 86$

$y = 37$

20- to 24-year-old women averaged 49 minutes grooming and men averaged 37 minutes.

7. Let x = the number of calories in a Mr. Goodbar.
Let y = the number of calories in a Mounds bar.
$$x + 2y = 780$$
$$2x + y = 786$$
Multiply the bottom equation by –2 and then add the equations to eliminate y.

$$
\begin{array}{r}
x + 2y = 780 \\
\underline{-4x - 2y = -1572} \\
-3x = -792
\end{array}
$$

$$x = 264$$

Back-substitute to find y.
$$x + 2y = 780$$
$$264 + 2y = 780$$
$$2y = 516$$
$$y = 258$$

There are 264 calories in a Mr. Goodbar and 258 calories in a Mounds bar.

9. Let x = the number of Mr. Goodbars.
Let y = the number of Mounds bars.
$$x + y = 5$$
$$16.3x + 14.1y - 70 = 7.1$$

Solve the first equation for y in terms of x.
$$x + y = 5$$
$$y = -x + 5$$

Substitute $-x + 5$ for y in the second equation.
$$16.3x + 14.1y - 70 = 7.1$$

$$16.3x + 14.1(\overbrace{-x + 5}^{y}) - 70 = 7.1$$
$$16.3x + 14.1(-x + 5) - 70 = 7.1$$
$$16.3x - 14.1x + 70.5 - 70 = 7.1$$
$$2.2x + 0.5 = 7.1$$
$$2.2x = 6.6$$
$$x = 3$$

Back-substitute to find y.
$$x + y = 5$$
$$3 + y = 5$$
$$y = 2$$

There are 3 Mr. Goodbars and 2 Mounds bars.

11. Let x = the price of one sweater.
Let y = the price of one shirt.
$$x + 3y = 42$$
$$3x + 2y = 56$$
Multiply the first equation by –3 and add the result to the second equation.

$$
\begin{array}{r}
-3x - 9y = -126 \\
\underline{3x + 2y = 56} \\
-7y = -70
\end{array}
$$

$$y = 10$$

Back-substitute 10 for y and solve for x.
$$x + 3y = 42$$
$$x + 3(10) = 42$$
$$x + 30 = 42$$
$$x = 12$$

The price of one sweater is $12 and the price of one shirt is $10.

13. Let x = the length of a badminton court.
Let y = the width of a badminton court.
Use the formula for the perimeter of a rectangle to write the first equation.
$$P = 2l + 2w$$
$$128 = 2x + 2y$$
Use the other information in the problem to write the second equation.
$$6x + 9y = 444$$
The two equations form the system.
$$2x + 2y = 128$$
$$6x + 9y = 444$$
Multiply the first equation by –3 and add the result to the second equation.

$$
\begin{array}{r}
-6x - 6y = -384 \\
\underline{6x + 9y = 444} \\
3y = 60
\end{array}
$$

$$y = 20$$

Back-substitute 20 for y and solve for x.
$$2x + 2y = 128$$
$$2x + 2(20) = 128$$
$$2x + 40 = 128$$
$$2x = 88$$
$$x = 44$$

The length is 44 feet and the width is 20 feet, so the dimensions of a standard badminton court are 44 feet by 20 feet.

15. Let x = the length of the lot.
Let y = the width of the lot.
Use the formula for the perimeter of a rectangle to write the first equation.
$2x + 2y = 320$
Use the other information in the problem to write the second equation.
$16x + 5(2y) = 2140$
These two equations form the system.
$2x + 2y = 320$
$16x + 10y = 2140$
Multiply the first equation by -5 and add the result to the second equation.
$-10x - 10y = -1600$

$$\underline{16x + 10y = \ \ 2140}$$
$$6x \quad\quad = \quad 540$$
$$x \quad\quad = \quad 90$$

Back-substitute 90 for x to find y.
$2(90) + 2y = 320$
$180 + 2y = 320$
$2y = 140$
$y = 70$
The length is 90 feet and the width is 70 feet, so the dimensions of the lot are 90 feet by 70 feet.

17. a. Let x = the number of minutes of long distance calls.
Let y = the monthly cost of a telephone plan.
Plan A: $y = 20 + 0.05x$
Plan B: $y = 5 + 0.10x$
Solve by substitution. Substitute $5 + 0.10x$ for y in the first equation.
$5 + 0.10x = 20 + 0.05x$
$5 + 0.05x = 20$
$0.05x = 15$
$x = 300$
Back-substitute 300 for x.
$y = 20 + 0.05x = 20 + 0.05(300) = 35$
The costs for the two plans will be equal for 300 minutes of long-distance calls per month. The cost for each plan will be $35.

b. $x = 10(20) = 200$

Plan A: $y = 20 + 0.05(200) = 30$

Plan B: $y = 5 + 0.10(200) = 25$

The monthly cost would be $30 for Plan A and $25 for Plan B, so Plan B should be selected to get the lower cost.

19. Let x = the number of dollars of merchandise purchased in a year.
Let y = the total cost for a year.
Plan A: $y = 100 + 0.80x$
Plan B: $y = 40 + 0.90x$
Substitute $40 = 0.90x$ for y in the first equation and solve for x.
$40 + 0.90x = 100 + 0.80x$
$40 + 0.10x = 100$
$0.10x = 60$
$x = 600$
Back-substitute 600 for x to find y.
$y = 100 + 0.80(600) = 580$.
If you purchase $600 worth of merchandise, you will pay the $580 under both plans.

21. Let x = the number of adult tickets sold.
Let y = the number of student tickets sold.
$x + y = 301$
$3x + y = 487$
Multiply the first equation by -1 and add it to the second equation.
$-x - y = -301$

$$\underline{3x + y = \ \ 487}$$
$$2x \quad\quad = 186$$
$$x = \ \ 93$$

Back-substitute to find y.
$x + y = 301$
$93 + y = 301$
$y = 208$
There were 93 adult tickets sold and 208 student tickets sold.

23. Let x = the cost of an item from column A.
Let y = the cost of an item from column B.
$x + y = 5.49$
$x + 2y = 6.99$
Multiply the first equation by -1 and add it to the second equation.
$-x - y = -5.49$

$$\underline{x + 2y = \ \ 6.99}$$
$$y = \ 1.50$$

Back-substitute to find x.
$x + y = 5.49$
$x + 1.50 = 5.49$
$x = 3.99$
The cost of an item from column A is $3.99 and the cost of an item from column B is $1.50.

25. Let x = the number of servings of macaroni.
Let y = the number of servings of broccoli.
$$3x + 2y = 14$$
$$16x + 4y = 48$$
Multiply the first equation by −2 and add to second equation.
$$-6x - 4y = -28$$
$$\underline{16x + 4y = \;\;48}$$
$$10x \qquad = 20$$
$$\;\; x \qquad = \;\;2$$
Back-substitute 2 for x to find y.
$$3(2) + 2y = 14$$
$$2y = 8$$
$$y = 4$$
It would take 2 servings of macaroni and 4 servings of broccoli to get 14 grams of protein and 48 grams of carbohydrate.

27. The sum of the measures of the three angles of any triangle is 180°, so
$$(x + 8y - 1) + (3y + 4) + (7x + 5) = 180.$$
Simplify this equation.
$$8x + 11y + 8 = 180$$
$$8x + 11y = 172$$
The base angles of an isosceles triangle have equal measures, so
$$3y + 4 = 7x + 5$$
Rewrite this equation in the form $Ax + By = C$.
$$7x + 5 = 3y + 4$$
$$7x - 3y = -1$$
Use the addition method to solve the system.
$$8x + 11y = 172$$
$$7x - 3y = -1$$
Multiply the first equation by 3 and the second equation by 11; then add the results.
$$24x + 33y = 516$$
$$\underline{77x - 33y = -11}$$
$$101x \qquad = 505$$
$$\;\; x \qquad = \;\;5$$
Back-substitute 5 for x to find y.
$$7(5) - 3y = -1$$
$$35 - 3y = -1$$
$$-3y = -36$$
$$y = 12$$
Use the values of x and y to find the angle measures.
Angle A: $(x + 8y - 1)° = (5 + 8 \cdot 12 - 1)° = 100°$

Angle B: $(3y + 4)° = (3 \cdot 12 + 4)° = 40°$

Angle C: $(7x + 5)° = (7 \cdot 5 + 5)° = 40°$

29. Use the motion formula to write equations.
Rowing with current:
$$r \cdot t = d$$
$$(x + y) \cdot 2 = 16$$
Rowing against current:
$$(x - y) \cdot 2 = 8$$
Rewrite each equation in the form $Ax + By = C$.
$$2x + 2y = 16$$
$$\underline{2x - 2y = \;\;8}$$
$$4x \qquad = 24$$
$$\;x \qquad = \;\;6$$
Back-substitute 6 for x to find y.
$$2(6) + 2y = 16$$
$$12 + 2y = 16$$
$$2y = 4$$
$$y = 2$$
The rowing rate in still water is 6 miles per hour and the rate of the current is 2 miles per hour.

31. – 33. Answers will vary.

35. does not make sense; Explanations will vary.
Sample explanation: The model is $y = 4 + 0.07x$.

37. does not make sense; Explanations will vary.
Sample explanation: The model is
$(4x - 2y + 4) + (12x + 6y + 12) = 180$.

39. Let x = the number of birds.
Let y = the number of lions.
Since each bird has one head and each lion has one head, $x + y = 30$.

Since each bird has two feet and each lion has four feet, $2x + 4y = 100$.

Solve the first equation for y. $y = 30 - x$

Substitute $30 - x$ for y in the second equation.
$$2x + 4(30 - x) = 100$$
$$2x + 120 - 4x = 100$$
$$-2x + 120 = 100$$
$$-2x = -20$$
$$x = 10$$
Back-substitute 10 for x to find y.
$$10 + y = 30$$
$$y = 20$$
There were 10 birds and 20 lions in the zoo.

41. Let x = the number of people in the downstairs apartment.

Let y = the number of people in the upstairs apartment.

If one of the people in the upstairs apartment goes downstairs, there will be the same number of people in both apartments, so $y - 1 = x + 1$.

If one of the people in the downstairs apartment goes upstairs, there will be twice as many people upstairs as downstairs, so $y + 1 = 2(x - 1)$.

Solve the first equation for y.

$y = x + 2$

Also solve the second equation for y.

$$y + 1 = 2x - 2$$
$$y = 2x - 3$$

Substitute $x + 2$ for y in the last equation.

$$x + 2 = 2x - 3$$
$$-x + 2 = -3$$
$$-x = -5$$
$$x = 5$$

Back-substitute to find y.

$y = 5 + 2 = 7$

There are 5 people downstairs and 7 people upstairs.

43. Answers will vary.

44.
$$2(x + 3) = 24 - 2(x + 4)$$
$$2x + 6 = 24 - 2x - 8$$
$$2x + 6 = 16 - 2x$$
$$4x = 10$$
$$x = \frac{10}{4}$$
$$x = \frac{5}{2}$$

The solution set is $\left\{ \dfrac{5}{2} \right\}$.

45.
$$5 + 6(x + 1) = 5 + 6x + 6$$
$$= 6x + 11$$

46. Find slope: $m = \dfrac{y_2 - y_1}{x_2 - x_1} = \dfrac{-10 - 6}{3 - (-5)} = \dfrac{-16}{8} = -2$

Use either point in the point-slope form and then solve for y.

$$y - y_1 = m(x - x_1)$$
$$y - (-10) = -2(x - 3)$$
$$y + 10 = -2x + 6$$
$$y = -2x - 4$$

47. $2x - y < 4$

Graph $2x - y = 4$ as a dashed line with x-intercept 2 and y-intercept -4. Use $(0, 0)$ as a test point. Since $2(0) - 0 < 4$ is true, shade the half-plane containing $(0, 0)$.

48. $y \geq x + 1$

Graph the line $y = x + 1$ using the slope of 1 and y-intercept of 1. Make the line solid because the inequality symbol is $\geq$. Use $(0, 0)$ as a test point. Since $0 \geq 0 + 1$ is false, shade the half-plane *not* containing $(0, 0)$.

49. $x \geq 2$

Graph $x = 2$ as a solid vertical line. Use $(0, 0)$ as a test point. Since $0 \geq 2$ is false, shade the half-plane *not* containing $(0, 0)$. This is the region to the right of the line $x = 2$.

5.5 Check Points

1. Point $B = (66, 130)$

$$4.9x - y \geq 165$$
$$4.9(66) - 130 \geq 165$$
$$193.4 \geq 165, \text{ true}$$

$$3.7x - y \leq 125$$
$$3.7(66) - 130 \leq 125$$
$$114.2 \leq 125, \text{ true}$$

Point B is a solution of the system.

2. $x + 2y > 4$

$2x - 3y \leq -6$

Graph $x + 2y > 4$ by graphing $x + 2y = 4$ as a dashed line using the x-intercept, 4, and the y-intercept, 2.
Use $(0,0)$ as a test point. $\quad x + 2y > 4$
$$0 + 2(0) > 4$$
$$0 > 4, \text{ false}$$

Because $0 + 2(0) > 4$ is false, shade the half-plane *not* containing $(0,0)$.

Graph $2x - 3y \leq -6$ by graphing $2x - 3y = -6$ as a solid line using the x-intercept, -3, and the y-intercept, 2.
Use $(0,0)$ as a test point. $\quad 2x - 3y \leq -6$
$$2(0) - 3(0) \leq -6$$
$$0 \leq -6, \text{ false}$$

Because $2(0) - 3(0) \leq -6$ is false, shade the half-plane *not* containing $(0,0)$.

The solution set of the system is the intersection of the two shaded regions.

$x + 2y > 4$
$2x - 3y \leq -6$

3. $y \geq x + 2$

$x \geq 1$

Graph $y \geq x + 2$ by graphing $y = x + 2$ as a solid line using the y-intercept, 2, and the slope, 1.
Use $(0,0)$ as a test point. $\quad y \geq x + 2$
$$0 \geq 0 + 2$$
$$0 \geq 2, \text{ false}$$

Because $0 \geq 0 + 2$ is false, shade the half-plane *not* containing $(0,0)$.

Graph $x \geq 1$ by graphing $x = 1$ as a solid vertical line through $x = 1$.
Use $(0,0)$ as a test point. $\quad x \geq 1$
$$0 \geq 1, \text{ false}$$

Because $0 \geq 1$ is false, shade the half-plane *not* containing $(0,0)$.

The solution set of the system is the intersection of the two shaded regions.

$y \geq x + 2$
$x \geq 1$

5.5 Exercise Set

1. $x + y \leq 4$

$x - y \leq 2$

Graph $x + y \leq 4$ by graphing $x + y = 4$ as a solid line using the x-intercept, 4, and the y-intercept, 4.
Because $(0,0)$ makes the inequality $x + y \leq 4$ true, shade the half-plane containing $(0,0)$.

Graph $x - y \leq 2$ by graphing $x - y = 2$ or $y = x - 2$ as a solid line with x-intercept 2 and y-intercept -2.
Because $(0,0)$ makes the inequality $x - y \leq 2$ true, shade the half-plane containing $(0,0)$.

The solution set of the system is the intersection of the shaded regions.

$x + y \leq 4$
$x - y \leq 2$

3. $2x - 4y \le 8$

$x + y \ge -1$

Graph $2x - 4y \le 8$ by graphing $2x - 4y = 8$ as a solid line using the x-intercept, 4, and the y-intercept, -2. Because $4(0) - 2(0) \le 8$ is true, shade the half-plane containing $(0,0)$.

Graph $x + y \ge -1$ by graphing $x + y = -1$ as a solid line using the x-intercept, -1, and the y-intercept, -1. Because $0 + 0 \ge -1$ is true, shade the half-plane containing $(0,0)$.

The solution set of the system is the intersection of the two shaded regions.

$2x - 4y \le 8$

$x + y \ge -1$

5. $x + 3y \le 6$

$x - 2y \le 4$

Graph $x + 3y \le 6$ by graphing $x + 3y = 6$ as a solid line using the x-intercept, 6, and the y-intercept, 2. Because $0 + 3(0) \le 6$ is true, shade the half-plane containing $(0,0)$.

Graph $x - 2y \le 4$ by graphing $x - 2y = 4$ as a solid line using the x-intercept, 4, and the y-intercept, -2. Because $0 - 2(0) \le 4$ is true, shade the half-plane containing $(0,0)$.

The solution set of the system is the intersection of the shaded regions.

$x + 3y \le 6$

$x - 2y \le 4$

7. $x - 2y > 4$

$2x + y \ge 6$

Graph $x - 2y > 4$ by graphing $x - 2y = 4$ as a dashed line using the x-intercept, 4, and the y-intercept, -2. Because $0 - 2(0) > 4$ is false, shade the half-plane *not* containing $(0,0)$.

Graph $2x + y \ge 6$ by graphing $2x + y = 6$ as a solid line using the x-intercept, 3, and the y-intercept, 6. Because $2(0) + 0 \ge 6$ is false, shade the half-plane *not* containing $(0,0)$.

The solution set of the system is the intersection of the two shaded regions.

$x - 2y > 4$

$2x + y \ge 6$

9. $x + y > 1$

$x + y < 4$

Graph $x + y > 1$ by graphing $x + y = 1$ as a dashed line using the x-intercept 1 and y-intercept 1. Because $0 + 0 > 1$ is false, *do not* shade the half-plane containing $(0,0)$.

Graph $x + y < 4$ by graphing $x + y = 4$ as a dashed line using the x-intercept 4 and y-intercept 4. Because $0 + 0 < 4$ is true, shade the half-plane containing $(0,0)$.

The solution set is the shaded region between the two dashed parallel lines.

$x + y > 1$

$x + y < 4$

11. $y \geq 2x + 1$

$y \leq 4$

Graph $y \geq 2x + 1$ by graphing $y = 2x + 1$ as a solid line using the slope, 2, and the y-intercept, 1. Because $0 \geq 2(0) + 1$ is false, shade the half-plane *not* containing $(0, 0)$.

Graph $y \leq 4$ by graphing $y = 4$ as a solid horizontal line with y-intercept 4. Because $0 \leq 4$ is true, shade the half-plane containing $(0, 0)$.

The solution set of the system is the intersection of the shaded regions.

13. $y > x - 1$

$x > 5$

Graph $y > x - 1$ by graphing $y = x - 1$ as a dashed line using the slope, 1, and the y-intercept, -1. Because $0 > 0 - 1$ is true, shade the half-plane containing $(0, 0)$.

Graph $x > 5$ by graphing $x = 5$ as a dashed vertical line with x-intercept 5. Because $0 > 5$ is false, shade the half-plane not containing $(0, 0)$.

The solution set of the system is the intersection of the two shaded regions.

15. $y \geq 2x - 3$

$y \leq 2x + 1$

Graph $y \geq 2x - 3$ by graphing $y = 2x - 3$ as a solid line using slope, 2, and y-intercept, -3. Since $0 \geq 2(0) - 3$ is true, shade the half plane containing $(0, 0)$.

Graph $y \leq 2x + 1$ by graphing $y = 2x + 1$ as a solid line using its slope, 2, and y-intercept, 1. Since $0 \leq 2(0) + 1$ is true, shade the half-plane containing $(0, 0)$.

The solution set of the system is the intersection of the shaded regions.

17. $y > 2x + 3$

$y \leq -x + 6$

Graph $y > 2x - 3$ by graphing $y = 2x - 3$ as a dashed line using its slope, 2, and y-intercept, -3. Since $0 > 2(0) - 3$ is true, shade the half-plane containing $(0, 0)$.

Graph $y \leq -x + 6$ by graphing $y = -x + 6$ as a solid line using its slope, -1, and y-intercept, 6. Since $0 \leq -0 + 6$ is true, shade the half-plane containing $(0, 0)$.

The solution set of the system is the intersection of the two shaded regions.

19. $x + 2y \le 4$

$y \ge x - 3$

Graph $x + 2y \le 4$ by graphing $x + 2y = 4$ as a solid line using its *x*-intercept, 4, and *y*-intercept, 2. Since $0 + 2(0) \le 4$ is true, shade the half-plane containing $(0,0)$.

Graph $y \ge x - 3$ by graphing $y = x - 3$ as a solid line, using its slope, 1, and *y*-intercept, −3. Since $0 \ge 0 - 3$ is true, shade the half-plane containing $(0,0)$.

The solution set of the system is the intersection of the two shaded regions.

21. $x \le 3$

$y \ge -2$

Graph $x \le 3$ by graphing $x = 3$ as a solid vertical line. Since $0 \le 3$ is true, shade the half-plane containing $(0,0)$.

Graph $y \ge -2$ by graphing $y = -2$ as a solid horizontal line. Since $0 \ge -2$ is true, shade the half-plane containing $(0,0)$.

The solution set of the system is the intersection of the shaded regions.

23. $x \ge 3$

$y < 2$

Graph $x \ge 3$ by graphing $x = 3$ as a solid vertical line. Since $0 \ge 3$ is false, shade the half-plane *not* containing $(0,0)$.

Graph $y < 2$ by graphing $y = 2$ as a dashed horizontal line. Since $0 < 2$ is true, shade the half-plane containing $(0,0)$.

The solution set of the system is the intersection of the two shaded regions.

25. $x \ge 0$

$y \le 0$

Graph $x \ge 0$ by graphing $x = 0$ (the *y*–axis) as a solid vertical line. Shade the half-plane to the right of the axis.

Graph $y \le 0$ by graphing $y = 0$ (the *x*–axis) as a solid horizontal line. Shade the half-plane below the axis.

The solution set of the system is the intersection of the two shaded regions. This is all of quadrant IV, including the portions of the axes that are the boundaries of this region.

27. $x \ge 0$

$y > 0$

Graph $x \ge 0$ by graphing $x = 0$ as a solid vertical line. This is the *y*-axis. Shade the half-plane to the right of the *y*-axis.

Graph $y > 0$ by graphing $y = 0$ as a dashed solid line. This is the *x*-axis. Shade the half-plane above the *x*-axis.

The solution set of the system is the intersection of the two shaded regions. This is all of quadrant I, including the portion of the *y*-axis, but excluding the portion of the *x*-axis, that are boundaries of this region.

29. $x + y \leq 5$

$x \geq 0$

$y \geq 0$

Graph $x + y \leq 5$ by graphing $x + y = 5$ as a solid line using its x-intercept, 5, and y-intercept, 5. Since $0 + 0 \leq 5$ is true, shade the half-plane containing $(0,0)$.

Graph $x \geq 0$ by graphing $x = 0$ (the y-axis) as a solid line. Shade the half-plane to the right of the y-axis.

Graph $y \geq 0$ by graphing $y = 0$ (the x-axis) as a solid line. Shade the half-plane above the x-axis.

The solution set of the system is the intersection of the shaded regions. This is the set of points satisfying $x + y \leq 5$ that lie in quadrant I, together with the portions of the axes that are boundaries of this region.

$x + y \leq 5$

$x \geq 0$

$y \geq 0$

31. $4x - 3y > 12$

$x \geq 0$

$y \leq 0$

Graph $4x - 3y > 12$ by graphing $4x - 3y = 12$ as a dashed line using x-intercept, 3, and y-intercept, −4. Since $4(0) - 3(0) > 12$ is false, shade the half-plane *not* including $(0,0)$.

Graph $x \geq 0$ by graphing $x = 0$ (the y-axis) as a solid line and shade the half-plane to the right of it.

Graph $y \leq 0$ by graphing $y = 0$ (the x-axis) as a solid line and shade the half-plane below it.

The solution set of the system is the intersection of the three shaded regions. Notice that this is the set of points satisfying $4x - 3y > 12$ that lie in quadrant IV, together with the portions of the axes that are boundaries of these regions.

$4x - 3y > 12$

$x \geq 0$

$y \leq 0$

33. $0 \leq x \leq 3$

$0 \leq y \leq 3$

Graph $0 \leq x \leq 3$ by graphing the vertical lines $x = 0$ (the y-axis) and $x = 3$ as solid lines. Shade the region between the parallel lines.

Graph $0 \leq y \leq 3$ by graphing the horizontal lines $y = 0$ (the x-axis) and $y = 3$ as solid lines. Shade the region between these horizontal lines.

The solution set of the system is the intersection of the shaded regions.

$0 \leq x \leq 3$

$0 \leq y \leq 3$

35. $x - y \leq 4$

$x + 2y \leq 4$

Graph $x - y \leq 4$ by graphing $x - y = 4$ as a solid line using the x-intercept, 4, and the y-intercept, −4. Since $0 - 0 \leq 4$ is true, shade the half-plane containing $(0,0)$.

Graph $x + 2y \leq 4$ by graphing $x + 2y = 4$ as a solid line using the x-intercept, 4, and the y-intercept, 2. Since $0 + 2(0) \leq 4$ is true, shade the half-plane containing $(0,0)$.

The solution set of the system is the intersection of the shaded regions.

$x - y \leq 4$

$x + 2y \leq 4$

37. $x + y \geq 1$

$x - y \geq 1$

$x \geq 4$

Graph $x + y \geq 1$ by graphing $x + y = 1$ as a solid line using the *x*-intercept, 1, and the *y*-intercept, 1. Since $0 + 0 \geq 1$ is false, shade the half-plane *not* containing $(0, 0)$.

Graph $x - y \geq 1$ by graphing $x - y = 1$ as a solid line using the *x*-intercept, 1, and the *y*-intercept, −1. Since $0 - 0 \geq 1$ is false, shade the half-plane *not* containing $(0, 0)$.

Graph $x \geq 4$ by graphing $x = 4$ as a solid vertical line and shade the half-plane to the right of it. The solution set of the system is the intersection of the shaded regions.

$x + y \geq 1$
$x - y \geq 1$
$x \geq 4$

39. $x + 2y < 6$

$y > 2x - 2$

$y \geq 2$

Graph $x + 2y < 6$ by graphing $x + 2y < 6$ as a dashed line using the *x*-intercept, 6, and the *y*-intercept, 3.

Since $0 + 2(0) < 6$ is true, shade the half-plane containing $(0, 0)$.

Graph $y > 2x - 2$ by graphing $y = 2x - 2$ as a dashed line using the slope, 2, and the *y*-intercept, −2. Since $0 > 2(0) - 2$ is true, shade the half-plane containing $(0, 0)$.

Graph $y \geq 2$ by graphing $y = 2$ as a solid horizontal line and shade the half-plane above it. The solution set of the system is the intersection of the shaded regions.

$x + 2y < 6$
$y > 2x - 2$
$y \geq 2$

41. $y \leq -3x + 3$

$y > -x - 1$

$y < x + 7$

Graph $y \leq -3x + 3$ by graphing $y = -3x + 3$ as a solid line with slope, −3, and *y*-intercept, 3. Since $0 \leq -3(0) + 3$ is true, shade the half-plane containing $(0, 0)$.

Graph $y > -x - 1$ by graphing $y = -x - 1$ as a dashed line using the slope, −1, and the *y*-intercept, −1.

Since $0 > -0 - 1$ is true, shade the half-plane containing $(0, 0)$.

Graph $y < x + 7$ by graphing $y = x + 7$ as a dashed line with slope, 1, and *y*-intercept, 7. Since $0 < 0 + 7$ is true, shade the half-plane containing $(0, 0)$.

The solution set of the system is the intersection of the shaded regions.

$y \leq -3x + 3$
$y \geq -x - 1$
$y < x + 7$

43. $y \geq 2x + 2$

$y < 2x - 3$

$x \geq 2$

Graph $y \geq 2x + 2$ by graphing $y = 2x + 2$ as a solid line with slope, 2, and y-intercept, 2. Since $0 \geq 2(0) + 2$ is false, shade the half-plane *not* containing $(0, 0)$.

Graph $y < 2x - 3$ by graphing $y = 2x - 3$ as a dashed line using the slope, 2, and the y-intercept, -3.

Since $0 < 2(0) - 3$ is false, shade the half-plane *not* containing $(0, 0)$.

Graph $x \geq 2$ by graphing $x = 2$ as a solid vertical line. Since $0 \geq 2$ is false, shade the half-plane containing $(0, 0)$.

The solution to the system is the intersection of the shaded regions. In this case, there is no region on the graph where the three shaded regions intersect, so there is no solution.

$y \geq 2x + 2$
$y < 2x - 3$
$x \geq 2$

45. Point $A = (66, 160)$

$$5.3x - y \geq 180$$
$$5.3(66) - 160 \geq 180$$
$$189.8 \geq 180, \text{ true}$$

$$4.1x - y \leq 14$$
$$4.1(66) - 160 \leq 140$$
$$110.6 \leq 140, \text{ true}$$

Point A is a solution of the system.

47. Point $= (72, 205)$

$$5.3x - y \geq 180$$
$$5.3(72) - 205 \geq 180$$
$$176.6 \geq 180, \text{ false}$$

$$4.1x - y \leq 14$$
$$4.1(72) - 205 \leq 140$$
$$90.2 \leq 140, \text{ true}$$

The data does not satisfy both inequalities. The person is not within the healthy weight region.

49. $165x + 110y \leq 330$

$165x + 110y \geq 165$

Graph $165x + 110y = 330$ as a solid line with x-intercept 2 and y-intercept 3. Draw the graph in quadrant I only. Use $(1, 1)$ as a test point. Since

$165(1) + 110(1) = 275 < 330$ is true, shade the region in quadrant I containing $(1, 1)$.

Graph $165x + 110y = 165$ as a solid line with x-intercept 1 and y-intercept 1.5. Draw the graph in quadrant I only. Use $(1, 3)$ as a test point. Since

$165(1) + 110(3) = 495 \geq 165$

is true, shade the region in quadrant I containing $(1, 3)$.

The graph of the system is the intersection of the two shaded regions.

165x + 110y ≤ 330

One point in the solution set is $(1, 1)$. This means that the patient is allowed to have 1 egg and 1 ounce of meat per day.

Another point in the solution set is $(0, 3)$ This means that the patient is also allowed to have no eggs and 3 ounces of meat per day.

51. Answers will vary.

53. makes sense

55. makes sense

57. $y \geq -x + 3$

$x > 5$

59. $x < 0$

$y < 0$

61. Let x = the number of \$35 tickets sold.
Let y = the number of \$50 tickets sold.
From the information given in the problem, we have the following inequalities.

$x + y \geq 25,000$

$35x + 50y \geq 1,025,000$

Also, the number of tickets sold and the amount of money in ticket sales cannot be negative, so we also have $x \geq 0$ and $y \geq 0$. so the system is as follows.

$x + y \geq 25,000$

$35x + 50y \geq 1,025,000$

$x \geq 0$

$y \geq 0$

Graph $x + y \geq 25,000$ by graphing $x + y = 25,000$ as a solid line using its x-intercept, 25,000, and y-intercept, 25,000. Since $0 + 0 \geq 25,000$ is false, shade the region *not* containing (0,0).
Graph $35x + 50y \geq 1,025,000$ by graphing $35x + 50y = 1,025,000$ using its x-intercept, approximately 29,286, and its y-intercept, 20,500. Since $35(0) + 50(0) \geq 1,025,000$ is false, shade the region *not* containing (0,0).
The inequalities $x \geq 0$ and $y \geq 0$ restrict the graph to quadrant I.

62. $(-6,1)$ and $(2,-1)$

$$m = \frac{-1-1}{2-(-6)} = \frac{-2}{8} = -\frac{1}{4}$$

63. $\dfrac{1}{5} + \left(-\dfrac{3}{4}\right) = \dfrac{4}{20} + \left(-\dfrac{15}{20}\right) = -\dfrac{11}{20}$

64. $7x = 10 + 6(11 - 2x)$

$7x = 10 + 66 - 12x$

$7x = 76 - 12x$

$19x = 76$

$x = \dfrac{76}{19}$

$x = 4$

The solution set is $\{4\}$.

65. $5x^3 + 12x^3 = (5 + 12)x^3 = 17x^3$

66. $-8x^2 + 6x^2 = (-8 + 6)x^2 = -2x^2$

67. $-9y^4 - (-2y^4) = -9y^4 + 2y^4$

$$= (-9 + 2)y^4$$

$$= -7y^4$$

Chapter 5 Review

1. $\qquad 4x - y = 9$

$\qquad 4(1) - (-5) = 9$

$\qquad\qquad 4 + 5 = 9$

$\qquad\qquad\qquad 9 = 9,\ \text{true}$

$\qquad\qquad 2x + 3y = -13$

$\qquad 2(1) + 3(-5) = -13$

$\qquad\qquad 2 - 15 = -13$

$\qquad\qquad -13 = -13,\ \text{true}$

Since the ordered pair $(1, -5)$ satisfies both equations, it is a solution of the given system.

2. $\qquad 2x + 3y = -4$

$\qquad 2(-5) + 3(2) = -4$

$\qquad\qquad -10 + 6 = -4$

$\qquad\qquad\qquad -4 = -4,\ \text{true}$

$\qquad\qquad x - 4y = -10$

$\qquad -5 - 4(-2) = -10$

$\qquad\qquad -5 + 8 = -10$

$\qquad\qquad\qquad 3 = -10,\ \text{false}$

Since $(-5,2)$ fails to satisfy *both* equations, it is not a solution of the given system.

3. $x + y = 2$

$-1 + 3 = 2$

$2 = 2$, true

$2x + y = -5$

$2(-1) + 3 = -5$

$-2 + 3 = -5$

$1 = -5$, false

Since $(-1, 3)$ fails to satisfy *both* equations, it is not a solution of the given system. Also, the second equation in the system, which can be rewritten as $y = -2x - 5$, is a line with slope -2 and y-intercept -5, while the graph shows a line with slope 2 and y-intercept 5.

4. $x + y = 2$

$x - y = 6$

Graph both lines on the same axes.

$x + y = 2$: x-intercept = 2; y-intercept 2

$x - y = 6$: x-intercept = 6, y-intercept = -6

The solution set is $\{(4, -2)\}$.

5. $2x - 3y = 12$

$-2x + y = -8$

Graph both equations.

$2x - 3y = 12$: x-intercept = 6; y-intercept = -4

$-2x + y = -8$: x-intercept = 4; y-intercept = -8

The solution set is $\{(3, -2)\}$.

6. $3x + 2y = 6$

$3x - 2y = 6$

Graph both equations.

$3x + 2y = 6$: x-intercept = 2; y-intercept = 3

$3x - 2y = 6$: x-intercept = 2; y-intercept = -3

The solution set is $\{(2, 0)\}$.

7. $y = \dfrac{1}{2} x$

$y = 2x - 3$

Graph both equations.

$y = \dfrac{1}{2} x$: slope = $\dfrac{1}{2}$; y-intercept = 0

$y = 2x - 3$: slope = 2; y-intercept = -3

The solution set is $\{(2, 1)\}$.

8. $x + 2y = 2$

$y = x - 5$

Graph both equations.

$x + 2y = 2$: x-intercept = 2; y-intercept = 1

$y = x - 5$: slope = 1; y-intercept = -5

The solution set is $\{(4, -1)\}$.

9. $x + 2y = 8$

    $3x + 6y = 12$

    Graph both equations.

    $x + 2y = 8$: x-intercept = 8; y-intercept = 4

    $3x + 6y = 12$: x-intercept = 4; y-intercept = 2

    The lines are parallel. The system is inconsistent and has no solution. The solution set is $\{\ \}$.

10. $2x - 4y = 8$

    $x - 2y = 4$

    Graph both equations.

    $2x - 4y = 8$: x-intercept = 4; y-intercept = -2

    $x - 2y = 4$: x-intercept = 4; y-intercept = -2

    The graphs of the two equations are the same line. The system is dependent and has infinitely many solutions.

    The solution set is $\{(x, y) | 2x - 4y = 8\}$ or

    $\{(x, y) | x - 2y = 4\}$.

11. $y = 3x - 1$

    $y = 3x + 2$

    Graph both equations.

    $y = 3x - 1$: slope = 3; y-intercept = -1

    $y = 3x + 2$: slope = 3; y-intercept = 2

    The lines are parallel, so the system is inconsistent and has no solution. The solution set is $\{\ \}$.

12. $x - y = 4$

    $x = -2$

    Graph both equations:

    $x - y = 4$: x-intercept = 4; y-intercept = -4

    $x = 2$: vertical line with x-intercept = -2

    The solution set is $\{(-2, -6)\}$.

13. $x = 2$

    $y = 5$

    The solution set is $\{(2, 5)\}$.

14. $x = 2$

    $x = 5$

    The lines are parallel, so the system inconsistent and has no solution.

    The solution set is $\{\ \}$.

15. $2x - 3y = 7$

$\qquad y = 3x - 7$

Substitute $3x - 7$ for y in the first equation.

$\qquad 2x - 3y = 7$

$\qquad 2x - 3(3x - 7) = 7$

$\qquad 2x - 9x + 21 = 7$

$\qquad -7x + 21 = 7$

$\qquad -7x = -14$

$\qquad x = 2$

Back-substitute 7 for x into the second equation and solve for y.

$y = 3x - 7$

$y = 3(2) - 7 = -1$

The solution set is $\{(2, -1)\}$.

16. $2x - y = 6$

$\qquad x = 13 - 2y$

Substitute $13 - 2y$ for x into the first equation.

$\qquad 2x - y = 6$

$\qquad 2(13 - 2y) - y = 6$

$\qquad 26 - 4y - y = 6$

$\qquad 26 - 5y = 6$

$\qquad -5y = -20$

$\qquad y = 4$

Back-substitute 4 for y in the second equation.

$x = 13 - 2y$

$x = 13 - 2(4) = 5$

The solution set is $\{(5, 4)\}$.

17. $2x - 5y = 1$

$\qquad 3x + y = -7$

Solve the second equation for y.

$3x + y = -7$

$\qquad y = -3x - 7$

Substitute $-3x - 7$ in the first equation.

$\qquad 2x - 5y = 1$

$\qquad 2x - 5(-3x - 7) = 1$

$\qquad 2x + 15x + 35 = 1$

$\qquad 17x + 35 = 1$

$\qquad 17x = -34$

$\qquad x = -2$

Back-substitute in the equation $y = -3x - 7$.

$y = -3x - 7$

$y = -3(-2) - 7 = -1$

The solution set is $\{(-2, -1)\}$.

18. $3x + 4y = -13$

$\qquad 5y - x = -21$

Solve the second equation for x.

$5y - x = -21$

$\qquad -x = -5y - 21$

$\qquad x = 5y + 21$

Substitute $5y + 21$ for x in the first equation.

$\qquad 3x + 4y = -13$

$\qquad 3(5y + 21) + 4y = -13$

$\qquad 15y + 63 + 4y = -13$

$\qquad 19y + 63 = -13$

$\qquad 19y = -76$

$\qquad y = -4$

Back-substitute.

$\qquad 3x + 4y = -13$

$\qquad 3x + 4(-4) = -13$

$\qquad 3x - 16 = -13$

$\qquad 3x = 3$

$\qquad x = 1$

The solution set is $\{(1, -4)\}$.

19. $y = 39 - 3x$

$\qquad y = 2x - 61$

Substitute $2x - 61$ for y in the first equation.

$2x - 61 = 39 - 3x$

$\qquad 5x - 61 = 39$

$\qquad 5x = 100$

$\qquad x = 20$

Back-substitute.

$y = 2x - 61 = 2(20) - 61 = -21$

The solution set is $\{(20, -21)\}$.

20. $4x + y = 5$

$12x + 3y = 15$

Solve the first equation for y.

$4x + y = 5$

$y = -4x + 5$

Substitute $-4x + 5$ for y in the second equation.

$12x + 3y = 15$

$12x + 3(-4x + 5) = 15$

$12x - 12x + 15 = 15$

$15 = 15, \text{ true}$

The true statement indicates that the given system has infinitely many solutions.

The solution set is $\{(x, y) | 4x + y = 5\}$ or

$\{(x, y) | 12x + 3y = 15\}$.

21. $4x - 2y = 10$

$y = 2x + 3$

Substitute $2x + 3$ for y in the first equation.

$4x - 2y = 10$

$4x - 2(2x + 3) = 10$

$4x - 4x - 6 = 10$

$-6 = 10, \text{ false}$

The false statement $-6 = 10$ indicates that the system is inconsistent and has no solution.

The solution set is $\{\ \}$.

22. $x - 4 = 0$

$9x - 2y = 0$

Solve the first equation for x.

$x - 4 = 0$

$x = 4$

Substitute 4 for x in the second equation.

$9x - 2y = 0$

$9(4) - 2y = 0$

$36 - 2y = 0$

$-2y = -36$

$y = 18$

The solution set is $\{(4, 18)\}$.

23. $8y = 4x$

$7x + 2y = -8$

Solve the first equation for y.

$8y = 4x$

$y = \dfrac{1}{2}x$

Substitute $\dfrac{1}{2}x$ for y in the second equation.

$7x + 2y = -8$

$7x + 2\left(\dfrac{1}{2}x\right) = -8$

$7x + x = -8$

$8x = -8$

$x = -1$

Back-substitute.

$y = \dfrac{1}{2}x = \dfrac{1}{2}(-1) = -\dfrac{1}{2}$

The solution set is $\left\{\left(-1, -\dfrac{1}{2}\right)\right\}$.

24. a. Demand model: $p = -50x + 2000$

Supply model: $p = 50x$

Use the substitution method.

$p = -50x + 2000$

$\overbrace{50x}^{p} = -50x + 2000$

$50x = -50x + 2000$

$100x = 2000$

$x = 20$

Back-substitute 20 for x and find p.

$p = 50x$

$p = 50(20) = 1000$

The solution set is $\{(20, 1000)\}$.

The equilibrium quantity is 20,000 and the equilibrium price is $1000.

b. When rents are $1000 per month, consumers will demand 20,000 apartments and suppliers will offer 20,000 apartments for rent.

25. $x + y = 6$

$2x + y = 8$

Multiply the first equation by -1 and add the result to the second equation to eliminate the y-terms.

$-x - y = -6$

$\underline{2x + y = \ 8}$

$x \qquad = 2$

Back-substitute into either of the original equations to solve for y.

$x + y = 6$

$2 + y = 6$

$y = 4$

The solution set is $\{(2, 4)\}$.

26. $3x - 4y = 1$

$12x - y = -11$

Multiply the first equation by -4 and add the result to the second equation.

$-12x + 16y = -4$

$\underline{12x - \ y = -11}$

$15y = -15$

$y = -1$

Back-substitute.

$3x - 4y = 1$

$3x - 4(-1) = 1$

$3x + 4 = 1$

$3x = -3$

$x = -1$

The solution set is $\{(-1, -1)\}$.

27. $3x - 7y = 13$

$6x + 5y = 7$

Multiply the first equation by -2.

$-6x + 14y = -26$

$\underline{6x + \ 5y = \ 7}$

$19y = -19$

$y = -1$

Back-substitute.

$3x - 7y = 13$

$3x - 7(-1) = 13$

$3x + 7 = 13$

$3x = 6$

$x = 2$

The solution set is $\{(2, -1)\}$.

28. $8x - 4y = 16$

$4x + 5y = 22$

Multiply the second equation by -2.

$8x - \ 4y = \ 16$

$\underline{-8x - 10y = -44}$

$-14y = -28$

$y = 2$

Back-substitute.

$8x - 4y = 16$

$8x - 4(2) = 16$

$8x - 8 = 16$

$8x = 24$

$x = 3$

The solution set is $\{(3, 2)\}$.

29. $5x - 2y = 8$

$3x - 5y = 1$

Multiply the first equation by 3.

Multiply the second equation by -5.

$15x - \ 6y = 24$

$\underline{-15x + 25y = -5}$

$19y = 19$

$y = 1$

Back-substitute.

$5x - 2y = 8$

$5x - 2(1) = 8$

$5x - 2 = 8$

$5x = 10$

$x = 2$

The solution set is $\{(2, 1)\}$.

30. $2x + 7y = 0$

$7x + 2y = 0$

Multiply the first equation by 7.
Multiply the second equation by -2.

$14x + 49y = 0$

$\underline{-14x - 4y = 0}$

$45y = 0$

$y = 0$

Back-substitute.

$2x + 7y = 0$

$2x + 7(0) = 0$

$2x = 0$

$x = 0$

The solution set is $\{(0,0)\}$.

31. $x + 3y = -4$

$3x + 2y = 3$

Multiply the first equation by -3.

$-3x - 9y = 12$

$\underline{3x + 2y = 3}$

$-7y = 15$

$y = -\dfrac{15}{7}$

Instead of back-substituting $-\dfrac{15}{7}$ and working with

fractions, go back to the original system. Multiply
the first equation by 2 and the second equation by
-3.

$2x + 6y = -8$

$\underline{-9x - 6y = -9}$

$-7x = -17$

$x = \dfrac{17}{7}$

The solution set is $\left\{\left(\dfrac{17}{7}, -\dfrac{15}{7}\right)\right\}$.

32. $2x + y = 5$

$2x + y = 7$

Multiply the first equation by -1.

$-2x - y = -5$

$\underline{2x + y = 7}$

$0 = 2, \text{ false}$

The false statement indicates that the system has no
solution. The solution set is $\{\ \}$.

33. $3x - 4y = -1$

$-6x + 8y = 2$

Multiply the first equation by 2.

$6x - 8y = -2$

$\underline{-6x + 8y = 2}$

$0 = 0, \text{ true}$

The true statement indicates that the system is
dependent and has infinitely many solutions.

The solution set is $\{(x, y) | 3x - 4y = -1\}$ or

$\{(x, y) | -6x + 8y = 2\}$.

34. $2x = 8y + 24$

$3x + 5y = 2$

Rewrite the first equation in the form $Ax + By = C$.

$2x - 8y = 24$

Multiply this equation by 3.
Multiply the second equation by -2.

$6x - 24y = 72$

$\underline{-6y - 10y = -4}$

$-34y = 68$

$y = -2$

Back-substitute.

$3x + 5y = 2$

$3x + 5(-2) = 2$

$3x - 10 = 2$

$3x = 12$

$x = 4$

The solution set is $\{(4, -2)\}$.

35. $5x - 7y = 2$

$3x = 4y$

Rewrite the second equation in the form
$Ax + By = C$.

$3x - 4y = 0$

Multiply this equation by -5.
Multiply the first equation by 3.

$15x - 21y = 6$

$\underline{-15x + 20y = 0}$

$-y = 6$

$y = -6$

Back-substitute.

$3x - 4y = 0$

$3x - 4(-6) = 0$

$3x + 24 = 0$

$3x = -24$

$x = -8$

The solution set is $\{(-8, -6)\}$.

36. $3x + 4y = -8$

$2x + 3y = -5$

Multiply the first equation by 2.
Multiply the second equation by -3.

$6x + 8y = -16$

$\underline{-6x - 9y = 15}$

$-y = -1$

$y = 1$

Back-substitute.

$3x + 4y = -8$

$3x + 4(1) = -8$

$3x + 4 = -8$

$3x = -12$

$x = -4$

The solution set is $\{(-4, 1)\}$.

37. $6x + 8y = 39$

$y = 2x - 2$

Substitute $2x - 2$ for y in the first equation.

$6x + 8y = 39$

$6x + 8(2x - 2) = 39$

$6x + 16x - 16 = 39$

$22x - 16 = 39$

$22x = 55$

$x = \dfrac{55}{22} = \dfrac{5}{2}$

Back-substitute $\dfrac{5}{2}$ for x into the second equation of the system.

$y = 2x - 2$

$y = 2\left(\dfrac{5}{2}\right) - 2 = 5 - 2 = 3$

The solution set is $\left\{\left(\dfrac{5}{2}, 3\right)\right\}$.

38. $x + 2y = 7$

$2x + y = 8$

Multiply the first equation by -2.

$-2x - 4y = -14$

$\underline{2x + y = \ \ 8}$

$-3y = -6$

$y = 2$

Back-substitute.

$x + 2y = 7$

$x + 2(2) = 7$

$x + 4 = 7$

$x = 3$

The solution set is $\{(3, 2)\}$.

39. $y = 2x - 3$

$y = -2x - 1$

Substitute $-2x - 1$ for y in the first equation.

$-2x - 1 = 2x - 3$

$-4x - 1 = -3$

$-4x = -2$

$x = \dfrac{1}{2}$

Back-substitute.

$y = 2x - 3$

$y = 2\left(\dfrac{1}{2}\right) - 3 = -2$

The solution set is $\left\{\left(\dfrac{1}{2}, -2\right)\right\}$.

40. $3x - 6y = 7$

$3x = 6y$

Solve the second equation for x.

$3x = 6y$

$x = 2y$

Substitute $2y$ for x in the first equation.

$3x - 6y = 7$

$3(2y) - 6y = 7$

$6y - 6y = 7$

$0 = 7$

The false statement indicates that the system has no solution. The solution set is $\{\ \}$.

41. $y - 7 = 0$

$7x - 3y = 0$

Solve the first equation for y.

$y - 7 = 0$

$y = 7$

Substitute 7 for y in the second equation.

$7x - 3y = 0$

$7x - 3(7) = 0$

$7x - 21 = 0$

$7x = 21$

$x = 3$

The solution set is $\{(3, 7)\}$.

42. Let $x =$ the selling price for Klint's work.
Let $y =$ the selling price for Picasso's work.

$x + y = 239$

$x - y = 31$

Add the equations to eliminate y and solve for x.

$x + y = 239$

$\underline{x - y = \ \ 31}$

$2x \quad = 270$

$x = 135$

Back-substitute to find y.

$x + y = 239$

$135 + y = 239$

$y = 104$

Klint's work sold for $135 million and Picasso's work sold for $104 million.

43. Let $x =$ the cholesterol content of one ounce of shrimp (in milligrams).
Let $y =$ the cholesterol content in one ounce of scallops.

$3x + 2y = 156$

$5x + 3y = 300 - 45$

Simplify the second equation.

$5x + 3y = 255$

Multiply this equation by 2.
Multiply the first equation by -3.

$-9x - 6y = -468$

$\underline{10x + 6y = \ \ 510}$

$x \qquad = \quad 42$

Back-substitute to find y.

$3x + 2y = 156$

$3(42) + 2y = 156$

$126 + 2y = 156$

$2y = 30$

$y = 15$

There are 42 mg of cholesterol in an ounce of shrimp and 15 mg in an ounce of scallops.

44. Let $x =$ the length of a tennis table top.
Let $y =$ the width.
Use the formula for perimeter of a rectangle to write the first equation and the other information in the problem to write the second equation.

$2x + 2y = 28$

$4x - 3y = 21$

Multiply the first equation by -2.

$-4x + 4y = -56$

$\underline{4x - 3y = \ \ 21}$

$-7y = -35$

$y = 5$

Back-substitute to find x.

$2x + 2(5) = 28$

$2x + 10 = 28$

$2x = 18$

$x = 9$

The length is 9 feet and the width is 5 feet, so the dimensions of the table are 9 feet by 5 feet.

45. Let x = the length of the garden.
Let y = the width of the garden.
The perimeter of the garden is 24 yards, so
$2x + 2y = 24$.

Since there are two lengths and two widths to be fenced, the information about the cost of fencing leads to the equation $3(2x) + 2(2y) = 62$.

Simplify the second equation.
$6x + 4y = 62$.

Multiply the first equation by −2.
$-4x - 4y = -48$

$$\underline{6x + 4y = 62}$$

$2x \quad = 14$
$x \quad = 7$

Back-substitute to find y.
$2(7) + 2y = 24$
$14 + 2y = 24$
$2y = 10$
$y = 5$

The length of the garden is 7 yards and the width is 5 yards.

46. Let x = daily cost for room.
Let y = daily cost for car.
First plan: $3x + 2y = 360$

Second plan: $4x + 3y = 500$

Multiply the first equation by 3.
Multiply the second equation by −2.
$9x + 6y = 1080$

$$\underline{-8x - 6y = -1000}$$

$x \quad = \quad 80$
Back-substitute to find y.
$3(80) + 2y = 360$
$240 + 2y = 360$
$2y = 120$
$y = 60$

The cost per day is $80 for the room and $60 for the car.

47. Let x = the number of minutes of long-distance calls.
Let y = the monthly cost of a telephone plan.
Plan A: $y = 15 + 0.05x$

Plan B: $y = 10 + 0.075x$

To determine the amount of calling time that will result in the same cost for both plans, solve this system by the substitution method. Substitute $15 + 0.05x$ for y in the first equation.
$15 + 0.05x = 10 + 0.075x$
$15 - 0.025x = 10$
$-0.025x = -5$
$$\frac{-0.025x}{-0.025} = \frac{-5}{-0.025}$$
$x = 200$

Back-substitute to find y.
$y = 15 + 0.05(200) = 25$

The costs for the two plans will be equal for 200 minutes of long-distance calls per month. The cost of each plan will be $25.

48. Let x = the number orchestra tickets.
Let y = the number balcony tickets.
$x + y = 9$
$90x + 60y = 720$

Solve the first equation for y.
$x + y = 9$
$y = -x + 9$

Use the substitution method.
$90x + 60y = 720$

$$90x + 60(\overbrace{-x+9}^{y}) = 720$$
$90x + 60(-x + 9) = 720$
$90x - 60x + 540 = 720$
$30x + 540 = 720$
$30x = 180$
$x = 6$

Back-substitute to find y.
$y = -x + 9$
$y = -6 + 9 = 3$

You purchased 6 orchestra tickets and 3 balcony tickets.

49. $3x - y \leq 6$

$x + y \geq 2$

Graph $3x - y \leq 6$ by graphing $3x - y = 6$ as a solid line using the x-intercept 2, and y-intercept −6. Because (0,0) makes the inequality true, shade the half-plane containing (0,0).
Graph $x + y \geq 2$ by graphing $x + y = 2$ as a solid line using the x-intercept 2, and y-intercept 2. Because (0,0) makes the inequality false, shade the half-plane *not* containing (0,0).
The solution set of the system is the intersection (overlap) of the two shaded regions.

3x − y ≤ 6
x + y ≥ 2

50. $x + y < 4$

$x - y < 4$

Graph $x + y < 4$ by graphing $x + y = 4$ as a dashed line using the x-intercept 4, and y-intercept 4. Because $0 + 0 < 4$ is true, shade the half-plane containing (0,0).
Graph $x - y < 4$ by graphing $x - y = 4$ as a dashed line using the x-intercept 4, and y-intercept −4. Because $0 - 0 < 4$ is true, shade the half-plane containing (0,0).
The solution set of the system is the intersection of the two shaded regions.

x + y < 4
x − y < 4

51. $y < 2x - 2$

$x \geq 3$

Graph $y < 2x - 2$ by graphing $y = 2x - 3$ as a dashed line using the slope 2 and y-intercept −2. Since $0 < 2(0) - 2$ is false, shade the half-plane *not* containing (0,0).
Graph $x \geq 3$ by graphing $x = 3$ as a solid vertical line with x-intercept 3. Since $0 \geq 3$ is false, shade the half-plane *not* containing (0,0).

The solution set of the system is the intersection of the two shaded regions.

y < 2x −2
x ≥ 3

52. $4x + 6y \leq 24$

$y > 2$

Graph $4x + 6y \leq 24$ by graphing $4x + 6y = 24$ as a solid line with x-intercept 6 and y-intercept 4. Since $4(0) + 6(0) \leq 24$ is true, shade the half plane containing (0,0).
Graph $y > 2$ by graphing the dashed horizontal line at $y = 2$. Since $0 > 2$ is false, shade the half-plane *not* containing (0,0), the half-plane above the line.
The solution set of the system is the intersection of the two shaded regions.

4x + 6y ≤ 24
y > 2

53. $x \leq 3$

$y \geq -2$

Graph $x \leq 3$ by graphing the solid vertical line at $x = 3$. Since $0 \leq 3$ is true, shade the half-plane containing (0,0).
Graph $y \geq -2$ by graphing $y = -2$ as a solid horizontal line. Since $0 \geq -2$ is true, shade the half-plane containing (0,0).
The solution set of the system is the intersection of the two shaded regions.

x ≤ 3
y ≥ −2

54. $y \geq \dfrac{1}{2}x - 2$

$y \leq \dfrac{1}{2}x + 1$

Graph $y \geq \dfrac{1}{2}x - 2$ by graphing $y = \dfrac{1}{2}x - 2$ as a

solid line with slope $\dfrac{1}{2}$ and y-intercept -2. Since

$0 \geq \dfrac{1}{2}(0) - 2$ is true, shade the half-plane

containing $(0,0)$.

Graph $y \leq \dfrac{1}{2}x + 1$ by graphing $y = \dfrac{1}{2}x + 1$ as a

solid line with slope $\dfrac{1}{2}$ and y-intercept 1. Since

$0 \leq \dfrac{1}{2}(0) + 1$ is true, shade the half-plane containing

$(0,0)$.

The solution set of the system is the intersection of the two shaded regions. This is the region between and including the two parallel lines.

$y \geq \dfrac{1}{2}x - 2$

$y \leq \dfrac{1}{2}x + 1$

55. $x \leq 0$

$y \geq 0$

Graph $x \leq 0$ by graphing $x = 0$ (the y-axis) as a solid line. Shade the half-plane to the left of the y-axis.

Graph $y \geq 0$ by graphing $y = 0$ (the x-axis) as a solid line. Shade the half-plane above the x-axis. The solution set of the system is the intersection of the two shaded regions. Notice that this is all of quadrant II, including the portions of the axes that are boundaries of the region.

$x \leq 0$

$y \geq 0$

Chapter 5 Test

1. $2x + y = 5$
$2(5) + (-5) = 5$
$10 + (-5) = 5$
      $5 = 5$, true

$x + 3y = -10$
$5 + 3(-5) = -10$
$5 + (-15) = -10$
    $-10 = -10$, true

Since the ordered pair $(5, -5)$ satisfies both equations, it is a solution of the given system.

2. $x + 5y = 7$
$-3 + 5(2) = 7$
$-3 + 10 = 7$
      $7 = 7$, true

$3x - 4y = 1$
$3(-3) - 4(2) = 1$
$-9 - 8 = 1$
    $-17 = 1$, false

Since the ordered pair $(-3,2)$ fails to satisfy *both* equations, it is not a solution of the given system.

3. $x + y = 6$
$4x - y = 4$

Graph both lines on the same axes.
$x + y = 6$: x-intercept = 6; y-intercept = 6
$4x - y = 4$: x-intercept: 1; y-intercept = -4

The solution set is $\{(2,4)\}$.

4. $2x + y = 8$

    $y = 3x - 2$

Graph both lines on the same axes.

$2x + y = 8$: *x*-intercept = 4; *y*-intercept = 8

$y = 3x - 2$: slope = 3; *y*-intercept = -2

The solution set is $\{(2, 4)\}$.

5. $x = y + 4$

  $3x + 7y = -18$

Substitute $y + 4$ for *x* in the second equation.

$3x + 7y = -18$

$3(y + 4) + 7y = -18$

$3y + 12 + 7y = -18$

$10y + 12 = -18$

$10y = -30$

$y = -3$

Back-substitute -3 for *y* in the first equation.

$x = y + 4$

$x = -3 + 4 = 1$

The solution set is $\{(1, -3)\}$.

6. $2x - y = 7$

  $3x + 2y = 0$

Solve the first equation for *y*.

$2x - y = 7$

$-y = -2x + 7$

$y = 2x - 7$

Substitute $2x - 7$ for *y* in the second equation.

$3x + 2y = 0$

$3x + 2(2x - 7) = 0$

$3x + 4x - 14 = 0$

$7x - 14 = 0$

$7x = 14$

$x = 2$

Back-substitute 2 for *x* in the equation $3x + 2y = 0$.

$3x + 2y = 0$

$3(2) + 2y = 0$

$6 + 2y = 0$

$2y = -6$

$y = -3$

The solution set is $\{(2, -3)\}$.

7. $2x - 4y = 3$

    $x = 2y + 4$

Substitute $2y + 4$ for *x* in the first equation.

$2x - 4y = 3$

$2(2y + 4) - 4y = 3$

$4y + 8 - 4y = 3$

$8 = 3$, false

The false statement indicates that the system has no solution. The solution set is $\{\ \}$.

8. $2x + y = 2$

  $\underline{4x - y = -8}$

  $6x \quad\quad = -6$

      $x = -1$

Back-substitute to find *y*.

$2x + y = 2$

$2(-1) + y = 2$

$-2 + y = 2$

$y = 4$

The solution set is $\{(-1, 4)\}$.

9. $2x + 3y = 1$

  $3x + 2y = -6$

Multiply the first equation by 3.

Multiply the second equation by -2.

$6x + 9y = 3$

$\underline{-6x - 4y = 12}$

    $5y = 15$

     $y = 3$

Back-substitute to find *x*.

$2x + 3y = 1$

$2x + 3(3) = 1$

$2x + 9 = 1$

$2x = -8$

$x = -4$

The solution set is $\{(-4, 3)\}$.

10. $3x - 2y = 2$

$-9x + 6y = -6$

Multiply the first equation by 3.

$9x - 6y = 6$

$\underline{-9x + 6y = -6}$

$0 = 0, \text{ true}$

The true statement $0 = 0$ indicates that the system is dependent and the equation has infinitely many solutions.

The solution set is $\left\{ (x, y) \big| 3x - 2y = 2 \right\}$ or $\left\{ (x, y) \big| -9x + 6y = -6 \right\}.$

11. Let x = the percentage of females named Mary.
Let y = the percentage of females named Patricia.
The system is $x + y = 3.7$

$x - y = 1.5$

Add the two equations:

$x + y = 3.7$

$\underline{x - y = 1.5}$

$2x = 5.2$

$x = 2.6$

Back substitute to find y.

$2.6 + y = 3.7$

$y = 1.1$

2.6% of females are named Mary and 1.1% are named Patricia.

12. Let x = the length of the garden.
Let y = the width of the garden.
The perimeter of the garden is 34 yards so $2x + 2y = 34$.

Since there are two lengths and two widths to be fenced, the information about the cost of fencing leads to the equation $2(2x) + 1(2y) = 58$.

Simplify the second equation.

$4x + 2y = 58$

Multiply this equation by -1 and add the result to the first equation.

$2x + 2y = 34$

$\underline{-4x - 2y = -58}$

$-2x = -24$

$x = 12$

Back substitute to find y.

$2(12) + 2y = 34$

$24 + 2y = 34$

$2y = 10$

$y = 5$

The length of the garden is 12 yards and the width is 5 yards.

13. Let x = the number of minutes of long-distance calls.
Let y = the monthly cost of a telephone plan.
Plan A: $y = 15 + 0.05x$

Plan B: $y = 5 + 0.07x$

To determine the amount of calling time that will result in the same cost for both plans, solve this system by the substitution method. Substitute $5 + 0.07x$ for y in the first equation.

$5 + 0.07x = 15 + 0.05x$

$5 + 0.02x = 15$

$0.02x = 10$

$\dfrac{0.02x}{0.02} = \dfrac{10}{0.02}$

$x = 500$

If $x = 500$, $y = 15 + 0.05(500) = 40.$

The cost of the two plans will be equal for 500 minutes per month. The cost of each plan will be $40.

14. $x - 3y > 6$

$2x + 4y \le 8$

Graph $x - 3y > 6$ by graphing $x - 3y = 6$ as a dashed line using the x-intercept 6 and y-intercept -2. Because $0 - 3(0) > 6$ is false, shade the half-plane *not* containing (0,0).

Graph $2x + 4y \le 8$ by graphing $2x + 4y = 8$ as a solid line using the x-intercept 4 and y-intercept 2. Because $2(0) + 4(0) \le 8$ is true, shade the half-plane containing (0,0).

The solution set of the system is the intersection (overlap) of the two shaded regions.

$x - 3y > 6$
$2x + 4y \le 8$

15. $y \ge 2x - 4$

$x < 2$

Graph $y \ge 2x - 4$ by graphing $y = 2x - 4$ as a solid line using the slope 2 and y-intercept -4. Since $0 \ge 2(0) - 4$ is true, shade the half-plane containing (0,0).

Graph $x < 2$ by graphing $x = 2$ as a dashed vertical line with x-intercept 2. Since $0 < 2$ is true, shade the half-plane containing (0,0).

The solution set of the system is the intersection (overlap) of the two shaded regions.

$y \ge 2x - 4$

$x < 2$

Cumulative Review (Chapters 1-5)

1. $-14 - \left[18 - (6 - 10) \right]$

$= -14 - \left[18 - (-4) \right]$

$= -14 - \left[18 + 4 \right]$

$= -14 - 22$

$= -14 + (-22)$

$= -36$

2. $6(3x - 2) - (x - 1) = 18x - 12 - x + 1$

$\qquad\qquad\qquad\quad = 17x - 11$

3. $17(x + 3) = 13 + 4(x - 10)$

$17x + 51 = 13 + 4x - 40$

$17x + 51 = 4x - 27$

$13x = -78$

$x = -6$

The solution set is $\{-6\}$.

4. $\dfrac{x}{4} - 1 = \dfrac{x}{5}$

To clear fractions, multiply both sides by 20.

$20\left(\dfrac{x}{4} - 1 \right) = 20\left(\dfrac{x}{5} \right)$

$5x - 20 = 4x$

$x - 20 = 0$

$x = 20$

The solution set is $\{20\}$.

5. $A = P + Prt$

$A - P = Prt$

$\dfrac{A - P}{Pr} = \dfrac{Prt}{Pr}$

$\dfrac{A - P}{Pr} = t \quad \text{or} \quad t = \dfrac{A - P}{Pr}$

6. $2x - 5 < 5x - 11$

$-3x - 5 < -11$

$-3x < -6$

$\dfrac{-3x}{-3} > \dfrac{-6}{-3}$

$x > 2$

The solution set is $\{x \mid x > 2\}$.

7. $x - 3y = 6$

x-intercept:

$x - 3y = 6$

$x - 3(0) = 6$

$x = 6$

y-intercept:

$x - 3y = 6$

$0 - 3y = 6$

$-3y = 6$

$y = -2$

Check point:

$x - 3y = 6$

$3 - 3y = 6$

$-3y = 3$

$y = -1$

A check point is $(3, -1)$.

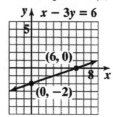

8.

x	$y = 0x + 4$	(x, y)
-6	$y = 0(-6) + 4 = 4$	$(-6, 4)$
-3	$y = 0(-3) + 4 = 4$	$(-3, 4)$
0	$y = 0(0) + 4 = 4$	$(0, 4)$
3	$y = 0(3) + 4 = 4$	$(3, 4)$
6	$y = 0(6) + 4 = 4$	$(6, 4)$

9. $y = -\dfrac{3}{5}x + 2$

slope $= -\dfrac{3}{5} = \dfrac{-3}{5}$; y-intercept $= 2$

Plot the point $(0,2)$. From this point, move 3 units down (because -3 is negative) and 5 units to the right to reach the point $(5, -1)$. Draw a line through $(0,2)$ and $(5, -1)$.

$y = -\dfrac{3}{5}x + 2$

10. $3x - 4y = 8$

$4x + 5y = -10$

To solve this system by the addition method, multiply the first equation by 4 and the second equation by -3. Then add the results.

$12x - 16y = 32$

$-12x - 15y = 30$

$\overline{\, -31y = 62}$

$y = -2$

Back-substitute to find x.

$3x - 4y = 8$

$3x - 4(-2) = 8$

$3x + 8 = 8$

$3x = 0$

$x = 0$

The solution set is $\{(0, -2)\}$.

11. $2x - 3y = 9$

$y = 4x - 8$

To solve this system by the substitution method, substitute $4x - 8$ for y in the first equation.

$2x - 3y = 9$

$2x - 3(4x - 8) = 9$

$2x - 12x + 24 = 9$

$-10x + 24 = 9$

$-10x = -15$

$x = \dfrac{3}{2}$

Back-substitute $\dfrac{3}{2}$ for x in the second equation.

$y = 4x - 8 = 4\left(\dfrac{3}{2}\right) - 8 = -2$

The solution set is $\left\{\left(\dfrac{3}{2}, -2\right)\right\}$.

12. $m = \dfrac{y_2 - y_1}{x_2 - x_1} = \dfrac{-5 - (-6)}{6 - 5} = \dfrac{1}{1} = 1$

13. $y - y_1 = m(x - x_1)$

$y - 6 = -4\left[x - (-1)\right]$

$y - 6 = -4(x + 1)$

slope-intercept form:

$y - 6 = -4x - 4$

$y = -4x + 2$

14. Use the formula for the area of a triangle.

$A = \dfrac{1}{2}bh$

$80 = \dfrac{1}{2} \cdot 16 \cdot h$

$80 = 8h$

$10 = h$

The height is 10 feet.

15. Let x = the cost of one pen.
Let y = the cost of one pad.

$$10x + 15y = 26$$
$$5x + 10y = 16$$

Multiply the second equation by -2, and add the result to the first equation.

$$10x + 15y = 26$$
$$\underline{-10x - 20y = -32}$$
$$-5y = -6$$
$$y = \frac{6}{5} = 1.20$$

Back-substitute 1.20 for y and solve for x.

$$10x + 15(1.20) = 26$$
$$10x + 18 = 26$$
$$10x = 8$$
$$x = \frac{8}{10} = 0.8$$

One pen costs $0.80 and one pad costs $1.20.

16. The integers in the given set are -93, 0, $\frac{7}{1}$ ($=7$) and $\sqrt{100}$ ($=10$).

17. The skim milk line has a positive slope. This means that skim milk consumption, in gallons per person, increased from 1945 through 2003.

18. The whole milk line has a negative slope. This means that whole milk consumption, in gallons per person, decreased from 1945 through 2003.

19. If y is whole milk consumption, in gallons per person and x is the number of years after 2003, then this can be modeled by the equation
$y = -0.57x + 7.6$.

To find when no whole milk will be consumed, let $y = 0$ and solve for x.

$$y = -0.57x + 7.6$$
$$0 = -0.57x + 7.6$$
$$0.57x = 7.6$$
$$x = \frac{7.6}{0.57}$$
$$x \approx 13$$

According to the model no whole milk will be consumed 13 years after 2003, or 2016.

20. To find when skim milk consumption will be 17.6 gallons per person, let $y = 15.6$ and solve for x.

$$y = 0.17x + 13.9$$
$$15.6 = 0.17x + 13.9$$
$$1.7 = 0.17x$$
$$\frac{1.7}{0.17} = x$$
$$x = 10$$

According to the model skim milk consumption will be 17.6 gallons per person 10 years after 2003, or 2013.

Chapter 6
Exponents and Polynomials

6.1 Check Points

1. $(-11x^3 + 7x^2 - 11x - 5) + (16x^3 - 3x^2 + 3x - 15)$

$= -11x^3 + 7x^2 - 11x - 5 + 16x^3 - 3x^2 + 3x - 15$

$= -11x^3 + 16x^3 + 7x^2 - 3x^2 - 11x + 3x - 5 - 15$

$= 5x^3 + 4x^2 - 8x - 20$

2. $-11x^3 + 7x^2 - 11x - 5$

$\underline{+16x^3 - 3x^2 + 3x - 15}$

$\quad 5x^3 + 4x^2 - 8x - 20$

3. $(9x^2 + 7x - 2) - (2x^2 - 4x - 6)$

$= 9x^2 + 7x - 2 - 2x^2 + 4x + 6$

$= 9x^2 - 2x^2 + 7x + 4x - 2 + 6$

$= 7x^2 + 11x + 4$

4. $(10x^3 - 5x^2 + 7x - 2) - (3x^3 - 8x^2 - 5x + 6)$

$= 10x^3 - 5x^2 + 7x - 2 - 3x^3 + 8x^2 + 5x - 6$

$= 10x^3 - 3x^3 - 5x^2 + 8x^2 + 7x + 5x - 2 - 6$

$= 7x^3 + 3x^2 + 12x - 8$

5. $\quad 8y^3 - 10y^2 - 14y - 2$

$\quad -\left(5y^3 \qquad -3y + 6\right)$

To subtract, add the opposite of the polynomial being subtracted.

$\quad 8y^3 - 10y^2 - 14y - 2$

$\underline{-5y^3 \qquad\quad + 3y - 6}$

$\quad 3y^3 - 10y^2 - 11y - 8$

6. Make a table of values.

x	$y = x^2 - 1$	(x, y)
-3	$y = (-3)^2 - 1 = 8$	$(-3, 8)$
-2	$y = (-2)^2 - 1 = 3$	$(-2, 3)$
-1	$y = (-1)^2 - 1 = 0$	$(-1, 0)$
0	$y = (0)^2 - 1 = -1$	$(0, -1)$
1	$y = (1)^2 - 1 = 0$	$(1, 0)$
2	$y = (2)^2 - 1 = 3$	$(2, 3)$
3	$y = (3)^2 - 1 = 8$	$(3, 8)$

6.1 Exercise Set

1. $3x + 7$ is a binomial of degree 1.

3. $x^2 - 2x$ is a binomial of degree 3.

5. $8x^2$ is a monomial of degree 2.

7. 5 is a monomial. Because it is a nonzero constant, its degree is 0.

9. $x^2 - 3x + 4$ is a trinomial of degree 2.

11. $7y^2 - 9y^4 + 5$ is a trinomial of degree 4.

13. $15x - 7x^3$ is a binomial of degree 3.

15. $-9y^{23}$ is a monomial of degree 23.

17. $(9x + 8) + (-17x + 5)$
$= 9x + 8 + (-17)x + 5$
$= 9x + 8 - 17x + 5$
$= (9x - 17x) + (8 + 5)$
$= -8x + 13$

19. $\left(4x^2 + 6x - 7\right) + \left(8x^2 + 9x - 2\right)$

$\quad = 4x^2 + 6x - 7 + 8x^2 + 9x - 2$

$\quad = \left(4x^2 + 8x^2\right) + \left(6x + 9x\right) + \left(-7 - 2\right)$

$\quad = 12x^2 + 15x - 9$

21. $\left(7x^2 - 11x\right) + \left(3x^2 - x\right)$

$\quad = 7x^2 - 11x + 3x^2 - x$

$\quad = \left(7x^2 + 3x^2\right) + \left(-11x - x\right)$

$\quad = 10x^2 - 12x$

23. $\left(4x^2 - 6x + 12\right) + \left(x^2 + 3x + 1\right)$

$\quad = 4x^2 - 6x + 12 + x^2 + 3x + 1$

$\quad = \left(4x^2 + x^2\right) + \left(-6x + 3x\right) + \left(12 + 1\right)$

$\quad = 5x^2 - 3x + 13$

25. $\left(4y^3 + 7y - 5\right) + \left(10y^2 - 6y + 3\right)$

$\quad = \left(4y^3 + 7y - 5\right) + \left(10y^2 - 6y + 3\right)$

$\quad = 4y^3 + 7y - 5 + 10y^2 - 6y + 3$

$\quad = 4y^3 + 10y^2 + \left(7y - 6y\right) + \left(-5 + 3\right)$

$\quad = 4y^3 + 10y^2 + y - 2$

27. $\quad = \left(2x^2 - 6x + 7\right) + \left(3x^3 - 3x\right)$

$\quad = 2x^2 - 6x + 7 + 3x^3 - 3x$

$\quad = 3x^3 + 2x^2 + \left(-6x - 3x\right) + 7$

$\quad = 3x^3 + 2x^2 - 9x + 7$

29. $\left(4y^2 + 8y + 11\right) + \left(-2y^3 + 5y + 2\right)$

$\quad = 4y^2 + 8y + 11 + \left(-2\right)y^3 + 5y + 2$

$\quad = -2y^3 + 4y^2 + \left(8y + 5y\right) + \left(11 + 2\right)$

$\quad = -2y^3 + 4y^2 + 13y + 13$

31. $\left(-2y^6 + 3y^4 - y^2\right) + \left(-y^6 + 5y^4 + 2y^2\right) = -2y^6 + 3y^4 - y^2 - y^6 + 5y^4 + 2y^2$

$\quad\quad\quad\quad\quad\quad\quad\quad\quad\quad\quad = \left(-2y^6 - y^6\right) + \left(3y^4 + 5y^4\right) + \left(-y^2 + 2y^2\right)$

$\quad\quad\quad\quad\quad\quad\quad\quad\quad\quad\quad = -3y^6 + 8y^4 + y^2$

33. $\left(9x^3 - x^2 - x - \dfrac{1}{3}\right) + \left(x^3 + x^2 + x + \dfrac{4}{3}\right) = \left(9x^3 + x^3\right) + \left(-x^2 + x^2\right) + \left(-x + x\right) + \left(-\dfrac{1}{3} + \dfrac{4}{3}\right)$

$$= 10x^3 + \dfrac{3}{3}$$

$$= 10x^3 + 1$$

35. $\left(\dfrac{1}{5}x^4 + \dfrac{1}{3}x^3 + \dfrac{3}{8}x^2 + 6\right) + \left(-\dfrac{3}{5}x^4 + \dfrac{2}{3}x^3 - \dfrac{1}{2}x^2 - 6\right)$

$$= \left[\dfrac{1}{5}x^4 + \left(-\dfrac{3}{5}x^4\right)\right] + \left(\dfrac{1}{3}x^2 + \dfrac{2}{3}x^3\right) + \left[\dfrac{3}{8}x^2 + \left(-\dfrac{1}{2}x^2\right)\right] + \left[6 + (-6)\right]$$

$$= -\dfrac{2}{5}x^4 + x^3 - \dfrac{1}{8}x^2$$

37. $\left(0.03x^5 - 0.1x^3 + x + 0.03\right) + \left(-0.02x^5 + x^4 - 0.7x + 0.3\right) = \left(0.03x^5 - 0.02x^5\right) + x^4 - 0.1x^3 + \left(x - 0.07x\right) + \left(0.03 + 0.3\right)$

$$= 0.01x^5 + x^4 - 0.1x^3 + 0.3x + 0.33$$

39. $\quad 5y^3 - 7y^2$

$\quad\ \underline{6y^3 + 4y^2}$

$\quad 11y^3 - 3y^2$

41. $\quad 3x^2 - 7x + 4$

$\quad \underline{-5x^2 + 6x - 3}$

$\quad -2x^2 - x + 1$

43. $\quad \dfrac{1}{4}x^4 - \dfrac{2}{3}x^3 - 5$

$\quad \underline{-\dfrac{1}{2}x^4 + \dfrac{1}{5}x^3 + 4.7}$

To add, rewrite using common denominators for common terms.

$\quad \dfrac{1}{4}x^4 - \dfrac{10}{15}x^3 - 5.0$

$\quad \underline{-\dfrac{1}{2}x^4 + \dfrac{3}{15}x^3 + 4.7}$

$\quad -\dfrac{1}{4}x^4 - \dfrac{7}{15}x^3 - 0.3$

45. $\quad y^3 + 5y^2 - 7y - 3$

$\quad \underline{-2y^3 + 3y^2 + 4y - 11}$

$\quad -y^3 + 8y^2 - 3y - 14$

47.

$$4x^3 - 6x^2 + 5x - 7$$
$$\underline{-9x^3 \qquad -4x + 3}$$
$$-5x^3 - 6x^2 + x - 4$$

49.

$$7x^4 - 3x^3 + x^2$$
$$\underline{\qquad x^3 - x^2 + 4x - 2}$$
$$7x^4 - 2x^3 \qquad + 4x - 2$$

51.

$$7x^2 - 9x + 3$$
$$4x^2 + 11x - 2$$
$$\underline{-3x^2 + 5x - 6}$$
$$8x^2 + 7x - 5$$

53.

$$1.2x^3 - 3x^2 + 9.1$$
$$7.8x^3 - 3.1x^2 + 8$$
$$\underline{\qquad 1.2x^2 - 6}$$
$$9x^3 - 4.9x^2 + 11.1$$

55.

$$\begin{aligned}
(x-8) - (3x+2) &= (x-8) + (-3x-2)\\
&= (x-3x) + (-8-2)\\
&= -2x - 10
\end{aligned}$$

57.

$$\begin{aligned}
&\left(x^2 - 5x - 3\right) - \left(6x^2 - 4x + 9\right)\\
&= \left(x^2 - 5x - 3\right) + \left(-6x^2 + 4x - 9\right)\\
&= \left(x^2 - 6x^2\right) + (-5x - 4x) + (-3 - 9)\\
&= -5x^2 - 9x - 12
\end{aligned}$$

59.

$$\begin{aligned}
&\left(x^2 - 5x\right) - \left(6x^2 - 4x\right)\\
&= \left(x^2 - 5x\right) + \left(-6x^2 + 4x\right)\\
&= \left(x^2 - 6x^2\right) + (-5x + 4x)\\
&= -5x^2 - x
\end{aligned}$$

61.

$$\begin{aligned}
&\left(x^2 - 8x - 9\right) - \left(5x^2 - 4x - 3\right)\\
&= \left(x^2 - 8x - 9\right) + \left(-5x^2 + 4x + 3\right)\\
&= -4x^2 - 4x - 6
\end{aligned}$$

63.

$$\begin{aligned}
(y-8) - (3y-2) &= (y-8) + (-3y+2)\\
&= -2y - 6
\end{aligned}$$

65.

$$\begin{aligned}
&\left(6y^3 + 2y^2 - y - 11\right) - \left(y^2 - 8y + 9\right)\\
&= \left(6y^3 + 2y^2 - y - 11\right) + \left(-y^2 + 8y - 9\right)\\
&= 6y^3 + y^2 + 7y - 20
\end{aligned}$$

67.

$$\begin{aligned}
&\left(7n^3 - n^7 - 8\right) - \left(6n^3 - n^7 - 10\right)\\
&= \left(7n^3 - n^7 - 8\right) + \left(-6n^3 + n^7 + 10\right)\\
&= \left(7n^3 - 6n^3\right) + \left(-n^7 + n^7\right) + (-8 + 10)\\
&= n^3 + 2
\end{aligned}$$

69.

$$\begin{aligned}
&\left(y^6 - y^3\right) - \left(y^2 - y\right)\\
&= \left(y^6 - y^3\right) + \left(-y^2 + y\right)\\
&= y^6 - y^3 - y^2 + y
\end{aligned}$$

71.

$$\begin{aligned}
&\left(7x^4 + 4x^2 + 5x\right) - \left(-19x^4 - 5x^2 - x\right)\\
&= \left(7x^4 + 4x^2 + 5x\right) + \left(19x^4 + 5x^2 + x\right)\\
&= 26x^4 + 9x^2 + 6x
\end{aligned}$$

73.

$$\begin{aligned}
&\left(\frac{3}{7}x^3 - \frac{1}{5}x - \frac{1}{3}\right) - \left(-\frac{2}{7}x^3 + \frac{1}{4}x - \frac{1}{3}\right)\\
&= \left(\frac{3}{7}x^3 - \frac{1}{5}x - \frac{1}{3}\right) + \left(\frac{2}{7}x^3 - \frac{1}{4}x + \frac{1}{3}\right)\\
&= \left(\frac{3}{7}x^3 + \frac{2}{7}x^3\right) + \left(-\frac{1}{5}x - \frac{1}{4}x\right) + \left(-\frac{1}{3} + \frac{1}{3}\right)\\
&= \left(\frac{3}{7}x^3 + \frac{2}{7}x^3\right) + \left(-\frac{4}{20}x - \frac{5}{20}x\right)\\
&= \frac{5}{7}x^3 - \frac{9}{20}x
\end{aligned}$$

75.

$$7x + 1$$
$$\underline{-(3x - 5)}$$

To subtract, add the opposite of the polynomial being subtracted.

$$7x + 1$$
$$\underline{-3x + 5}$$
$$4x + 6$$

77. $7x^2 - 3$

$\underline{-\left(-3x^2 + 4\right)}$

To subtract, add the opposite of the polynomial being subtracted.

$7x^2 - 3$

$\underline{3x^2 - 4}$

$10x^2 - 7$

79. $7y^2 - 5y + 2$

$\underline{-\left(11y^2 + 2y - 3\right)}$

To subtract, add the opposite of the polynomial being subtracted.

$7y^2 - 5y + 2$

$\underline{+-11y^2 - 2y + 3}$

$-4y^2 - 7y + 5$

81. $7x^3 + 5x^2 - 3$

$\underline{-\left(-2x^3 - 6x^2 + 5\right)}$

To subtract, add the opposite of the polynomial being subtracted.

$7x^3 + 5x^2 - 3$

$\underline{2x^3 + 6x^2 - 5}$

$9x^3 + 11x^2 - 8$

83. $5y^3 + 6y^2 - 3y + 10$

$\underline{-\left(6y^3 - 2y^2 - 4y - 4\right)}$

To subtract, add the opposite of the polynomial being subtracted.

$5y^3 + 6y^2 - 3y + 10$

$\underline{+-6y^3 + 2y^2 + 4y + 4}$

$-y^3 + 8y^2 + y + 14$

85. $7x^4 - 3x^3 + 2x^2$

$\underline{-\left(- x^3 - x^2 + x - 2\right)}$

To subtract, add the opposite of the polynomial being subtracted.

$7x^4 - 3x^3 + 2x^2$

$\underline{+x^3 + x^2 - x + 2}$

$7x^4 - 2x^3 + 3x^2 - x + 2$

87. $0.07x^3 - 0.01x^2 + 0.02x$

$\underline{-\left(0.02x^3 - 0.03x^2 - x\right)}$

To subtract, add the opposite of the polynomial being subtracted.

$0.07x^3 - 0.01x^2 + 0.02x$

$\underline{-0.02x^3 + 0.03x^2 + x}$

$0.05x^3 + 0.02x^2 + 1.02x$

89.

x	$y = x^2$	(x, y)
-3	$y = (-3)^2 = 9$	$(-3, 9)$
-2	$y = (-2)^2 = 4$	$(-2, 4)$
-1	$y = (-1)^2 = 1$	$(-1, 1)$
0	$y = (0)^2 = 0$	$(0, 0)$
1	$y = (1)^2 = 1$	$(1, 1)$
2	$y = (2)^2 = 4$	$(2, 4)$
3	$y = (3)^2 = 9$	$(3, 9)$

91.

x	$y = x^2 + 1$	(x, y)
-3	$y = (-3)^2 + 1 = 10$	$(-3, 10)$
-2	$y = (-2)^2 + 1 = 5$	$(-2, 5)$
-1	$y = (-1)^2 + 1 = 2$	$(-1, 2)$
0	$y = (0)^2 + 1 = 1$	$(0, 1)$
1	$y = (1)^2 + 1 = 2$	$(1, 2)$
2	$y = (2)^2 + 1 = 5$	$(2, 5)$
3	$y = (3)^2 + 1 = 10$	$(3, 10)$

93.

x	$y = 4 - x^2$	(x, y)
-3	$y = 4 - (-3)^2 = -5$	$(-3, -5)$
-2	$y = 4 - (-2)^2 = 0$	$(-2, 0)$
-1	$y = 4 - (-1)^2 = 3$	$(-1, 3)$
0	$y = 4 - (0)^2 = 4$	$(0, 4)$
1	$y = 4 - (1)^2 = 3$	$(1, 3)$
2	$y = 4 - (2)^2 = 0$	$(2, 0)$
3	$y = 4 - (3)^2 = -5$	$(3, -5)$

95. $\left[\left(4x^2 + 7x - 5\right) - \left(2x^2 - 10x + 3\right)\right] - \left(x^2 + 5x - 8\right)$

$= \left[2x^2 + 17x - 8\right] - x^2 - 5x + 8$

$= x^2 + 12x$

97. $\left[\left(4y^2 - 3y + 8\right) - \left(5y^2 + 7y - 4\right)\right] - \left[\left(8y^2 + 5y - 7\right) + \left(-10y^2 + 4y + 3\right)\right]$

$= \left[-y^2 - 10y + 12\right] - \left[-2y^2 + 9y - 4\right]$

$= y^2 - 19y + 16$

99. $\left[\left(4x^3 + x^2\right) + \left(-x^3 + 7x - 3\right)\right] - \left(x^3 - 2x^2 + 2\right)$

$= \left[3x^3 + x^2 + 7x - 3\right] + \left(-x^3 + 2x^2 - 2\right)$

$= 2x^3 + 3x^2 + 7x - 5$

101. $\left[\left(-5 + y^2 + 4y^3\right) - \left(-8 - y + 7y^3\right)\right] - \left(-y^2 + 7y^3\right)$

$= \left[-3y^3 + y^2 + y + 3\right] + \left(y^2 - 7y^3\right)$

$= -10y^3 + 2y^2 + y + 3$

103. a. $M - W = (-18x^3 + 923x^2 - 9603x + 48,446) - (17x^3 - 450x^2 + 6392x - 14,764)$

$M - W = -18x^3 + 923x^2 - 9603x + 48,446 - 17x^3 + 450x^2 - 6392x + 14,764$

$M - W = -18x^3 - 17x^3 + 923x^2 + 450x^2 - 9603x - 6392x + 48,446 + 14,764$

$M - W = -35x^3 + 1373x^2 - 15,995x + 63,210$

b. $M - W = -35x^3 + 1373x^2 - 15,995x + 63,210$

$M - W = -35(14)^3 + 1373(14)^2 - 15,995(14) + 63,210 = 12,348$

The difference in the median income between men and women with 14 years experience is $12,348.

c. $44,404 - 33,481 = 10,923$

The actual difference displayed in the graph in the median income between men and women with 14 years experience is $10,923.

The model overestimates this difference by $12,348 - $10,923 = $1425.

105. a. $M = 177x^2 + 288x + 7075$

$M = 177(16)^2 + 288(16) + 7075 = 56,995$

The model estimates the median annual income for a man with 16 years of education to be $56,995.

The model underestimates the actual value of $57,220 shown in the bar graph by $225.

b. The solution found in part (a) is represented by the point (16, 56,995) on the graph for men.

c. According to the graph in part (b) the median annual income for a woman with 16 years of education is about $42,000 (although answers will vary).

107. – 113. Answers will vary.

115. does not make sense; Explanations will vary. Sample explanation: The term of highest degree of a polynomial is not necessarily the first term. For example, the degree of $8x^2 - 7x + 9x^3 + 5$ is 3.

117. does not make sense; Explanations will vary. Sample explanation: $y = x^2 - 4$ is not a linear equation. Using two points and a checkpoint is an appropriate method for graphing a linear equation.

119. false; Changes to make the statement true will vary. A sample change is: The expression $\dfrac{1}{5x^2} + \dfrac{1}{3x}$ is not a polynomial expression (variables must not be in the denominator).

121. false; Changes to make the statement true will vary. A sample change is: The coefficient of x is –5.

123. $\left(5t - 3t^2 + t^3\right) - \left(t - t^2 + \dfrac{1}{3}t^3\right)$

$= \left(5t - 3t^2 + t^3\right) + \left(-t + t^2 - \dfrac{1}{3}t^3\right)$

$= (5t - t) + \left(-3t^2 + t^2\right) + \left(t^3 - \dfrac{1}{3}t^3\right)$

$= 4t - 2t^2 + \dfrac{2}{3}t^3$

$= \dfrac{2}{3}t^3 - 2t^2 + 4t$

125. $(-10)(-7) \div (1-8) = (-10)(-7) \div (-7)$
$$= 70 \div (-7) = -10$$

126. $-4.6 - (-10.2) = -4.6 + 10.2 = 5.6$

127. $3(x-2) = 9(x+2)$
$3x - 6 = 9x + 18$
$3x - 6 - 9x = 9x + 18 - 9x$
$-6x - 6 = 18$
$-6x - 6 + 6 = 18 + 6$
$-6x = 24$
$\dfrac{-6x}{-6} = \dfrac{24}{-6}$
$x = -4$
The solution set is $\{-4\}$.

128. $x^3 \cdot x^4 = (x \cdot x \cdot x) \cdot (x \cdot x \cdot x \cdot x) = x^7$

129. $3x(x+5) = 3x \cdot x + 3x \cdot 5 = 3x^2 + 15x$

130. $x(x+2) + 3(x+2) = x^2 + 2x + 3x + 6 = x^2 + 5x + 6$

6.2 Check Points

1. a. $2^2 \cdot 2^4 = 2^{2+4} = 2^6$ or 64

b. $x^6 \cdot x^4 = x^{6+4} = x^{10}$

c. $y \cdot y^7 = y^{1+7} = y^8$

d. $y^4 \cdot y^3 \cdot y^2 = y^{4+3+2} = y^9$

2. a. $\left(3^4\right)^5 = 3^{4 \cdot 5} = 3^{20}$

b. $\left(x^9\right)^{10} = x^{9 \cdot 10} = x^{90}$

c. $\left[(-5)^7\right]^3 = (-5)^{7 \cdot 3} = (-5)^{21}$

3. a. $(2x)^4 = 2^4 x^4 = 16x^4$

b. $\left(-4y^2\right)^3 = (-4)^3 \left(y^2\right)^3 = (-4)^3 y^{2 \cdot 3} = -64y^6$

4. a. $(7x^2)(10x) = (7 \cdot 10)(x^2 \cdot x) = 70x^3$

b. $(-5x^4)(4x^5) = (-5 \cdot 4)(x^4 \cdot x^5) = -20x^9$

5. a. $3x(x+5) = 3x \cdot x + 3x \cdot 5 = 3x^2 + 15x$

b. $6x^2(5x^3 - 2x + 3)$
$= 6x^2 \cdot 5x^3 - 6x^2 \cdot 2x + 6x^2 \cdot 3$
$= 30x^5 - 12x^3 + 18x^2$

6. a. $(x+4)(x+5) = x^2 + 5x + 4x + 20$
$$= x^2 + 9x + 20$$

b. $(5x+3)(2x-7) = 10x^2 - 35x + 6x - 21$
$$= 10x^2 - 29x - 21$$

7. $(5x+2)(x^2 - 4x + 3)$
$= 5x \cdot x^2 - 5x \cdot 4x + 5x \cdot 3 + 2 \cdot x^2 - 2 \cdot 4x + 2 \cdot 3$
$= 5x^3 - 20x^2 + 15x + 2x^2 - 8x + 6$
$= 5x^3 - 20x^2 + 2x^2 + 15x - 8x + 6$
$= 5x^3 - 18x^2 + 7x + 6$

8.
$$2x^3 - 5x^2 + 4x$$
$$3x^2 - 2x$$
$$\overline{ -4x^4 + 10x^3 - 8x^2}$$
$$\underline{6x^5 - 15x^4 + 12x^3}$$
$$6x^5 - 19x^4 + 22x^3 - 8x^2$$

6.2 Exercise Set

1. $x^{15} \cdot x^3 = x^{15+3} = x^{18}$

3. $y \cdot y^{11} = y^1 \cdot y^{11} = y^{1+11} = y^{12}$

5. $x^2 \cdot x^6 \cdot x^3 = x^{2+6+3} = x^{11}$

7. $7^9 \cdot 7^{10} = 7^{9+10} = 7^{19}$

9. $\left(6^9\right)^{10} = 6^{9 \cdot 10} = 6^{90}$

11. $\left(x^{15}\right)^3 = x^{15 \cdot 3} = x^{45}$

13. $\left[(-20)^3\right]^3 = (-20)^{3\cdot3} = (-20)^9$

15. $(2x)^3 = 2^3 \cdot x^3 = 8x^3$

17. $(-5x)^2 = (-5)^2 x^2 = 25x^2$

19. $\left(4x^3\right)^2 = 4^2\left(x^3\right)^2 = 16x^6$

21. $\left(-2y^6\right)^4 = (-2)^4\left(y^6\right)^4 = 16y^{24}$

23. $\left(-2x^7\right)^5 = (-2)^5\left(x^7\right)^5 = -32x^{35}$

25. $(7x)(2x) = (7\cdot2)(x\cdot x) = 14x^2$

27. $(6x)\left(4x^2\right) = (6\cdot4)\left(x\cdot x^2\right) = 24x^3$

29. $\left(-5y^4\right)\left(3y^3\right) = (-5\cdot3)\left(y^4\cdot y^3\right) = -15y^7$

31. $\left(-\dfrac{1}{2}a^3\right)\left(-\dfrac{1}{4}a^2\right) = \left(-\dfrac{1}{2}\cdot-\dfrac{1}{4}\right)\left(a^3\cdot a^2\right)$

$\qquad = \dfrac{1}{8}a^5$

33. $\left(2x^2\right)(-3x)\left(8x^4\right)$

$\qquad = (2\cdot-3\cdot8)\left(x^2\cdot x\cdot x^4\right) = -48x^7$

35. $4x(x+3) = 4x\cdot x + 4x\cdot3$

$\qquad = 4x^2 + 12x$

37. $x(x-3) = x\cdot x - x\cdot3$

$\qquad = x^2 - 3x$

39. $2x(x-6) = 2x\cdot x - 2x\cdot6$

$\qquad = 2x^2 - 12x$

41. $-4y(3y+5) = -4y\cdot3y - 4y\cdot5$

$\qquad = -12y^2 - 20y$

43. $4x^2(x+2) = 4x^2\cdot x + 4x^2\cdot2$

$\qquad = 4x^3 + 8x^2$

45. $2y^2\left(y^2+3y\right) = 2y^2\cdot y^2 + 2y^2\cdot3y$

$\qquad = 2y^4 + 6y^3$

47. $2y^2\left(3y^2-4y+7\right)$

$\qquad = 2y^2\left(3y^2\right) + 2y^2(-4y) + 2y^2(7)$

$\qquad = 6y^4 - 8y^3 + 14y^2$

49. $\left(3x^3+4x^2\right)(2x) = 3x^3\cdot2x + 4x^2\cdot2x$

$\qquad = 6x^4 + 8x^3$

51. $\left(x^2+5x-3\right)(-2x)$

$\qquad = x^2(-2x) + 5x(-2x) - 3(-2x)$

$\qquad = -2x^3 - 10x^2 + 6x$

53. $-3x^2\left(-4x^2+x-5\right)$

$\qquad = -3x^2\left(-4x^2\right) - 3x^2(x) - 3x^2(-5)$

$\qquad = 12x^4 - 3x^3 + 15x^2$

55. $(x+3)(x+5)$

$\qquad = x(x+5) + 3(x+5)$

$\qquad = x\cdot x + x\cdot5 + 3\cdot x + 3\cdot5$

$\qquad = x^2 + 5x + 3x + 15$

$\qquad = x^2 + 8x + 15$

57. $(2x+1)(x+4)$

$\qquad = 2x(x+4) + 1(x+4)$

$\qquad = 2x^2 + 8x + x + 4$

$\qquad = 2x^2 + 9x + 4$

59. $(x+3)(x-5) = x(x-5) + 3(x-5)$

$\qquad = x^2 - 5x + 3x - 15$

$\qquad = x^2 - 2x - 15$

61. $(x-11)(x+9) = x(x+9) - 11(x+9)$

$\qquad = x^2 + 9x - 11x - 99$

$\qquad = x^2 - 2x - 99$

63. $(2x-5)(x+4)$

$= 2x(x+4) - 5(x+4)$

$= 2x^2 + 8x - 5x - 20$

$= 2x^2 + 3x - 20$

65. $\left(\dfrac{1}{4}x + 4\right)\left(\dfrac{3}{4}x - 1\right)$

$= \dfrac{1}{4}x\left(\dfrac{3}{4}x - 1\right) + 4\left(\dfrac{3}{4}x - 1\right)$

$= \dfrac{1}{4}x \cdot \dfrac{3}{4}x + \dfrac{1}{4}x(-1)$

$\quad + 4\left(\dfrac{3}{4}x\right) + 4(-1)$

$= \dfrac{3}{16}x^2 - \dfrac{1}{4}x + \dfrac{12}{4}x - 4$

$= \dfrac{3}{16}x^2 + \dfrac{11}{4}x - 4$

67. $(x+1)(x^2 + 2x + 3)$

$= x(x^2 + 2x + 3) + 1(x^2 + 2x + 3)$

$= x^3 + 2x^2 + 3x + x^2 + 2x + 3$

$= x^3 + 3x^2 + 5x + 3$

69. $(y-3)(y^2 - 3y + 4)$

$= y(y^2 - 3y + 4) - 3(y^2 - 3y + 4)$

$= y^3 - 3y^2 + 4y - 3y^2 + 9y - 12$

$= y^3 - 6y^2 + 13y - 12$

71. $(2a-3)(a^2 - 3a + 5)$

$= 2a(a^2 - 3a + 5) - 3(a^2 - 3a + 5)$

$= 2a^3 - 6a^2 + 10a - 3a^2 + 9a - 15$

$= 2a^3 - 9a^2 + 19a - 15$

73. $(x+1)(x^3 + 2x^2 + 3x + 4)$

$= x(x^3 + 2x^2 + 3x + 4) + 1(x^3 + 2x^2 + 3x + 4)$

$= x^4 + 2x^3 + 3x^2 + 4x + x^3 + 2x^2 + 3x + 4$

$= x^4 + (2x^3 + x^3) + (3x^2 + 2x^2) + (4x + 3x) + 4$

$= x^4 + 3x^3 + 5x^2 + 7x + 4$

75. $\left(x - \dfrac{1}{2}\right)(4x^3 - 2x^2 + 5x - 6)$

$= x(4x^3 - 2x^2 + 5x - 6) - \dfrac{1}{2}(4x^3 - 2x^2 + 5x - 6)$

$= 4x^4 - 2x^3 + 5x^2 - 6x - 2x^3 + x^2 - \dfrac{5}{2}x + 3$

$= 4x^4 - 4x^3 + 6x^2 - \dfrac{17}{2}x + 3$

77. $(x^2 + 2x + 1)(x^2 - x + 2)$

$= x^2(x^2 - x + 2) + 2x(x^2 - x + 2) + 1(x^2 - x + 2)$

$= x^4 - x^3 + 2x^2 + 2x^3 - 2x^2 + 4x + x^2 - x + 2$

$= x^4 + x^3 + x^2 + 3x + 2$

79.

$$
\begin{array}{r}
x^2 - 5x + 3 \\
x + 8 \\
\hline
8x^2 - 40x + 24 \\
x^3 - 5x^2 + 3x \\
\hline
x^3 + 3x^2 - 37x + 24
\end{array}
$$

81.

$$
\begin{array}{r}
x^2 - 3x + 9 \\
2x - 3 \\
\hline
-3x^2 + 9x - 27 \\
2x^3 - 6x^2 + 18x \\
\hline
2x^3 - 9x^2 + 27x - 27
\end{array}
$$

83.

$$
\begin{array}{r}
2x^3 + x^2 + 2x + 3 \\
x + 4 \\
\hline
8x^3 + 4x^2 + 8x + 12 \\
2x^4 + x^3 + 2x^2 + 3x \\
\hline
2x^4 + 9x^3 + 6x^2 + 11x + 12
\end{array}
$$

85.

$$
\begin{array}{r}
4z^3 - 2z^2 + 5z - 4 \\
3z - 2 \\
\hline
-8z^3 + 4z^2 - 10z + 8 \\
12z^4 - 5z^3 + 15z^2 - 12z \\
\hline
12z^4 - 14z^3 + 19z^2 - 22z + 8
\end{array}
$$

87.
$$7x^3 - 5x^2 + 6x$$
$$\underline{\hspace{1cm} 3x^2 - 4x}$$
$$-28x^4 + 20x^3 - 24x^2$$
$$\underline{21x^5 - 15x^4 + 18x^3}$$
$$21x^5 - 43x^4 + 38x^3 - 24x^2$$

89.
$$2y^5 \qquad -3y^3 + y^2 - 2y + 3$$
$$\underline{\hspace{4cm} 2y - 1}$$
$$-2y^5 \qquad + 3y^3 - y^2 + 2y - 3$$
$$\underline{4y^6 - \qquad 6y^4 + 2y^3 - 4y^2 + 6y}$$
$$4y^6 - 2y^5 - 6y^4 + 5y^3 - 5y^2 + 8y - 3$$

91.
$$x^2 + 7x - 3$$
$$\underline{\hspace{0.8cm} x^2 - x - 1}$$
$$-x^2 - 7x + 3$$
$$-x^3 - 7x^2 + 3x$$
$$\underline{x^4 + 7x^3 - 3x^2 \hspace{1cm}}$$
$$x^4 + 6x^3 - 11x^2 - 4x + 3$$

93. $(x+4)(x-5) - (x+3)(x-6)$
$$= \left(x^2 - x - 20\right) - \left(x^2 - 3x - 18\right)$$
$$= \left(x^2 - x - 20\right) + \left(-x^2 + 3x + 18\right)$$
$$= 2x - 2$$

95. $4x^2\left(5x^3 + 3x - 2\right) - 5x^3\left(x^2 - 6\right)$
$$= \left(20x^5 + 12x^3 - 8x^2\right) + \left(-5x^5 + 30x^3\right)$$
$$= 15x^5 + 42x^3 - 8x^2$$

97. $(y+1)\left(y^2 - y + 1\right) + (y-1)\left(y^2 + y + 1\right)$
$$= y\left(y^2 - y + 1\right) + 1\left(y^2 - y + 1\right)$$
$$\quad + y\left(y^2 + y + 1\right) - 1\left(y^2 + y + 1\right)$$
$$= y^3 - y^2 + y + y^2 - y + 1$$
$$\quad + y^3 + y^2 + y - y^2 - y - 1$$
$$= 2y^3$$

99. $(y+6)^2 - (y-2)^2$
$$= (y+6)(y+6) - (y-2)(y-2)$$
$$= \left(y^2 + 12y + 36\right) - \left(y^2 - 4y + 4\right)$$
$$= 16y + 32$$

101. Use the formula for the area of a rectangle.
$$A = l \cdot w$$
$$A = (x+5)(2x-3)$$
$$= x(2x-3) + 5(2x-3)$$
$$= 2x^2 - 3x + 10x - 15$$
$$= 2x^2 + 7x - 15$$
The area of the rug is $2x^2 + 7x - 15$ square feet.

103. a. $(x+2)(2x+1)$

b. $x \cdot 2x + 2 \cdot 2x + x \cdot 1 + 2 \cdot 1$
$$= 2x^2 + 4x + x + 2$$
$$= 2x^2 + 5x + 2$$

c. $(x+2)(2x+1) = x(2x+1) + 2(2x+1)$
$$= 2x^2 + x + 4x + 2$$
$$= 2x^2 + 5x + 2$$

105. When multiplying numbers with the same base, keep the base and add the exponents.

Example: $2^3 \cdot 2^5 = 2^{3+5} = 2^8$

107. – 111. Answers will vary.

113. makes sense

115. makes sense

117. false; Changes to make the statement true will vary. A sample change is: $4x^3 \cdot 3x^4 = 4 \cdot 3x^{3+4} = 12x^7$

119. true

121. The area of the outer square is
$$(x+4)(x+4) = x(x+4) + 4(x+4)$$
$$= x^2 + 4x + 4x + 16$$
$$= x^2 + 8x + 16$$

The area of the inner square is x^2. The area of the shaded region is the difference between the areas of the two squares, which is
$$\left(x^2 + 8x + 16\right) - x^2 = 8x + 16$$

123. $\left(-8x^4\right)\left(-\dfrac{1}{4}xy^3\right) = 2x^5y^3$, so the missing factor is $-8x^4$.

124.
$$4x - 7 > 9x - 2$$
$$4x - 7 - 9x > 9x - 2 - 9x$$
$$-5x - 7 > -2$$
$$-5x - 7 + 7 > -2 + 7$$
$$-5x > 5$$
$$\frac{-5x}{-5} < \frac{5}{-5}$$
$$x < -1$$
Solution: $(-\infty, -1)$

125. $3x - 2y = 6$
x-intercept:
$$3x - 2y = 6$$
$$3x - 2(0) = 6$$
$$3x = 6$$
$$x = 2$$
y-intercept:
$$3x - 2y = 6$$
$$3(0) - 2y = 6$$
$$-2y = 6$$
$$y = -3$$
checkpoint:
$$3x - 2y = 6$$
$$3(4) - 2y = 6$$
$$12 - 2y = 6$$
$$-2y = -6$$
$$y = 3$$
A checkpoint is (4,3).

$3x - 2y = 6$

126. $m = \dfrac{y_2 - y_1}{x_2 - x_2} = \dfrac{6 - 8}{1 - (-2)} = -\dfrac{2}{3}$

127. **a.** $(x+3)(x+4) = x^2 + 4x + 3x + 12$
$$= x^2 + 7x + 12$$

b. $(x+5)(x+20) = x^2 + 5x + 20x + 100$
$$= x^2 + 25x + 100$$

A fast method is $(x+a)(x+b) = x^2 + (a+b)x + ab$.

128. **a.** $(x+3)(x-3) = x^2 + 3x - 3x - 9$
$$= x^2 - 9$$

b. $(x+5)(x-5) = x^2 + 5x - 5x - 25$
$$= x^2 - 25$$

A fast method is $(x+a)(x-a) = x^2 - a^2$.

129. **a.** $(x+3)^2 = (x+3)(x+3)$
$$= x^2 + 3x + 3x + 9$$
$$= x^2 + 6x + 9$$

b. $(x+5)^2 = (x+5)(x+5)$
$$= x^2 + 5x + 5x + 9$$
$$= x^2 + 10x + 25$$

A fast method is $(x+a)^2 = x^2 + 2ax + a^2$.

6.3 Check Points

1. $(x+5)(x+6) = x^2 + 6x + 5x + 30$
$$= x^2 + 11x + 30$$

2. $(7x+5)(4x-3) = 28x^2 - 21x + 20x - 15$
$$= 28x^2 - x - 15$$

3. $(4-2x)(5-3x) = 20 - 12x - 10x + 6x^2$
$$= 20 - 22x + 6x^2$$
$$= 6x^2 - 22x + 20$$

4. a. $(7y+8)(7y-8) = \overbrace{(7y)^2}^{\substack{\text{first term}\\\text{squared}}} - \overbrace{8^2}^{\substack{\text{second term}\\\text{squared}}}$

$\qquad\qquad\qquad = 49y^2 - 64$

b. $(4x-5)(4x+5) = \overbrace{(4x)^2}^{\substack{\text{first term}\\\text{squared}}} - \overbrace{5^2}^{\substack{\text{second term}\\\text{squared}}}$

$\qquad\qquad\qquad = 16x^2 - 25$

c. $(2a^3+3)(2a^3-3) = \overbrace{(2a^3)^2}^{\substack{\text{first term}\\\text{squared}}} - \overbrace{3^2}^{\substack{\text{second term}\\\text{squared}}}$

$\qquad\qquad\qquad = 4a^6 - 9$

5. a. $(x+10)^2 = \overbrace{x^2}^{\substack{\text{first term}\\\text{squared}}} + \overbrace{2\cdot10x}^{\substack{2\cdot\text{product}\\\text{of the terms}}} + \overbrace{10^2}^{\substack{\text{last term}\\\text{squared}}}$

$\qquad\qquad = x^2 + 20x + 100$

b. $(5x+4)^2 = \overbrace{(5x)^2}^{\substack{\text{first term}\\\text{squared}}} + \overbrace{2\cdot20x}^{\substack{2\cdot\text{product}\\\text{of the terms}}} + \overbrace{4^2}^{\substack{\text{last term}\\\text{squared}}}$

$\qquad\qquad = 25x^2 + 40x + 16$

6. a. $(x-9)^2 = \overbrace{x^2}^{\substack{\text{first term}\\\text{squared}}} - \overbrace{2\cdot9x}^{\substack{2\cdot\text{product}\\\text{of the terms}}} + \overbrace{9^2}^{\substack{\text{last term}\\\text{squared}}}$

$\qquad\qquad = x^2 - 18x + 81$

b. $(7x-3)^2 = \overbrace{(7x)^2}^{\substack{\text{first term}\\\text{squared}}} - \overbrace{2\cdot21x}^{\substack{2\cdot\text{product}\\\text{of the terms}}} + \overbrace{3^2}^{\substack{\text{last term}\\\text{squared}}}$

$\qquad\qquad = 49x^2 - 42x + 9$

6.3 Exercise Set

1. $(x+4)(x+6) = x^2 + 6x + 4x + 24$

$\qquad\qquad\qquad = x^2 + 10x + 24$

3. $(y-7)(y+3) = y^2 + 3y - 7y - 21$

$\qquad\qquad\qquad = y^2 - 4y - 21$

5. $(2x-3)(x+5) = 2x^2 + 10x - 3x - 15$

$\qquad\qquad\qquad = 2x^2 + 7x - 15$

7. $(4y+3)(y-1) = 4y^2 - 4y + 3y - 3$

$\qquad\qquad\qquad = 4y^2 - y - 3$

9. $(2x-3)(5x+3) = 10x^2 + 6x - 15x - 9$

$\qquad\qquad\qquad = 10x^2 - 9x - 9$

11. $(3y-7)(4y-5) = 12y^2 - 15y - 28y + 35$

$\qquad\qquad\qquad = 12y^2 - 43y + 35$

13. $(7+3x)(1-5x) = 7 - 35x + 3x - 15x^2$

$\qquad\qquad\qquad = -15x^2 - 32x + 7$

15. $(5-3y)(6-2y) = 30 - 10y - 18y + 6y^2$

$\qquad\qquad\qquad = 30 - 28y + 6y^2$

$\qquad\qquad\qquad = 6y^2 - 28y + 30$

17. $(5x^2-4)(3x^2-7)$

$\quad = (5x^2)(3x^2) + (5x^2)(-7) + (-4)(3x^2) + (-4)(-7)$

$\quad = 15x^4 - 35x^2 - 12x^2 + 28$

$\quad = 15x^4 - 47x^2 + 28$

19. $(6x-5)(2-x) = 12x - 6x^2 - 10 + 5x$

$\qquad\qquad\qquad = -6x^2 + 17x - 10$

21. $(x+5)(x^2+3) = x^3 + 3x + 5x^2 + 15$

$\qquad\qquad\qquad = x^3 + 5x^2 + 3x + 15$

23. $(8x^3+3)(x^2+5) = 8x^5 + 40x^3 + 3x^2 + 15$

25. $(x+3)(x-3) = x^2 - 3^2 = x^2 - 9$

27. $(3x+2)(3x-2) = (3x)^2 - 2^2 = 9x^2 - 4$

29. $(3r-4)(3r+4) = (3r)^2 - 4^2$

$\qquad\qquad\qquad = 9r^2 - 16$

31. $(3+r)(3-r) = 3^2 - r^2 = 9 - r^2$

33. $(5-7x)(5+7x) = 5^2 - (7x^2) = 25 - 49x^2$

35. $\left(2x+\dfrac{1}{2}\right)\left(2x-\dfrac{1}{2}\right)=(2x)^2-\left(\dfrac{1}{2}\right)^2$

$\qquad\qquad\qquad =4x^2-\dfrac{1}{4}$

37. $\left(y^2+1\right)\left(y^2-1\right)=\left(y^2\right)^2-1^2=y^4-1$

39. $\left(r^3+2\right)\left(r^3-2\right)=\left(r^3\right)^2-2^2=r^6-4$

41. $\left(1-y^4\right)\left(1+y^4\right)=1^2-\left(y^4\right)^2=1-y^8$

43. $\left(x^{10}+5\right)\left(x^{10}-5\right)=\left(x^{10}\right)^2-5^2$

$\qquad\qquad\qquad\qquad =x^{20}-25$

45. $(x+2)^2=x^2+2(2x)+2^2$

$\qquad\qquad =x^2+4x+4$

47. $(2x+5)^2=(2x)^2+2(2x)(5)+5^2$

$\qquad\qquad\quad =4x^2+20x+25$

49. $(x-3)^2=x^2-2(3x)+3^2$

$\qquad\qquad =x^2-6x+9$

51. $(3y-4)^2=(3y)^2-2(3y)(4)+4^2$

$\qquad\qquad\quad =9y^2-24y+16$

53. $\left(4x^2-1\right)^2=\left(4x^2\right)^2-2\left(4x^2\right)(1)+1^2$

$\qquad\qquad\qquad =16x^4-8x^2+1$

55. $(7-2x)^2=7^2-2(7)(2x)+(2x)^2$

$\qquad\qquad\quad =49-28x+4x^2$

57. $\left(2x+\dfrac{1}{2}\right)^2=4x^2+2(2x)\left(\dfrac{1}{2}\right)+\left(\dfrac{1}{2}\right)^2$

$\qquad\qquad\quad =4x^2+2x+\dfrac{1}{4}$

59. $\left(4y-\dfrac{1}{4}\right)^2=(4y)^2-2(4y)\left(\dfrac{1}{4}\right)+\left(\dfrac{1}{4}\right)^2$

$\qquad\qquad\quad =16y^2-2y+\dfrac{1}{16}$

61. $\left(x^8+3\right)^2=\left(x^8\right)^2+2\left(x^8\right)(3)+3^2$

$\qquad\qquad\quad =x^{16}+6x^8+9$

63. $(x-1)\left(x^2+x+1\right)$

$\qquad =x\left(x^2+x+1\right)-1\left(x^2+x+1\right)$

$\qquad =x^3+x^2+x-x^2-x-1$

$\qquad =x^3-1$

65. $(x-1)^2=x^2-2(x)(1)+1^2$

$\qquad\qquad =x^2-2x+1$

67. $(3y+7)(3y-7)=\left(3y^2\right)-7^2$

$\qquad\qquad\qquad\quad =9y^2-49$

69. $3x^2\left(4x^2+x+9\right)$

$\qquad =3x^2\left(4x^2\right)+3x^2(x)+3x^2(9)$

$\qquad =12x^4+3x^3+27x^2$

71. $(7y+3)(10y-4)$

$\qquad =70y^2-28y+30y-12$

$\qquad =70y^2+2y-12$

73. $\left(x^2+1\right)^2=\left(x^2\right)^2+2\left(x^2\right)(1)+1^2$

$\qquad\qquad\quad =x^4+2x^2+1$

75. $\left(x^2+1\right)\left(x^2+2\right)$

$\qquad =x^2\cdot x^2+x^2\cdot 2+1\cdot x^2+1\cdot 2$

$\qquad =x^4+3x^2+2$

77. $\left(x^2+4\right)\left(x^2-4\right)=\left(x^2\right)^2-4^2$

$\qquad\qquad\qquad\quad =x^4-16$

79. $\left(2-3x^5\right)^2 = 2^2 - 2(2)\left(3x^5\right) + \left(3x^5\right)^2$

$$= 4 - 12x^5 + 9x^{10}$$

81. $\left(\dfrac{1}{4}x^2 + 12\right)\left(\dfrac{3}{4}x^2 - 8\right)$

$$= \dfrac{1}{4}x^2\left(\dfrac{3}{4}x^2\right) + \dfrac{1}{4}x^2(-8) + 12\left(\dfrac{3}{4}x^2\right) + 12(-8)$$

$$= \dfrac{3}{16}x^4 - 2x^2 + 9x^2 - 96$$

$$= \dfrac{3}{16}x^2 + 7x^2 - 96$$

83. $A = \left(x+1\right)^2 = x^2 + 2x + 1$

85. $A = \left(2x-3\right)\left(2x+3\right) = \left(2x\right)^2 - 3^2$

$$= 4x^2 - 9$$

87. Area of outer rectangle:

$(x+9)(x+3) = x^2 + 12x + 27$

Area of inner rectangle:

$(x+5)(x+1) = x^2 + 6x + 5$

Area of shaded region:

$\left(x^2 + 12x + 27\right) - \left(x^2 + 6x + 5\right) = 6x + 22$

89. $\left[\left(2x+3\right)\left(2x-3\right)\right]^2$

$$= \left[4x^2 - 9\right]^2$$

$$= 16x^4 - 72x^2 + 81$$

91. $\left(4x^2 + 1\right)\left[\left(2x+1\right)\left(2x-1\right)\right]$

$$= \left(4x^2 + 1\right)\left[4x^2 - 1\right]$$

$$= 16x^4 - 1$$

93. $(x+2)^3$

$$= (x+2)(x+2)^2$$

$$= (x+2)\left(x^2 + 4x + 4\right)$$

$$= x\left(x^2 + 4x + 4\right) + 2\left(x^2 + 4x + 4\right)$$

$$= x^3 + 4x^2 + 4x + 2x^2 + 8x + 8$$

$$= x^3 + 6x^2 + 12x + 8$$

95. $\left[(x+3) - y\right]\left[(x+3) + y\right]$

$$= (x+3)^2 - y^2$$

$$= x^2 + 6x + 9 - y^2$$

97. $(x+2)(x+1)$

The area of the larger garden is given by $(x+2)(x+1)$ square yards.

99. If the original garden measures $x = 6$ yards on a side, the area of the larger garden would be

$(6)^2 + 3(6) + 2 = 56$ square yards.

This corresponds to the point $(6, 56)$ on the graph.

101. $A_{\text{total}} = \left(x+2\right)^2 = x^2 + 2 \cdot (2x) + 2^2 = x^2 + 4x + 4$

The total area is $(x^2 + 4x + 4)$ square inches.

103. – 107. Answers will vary.

109. makes sense

111. makes sense

113. true

115. false; Changes to make the statement true will vary. A sample change is: $(x-5)^2 = x^2 - 10x + 25$.

117. $V = l \cdot w \cdot h$

$$= (10 - 2x)(8 - 2x)(x)$$

$$= \left(80 - 20x - 16x + 4x^2\right)(x)$$

$$= \left(80 - 36x + 4x^2\right)(x)$$

$$= 80x - 36x^2 + 4x^3$$

$$= 4x^3 - 36x^2 + 80x$$

The volume of the box is $(4x^3 - 36x^2 + 80x)$ cubic units.

119. Let $y_1 = (x+1)^2$ and $y_2 = x^2 + 1$.

The graphs do not coincide so the multiplication is not correct.

To correct, let $y_2 = x^2 + 2x + 1$

121. Let $y_1 = (x+1)(x-1)$ and $y_2 = x^2 - 1$.

The graphs coincide so the multiplication is correct.

$(x+1)(x-1) = x^2 - x + x - 1 = x^2 - 1$

123. $2x + 3y = 1$

$y = 3x - 7$

The substitution method is a good choice because the second equation is already solved for y.
Substitute $3x - 7$ for y into the first equation.

$2x + 3y = 1$

$2x + 3(3x - 7) = 1$

$2x + 9x - 21 = 1$

$11x - 21 = 1$

$11x = 22$

$x = 2$

Back-substitute to find y.

$y = 3x - 7$

$y = 3(2) - 7 = 6 + 7 = -1$

The solution set is $\{(2, -1)\}$.

124. $3x + 4y = 7$

$2x + 7y = 9$

The addition method is a good choice because both equations are written in the form $Ax + By = C$. To eliminate x, multiply the first equation by 2 and the second equation by -3. Then add the results.

$\begin{array}{r} 6x + 8y = 14 \\ \underline{-6x - 21y = -27} \\ -13y = -13 \\ y = 1 \end{array}$

Back-substitute 1 for y in either equation of the original system.

$3x + 4y = 7$

$3x + 4(1) = 7$

$3x + 4 = 7$

$3x = 3$

$x = 1$

The solution set is $\{(1, 1)\}$.

125. $y \le \dfrac{1}{3}x$

Graph $y = \dfrac{1}{3}x$ as a solid line using its slope, $\dfrac{1}{3}$, and y-intercept, 0. Since $(0,0)$ is on the line, chose a different point as a test point, for example, $(3, 2)$.

Since $2 \le \dfrac{1}{3}(3)$ is false, shade the half-plane *not* containing $(3, 2)$.

126. $x^3 y + 2xy^2 + 5x - 2$

$= (-2)^3 (3) + 2(-2)(3)^2 + 5(-2) - 2$

$= (-8)(3) + 2(-2)(9) + 5(-2) - 2$

$= -24 - 36 - 10 - 2$

$= -72$

127. $5xy + 6xy = (5 + 6)xy = 11xy$

128. $(x + 2y)(3x + 5y) = x \cdot 3x + x \cdot 5y + 2y \cdot 3x + 2y \cdot 5y$

$= 3x^2 + 5xy + 6xy + 10y^2$

$= 3x^2 + 11xy + 10y^2$

6.4 Check Points

1. $3x^3 y + xy^2 + 5y + 6$

$= 3(-1)^3 (5) + (-1)(5)^2 + 5(5) + 6$

$= 3(-1)(5) + (-1)(25) + 5(5) + 6$

$= -15 - 25 + 25 + 6$

$= -9$

2. $8x^4y^5 - 7x^3y^2 - x^2y - 5x + 11$

Term	Coefficient	Degree
$8x^4y^5$	8	$4+5=9$
$-7x^3y^2$	-7	$3+2=5$
$-x^2y$	-1	$2+1=3$
$-5x$	-5	1
11	11	0

The degree of the polynomial is the highest degree of all its terms, which is 9.

3. $(-8x^2y - 3xy + 6) + (10x^2y + 5xy - 10)$

$= -8x^2y - 3xy + 6 + 10x^2y + 5xy - 10$

$= -8x^2y + 10x^2y - 3xy + 5xy + 6 - 10$

$= 2x^2y + 2xy - 4$

4. $(7x^3 - 10x^2y + 2xy^2 - 5) - (4x^3 - 12x^2y - 3xy^2 + 5)$

$= 7x^3 - 10x^2y + 2xy^2 - 5 - 4x^3 + 12x^2y + 3xy^2 - 5$

$= 7x^3 - 4x^3 - 10x^2y + 12x^2y + 2xy^2 + 3xy^2 - 5 - 5$

$= 3x^3 + 2x^2y + 5xy^2 - 10$

5. $(6xy^3)(10x^4y^2) = (6 \cdot 10)(x \cdot x^4)(y^3 \cdot y^2)$

$= 60x^{1+4}y^{3+2}$

$= 60x^5y^5$

6. $6xy^2(10x^4y^5 - 2x^2y + 3)$

$= 6xy^2 \cdot 10x^4y^5 - 6xy^2 \cdot 2x^2y + 6xy^2 \cdot 3$

$= 60x^{1+4}y^{2+5} - 12x^{1+2}y^{2+1} + 18xy^2$

$= 60x^5y^7 - 12x^3y^3 + 18xy^2$

7. a. $(7x - 6y)(3x - y)$

$$= \overbrace{(7x)(3x)}^{F} + \overbrace{(7x)(-y)}^{O} + \overbrace{(-6y)(3x)}^{I} + \overbrace{(-6y)(-y)}^{L}$$

$= 21x^2 - 7xy - 18xy + 6y^2$

$= 21x^2 - 25xy + 6y^2$

b. $\overbrace{(2x+4y)^2}^{(A+B)^2} = \overbrace{(2x)^2}^{A^2} + \overbrace{2(2x)(4y)}^{2 \cdot A \cdot B} + \overbrace{(4y)^2}^{B^2}$

$= 4x^2 + 16xy + 16y^2$

$= 4x^2 + 16xy + 16y^2$

8. a.
$$\overbrace{(6xy^2+5x)(6xy^2-5x)}^{(A+B)\cdot(A-B)} = \overbrace{(6xy^2)^2}^{A^2} - \overbrace{(5x)^2}^{B^2}$$
$$= 36x^2y^4 - 25x^2$$

b. $(x-y)(x^2+xy+y^2) = x(x^2+xy+y^2) - y(x^2+xy+y^2)$
$$= x\cdot x^2 + x\cdot xy + x\cdot y^2 - y\cdot x^2 - y\cdot xy - y\cdot y^2$$
$$= x^3 + x^2y + xy^2 - x^2y - xy^2 - y^3$$
$$= x^3 + x^2y - x^2y + xy^2 - xy^2 - y^3$$
$$= x^3 - y^3$$

6.4 Exercise Set

1. $x^2 + 2xy + y^2 = 2^2 + 2(2)(-3) + (-3)^2$
$$= 4 - 12 + 9 = 1$$

3. $xy^3 - xy + 1 = 2(-3)^3 - 2(-3) + 1$
$$= 2(-27) + 6 + 1$$
$$= -54 + 6 + 1 = -47$$

5. $2x^2y - 5y + 3 = 2(2^2)(-3) - 5(-3) + 3$
$$= 2(4)(-3) - 5(-3) + 3$$
$$= -24 + 15 + 3$$
$$= -6$$

7. $x^3y^2 - 5x^2y^7 + 6y^2 - 3$

Term	Coefficient	Degree
x^3y^2	1	$3+2=5$
$-5x^2y^7$	-5	$2+7=9$
$6y^2$	6	2
-3	-3	0

The degree of the polynomial is the highest degree of all its terms, which is 9.

9. $\left(5x^2y - 3xy\right) + \left(2x^2y - xy\right)$
$$= \left(5x^2y + 2x^2y\right) + \left(-3xy - xy\right)$$
$$= 7x^2y - 4xy$$

11. $\left(4x^2y+8xy+11\right)+\left(-2x^2y+5xy+2\right)$

$=\left(4x^2y-2x^2y\right)+\left(8xy+5xy\right)+\left(11+2\right)$

$=2x^2y+13xy+13$

13. $\left(7x^4y^2-5x^2y^2+3xy\right)+\left(-18x^4y^2-6x^2y^2-xy\right)$

$=\left(7x^4y^2-18x^4y^2\right)+\left(-5x^2y^2-6x^2y^2\right)+\left(3xy-xy\right)$

$=-11x^4y^2-11x^2y^2+2xy$

15. $\left(x^3+7xy-5y^2\right)-\left(6x^3-xy+4y^2\right)$

$=\left(x^3+7xy-5y^2\right)+\left(-6x^3+xy-4y^2\right)$

$=\left(x^3-6x^3\right)+\left(7xy+xy\right)+\left(-5y^2-4y^2\right)$

$=-5x^3+8xy-9y^2$

17. $\left(3x^4y^2+5x^3y-3y\right)-\left(2x^4y^2-3x^3y-4y+6x\right)$

$=\left(3x^4y^2+5x^3y-3y\right)+\left(-2x^4y^2+3x^3y+4y-6x\right)$

$=\left(3x^4y^2-2x^4y^2\right)+\left(5x^3y+3x^3y\right)+\left(-3y+4y\right)+\left(-6x\right)$

$=x^4y^2+8x^3y+y-6x$

19. $\left(x^3-y^3\right)-\left(-4x^3-x^2y+xy^2+3y^3\right)$

$=\left(x^3-y^3\right)+\left(4x^3+x^2y-xy^2-3y^3\right)$

$=\left(x^3+4x^3\right)+\left(-y^3-3y^3\right)+x^2y-xy^2$

$=5x^3-4y^3+x^2y-xy^2$

$=5x^3+x^2y-xy^2-4y^3$

21. $\quad 5x^2y^2-4xy^2+6y^2$

$\quad \underline{-8x^2y^2+5xy^2\ -y^2}$

$\quad -3x^2y^2+\ xy^2\ +5y^2$

23. $\quad 3a^2b^4-5ab^2+7ab$

$\quad -\left(\underline{-5a^2b^4-8ab^2\ -ab}\right)$

To subtract, add the opposite of the polynomial being subtracted.

$\quad 3a^2b^4-5ab^2+\ 7ab$

$\quad \underline{+5a^2b^4+8ab^2\ +\ ab}$

$\quad\ \ 8a^2b^4+3ab^2\ +8ab$

25. $\left[\left(7x+13y\right)+\left(-26x+19y\right)\right]-\left(11x-5y\right)=7x+13y-26x+19y-11x+5y$

$$=7x-26x-11x+13y+19y+5y$$

$$=-30x+37y$$

27. $\left(5x^2y\right)\left(8xy\right)=\left(5\cdot 8\right)\left(x^2\cdot x\right)\left(y\cdot y\right)$

$$=40x^3y^2$$

29. $\left(-8x^3y^4\right)\left(3x^2y^5\right)=\left(-8\cdot 3\right)\left(x^3\cdot x^2\right)\left(y^4\cdot y^5\right)$

$$=-24x^5y^9$$

31. $9xy\left(5x+2y\right)=9xy\left(5x\right)+9xy\left(2y\right)$

$$=45x^2y+18xy^2$$

33. $5xy^2\left(10x^2-3y\right)=5xy^2\left(10x^2\right)-5xy^2\left(3y\right)$

$$=50x^3y^2-15xy^3$$

35. $4ab^2\left(7a^2b^3+2ab\right)=4ab^2\left(7a^2b^3\right)+4ab^2\left(2ab\right)$

$$=28a^3b^5+8a^2b^3$$

37. $-b\left(a^2-ab+b^2\right)=-b\left(a^2\right)-b\left(-ab\right)-b\left(b^2\right)$

$$=-a^2b+ab^2-b^3$$

39. $\left(x+5y\right)\left(7x+3y\right)$

$$=x\left(7x\right)+x\left(3y\right)+5y\left(7x\right)+5y\left(3y\right)$$

$$=7x^2+3xy+35xy+15y^2$$

$$=7x^2+38xy+15y^2$$

41. $\left(x-3y\right)\left(2x+7y\right)$

$$=x\left(2x\right)+x\left(7y\right)-3y\left(2x\right)-3y\left(7y\right)$$

$$=2x^2+7xy-6xy-21y^2$$

$$=2x^2+xy-21y^2$$

43. $\left(3xy-1\right)\left(5xy+2\right)$

$$=3xy\left(5xy\right)+3xy\left(2\right)-1\left(5xy\right)-1\left(2\right)$$

$$=15x^2y^2+6xy-5xy-2$$

$$=15x^2y^2+xy-2$$

45. $\left(2x+3y\right)^2=\left(2x\right)^2+2\left(2x\right)\left(3y\right)+\left(3y\right)^2$

$$=4x^2+12xy+9y^2$$

47. $(xy-3)^2 = (xy)^2 - 2(xy)(3) + (-3)^2$
$\qquad = x^2y^2 - 6xy + 9$

49. $\left(x^2 + y^2\right)^2 = \left(x^2\right)^2 + 2\left(x^2\right)\left(y^2\right) + \left(y^2\right)^2$
$\qquad = x^4 + 2x^2y^2 + y^4$

51. $\left(x^2 - 2y^2\right)^2$
$\qquad = \left(x^2\right) - 2\left(x^2\right)\left(2y^2\right) + \left(-2y^2\right)^2$
$\qquad = x^4 - 4x^2y^2 + 4y^4$

53. $(3x+y)(3x-y) = (3x)^2 - y^2 = 9x^2 - y^2$

55. $(ab+1)(ab-1) = (ab)^2 - 1^2 = a^2b^2 - 1$

57. $\left(x + y^2\right)\left(x - y^2\right) = x^2 - \left(y^2\right)^2 = x^2 - y^4$

59. $\left(3a^2b + a\right)\left(3a^2b - a\right) = \left(3a^2b\right)^2 - a^2$
$\qquad = 9a^4b^2 - a^2$

61. $\left(3xy^2 - 4y\right)\left(3xy^2 + 4y\right) = \left(3xy^2\right)^2 - (4y)^2$
$\qquad = 9x^2y^4 - 16y^2$

63. $(a+b)\left(a^2 - b^2\right)$
$\qquad = a\left(a^2\right) + a\left(-b^2\right) + b\left(a^2\right) + b\left(-b^2\right)$
$\qquad = a^3 - ab^2 + a^2b - b^3$

65. $(x+y)\left(x^2 + 3xy + y^2\right)$
$\qquad = x\left(x^2 + 3xy + y^2\right) + y\left(x^2 + 3xy + y^2\right)$
$\qquad = x^3 + 3x^2y + xy^2 + x^2y + 3xy^2 + y^3$
$\qquad = x^3 + 4x^2y + 4xy^2 + y^3$

67. $(x-y)\left(x^2 - 3xy + y^2\right)$
$\qquad = x\left(x^2 - 3xy + y^2\right) - y\left(x^2 - 3xy + y^2\right)$
$\qquad = x^3 - 3x^2y + xy^2 - x^2y + 3xy^2 - y^3$
$\qquad = x^3 - 4x^2y + 4xy^2 - y^3$

69. $(xy+ab)(xy-ab) = (xy)^2 - (ab)^2$
$\qquad = x^2y^2 - a^2b^2$

71. $\left(x^2 + 1\right)\left(x^4y + x^2 + 1\right)$
$\qquad = x^2\left(x^4y + x^2 + 1\right) + 1\left(x^4y + x^2 + 1\right)$
$\qquad = x^6y + x^4 + x^2 + x^4y + x^2 + 1$
$\qquad = x^6y + x^4y + x^4 + 2x^2 + 1$

73. $\left(x^2y^2 - 3\right)^2$
$\qquad = \left(x^2y^2\right)^2 - 2\left(x^2y^2\right)(3) + (-3)^2$
$\qquad = x^4y^4 - 6x^2y^2 + 9$

75. $(x+y+1)(x+y-1)$
$\qquad = x(x+y-1) + y(x+y-1) + 1(x+y-1)$
$\qquad = x^2 + xy - x + yx + y^2 - y + x + y - 1$
$\qquad = x^2 + 2xy + y^2 - 1$

77. $A = (3x+5y)(x+y)$
$\qquad = 3x(x) + 3x(y) + 5y(x) + 5y(y)$
$\qquad = 3x^2 + 3xy + 5xy + 5y^2$
$\qquad = 3x^2 + 8xy + 5y^2$

The area of the shaded region is $3x^2 + 8xy + 5y^2$
square units.

79. Area of shaded region $= \overbrace{(x+y)^2}^{\substack{\text{Area of}\\\text{larger square}}} - \overbrace{x^2}^{\substack{\text{Area of}\\\text{smaller square}}}$
$\qquad = (x^2 + 2xy + y^2) - x^2$
$\qquad = 2xy + y^2$

81. $\left[\left(x^3y^3 + 1\right)\left(x^3y^3 - 1\right)\right]^2$
$\qquad = \left[\left(x^3y^3\right)^2 - (1)^2\right]^2$
$\qquad = \left[x^6y^6 - 1\right]^2$
$\qquad = \left(x^6y^6\right)^2 - 2\left(x^6y^6\right)(1) + (1)^2$
$\qquad = x^{12}y^{12} - 2x^6y^6 + 1$

83. $(xy-3)^2(xy+3)^2$

$= \left[(xy-3)(xy+3)\right]^2$

$= \left[(xy)^2-3^2\right]^2$

$= \left[x^2y^2-9\right]^2$

$= \left(x^2y^2\right)^2 - 2\left(x^2y^2\right)(9)+(9)^2$

$x^4y^4 - 18x^2y^2 + 81$

85. $[x+y+z]\left[x-(y+z)\right]$

$= \left[x+(y+z)\right]\left[x-(y+z)\right]$

$= x^2 - (y+z)^2$

$= x^2 - \left(y^2 + 2yz + z^2\right)$

$= x^2 - y^2 - 2yz - z^2$

87. $N = \dfrac{1}{4}x^2y - 2xy + 4y;\ x = 10,\ y = 16$

$N = \dfrac{1}{4}x^2y - 2xy + 4y$

$= \dfrac{1}{4}(10)^2(16) - 2(10)(16) + 4(16)$

$= \dfrac{1}{4}(100)(16) - 2(10)(16) + 4(16)$

$= 400 - 320 + 64$

$= 144$

Each tree provides 144 board feet of lumber, so 20 trees will provide 20(144) = 2880 board feet. This is not enough lumber to complete the job. Since 3000 − 2880 = 120, the contractor will need 120 more board feet.

89. $v_0 = 80,\ s_0 = 96$ and $t = 2$

$s = -16t^2 + v_0t + s_0$

$s = -16t^2 + 80t + 96$

$s = -16(2)^2 + 80(2) + 96$

$= -16(4) + 80(6) + 96$

$= -64 + 160 + 96$

$= 192$

The ball will be 192 feet above the ground 2 seconds after being thrown.

91. $v_0 = 80,\ s_0 = 96$ and $t = 6$

$s = -16t^2 + v_0t + s_0$

$s = -16t^2 + 80t + 96$

$s = -16(6)^2 + 80(6) + 96$

$= -16(36) + 80(6) + 96$

$= -576 + 480 + 96 = 0$

The ball will be 0 feet above the ground after 6 seconds. This means that the ball hits the ground 6 seconds after being thrown.

93. The ball is falling from 2.5 seconds to 6 seconds. The graph is decreasing over this interval.

95. $(2, 192)$

97. The ball reaches its maximum height 2.5 seconds after it is thrown.

$v_0 = 80,\ s_0 = 96$ and $t = 2.5$

$s = -16t^2 + v_0t + s_0$

$s = -16t^2 + 80t + 96$

$s = -16(2.5)^2 + 80(2.5) + 96$

$= -16(6.25) + 80(2.5) + 96$

$= -100 + 200 + 96$

$= 196$

The maximum height is 196 feet.

99. Answers will vary.

101. makes sense

103. does not make sense; Explanations will vary. Sample explanation: FOIL is used to multiply a binomial by a binomial.

105. false; Changes to make the statement true will vary.

A sample change is: The term $-3x^{16}y^9$ has degree $16 + 9 = 25$.

107. true

109. Area of rectangle:

$(x+10y)(x+8y) = x^2 + 18xy + 80y^2$

Area of two corner squares: $x^2 + x^2 = 2x^2$

Area of shaded region:

$\left(x^2 + 18xy + 80y^2\right) - 2x^2 = -x^2 + 18xy + 80y^2$

111. Note that the shed consists of a rectangular solid with half a cylinder on top.

Radius of cylinder: x

Length of cylinder: y

Width of base: $2x$

Length of base: y

Height of base: x

Volume of rectangular solid: $l \cdot w \cdot h$

Volume of cylinder: $\pi r^2 \cdot l$

Volume of half-cylinder: $\dfrac{1}{2}\pi r^2 \cdot l$

$V_{\text{shed}} = V_{\text{base}} + V_{\text{top}}$

$\quad = l \cdot w \cdot h + \dfrac{1}{2}\pi r^2 \cdot l$

$\quad = y \cdot 2x \cdot x + \dfrac{1}{2}\pi \cdot (x)^2 \cdot y$

$\quad = 2x^2 y + \dfrac{1}{2}\pi x^2 y$

112. $R = \dfrac{L + 3W}{2}$; for W

$\qquad R = \dfrac{L + 3W}{2}$

$\qquad 2R = 2\left(\dfrac{L + 3W}{2}\right)$

$\qquad 2R = L + 3W$

$\qquad 2R - L = L + 3W - L$

$\qquad 2R - L = 3W$

$\qquad \dfrac{2R - L}{3} = \dfrac{3W}{3}$

$\qquad \dfrac{2R - L}{3} = W$ or $W = \dfrac{2R - L}{3}$

113. $-6.4 - (-10.2) = -6.4 + 10.2 = 3.8$

114. $\dfrac{63}{x} = \dfrac{3}{5}$

$\quad 3x = 63 \cdot 5$

$\quad 3x = 315$

$\quad \dfrac{3x}{3} = \dfrac{315}{3}$

$\quad x = 105$

The solution set is $\{105\}$.

115. $\dfrac{x^7}{x^3} = \dfrac{\cancel{x} \cdot \cancel{x} \cdot \cancel{x} \cdot x \cdot x \cdot x \cdot x}{\cancel{x} \cdot \cancel{x} \cdot \cancel{x}} = x^4$

116. $\dfrac{(x^2)^3}{5^3} = \dfrac{x^6}{125}$

117. $\dfrac{(2a^3)^5}{(b^4)^5} = \dfrac{2^5(a^3)^5}{b^{20}} = \dfrac{32a^{15}}{b^{20}}$

Mid-Chapter Check Point

1. $\left(11x^2 y^3\right)\left(-5x^2 y^3\right)$

$\quad = -55x^{2+2}y^{3+3} = -55x^4 y^6$

2. $11x^2 y^3 - 5x^2 y^3 = 6x^2 y^3$

3. $(3x + 5)(4x - 7)$

$\quad = 12x^2 - 21x + 20x - 35$

$\quad = 12x^2 - x - 35$

4. $(3x + 5) - (4x - 7)$

$\quad = (3x + 5) + (-4x + 7)$

$\quad = -x + 12$

5. $(2x - 5)\left(x^2 - 3x + 1\right)$

$\quad = 2x\left(x^2 - 3x + 1\right) - 5\left(x^2 - 3x + 1\right)$

$\quad = 2x^3 - 6x^2 + 2x - 5x^2 + 15x - 5$

$\quad = 2x^3 - 11x^2 + 17x - 5$

6. $(2x - 5) + \left(x^2 - 3x + 1\right)$

$\quad = x^2 - x - 4$

7. $(8x - 3)^2$

$\quad = (8x)^2 - 2(8x)(3) + 3^2$

$\quad = 64x^2 - 48x + 9$

8. $\left(-10x^4\right)\left(-7x^5\right) = 70x^9$

9. $\left(x^2 + 2\right)\left(x^2 - 2\right)$

$\quad = \left(x^2\right)^2 - 2^2$

$\quad = x^4 - 4$

10. $\left(x^2+2\right)^2$

$= \left(x^2\right)^2 + 2\left(x^2\right)(2) + 2^2$

$= x^4 + 4x^2 + 4$

11. $(9a-10b)(2a+b)$

$= 18a^2 + 9ab - 20ba - 10b^2$

$= 18a^2 + 9ab - 20ab - 10b^2$

$= 18a^2 - 11ab - 10b^2$

12. $7x^2\left(10x^3 - 2x + 3\right)$

$= 70x^5 - 14x^3 + 21x^2$

13. $\left(3a^2b^3 - ab + 4b^2\right) - \left(-2a^2b^3 - 3ab + 5b^2\right)$

$= \left(3a^2b^3 - ab + 4b^2\right) + \left(2a^2b^3 + 3ab - 5b^2\right)$

$= 5a^2b^3 + 2ab - b^2$

14. $2(3y-5)(3y+5) = 2\left(9y^2 - 25\right)$

$\qquad\qquad\qquad = 18y^2 - 50$

15. $\left(-9x^3 + 5x^2 - 2x + 7\right)$

$\quad + \left(11x^3 - 6x^2 + 3x - 7\right)$

$= \left(-9x^3 + 11x^3\right) + \left(5x^2 - 6x^2\right)$

$\quad + (-2x + 3x) + (7 - 7)$

$= 2x^3 - x^2 + x$

16. $10x^2 - 8xy - 3\left(y^2 - xy\right)$

$= 10x^2 - 8xy - 3y^2 + 3xy$

$= 10x^2 - 5xy - 3y^2$

17. $\left(-2x^5 + x^4 - 3x + 10\right)$

$\quad - \left(2x^5 - 6x^4 + 7x - 13\right)$

$= \left(-2x^5 + x^4 - 3x + 10\right)$

$\quad + \left(-2x^5 + 6x^4 - 7x + 13\right)$

$= -4x^5 + 7x^4 - 10x + 23$

18. $(x+3y)\left(x^2 - 3xy + 9y^2\right)$

$= x\left(x^2 - 3xy + 9y^2\right) + 3y\left(x^2 - 3xy + 9y^2\right)$

$= x^3 - 3x^2y + 9xy^2 + 3x^2y - 9xy^2 + 27y^3$

$= x^3 + 27y^3$

19. $\left(5x^4 + 4\right)\left(2x^3 - 1\right)$

$= 10x^7 - 5x^4 + 8x^3 - 4$

20. $(y-6z)^2 = y^2 - 2(y)(6z) + (6z)^2$

$\qquad\qquad = y^2 - 12yz + 36z^2$

21. $(2x+3)(2x-3) - (5x+4)(5x-4)$

$= \left(4x^2 - 9\right) - \left(25x^2 - 16\right)$

$= \left(4x^2 - 9\right) + \left(-25x^2 + 16\right)$

$= -21x^2 + 7$

22.

x	$y = 1 - x^2$	(x, y)
-3	$y = 1 - (-3)^2 = -8$	$(-3, -8)$
-2	$y = 1 - (-2)^2 = -3$	$(-2, -3)$
-1	$y = 1 - (-1)^2 = 0$	$(-1, 0)$
0	$y = 1 - (0)^2 = 1$	$(0, 1)$
1	$y = 1 - (1)^2 = 0$	$(1, 0)$
2	$y = 1 - (2)^2 = -3$	$(2, -3)$
3	$y = 1 - (3)^2 = -8$	$(3, -8)$

6.5 Check Points

1. a. $\dfrac{5^{12}}{5^4} = 5^{12-4} = 5^8$

b. $\dfrac{x^9}{x^2} = x^{9-2} = x^7$

c. $\dfrac{y^{20}}{y} = y^{20-1} = y^{19}$

2. a. $14^0 = 1$

b. $(-10)^0 = 1$

c. $-10^0 = -1 \cdot 10^0 = -1 \cdot 1 = -1$

d. $20x^0 = 20 \cdot 1 = 20$

e. $(20x)^0 = 1$

3. a. $\left(\dfrac{x}{5}\right)^2 = \dfrac{x^2}{5^2} = \dfrac{x^2}{25}$

b. $\left(\dfrac{x^4}{2}\right)^3 = \dfrac{x^{4 \cdot 3}}{2^3} = \dfrac{x^{12}}{8}$

c. $\left(\dfrac{2a^{10}}{b^3}\right)^4 = \dfrac{2^4(a^{10})^4}{(b^3)^4} = \dfrac{16a^{40}}{b^{12}}$

4. a. $\dfrac{-20x^{12}}{10x^4} = \dfrac{-20}{10}x^{12-4} = -2x^8$

b. $\dfrac{3x^4}{15x^4} = \dfrac{3}{15}x^{4-4} = \dfrac{1}{5}x^0 = \dfrac{1}{5}$

c. $\dfrac{9x^6y^5}{3xy^2} = \dfrac{9}{3} \cdot x^{6-1}y^{5-2} = 3x^5y^3$

5. $\dfrac{-15x^9 + 6x^5 - 9x^3}{3x^2} = \dfrac{-15x^9}{3x^2} + \dfrac{6x^5}{3x^2} - \dfrac{9x^3}{3x^2}$

$= -5x^7 + 2x^3 - 3x$

6. $\dfrac{25x^9 - 7x^4 + 10x^3}{5x^3} = \dfrac{25x^9}{5x^3} - \dfrac{7x^4}{5x^3} + \dfrac{10x^3}{5x^3}$

$= 5x^6 - \dfrac{7}{5}x + 2$

7. $\dfrac{18x^7y^6 - 6x^2y^3 + 60xy^2}{6xy^2}$

$= \dfrac{18x^7y^6}{6xy^2} - \dfrac{6x^2y^3}{6xy^2} + \dfrac{60xy^2}{6xy^2}$

$= 3x^6y^4 - xy + 10$

6.5 Exercise Set

1. $\dfrac{3^{20}}{3^5} = 3^{20-5} = 3^{15}$

3. $\dfrac{x^6}{x^2} = x^{6-2} = x^4$

5. $\dfrac{y^{13}}{y^5} = y^{13-5} = y^8$

7. $\dfrac{5^6 \cdot 2^8}{5^3 \cdot 2^4} = 5^{6-3} \cdot 2^{8-4} = 5^3 \cdot 2^4$

9. $\dfrac{x^{100}y^{50}}{x^{25}y^{10}} = x^{100-25}y^{50-10} = x^{75}y^{40}$

11. $2^0 = 1$

13. $(-2)^0 = 1$

15. $-2^0 = -\left(2^0\right) = -(1) = -1$

17. $100y^0 = 100 \cdot 1 = 100$

19. $(100y)^0 = 1$

21. $-5^0 + (-5)^0 = -1 + 1 = 0$

23. $-\pi^0 - (-\pi)^0 = -1 - 1 = -2$

25. $\left(\dfrac{x}{3}\right)^2 = \dfrac{x^2}{3^2} = \dfrac{x^2}{9}$

27. $\left(\dfrac{x^2}{4}\right)^3 = \dfrac{\left(x^2\right)^3}{4^3} = \dfrac{x^{2\cdot3}}{4^3} = \dfrac{x^6}{64}$

29. $\left(\dfrac{2x^3}{5}\right)^2 = \dfrac{2^2\left(x^3\right)^2}{5^2} = \dfrac{4x^6}{25}$

31. $\left(\dfrac{-4}{3a^3}\right)^3 = \dfrac{(-4)^3}{3^3\left(a^3\right)^3} = \dfrac{-64}{27a^9} = -\dfrac{64}{27a^9}$

33. $\left(\dfrac{-2a^7}{b^4}\right)^5 = \dfrac{\left(-2a^7\right)^5}{\left(b^4\right)^5} = \dfrac{(-2)^5\left(a^7\right)^5}{\left(b^4\right)^5}$

$= \dfrac{-32a^{35}}{b^{20}} = -\dfrac{32a^{35}}{b^{20}}$

35. $\left(\dfrac{x^2y^3}{2z}\right)^4 = \dfrac{\left(x^2\right)^4\left(y^3\right)^4}{2^4z^4} = \dfrac{x^8y^{12}}{16z^4}$

37. $\dfrac{30x^{10}}{10x^5} = \dfrac{30}{10}x^{10-5} = 3x^5$

39. $\dfrac{-8x^{22}}{4x^2} = \dfrac{-8}{4}x^{22-2} = -2x^{20}$

41. $\dfrac{-9y^8}{18y^5} = \dfrac{-9}{18}y^{8-5} = -\dfrac{1}{2}y^3$

43. $\dfrac{7y^{17}}{5y^5} = \dfrac{7}{5}y^{17-5} = \dfrac{7}{5}y^{12}$

45. $\dfrac{30x^7y^5}{5x^2y} = \dfrac{30}{5}x^{7-2}y^{5-1} = 6x^5y^4$

47. $\dfrac{-18x^{14}y^2}{36x^2y^2} = \dfrac{-18}{36}x^{14-2}y^{2-2}$

$= -\dfrac{1}{2}x^{12}y^0 = -\dfrac{1}{2}x^{12}\cdot1$

$= -\dfrac{1}{2}x^{12}$

49. $\dfrac{9x^{20}y^{20}}{7x^{20}y^{20}} = \dfrac{9}{7}x^{20-20}y^{20-20}$

$= \dfrac{9}{7}x^0y^0 = \dfrac{9}{7}\cdot1\cdot1 = \dfrac{9}{7}$

51. $\dfrac{-5x^{10}y^{12}z^6}{50x^2y^3z^2} = -\dfrac{1}{10}x^{10-2}y^{12-3}z^{6-2}$

$= -\dfrac{1}{10}x^8y^9z^4$

53. $\dfrac{10x^4+2x^3}{2} = \dfrac{10x^4}{2} + \dfrac{2x^3}{2} = 5x^4 + x^3$

55. $\dfrac{14x^4-7x^3}{7x} = \dfrac{14x^4}{7x} - \dfrac{7x^3}{7x}$

$= 2x^{4-1} - x^{3-1} = 2x^3 - x^2$

57. $\dfrac{y^7-9y^2+y}{y} = \dfrac{y^7}{y} - \dfrac{9y^2}{y} + \dfrac{y}{y}$

$= y^{7-1} - 9y^{2-1} + y^{1-1}$

$= y^6 - 9y^1 + y^0$

$= y^6 - 9y + 1$

59. $\dfrac{24x^3-15x^2}{-3x} = \dfrac{24x^3}{-3x} + \dfrac{-15x^2}{-3x}$

$= -8x^{3-1} + 5x^{2-1} = -8x^2 + 5x$

61. $\dfrac{18x^5+6x^4+9x^3}{3x^2} = \dfrac{18x^5}{3x^2} + \dfrac{6x^4}{3x^2} + \dfrac{9x^3}{3x^2}$

$= 6x^3 + 2x^2 + 3x$

63. $\dfrac{12x^4-8x^3+40x^2}{4x} = \dfrac{12x^4}{4x} - \dfrac{8x^3}{4x} + \dfrac{40x^2}{4x}$

$= 3x^3 - 2x^2 + 10x$

65. $\left(4x^2-6x\right) \div x = \dfrac{4x^2-6x}{x} = \dfrac{4x^2}{x} - \dfrac{6x}{x}$

$= 4x - 6$

67. $\dfrac{30z^3+10z^2}{-5z} = \dfrac{30z^3}{-5z} + \dfrac{10z^2}{-5z} = -6z^2 - 2z$

69. $\dfrac{8x^3+6x^2-2x}{2x} = \dfrac{8x^3}{2x} + \dfrac{6x^2}{2x} - \dfrac{2x}{2x}$

$= 4x^2 + 3x - 1$

71. $\dfrac{25x^7 - 15x^5 - 5x^4}{5x^3} = \dfrac{25x^7}{5x^3} - \dfrac{15x^5}{5x^3} - \dfrac{5x^4}{5x^3}$

$$= 5x^4 - 3x^2 - x$$

73. $\dfrac{18x^7 - 9x^6 + 20x^5 - 10x^4}{-2x^4}$

$$= \dfrac{18x^7}{-2x^4} - \dfrac{9x^6}{-2x^4} + \dfrac{20x^5}{-2x^4} - \dfrac{10x^4}{-2x^4}$$

$$= -9x^3 + \dfrac{9}{2}x^2 - 10x + 5$$

75. $\dfrac{12x^2y^2 + 6x^2y - 15xy^2}{3xy}$

$$= \dfrac{12x^2y^2}{3xy} + \dfrac{6x^2y}{3xy} - \dfrac{15xy^2}{3xy}$$

$$= 4xy + 2x - 5y$$

77. $\dfrac{20x^7y^4 - 15x^3y^2 - 10x^2y}{-5x^2y}$

$$= \dfrac{20x^7y^4}{-5x^2y} + \dfrac{-15x^3y^2}{-5x^2y} + \dfrac{-10x^2y}{-5x^2y}$$

$$= -4x^5y^3 + 3xy + 2$$

79. $\dfrac{2x^3(4x+2) - 3x^2(2x-4)}{2x^2}$

$$= \dfrac{8x^4 + 4x^3 - 6x^3 + 12x^2}{2x^2}$$

$$= \dfrac{8x^4 - 2x^3 + 12x^2}{2x^2}$$

$$= \dfrac{8x^4}{2x^2} - \dfrac{2x^3}{2x^2} + \dfrac{12x^2}{2x^2}$$

$$= 4x^2 - x + 6$$

81. $\left(\dfrac{18x^2y^4}{9xy^2}\right) - \left(\dfrac{15x^5y^6}{5x^4y^4}\right) = 2xy^2 - 3xy^2$

$$= -xy^2$$

83. $\dfrac{(y+5)^2 + (y+5)(y-5)}{2y}$

$$= \dfrac{(y^2 + 10y + 25) + (y^2 - 25)}{2y}$$

$$= \dfrac{2y^2 + 10y}{2y} = \dfrac{2y^2}{2y} + \dfrac{10y}{2y} = y + 5$$

85. $\dfrac{12x^{15n} - 24x^{12n} + 8x^{3n}}{4x^{3n}}$

$$= \dfrac{12x^{15n}}{4x^{3n}} - \dfrac{24x^{12n}}{4x^{3n}} + \dfrac{8x^{3n}}{4x^{3n}}$$

$$= 3x^{12n} - 6x^{9n} + 2$$

87. a. Average $= \dfrac{\text{Receipts}}{\text{Admissions}} = \dfrac{7661}{1421} = 5.39$

The average admission charge for a film in 2000 was $5.39.

b. Average $= \dfrac{\text{Receipts}}{\text{Admissions}} = \dfrac{3.6x^2 + 158x + 2790}{-0.2x^2 + 21x + 1015}$

c. $\dfrac{3.6x^2 + 158x + 2790}{-0.2x^2 + 21x + 1015} = \overbrace{\dfrac{3.6(20)^2 + 158(20) + 2790}{-0.2(20)^2 + 21(20) + 1015}}^{\text{2000 is 20 years after 1980.}}$

$$= \dfrac{7390}{1355}$$

$$= 5.45$$

According to the model, the average admission charge for a film in 2000 was $5.45. This overestimates the actual value by $0.06.

d. Polynomial division cannot be performed using the methods in this section because the divisor is not a monomial.

89. – 95. Answers will vary.

97. does not make sense; Explanations will vary. Sample explanation: The quotient rule involves subtracting exponents.

99. does not make sense; Explanations will vary. Sample explanation: Divide each term of the polynomial by the monomial.

101. false; Changes to make the statement true will vary. A sample change is:

$$\dfrac{12x^3 - 6x}{2x} = \dfrac{12x^3}{2x} - \dfrac{6x}{2x} = 6x^2 - 3$$

103. true

105. $\dfrac{?x^8 - ?x^6}{3x^?} = 3x^5 - 4x^3$

To get 3 as the coefficient of the first term of the quotient, the coefficient of the first term of the dividend must be 9. For the exponent in the first term of the quotient to be 5, the exponent in the divisor must be 3. Since now know that the divisor is $3x^3$, the coefficient of the second term in the dividend must be 12. Therefore,

$$\dfrac{?x^8 - ?x^6}{3x^?} = \dfrac{9x^8 - 12x^6}{3x^3}$$

107. $|-20.3| = 20.3$

108.
$$\begin{array}{r} 0.875 \\ 8\overline{)7.000} \\ \underline{64} \\ 60 \\ \underline{56} \\ 40 \\ \underline{40} \\ 0 \end{array}$$

$\dfrac{7}{8} = 0.875$

109. $y = \dfrac{1}{3}x + 2$

slope $= \dfrac{1}{3}$; y-intercept $= 2$

Plot (0,2). From this point move 1 unit *up* and 3 units to the *right* to reach the point (3,3). Draw a line through (0,2) and (3,3).

$y = \dfrac{1}{3}x + 2$

110.
$$\begin{array}{r} 26 \\ 19\overline{)494} \\ \underline{38} \\ 114 \\ \underline{114} \\ 0 \end{array}$$

The quotient is 26 and the remainder is 0.

111.
$$\begin{array}{r} 123 \\ 24\overline{)2958} \\ \underline{24} \\ 55 \\ \underline{48} \\ 78 \\ \underline{72} \\ 6 \end{array}$$

The quotient is 123 and the remainder is 6.

112.
$$\begin{array}{r} 257 \\ 98\overline{)25187} \\ \underline{196} \\ 558 \\ \underline{490} \\ 687 \\ \underline{686} \\ 1 \end{array}$$

The quotient is 257 and the remainder is 1.

6.6 Check Points

1.
$$\begin{array}{r} x+5 \\ x+9\overline{)x^2 +14x + 45} \\ \underline{x^2 + 9x} \\ 5x + 45 \\ \underline{5x + 45} \\ 0 \end{array}$$

$$\dfrac{x^2 + 14x + 45}{x + 9} = x + 5$$

2. $\dfrac{6x + 8x^2 - 12}{2x + 3} = \dfrac{8x^2 + 6x - 12}{2x + 3}$

$$\begin{array}{r} 4x - 3 \\ 2x+3\overline{)8x^2 + 6x - 12} \\ \underline{8x^2 + 12x} \\ -6x - 12 \\ \underline{-6x - 9} \\ -3 \end{array}$$

$$\dfrac{6x + 8x^2 - 12}{2x + 3} = 4x - 3 - \dfrac{3}{2x + 3}$$

3. Rewriting $x^3 - 1$ using coefficients of 0 on the missing terms gives $x^3 + 0x^2 + 0x - 1$.

$$
\begin{array}{r}
x^2 + x + 1 \\
x - 1 \overline{)x^3 + 0x^2 + 0x - 1} \\
\underline{x^3 - x^2} \\
x^2 + 0x \\
\underline{x^2 - x} \\
x - 1 \\
\underline{x - 1} \\
0
\end{array}
$$

$$\frac{x^3 - 1}{x - 1} = x^2 + x + 1$$

6.6 Exercise Set

1.
$$
\begin{array}{r}
x + 4 \\
x + 2 \overline{)x^2 + 6x + 8} \\
\underline{x^2 + 2x} \\
4x + 8 \\
\underline{4x + 8} \\
0
\end{array}
$$

$$\frac{x^2 + 6x + 8}{x + 2} = x + 4$$

3.
$$
\begin{array}{r}
2x + 5 \\
x - 2 \overline{)2x^2 + x - 10} \\
\underline{2x^2 - 4x} \\
5x - 10 \\
\underline{5x - 10} \\
0
\end{array}
$$

$$\frac{2x^2 + x - 10}{x - 2} = 2x + 5$$

5.
$$
\begin{array}{r}
x - 2 \\
x - 3 \overline{)x^2 - 5x + 6} \\
\underline{x^2 - 3x} \\
-2x + 6 \\
\underline{-2x + 6} \\
0
\end{array}
$$

$$\frac{x^2 - 5x + 6}{x - 3} = x - 2$$

7.
$$
\begin{array}{r}
2y + 1 \\
y + 2 \overline{)2y^2 + 5y + 2} \\
\underline{2y^2 + 4y} \\
y + 2 \\
\underline{y + 2} \\
0
\end{array}
$$

$$\frac{2y^2 + 5y + 2}{y + 2} = 2y + 1$$

9.
$$
\begin{array}{r}
x - 5 \\
x + 2 \overline{)x^2 - 3x + 4} \\
\underline{x^2 + 2x} \\
-5x + 4 \\
\underline{-5x - 10} \\
14
\end{array}
$$

$$\frac{x^2 - 3x + 4}{x + 2} = x - 5 + \frac{14}{x + 2}$$

11.
$$
\begin{array}{r}
y + 3 \\
y + 2 \overline{)y^2 + 5y + 10} \\
\underline{y^2 + 2y} \\
3y + 10 \\
\underline{3y + 6} \\
4
\end{array}
$$

$$\frac{5y + 10 + y^2}{y + 2} = \frac{y^2 + 5y + 10}{y + 2} = y + 3 + \frac{4}{y + 2}$$

13.
$$
\begin{array}{r}
x^2 - 5x + 2 \\
x - 1 \overline{)x^3 - 6x^2 + 7x - 2} \\
\underline{x^3 - x^2} \\
-5x^2 + 7x \\
\underline{-5x^2 + 5x} \\
2x - 2 \\
\underline{2x - 2} \\
0
\end{array}
$$

$$\frac{x^3 - 6x^2 + 7x - 2}{x - 1} = x^2 - 5x + 2$$

15.

$$2y-3\overline{)12y^2-20y+3}$$ quotient $6y-1$

$$\underline{12y^2-18y}$$
$$-2y+3$$
$$\underline{-2y+3}$$
$$0$$

$$\frac{12y^2-20y+3}{2y-3}=6y-1$$

17.

$$2a-1\overline{)4a^2+4a-3}$$ quotient $2a+3$

$$\underline{4a^2-2a}$$
$$6a-3$$
$$\underline{6a-3}$$
$$0$$

$$\frac{4a^2+4a-3}{2a-1}=2a+3$$

19.

$$2y+1\overline{)2y^3-y^2+3y+2}$$ quotient y^2-y+2

$$\underline{2y^3+y^2}$$
$$-2y^2+3y$$
$$\underline{-2y^2-\ y}$$
$$4y+2$$
$$\underline{4y+2}$$
$$0$$

$$\frac{3y-y^2+2y^3+2}{2y+1}$$

$$=\frac{2y^3-y^2+3y+2}{2y+1}=y^2-y+2$$

21.

$$2x-5\overline{)6x^2-5x-30}$$ quotient $3x+5$

$$\underline{6x^2-15x}$$
$$10x-30$$
$$\underline{10x-25}$$
$$-5$$

$$\frac{6x^2-5x-30}{2x-5}=3x+5-\frac{5}{2x-5}$$

23.

$$x-2\overline{)x^3+0x^2+4x-3}$$ quotient x^2+2x+8

$$\underline{x^3-2x^2}$$
$$2x^2+4x$$
$$\underline{2x^2-4x}$$
$$8x-\ 3$$
$$\underline{8x-16}$$
$$13$$

$$\frac{x^2+4x-3}{x-2}=x^2+2x+8+\frac{13}{x-2}$$

25.

$$2y+3\overline{)4y^3+8y^2+5y+9}$$ quotient $2y^2+y+1$

$$\underline{4y^3+6y^2}$$
$$2y^2+5y$$
$$\underline{2y^2+3y}$$
$$2y+9$$
$$\underline{2y+3}$$
$$6$$

$$\frac{4y^3+8y^2+5y+9}{2y+3}=2y^2+y+1+\frac{6}{2y+3}$$

27.

$$3y+2\overline{)6y^3-5y^2+0y+5}$$ quotient $2y^2-3y+2$

$$\underline{6y^3+4y^2}$$
$$-9y^2+0y$$
$$\underline{-9y^2-6y}$$
$$6y+5$$
$$\underline{6y+4}$$
$$1$$

$$\frac{6y^3-5y^2+5}{3y+2}=2y^2-3y+2+\frac{1}{3y+2}$$

29.
$$
\begin{array}{r}
9x^2+3x+1 \\
3x-1\overline{)27x^3+0x^2+0x-1} \\
\underline{27x^3-9x^2} \\
9x^2+0x \\
\underline{9x^2-3x} \\
3x-1 \\
\underline{3x-1} \\
0
\end{array}
$$

$$\frac{27x^3-1}{3x-1}=9x^2+3x+1$$

31.
$$
\begin{array}{r}
y^3-9y^2+27y-27 \\
y-3\overline{)y^4-12y^3+54y^2-108y+81} \\
\underline{y^4-3y^3} \\
-9y^3+54y^2 \\
\underline{-9y^3+27y^2} \\
27y^2-108y \\
\underline{27y^2-81y} \\
-27y+81 \\
\underline{-27y+81} \\
0
\end{array}
$$

$$\frac{81-12y^3+54y^2+y^4-108y}{y-3}$$
$$=\frac{y^4-12y^3+54y^2-108y+81}{y-3}$$
$$=y^3-9y^2+27y-27$$

33.
$$
\begin{array}{r}
2y+4 \\
2y-1\overline{)4y^2+6y+0} \\
\underline{4y^2-2y} \\
8y+0 \\
\underline{8y-4} \\
4
\end{array}
$$

$$\frac{4y^2+6y}{2y-1}=2y+4+\frac{4}{2y-1}$$

35.
$$
\begin{array}{r}
y^3+y^2-y-1 \\
y-1\overline{)y^4+0y^3-2y^2+0y+5} \\
\underline{y^4-y^3} \\
y^3-2y^2 \\
\underline{y^3-y^2} \\
-y^2+0y \\
\underline{-y^2+y} \\
-y+5 \\
\underline{-y+1} \\
4
\end{array}
$$

$$\frac{y^4-2y^2+5}{y-1}=y^3+y^2-y-1+\frac{4}{y-1}$$

37.
$$
\begin{array}{r}
4x-3 \\
x^2+0x+2\overline{)4x^3-3x^2+x+1} \\
\underline{4x^3+0x^2+8x} \\
-3x^2-7x+1 \\
\underline{-3x^2+0x-6} \\
-7x+7
\end{array}
$$

$$\frac{4x^3-3x^2+x+1}{x^2+2}=4x-3+\frac{-7x+7}{x^2+2}$$

39.
$$
\begin{array}{r}
x^2+ax+a^2 \\
x-a\overline{)x^3+0x^2+0x-a^3} \\
\underline{x^3-ax^2} \\
ax^2+0x \\
\underline{ax^2-a^2x} \\
a^2x-a^3 \\
\underline{a^2x-a^3} \\
0
\end{array}
$$

$$\frac{x^3+0x^2+0x-a^3}{x-a}=x^2+ax+a^2$$

41.

$$3x^2+2x-4\overline{)6x^4-5x^3-8x^2+16x-8}$$

quotient: $2x^2-3x+2$

$$6x^4+4x^3-8x^2$$
$$-9x^3+0x^2+16x$$
$$-9x^3-6x^2+12x$$
$$6x^2+4x-8$$
$$6x^2+4x-8$$
$$0$$

$$\frac{6x^4-5x^3-8x^2+16x-8}{3x^2+2x-4}=2x^2-3x+2$$

43. First, compute the difference:

$$\left(4x^3+x^2-2x+7\right)-\left(3x^3-2x^2-7x+4\right)$$

$$=x^3+3x^2+5x+3$$

Now, complete the division:

$$\frac{x^3+3x^2+5x+3}{x+1}$$

$$x+1\overline{)x^3+3x^2+5x+3}$$

quotient: x^2+2x+3

$$x^3+x^2$$
$$2x^2+5x$$
$$2x^2+2x$$
$$3x+3$$
$$3x+3$$
$$0$$

$$\frac{x^3+3x^2+5x+3}{x+1}=x^2+2x+3$$

45. $A=l\cdot w$ so $l=\dfrac{A}{w}=\dfrac{x^3+3x^2+5x+3}{x+1}$

$$x+1\overline{)x^3+3x^2+5x+3}$$

quotient: x^2+2x+3

$$x^3+x^2$$
$$2x^2+5x$$
$$2x^2+2x$$
$$3x+3$$
$$3x+3$$
$$0$$

The base of the parallelogram is $\left(x^2+2x+3\right)$ units.

47. a. Substitute $n=3$ into the formula:

$$\frac{30,000x^3-30,000}{x-1}$$

b. Factor out 30,000 from the numerator:

$$\frac{30,000x^3-30,000}{x-1}=30,000\frac{x^3-1}{x-1}$$

Now use the formula from #39 with $a=1$:

$$\frac{x^3-a^3}{x-a}=x^2+ax+a^2$$

$$\frac{x^3-1}{x-1}=\frac{x^3-1^3}{x-1}$$

$$=x^2+1\cdot x+1^2=x^2+x+1$$

So $\dfrac{30,000x^3-30,000}{x-1}=30,000\cdot\dfrac{x^3-1}{x-1}$

$$=30,000\left(x^2+x+1\right)$$

$$=30,000x^2+30,000x+30,000$$

c. Substitute in $x=1.05$ into your formulas from parts (a) and (b) above:

$$\frac{30,000x^3-30,000}{x-1}$$

$$=\frac{30,000(1.05)^3-30,000}{(1.05)-1}=94,575$$

$$30,000x^2+30,000x+30,000$$

$$=30,000(1.05)^2+30,000(1.05)$$

$$+30,000$$

$$=94,575$$

Total salary over three years is $94,575.

49. – 51. Answers will vary.

53. makes sense

55. does not make sense; Explanations will vary. Sample explanation: The correct answer is x^2-x+1.

57. false; Changes to make the statement true will vary. A sample change is: The remainder is -9.

59. true

61. We can find the polynomial by multiplying the divisor by the quotient and adding the remainder.

$(x-3)(2x+4)+17$

$= 2x^2 + 4x - 6x - 12 + 17$

$= 2x^2 - 2x + 5$

63. Answers will vary. The quotient starts with x to a power that is one less than the power in the dividend. It is made up of terms that are all powers of x down to 1, but with alternating signs. The remainder is always -2. Following this pattern,

$$\frac{x^7-1}{x+1} = x^6 - x^5 + x^4 - x^3 + x^2 - x + 1 - \frac{2}{x+1}$$

$$\begin{array}{r}
x^6 - x^5 + x^4 - x^3 + x^2 - x + 1 \\
x+1\overline{)x^7 + 0x^6 + 0x^5 + 0x^4 + 0x^3 + 0x^2 + 0x - 1}
\end{array}$$

$\underline{x^7 + x^6}$

$-x^6 + 0x^5$

$\underline{-x^6 - x^5}$

$x^5 + 0x^4$

$\underline{x^5 + x^4}$

$-x^4 + 0x^3$

$\underline{-x^4 - x^3}$

$x^3 + 0x^2$

$\underline{x^3 + x^2}$

$-x^2 + 0x$

$\underline{-x^2 - x}$

$x - 1$

$\underline{x + 1}$

-2

Long division yields the same result.

65. Let $y_1 = \dfrac{x^2-25}{x-5}$ and $y_2 = x-5$.

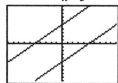

The graphs do not coincide so the division is incorrect.

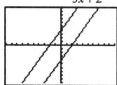

$$\begin{array}{r}
x+5 \\
x-5\overline{)x^2 + 0x - 25}
\end{array}$$

$\underline{x^2 - 5x}$

$5x - 25$

$\underline{5x - 25}$

0

The right side should be $x+5$.

67. Let $y_1 = \dfrac{6x^2+16x+8}{3x+2}$ and $y_2 = 2x-4$.

The graphs do not coincide so the division is incorrect.

$$\begin{array}{r}
2x+4 \\
3x+2\overline{)6x^2 + 16x + 8}
\end{array}$$

$\underline{6x^2 + 4x}$

$12x + 8$

$\underline{12x + 8}$

0

The right side should be $2x+4$.

69. $2x - y \geq 4$

$x + y \leq -1$

Graph $2x - y \geq 4$:

Graph $2x - y = 4$ as a solid line with x-intercept 2 and y-intercept -4. Since $2(0) - 0 \geq 4$ is false, shade the half-plane *not* containing $(0,0)$.

Graph $x + y \leq -1$;

Graph $x + y = -1$ as a solid line with x-intercept 1, and y-intercept 1. Since $0 + 0 \leq -1$ is false, shade the half-plane not containing $(0,0)$.

The solution set of the system is the intersection (overlap) of the two shaded regions.

$2x - y \geq 4$
$x + y \leq -1$

70. $P = 6\% = 0.06,\ B = 20$

$A = PB$

$A = (0.06)(20)$

$A = 1.2$

1.2 is 6% of 20.

71. $\dfrac{x}{3} + \dfrac{2}{5} = \dfrac{x}{5} - \dfrac{2}{5}$

To clear fractions, multiply by the LCD, 15.

$$15\left(\dfrac{x}{3} + \dfrac{2}{5}\right) = 15\left(\dfrac{x}{5} - \dfrac{2}{5}\right)$$

$$15\left(\dfrac{x}{3}\right) + 15\left(\dfrac{2}{5}\right) = 15\left(\dfrac{x}{5}\right) - 15\left(\dfrac{2}{5}\right)$$

$$5x + 6 = 3x - 6$$

$$2x + 6 = -6$$

$$2x = -12$$

$$x = -6$$

The solution set is $\{-6\}$.

72. a. $\dfrac{7^3}{7^5} = \dfrac{\cancel{7} \cdot \cancel{7} \cdot \cancel{7}}{\cancel{7} \cdot \cancel{7} \cdot \cancel{7} \cdot 7 \cdot 7} = \dfrac{1}{7^2}$

$\dfrac{7^3}{7^5} = 7^{3-5} = 7^{-2}$

b. $\dfrac{1}{7^2} = 7^{-2}$

73. $\dfrac{(2x^3)^4}{x^{10}} = \dfrac{2^4(x^3)^4}{x^{10}} = \dfrac{16x^{12}}{x^{10}} = 16x^{12-10} = 16x^2$

74. $\left(\dfrac{x^5}{x^2}\right)^3 = (x^{5-2})^3 = (x^3)^3 = x^9$

6.7 Check Points

1. a. $6^{-2} = \dfrac{1}{6^2} = \dfrac{1}{36}$

b. $5^{-3} = \dfrac{1}{5^3} = \dfrac{1}{125}$

c. $(-3)^{-4} = \dfrac{1}{(-3)^4} = \dfrac{1}{81}$

d. $-3^{-4} = -\dfrac{1}{3^4} = -\dfrac{1}{81}$

e. $8^{-1} = \dfrac{1}{8^1} = \dfrac{1}{8}$

2. a. $\dfrac{2^{-3}}{7^{-2}} = \dfrac{7^2}{2^3} = \dfrac{49}{8}$

b. $\left(\dfrac{4}{5}\right)^{-2} = \dfrac{5^2}{4^2} = \dfrac{25}{16}$

c. $\dfrac{1}{7y^{-2}} = \dfrac{y^2}{7}$

d. $\dfrac{x^{-1}}{y^{-8}} = \dfrac{y^8}{x^1} = \dfrac{y^8}{x}$

3. $x^{-12} \cdot x^2 = x^{-12+2} = x^{-10} = \dfrac{1}{x^{10}}$

4. a. $\dfrac{x^2}{x^{10}} = x^{2-10} = x^{-8} = \dfrac{1}{x^8}$

b. $\dfrac{75x^3}{5x^9} = \dfrac{75}{5} \cdot \dfrac{x^3}{x^9} = 15x^{3-9} = 15x^{-6} = \dfrac{15}{x^6}$

c. $\dfrac{50y^8}{-25y^{14}} = \dfrac{50}{-25} \cdot \dfrac{y^8}{y^{14}} = -2y^{8-14} = -2y^{-6} = -\dfrac{2}{y^6}$

5. $\dfrac{(6x^4)^2}{x^{11}} = \dfrac{6^2(x^4)^2}{x^{11}} = \dfrac{36x^{4 \cdot 2}}{x^{11}} = \dfrac{36x^8}{x^{11}}$

$= 36x^{8-11} = 36x^{-3} = \dfrac{36}{x^3}$

6. $\left(\dfrac{x^8}{x^4}\right)^{-5} = \left(x^4\right)^{-5} = x^{-20} = \dfrac{1}{x^{20}}$

7. a. $7.4 \times 10^9 = 7,400,000,000$

   b. $3.017 \times 10^{-6} = 0.000003017$

8. a. $7,410,000,000 = 7.41 \times 10^9$

   b. $0.000000092 = 9.2 \times 10^{-8}$

9. a. $(3 \times 10^8)(2 \times 10^2) = (3 \times 2) \times (10^8 \times 10^2)$
$$= 6 \times 10^{8+2}$$
$$= 6 \times 10^{10}$$

   b. $\dfrac{8.4 \times 10^7}{4 \times 10^{-4}} = \dfrac{8.4}{4} \cdot \dfrac{10^7}{10^{-4}}$
$$= 2.1 \times 10^{7-(-4)}$$
$$= 2.1 \times 10^{11}$$

   c. $(4 \times 10^{-2})^3 = 4^3 \times (10^{-2})^3$
$$= 64 \times 10^{-6}$$
$$= 6.4 \times 10^{-5}$$

10. $\dfrac{13 \times 10^9}{5.1 \times 10^6} = \dfrac{13}{5.1} \times \dfrac{10^9}{10^6} \approx 2.5 \times 10^3 = 2500$

The average grant was about \$2500.

6.7 Exercise Set

1. $8^{-2} = \dfrac{1}{8^2} = \dfrac{1}{64}$

3. $5^{-3} = \dfrac{1}{5^3} = \dfrac{1}{125}$

5. $(-6)^{-2} = \dfrac{1}{(-6)^2} = \dfrac{1}{36}$

7. $-6^{-2} = -\dfrac{1}{6^2} = -\dfrac{1}{36}$

9. $4^{-1} = \dfrac{1}{4^1} = \dfrac{1}{4}$

11. $2^{-1} + 3^{-1} = \dfrac{1}{2^1} + \dfrac{1}{3^1} = \dfrac{1}{2} + \dfrac{1}{3}$
$$= \dfrac{3}{6} + \dfrac{2}{6} = \dfrac{5}{6}$$

13. $\dfrac{1}{3^{-2}} = 3^2 = 9$

15. $\dfrac{1}{(-3)^{-2}} = (-3)^2 = 9$

17. $\dfrac{2^{-3}}{8^{-2}} = \dfrac{8^2}{2^3} = \dfrac{64}{8} = 8$

19. $\left(\dfrac{1}{4}\right)^{-2} = \dfrac{1^{-2}}{4^{-2}} = \dfrac{4^2}{1^2} = \dfrac{16}{1} = 16$

21. $\left(\dfrac{3}{5}\right)^{-3} = \dfrac{3^{-3}}{5^{-3}} = \dfrac{5^3}{3^3} = \dfrac{125}{27}$

23. $\dfrac{1}{6x^{-5}} = \dfrac{1 \cdot x^5}{6} = \dfrac{x^5}{6}$

25. $\dfrac{x^{-8}}{y^{-1}} = \dfrac{y^1}{x^8} = \dfrac{y}{x^8}$

27. $\dfrac{3}{(-5)^{-3}} = 3 \cdot (-5)^3 = 5(-125) = -375$

29. $x^{-8} \cdot x^3 = x^{-8+3} = x^{-5} = \dfrac{1}{x^5}$

31. $\left(4x^{-5}\right)\left(2x^2\right) = 8x^{-5+2} = 8x^{-3} = \dfrac{8}{x^3}$

33. $\dfrac{x^3}{x^9} = x^{3-9} = x^{-6} = \dfrac{1}{x^6}$

35. $\dfrac{y}{y^{100}} = \dfrac{y^1}{y^{100}} = y^{1-100} = y^{-99} = \dfrac{1}{y^{99}}$

37. $\dfrac{30z^5}{10z^{10}} = \dfrac{30}{10} \cdot \dfrac{z^5}{z^{10}} = 3z^{5-10}$
$$= -3z^{-5} = \dfrac{3}{z^5}$$

39. $\dfrac{-8x^3}{2x^7} = \dfrac{-8}{2} \cdot \dfrac{x^3}{x^7} = -4x^{-4} = -\dfrac{4}{x^4}$

41. $\dfrac{-9a^5}{27a^8} = \dfrac{-9}{27} \cdot \dfrac{a^5}{a^8} = -\dfrac{1}{3}a^{-3} = -\dfrac{1}{3a^3}$

43. $\dfrac{7w^5}{5w^{13}} = \dfrac{7}{5} \cdot \dfrac{w^5}{w^{13}} = \dfrac{7}{5}w^{-8} = \dfrac{7}{5w^8}$

45. $\dfrac{x^3}{\left(x^4\right)^2} = \dfrac{x^3}{x^{4 \cdot 2}} = \dfrac{x^3}{x^8} = x^{-5} = \dfrac{1}{x^5}$

47. $\dfrac{y^{-3}}{\left(y^4\right)^2} = \dfrac{y^{-3}}{y^8} = y^{-3-8} = y^{-11} = \dfrac{1}{y^{11}}$

49. $\dfrac{\left(4x^3\right)^2}{x^8} = \dfrac{4^2 x^6}{x^8} = 16x^{-2} = \dfrac{16}{x^2}$

51. $\dfrac{\left(6y^4\right)^3}{y^{-5}} = \dfrac{6^3 y^{12}}{y^{-5}} = 216y^{12-(-5)} = 216y^{17}$

53. $\left(\dfrac{x^4}{x^2}\right)^{-3} = \left(x^2\right)^{-3} = x^{-6} = \dfrac{1}{x^6}$

55. $\left(\dfrac{4x^5}{2x^2}\right)^{-4} = \left(2x^3\right)^{-4} = 2^{-4}x^{-12} = \dfrac{1}{2^4 x^{12}}$

$\qquad = \dfrac{1}{16x^{12}}$

57. $\left(3x^{-1}\right)^{-2} = 3^{-2}\left(x^{-1}\right)^{-2} = 3^{-2}x^2$

$\qquad = \dfrac{x^2}{3^2} = \dfrac{x^2}{9}$

59. $\left(-2y^{-1}\right)^{-3} = (-2)^{-3}\left(y^{-1}\right)^{-3} = \dfrac{y^3}{(-2)^3}$

$\qquad = \dfrac{y^3}{-8} = -\dfrac{y^3}{8}$

61. $\dfrac{2x^5 \cdot 3x^7}{15x^6} = \dfrac{6x^{12}}{15x^6} = \dfrac{6}{15} \cdot \dfrac{x^{12}}{x^6}$

$\qquad = \dfrac{2}{5} \cdot x^6 = \dfrac{2x^6}{5}$

63. $\left(x^3\right)^5 \cdot x^{-7} = x^{15} \cdot x^{-7} = x^{15+(-7)} = x^8$

65. $\left(2y^3\right)^4 y^{-6} = 2^4\left(y^3\right)^4 y^{-6} = 16y^{12}y^{-6}$

$\qquad = 16y^6$

67. $\dfrac{\left(y^3\right)^4}{\left(y^2\right)^7} = \dfrac{y^{12}}{y^{14}} = y^{-2} = \dfrac{1}{y^2}$

69. $\left(y^{10}\right)^{-5} = y^{(10)(-5)} = y^{-50} = \dfrac{1}{y^{50}}$

71. $\left(a^4 b^5\right)^{-3} = \left(a^4\right)^{-3}\left(b^5\right)^{-3} = a^{-12}b^{-15}$

$\qquad = \dfrac{1}{a^{12}b^{15}}$

73. $\left(a^{-2}b^6\right)^{-4} = a^8 b^{-24} = \dfrac{a^8}{b^{24}}$

75. $\left(\dfrac{x^2}{2}\right)^{-2} = \dfrac{x^{-4}}{2^{-2}} = \dfrac{2^2}{x^4} = \dfrac{4}{x^4}$

77. $\left(\dfrac{x^2}{y^3}\right)^{-3} = \dfrac{\left(x^2\right)^{-3}}{\left(y^3\right)^{-3}} = \dfrac{x^{-6}}{y^{-9}} = \dfrac{y^9}{x^6}$

79. $8.7 \times 10^2 = 870$ (Move decimal point 2 places to the right.)

81. $9.23 \times 10^5 = 923{,}000$ (Move right 5.)

83. $3.4 \times 10^0 = 3.4$ (Don't move decimal point.)

85. $7.9 \times 10^{-1} = 0.79$ (Move left 1.)

87. $2.15 \times 10^{-2} = 0.0215$ (Move left 2.)

89. $7.86 \times 10^{-4} = 0.000786$ (Move left 4.)

91. $32,400 = 3.24 \times 10^4$

93. $220,000,000 = 2.2 \times 10^8$

95. $713 = 7.13 \times 10^2$

97. $6751 = 6.751 \times 10^3$

99. $0.0027 = 2.7 \times 10^{-3}$

101. $0.000020 = 2.02 \times 10^{-5}$

103. $0.005 = 5 \times 10^{-3}$

105. $3.14159 = 3.14159 \times 10^0$

107. $\left(2 \times 10^3\right)\left(3 \times 10^2\right) = 6 \times 10^{3+2} = 6 \times 10^5$

109. $\left(2 \times 10^5\right)\left(8 \times 10^3\right) = 16 \times 10^{5+3} = 16 \times 10^8$
$$= 1.6 \times 10^9$$

111. $\dfrac{12 \times 10^6}{4 \times 10^2} = 3 \times 10^{6-2} = 3 \times 10^4$

113. $\dfrac{15 \times 10^4}{5 \times 10^{-2}} = 3 \times 10^{4+2} = 3 \times 10^6$

115. $\dfrac{15 \times 10^{-4}}{5 \times 10^2} = 3 \times 10^{-4-2} = 3 \times 10^{-6}$

117. $\dfrac{180 \times 10^6}{2 \times 10^3} = 90 \times 10^{6-3} = 90 \times 10^3$
$$= 9 \times 10^4$$

119. $\dfrac{3 \times 10^4}{12 \times 10^{-3}} = 0.25 \times 10^{4+3} = 0.25 \times 10^7$
$$= 2.5 \times 10^6$$

121. $\left(5 \times 10^2\right)^3 = 5^3 \times 10^{2(3)} = 125 \times 10^6$
$$= 1.25 \times 10^8$$

123. $\left(3 \times 10^{-2}\right)^4 = 3^4 \times 10^{-2(4)} = 81 \times 10^{-8}$
$$= 8.1 \times 10^{-7}$$

125. $\left(4 \times 10^6\right)^{-1} = 4^{-1} \times 10^{6(-1)} = 0.25 \times 10^{-6}$
$$= 2.5 \times 10^{-7}$$

127. $\dfrac{\left(x^{-2}y\right)^{-3}}{\left(x^2 y^{-1}\right)^3} = \dfrac{x^6 y^{-3}}{x^6 y^{-3}}$
$$= x^{6-6} y^{-3-(-3)} = x^0 y^0 = 1$$

129. $\left(2x^{-3} y z^{-6}\right)\left(2x\right)^{-5} = 2x^{-3} y z^{-6} \cdot 2^{-5} x^{\cdot -5}$
$$= 2^{-4} x^{-8} y z^{-6} = \dfrac{y}{2^4 x^8 z^6} = \dfrac{y}{16 x^8 z^6}$$

131. $\left(\dfrac{x^3 y^4 z^5}{x^{-3} y^{-4} z^{-5}}\right)^{-2} = \left(x^6 y^8 z^{10}\right)^{-2}$
$$= x^{-12} y^{-16} z^{-20} = \dfrac{1}{x^{12} y^{16} z^{20}}$$

133. $\dfrac{\left(2^{-1} x^{-2} y^{-1}\right)^{-2} \left(2x^{-4} y^3\right)^{-2} \left(16 x^{-3} y^3\right)^0}{\left(2x^{-3} y^{-5}\right)^2}$
$$= \dfrac{\left(2^2 x^2 y^2\right)\left(2^{-2} x^8 y^{-6}\right)(1)}{\left(2^2 x^{-6} y^{-10}\right)}$$
$$= \dfrac{x^{18} y^6}{4}$$

135. $\dfrac{\left(5 \times 10^3\right)\left(1.2 \times 10^{-4}\right)}{\left(2.4 \times 10^2\right)} = 2.5 \times 10^{-3}$

137. $\dfrac{\left(1.6 \times 10^4\right)\left(7.2 \times 10^{-3}\right)}{\left(3.6 \times 10^8\right)\left(4 \times 10^{-3}\right)} = 0.8 \times 10^{-4}$
$$= 8 \times 10^{-5}$$

139. $9200 = 9.2 \times 10^3$

141. $0.00000000000000025 = 2.5 \times 10^{-16}$

143. $90.5 \times 10^6 = 9.05 \times 10^1 \times 10^6 = 9.05 \times 10^7$

145. $465 \times 10^9 = 4.65 \times 10^2 \times 10^9 = 4.65 \times 10^{11}$

147. a. 2.27×10^{12}

b. $298 \times 10^6 = 2.98 \times 10^2 \times 10^6 = 2.98 \times 10^8$

c. $\dfrac{2.27 \times 10^{12}}{2.98 \times 10^8} = \dfrac{2.27}{2.98} \cdot \dfrac{10^{12}}{10^8} \approx 0.7617 \times 10^4 = 7617$

The amount per citizen would be \$7617.

149. $120(3.1 \times 10^8) = 372 \times 10^8$
$$= 3.72 \times 10^2 \times 10^8 = 3.72 \times 10^{10}$$
The total annual spending in the United States on ice cream is about $\$3.72 \times 10^{10}$.

151. $\dfrac{2.325 \times 10^5}{1.86 \times 10^5} = 1.25$ seconds

153. – 157. Answers will vary.

159. does not make sense; Explanations will vary.
Sample explanation: $36(x^3)^9 = 36x^{27} \neq 36x^{12}$

161. does not make sense; Explanations will vary.
Sample explanation: This value is much greater than the world population.

163. false; Changes to make the statement true will vary.
A sample change is: $4^{-2} > 4^{-3}$

165. false; Changes to make the statement true will vary.
A sample change is: $(-2)^4 = 16$ and
$2^{-4} = \dfrac{1}{2^4} = \dfrac{1}{16}$.

167. false; Changes to make the statement true will vary.
A sample change is: $534.7 = 5.347 \times 10^2$

169. false; Changes to make the statement true will vary.
A sample change is:
$\left(7 \times 10^5\right) + \left(2 \times 10^{-3}\right)$
$= \left(7 \times 10^5\right) + \left(0.00000002 \times 10^5\right)$
$= \left(7 + 0.00000002\right) \times 10^5$
$= 7.00000002 \times 10^5$

171. $2^{-1} + 2^{-2} = \dfrac{1}{2^1} + \dfrac{1}{2^2}$
$$= \dfrac{1}{2} + \dfrac{1}{4}$$
$$= \dfrac{2}{4} + \dfrac{1}{4} = \dfrac{3}{4}$$

Dr. Frankenstein has gathered enough bits and pieces for $\dfrac{3}{4}$ of his creature. He still needs parts for
$1 - \dfrac{3}{4} = \dfrac{1}{4}$.

173. The calculator verifies your results.

175. The calculator verifies your results.

176. Let x = the number of deer in the park.

$$\dfrac{\substack{\text{Original number} \\ \text{of tagged deer}}}{\substack{\text{Total number} \\ \text{of deer}}} = \dfrac{\substack{\text{Number of tagged} \\ \text{deer in sample}}}{\substack{\text{Number of deer} \\ \text{in sample}}}$$

$$\dfrac{25}{x} = \dfrac{4}{36}$$
$$4x = 900$$
$$x = 225$$

There are approximately 225 deer in the park.

177. $24 \div 8 \cdot 3 + 28 \div (-7) = 3 \cdot 3 + 28 \div (-7)$
$$= 9 + (-4) = 5$$

178. The whole numbers in the given set are 0 and $\sqrt{16} (= 4)$.

179. $4x^3(4x^2 - 3x + 1) = 4x^3 \cdot 4x^2 - 4x^3 \cdot 3x + 4x^3 \cdot 1$
$$= 16x^5 - 12x^4 + 4x^3$$

180. $9xy(3xy^2 - y + 9) = 9xy \cdot 3xy^2 - 9xy \cdot y + 9xy \cdot 9$
$$= 27x^2y^3 - 9xy^2 + 81xy$$

181. $(x + 3)(x^2 + 5) = (x)(x^2) + (x)(5) + (3)(x^2) + (3)(5)$
$$= x^3 + 5x + 3x^2 + 15$$
$$= x^3 + 3x^2 + 5x + 15$$

Chapter 6 Review

1. $7x^4 + 9x$ is a binomial of degree 4.

2. $3x + 5x^2 - 2$ is a trinomial of degree 2.

3. $16x$ is a monomial of degree 1.

4. $\left(-6x^3 + 7x^2 - 9x + 3\right) + \left(14x^3 + 3x^2 - 11x - 7\right)$

   $= \left(-6x^3 + 14x^3\right) + \left(7x^2 + 3x^2\right) + (-9x - 11x) + (3 - 7)$

   $= 8x^3 + 10x^2 - 20x - 4$

5. $\left(9y^3 - 7y^2 + 5\right) + \left(4y^3 - y^2 + 7y - 10\right)$

   $= \left(9y^3 + 4y^3\right) + \left(-7y^2 - y^2\right) + 7y + (5 - 10)$

   $= 13y^3 - 8y^2 + 7y - 5$

6. $\left(5y^2 - y - 8\right) - \left(-6y^2 + 3y - 4\right)$

   $= \left(5y^2 - y - 8\right) + \left(6y^2 - 3y + 4\right)$

   $= \left(5y^2 + 6y^2\right) + (-y - 3y) + (-8 + 4)$

   $= 11y^2 - 4y - 4$

7. $\left(13x^4 - 8x^3 + 2x^2\right) - \left(5x^4 - 3x^3 + 2x^2 - 6\right)$

   $= \left(13x^4 - 8x^3 + 2x^2\right)$

   $\quad + \left(-5x^4 + 3x^3 - 2x^2 + 6\right)$

   $= \left(13x^4 - 5x^4\right) + \left(-8x^3 + 3x^3\right)$

   $\quad + \left(2x^2 - 2x^2\right) + 6$

   $= 8x^4 - 5x^3 + 6$

8. $\left(-13x^4 - 6x^2 + 5x\right) - \left(x^4 + 7x^2 - 11x\right)$

   $= \left(-13x^4 - 6x^2 + 5x\right) + \left(-x^4 - 7x^2 + 11x\right)$

   $= \left(-13x^4 - x^4\right) + \left(-6x^2 - 7x^2\right) + (5x + 11x)$

   $= -14x^4 - 13x^2 + 16x$

9. $7y^4 - 6y^3 + 4y^2 - 4y$

   $\underline{\qquad y^3 - \ y^2 + 3y - 4}$

   $7y^4 - 5y^3 + 3y^2 - \ y - 4$

10. $7x^2 - 9x + 2$

    $\underline{-\left(4x^2 - 2x - 7\right)}$

    To subtract, add the opposite of the polynomial being subtracted.

    $7x^2 - 9x + 2$

    $\underline{-4x^2 + 2x + 7}$

    $3x^2 - 7x + 9$

11. $5x^3 - 6x^2 - \ 9x + 14$

    $\underline{-\left(-5x^3 + 3x^2 - 11x + \ 3\right)}$

    To subtract, add the opposite of the polynomial being subtracted.

    $5x^3 - 6x^2 - \ 9x + 14$

    $\underline{5x^3 - 3x^2 + 11x - \ 3}$

    $10x^3 - 9x^2 + \ 2x + 11$

12.

x	$y = x^2 + 3$	(x, y)
-3	$y = (-3)^2 + 3 = 12$	$(-3, 12)$
-2	$y = (-2)^2 + 3 = 7$	$(-2, 7)$
-1	$y = (-1)^2 + 3 = 4$	$(-1, 4)$
0	$y = (0)^2 + 3 = 3$	$(0, 3)$
1	$y = (1)^2 + 3 = 4$	$(1, 4)$
2	$y = (2)^2 + 3 = 7$	$(2, 7)$
3	$y = (3)^2 + 3 = 12$	$(3, 12)$

13.

x	$y = 1 - x^2$	(x, y)
-3	$y = 1 - (-3)^2 = -8$	$(-3, -8)$
-2	$y = 1 - (-2)^2 = -3$	$(-2, -3)$
-1	$y = 1 - (-1)^2 = 0$	$(-1, 0)$
0	$y = 1 - (0)^2 = 1$	$(0, 1)$
1	$y = 1 - (1)^2 = 0$	$(1, 0)$
2	$y = 1 - (2)^2 = -3$	$(2, -3)$
3	$y = 1 - (3)^2 = -8$	$(3, -8)$

14. $x^{20} \cdot x^3 = x^{20+3} = x^{23}$

15. $y \cdot y^5 \cdot y^8 = y^1 \cdot y^5 \cdot y^8 = y^{1+5+8} = y^{14}$

16. $\left(x^{20}\right)^5 = x^{20 \cdot 5} = x^{100}$

17. $(10y)^2 = 10^2 y^2 = 100 y^2$

18. $\left(-4x^{10}\right)^3 = (-4)^3 \left(x^{10}\right)^3 = -64x^{30}$

19. $(5x)\left(10x^3\right) = (5 \cdot 10)\left(x^1 \cdot x^3\right) = 50x^4$

20. $\left(-12y^7\right)\left(3y^4\right) = -36y^{11}$

21. $\left(-2x^5\right)\left(-3x^4\right)\left(5x^3\right) = 30x^{12}$

22. $7x\left(3x^2 + 9\right) = 7x\left(3x^2\right) + (7x)(9)$
$$= 21x^3 + 63x$$

23. $5x^3\left(4x^2 - 11x\right) = 5x^3\left(4x^2\right) - 5x^3(11x)$
$$= 20x^5 - 55x^4$$

24. $3y^2\left(-7y^2 + 3y - 6\right)$
$$= 3y^2\left(-7y^2\right) + 3y^2(3y) + 3y^2(-6)$$
$$= -21y^4 + 9y^3 - 18y^2$$

25. $2y^5\left(8y^3 - 10y^2 + 1\right)$
$$= 2y^5\left(8y^3\right) + 2y^5\left(-10y^2\right) + 2y^5(1)$$
$$= 16y^8 - 20y^7 + 2y^5$$

26. $(x+3)\left(x^2 - 5x + 2\right)$
$$= x\left(x^2 - 5x + 2\right) + 3\left(x^2 - 5x + 2\right)$$
$$= x^3 - 5x^2 + 2x + 3x^2 - 15x + 6$$
$$= x^3 - 2x^2 - 13x + 6$$

27. $(3y-2)\left(4y^2 + 3y - 5\right)$
$$= 3y\left(4y^2 + 3y - 5\right) - 2\left(4y^2 + 3y - 5\right)$$
$$= 12y^3 + 9y^2 - 15y - 8y^2 - 6y + 10$$
$$= 12y^3 + y^2 - 21y + 10$$

28. $y^2 - 4y + 7$
$$\underline{\qquad 3y - 5 \qquad}$$
$$-5y^2 + 20y - 35$$
$$\underline{3y^3 - 12y^2 + 21y \qquad}$$
$$3y^3 - 17y^2 + 41y - 35$$

29. $4x^3 - 2x^2 - 6x - 1$
$$\underline{\qquad\qquad 2x + 3}$$
$$12x^3 - 6x^2 - 18x - 3$$
$$\underline{8x^4 - 4x^3 - 12x^2 - 2x \qquad}$$
$$8x^4 + 8x^3 - 18x^2 - 20x - 3$$

30. $(x+6)(x+2)$
$$= x \cdot x + x \cdot 2 + 6 \cdot x + 6 \cdot 2$$
$$= x^2 + 2x + 6x + 12$$
$$= x^2 + 8x + 12$$

31. $(3y-5)(2y+1) = 6y^2 + 3y - 10y - 5$
$$= 6y^2 - 7y - 5$$

32. $\left(4x^2-2\right)\left(x^2-3\right)$

$\qquad = 4x^2 \cdot x^2 + 4x^2\left(-3\right) - 2\cdot x^2 - 2\left(-3\right)$

$\qquad = 4x^4 - 12x^2 - 2x^2 + 6$

$\qquad = 4x^4 - 14x^2 + 6$

33. $\left(5x+4\right)\left(5x-4\right) = \left(5x\right)^2 - 4^2$

$\qquad\qquad\qquad\qquad = 25x^2 - 16$

34. $\left(7-2y\right)\left(7+2y\right) = 7^2 - \left(2y\right)^2$

$\qquad\qquad\qquad\qquad\quad = 49 - 4y^2$

35. $\left(y^2+1\right)\left(y^2-1\right) = \left(y^2\right)^2 - 1^2 = y^4 - 1$

36. $\left(x+3\right)^2 = x^2 + 2\left(x\right)\left(3\right) + 3^2$

$\qquad\qquad\quad = x^2 + 6x + 9$

37. $\left(3y+4\right)^2 = \left(3y\right)^2 + 2\left(3y\right)\left(4\right) + 16$

$\qquad\qquad\qquad = 9y^2 + 24y + 16$

38. $\left(y-1\right)^2 = y^2 - 2y + 1$

39. $\left(5y-2\right)^2 = \left(5y\right)^2 - 2\left(5y\right)\left(2\right) + 2^2$

$\qquad\qquad\qquad = 25y^2 - 20y + 4$

40. $\left(x^2+4\right)^2 = \left(x^2\right)^2 + 2\left(x^2\right)\left(4\right) + 4^2$

$\qquad\qquad\qquad = x^4 + 8x^2 + 16$

41. $\left(x^2+4\right)\left(x^2-4\right) = \left(x^2\right)^2 - 4^2 = x^4 - 16$

42. $\left(x^2+4\right)\left(x^2-5\right) = \left(x^2\right)^2 - 5x^2 + 4x^2 - 20$

$\qquad\qquad\qquad\qquad\quad = x^4 - x^2 - 20$

43. $A = \left(x+3\right)\left(x+4\right)$

$\qquad = x^2 + 4x + 3x + 12$

$\qquad = x^2 + 7x + 12$

44. $A = \left(x+30\right)\left(x+20\right)$

$\qquad = x^2 + 20x + 30x + 600$

$\qquad = x^2 + 50x + 600$

The area of the expanded garage is

$\left(x^2 + 50x + 600\right)$ yards^2.

45. $2x^3y - 4xy^2 + 5y + 6$

$\qquad = 2\left(-1\right)^3\left(2\right) - 4\left(-1\right)\left(2\right)^2 + 5\left(2\right) + 6$

$\qquad = 2\left(-1\right)\left(2\right) + 4\left(1\right)\left(4\right) + 5\left(2\right) + 6$

$\qquad = -4 + 16 + 10 + 6 = 28$

46. $4x^2y + 9x^3y^2 - 17x^4 - 12$

Term	Coefficient	Degree
$4x^2y$	4	$2+1=3$
$9x^3y^2$	9	$3+2=5$
$-17x^4$	-17	4
-12	-12	0

The degree of the polynomial is the highest degree of all its terms, which is 5.

47. $\left(7x^2-8xy+y^2\right)+\left(-8x^2-9xy+4y^2\right)$

$\qquad = \left(7x^2-8x^2\right)+\left(-8xy-9xy\right)+\left(y^2+4y^2\right)$

$\qquad = -x^2 - 17xy + 5y^2$

48. $\left(13x^3y^2 - 5x^2y - 9x^2\right) - \left(11x^3y^2 - 6x^2y - 3x^2 + 4\right)$

$\quad = \left(13x^3y^2 - 5x^2y - 9x^2\right) + \left(-11x^3y^2 + 6x^2y + 3x^2 - 4\right)$

$\quad = \left(13x^3y^2 - 11x^3y^2\right) + \left(-5x^2y + 6x^2y\right) + \left(-9x^2 + 3x^2\right) - 4$

$\quad = 2x^3y^2 + x^2y - 6x^2 - 4$

49. $\left(-7x^2y^3\right)\left(5x^4y^6\right) = (-7)(-5)x^{2+4}y^{3+6}$

$\quad\quad\quad\quad\quad\quad\quad = -35x^6y^9$

50. $5ab^2\left(3a^2b^3 - 4ab\right)$

$\quad = 5ab^2\left(3a^2b^3\right) + 5ab^2\left(-4ab\right)$

$\quad = 15a^3b^5 - 20a^2b^3$

51. $(x + 7y)(3x - 5y)$

$\quad = x(3x) + x(-5y) + 7y(3x) + 7y(-5y)$

$\quad = 3x^2 - 5xy + 21xy - 35y^2$

$\quad = 3x^2 + 16xy - 35y^2$

52. $(4xy - 3)(9xy - 1)$

$\quad = 4xy(9xy) + 4xy(-1) - 3(9xy) - 3(-1)$

$\quad = 36x^2y^2 - 4xy - 27xy + 3$

$\quad = 36x^2y^2 - 31xy + 3$

53. $(3x + 5y)^2 = (3x)^2 + 2(3x)(5y) + (5y)^2$

$\quad\quad\quad\quad\quad = 9x^2 + 30xy + 25y^2$

54. $(xy - 7)^2 = (xy)^2 - 2(xy)(7) + 7^2$

$\quad\quad\quad\quad = x^2y^2 - 14xy + 49$

55. $(7x + 4y)(7x - 4y) = (7x)^2 - (4y)^2$

$\quad\quad\quad\quad\quad\quad\quad = 49x^2 - 16y^2$

56. $(a - b)\left(a^2 + ab + b^2\right)$

$\quad = a\left(a^2 + ab + b^2\right) - b\left(a^2 + ab + b^2\right)$

$\quad = a^3 + a^2b + ab^2 - a^2b - ab^2 - b^3$

$\quad = a^3 + \left(a^2b - a^2b\right) + \left(ab^2 - ab^2\right) - b^3$

$\quad = a^3 - b^3$

57. $\dfrac{6^{40}}{6^{10}} = 6^{40-10} = 6^{30}$

58. $\dfrac{x^{18}}{x^3} = x^{18-3} = x^{15}$

59. $(-10)^0 = 1$

60. $-10^0 = -(1) = -1$

61. $400x^0 = 400 \cdot 1 = 400$

62. $\left(\dfrac{x^4}{2}\right)^3 = \dfrac{\left(x^4\right)^3}{2^3} = \dfrac{x^{4 \cdot 3}}{8} = \dfrac{x^{12}}{8}$

63. $\left(\dfrac{-3}{2y^6}\right)^4 = \dfrac{(-3)^4}{\left(2y^6\right)^4} = \dfrac{81}{\left(2^4 y^6\right)^4} = \dfrac{81}{16y^{24}}$

64. $\dfrac{-15y^8}{3y^2} = \dfrac{-15}{3} \cdot \dfrac{y^8}{y^2} = -5y^6$

65. $\dfrac{40x^8 y^6}{5xy^3} = \dfrac{40}{5} \cdot \dfrac{x^8}{x^1} \cdot \dfrac{y^6}{y^3} = 8x^7 y^3$

66. $\dfrac{18x^4 - 12x^2 + 36x}{6x} = \dfrac{18x^4}{6x} - \dfrac{12x^2}{6x} + \dfrac{36x}{6x}$
$= 3x^2 - 2x + 6$

67. $\dfrac{30x^8 - 25x^7 - 40x^5}{-5x^3}$
$= \dfrac{30x^8}{-5x^3} - \dfrac{25x^7}{-5x^3} - \dfrac{40x^5}{-5x^3}$
$= -6x^5 + 5x^4 + 8x^2$

68. $\dfrac{27x^3 y^2 - 9x^2 y - 18xy^2}{3xy}$
$= \dfrac{27x^3 y^2}{3xy} - \dfrac{9x^2 y}{3xy} - \dfrac{18xy^2}{3xy}$
$= 9x^2 y - 3x - 6y$

69.
$$\begin{array}{r}
2x+7 \\
x-2 \overline{\smash{\big)}\, 2x^2 + 3x - 14} \\
\underline{2x^2 - 4x} \\
7x - 14 \\
\underline{7x - 14} \\
0
\end{array}$$

$\dfrac{2x^2 + 3x - 14}{x - 2} = 2x + 7$

70.
$$\begin{array}{r}
x^2 - 3x + 5 \\
2x+1 \overline{\smash{\big)}\, 2x^3 - 5x^2 + 7x + 5} \\
\underline{2x^3 + x^2} \\
-6x^2 + 7x \\
\underline{-6x^2 - 3x} \\
10x + 5 \\
\underline{10x + 5} \\
0
\end{array}$$

$\dfrac{2x^3 - 5x^2 + 7x + 5}{2x + 1} = x^2 - 3x + 5$

71.
$$\begin{array}{r}
x^2 + 5x + 2 \\
x-7 \overline{\smash{\big)}\, x^3 - 2x^2 - 33x - 7} \\
\underline{x^3 - 7x^2} \\
5x^2 - 33x \\
\underline{5x^2 - 35x} \\
2x - 7 \\
\underline{2x - 14} \\
7
\end{array}$$

$\dfrac{x^3 - 2x^2 - 33x - 7}{x - 7} = x^2 + 5x + 2 + \dfrac{7}{x - 7}$

72.

$$y-3\overline{\smash{\big)}\,y^3+0y^2+0y-27}$$

quotient: y^2+3y+9

$$\underline{y^3-3y^2}$$
$$3y^2+0y$$
$$\underline{3y^2-9y}$$
$$9y-27$$
$$\underline{9y-27}$$
$$0$$

$$\frac{y^2-27}{y-3}=y^2+3y+9$$

73. $7^{-2}=\dfrac{1}{7^2}=\dfrac{1}{49}$

74. $(-4)^{-3}=\dfrac{1}{(-4)^3}=\dfrac{1}{-64}=-\dfrac{1}{64}$

75. $2^{-1}+4^{-1}=\dfrac{1}{2}+\dfrac{1}{4}=\dfrac{3}{4}$

76. $\dfrac{1}{5^{-2}}=5^2=25$

77. $\left(\dfrac{2}{5}\right)^{-3}=\dfrac{2^{-3}}{5^{-3}}=\dfrac{5^3}{2^3}=\dfrac{125}{8}$

78. $\dfrac{x^3}{x^9}=x^{3-9}=x^{-6}=\dfrac{1}{x^6}$

79. $\dfrac{30y^6}{5y^8}=\dfrac{30}{5}\cdot\dfrac{y^6}{y^8}=6y^{-2}=\dfrac{6}{y^2}$

80. $\left(5x^{-7}\right)\left(6x^2\right)=(5\cdot6)\left(x^{-7+2}\right)$
$$=30x^{-5}=\dfrac{30}{x^5}$$

81. $\dfrac{x^4\cdot x^{-2}}{x^{-6}}=\dfrac{x^{4+(-2)}}{x^{-6}}=\dfrac{x^2}{x^{-6}}$
$$=x^{2-(-6)}=x^8$$

82. $\dfrac{\left(3y^3\right)^4}{y^{10}}=\dfrac{3^4y^{3(4)}}{y^{10}}=\dfrac{81y^{12}}{y^{10}}$
$$=81y^{12-10}=81y^2$$

83. $\dfrac{y^{-7}}{\left(y^4\right)^3}=\dfrac{y^{-7}}{y^{12}}=y^{-7-12}=y^{-19}=\dfrac{1}{y^{19}}$

84. $\left(2x^{-1}\right)^{-3}=2^{-3}\left(x^{-1}\right)^{-3}=2^{-3}x^3$
$$=\dfrac{x^3}{2^3}=\dfrac{x^3}{8}$$

85. $\left(\dfrac{x^7}{x^4}\right)^{-2}=\left(x^3\right)^{-2}=x^{-6}=\dfrac{1}{x^6}$

86. $\dfrac{\left(y^3\right)^4}{\left(y^{-2}\right)^4}=\dfrac{y^{12}}{y^{-8}}=y^{12-(-8)}=y^{20}$

87. $2.3\times10^4=23,000$

88. $1.76\times10^{-3}=0.00176$

89. $9\times10^{-1}=0.9$

90. $73,900,000=7.39\times10^7$

91. $0.00062=6.2\times10^{-4}$

92. $0.38=3.8\times10^{-1}$

93. $3.8=3.8\times10^0$

94. $\left(6\times10^{-3}\right)\left(1.5\times10^6\right)=6(1.5)\times10^{-3+6}$
$$=9\times10^3$$

95. $\dfrac{2\times10^2}{4\times10^{-3}}=0.5\cdot10^{2+3}=0.5\times10^5$
$$=5\times10^{-1}\times10^5$$
$$=5.0\times10^4$$

96. $\left(4\times10^{-2}\right)^2=4^2\times10^{-2(2)}=16\times10^{-4}$
$$=1.6\times10^1\times10^{-4}=1.6\times10^{1-4}$$
$$=1.6\times10^{-3}$$

97. $257\times10^9=2.57\times10^2\times10^9=2.57\times10^{11}$

98. $175 \times 10^6 = 1.75 \times 10^2 \times 10^6 = 1.75 \times 10^8$

99. $\dfrac{2.57 \times 10^{11}}{1.75 \times 10^8} = \dfrac{2.57}{1.75} \cdot \dfrac{10^{11}}{10^8} \approx 1.469 \times 10^3 = 1469$

Chapter 6 Test

1. $9x + 6x^2 - 4$ is a trinomial of degree 2.

2. $\left(7x^3 + 3x^2 - 5x - 11\right) + \left(6x^3 - 2x^2 + 4x - 13\right)$

$= \left(7x^3 + 6x^3\right) + \left(3x^2 - 2x^2\right) + \left(-5x + 4x\right) + \left(-11 - 13\right)$

$= 13x^3 + x^2 - x - 24$

3. $\left(9x^3 - 6x^2 - 11x - 4\right) - \left(4x^3 - 8x^2 - 13x + 5\right)$

$= \left(9x^3 - 6x^2 - 11x - 4\right) + \left(-4x^3 + 8x^2 + 13x - 5\right)$

$= \left(9x^3 - 4x^3\right) + \left(-6x^2 + 8x^2\right) + \left(-11x + 13x\right) + \left(-4 - 5\right)$

$= 5x^3 + 2x^2 + 2x - 9$

4.

x	$y = x^2 - 3$	(x, y)
-3	$y = (-3)^2 - 3 = 6$	$(-3, 6)$
-2	$y = (-2)^2 - 3 = 1$	$(-2, 1)$
-1	$y = (-1)^2 - 3 = -2$	$(-1, -2)$
0	$y = (0)^2 - 3 = -3$	$(0, -3)$
1	$y = (1)^2 - 3 = -2$	$(1, -2)$
2	$y = (2)^2 - 3 = 1$	$(2, 1)$
3	$y = (3)^2 - 3 = 6$	$(3, 6)$

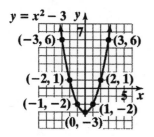

5. $\left(-7x^3\right)\left(5x^8\right) = \left(-7 \cdot 5\right)\left(x^{3+8}\right) = -35x^{11}$

6. $6x^2\left(8x^3-5x-2\right)$

$=6x^2\left(8x^3\right)+6x^2\left(-5x\right)+6x^2\left(-2\right)$

$=48x^5-30x^3-12x^2$

7. $\left(3x+2\right)\left(x^2-4x-3\right)$

$=3x\left(x^2-4x-3\right)+2\left(x^2-4x-3\right)$

$=3x^3-12x^2-9x+2x^2-8x-6$

$=3x^3-10x^2-17x-6$

8. $\left(3y+7\right)\left(2y-9\right)$

$=6y^2+14y-27y-63$

$=6y^2-13y-63$

9. $\left(7x+5\right)\left(7x-5\right)=\left(7x\right)^2-5^2$

$=49x^2-25$

10. $\left(x^2+3\right)^2=\left(x^2\right)^2+2\left(x^2\right)\left(3\right)+3^2$

$=x^4+6x^2+9$

11. $\left(5x-3\right)^2=\left(5x\right)^2-2\left(5x\right)\left(3\right)+3^2$

$=25x^2-30x+9$

12. $4x^2y+5xy-6x$

$=4\left(-2\right)^2\left(3\right)+5\left(-2\right)\left(3\right)-6\left(-2\right)$

$=4\left(4\right)\left(3\right)+5\left(-2\right)\left(3\right)-6\left(-2\right)$

$=48-30+12=30$

13. $\left(8x^2y^3-xy+2y^2\right)-\left(6x^2y^3-4xy-10y^2\right)$

$=\left(8x^2y^3-xy+2y^2\right)+\left(-6x^2y^3+4xy+10y^2\right)$

$=\left(8x^2y^3-6x^2y^3\right)+\left(-xy+4xy\right)+\left(2y^2+10y^2\right)$

$=2x^2y^3+3xy+12y^2$

14. $\left(3a-7b\right)\left(4a+5b\right)$

$=\left(3a\right)\left(4a\right)+\left(3a\right)\left(5b\right)-\left(7b\right)\left(4a\right)-\left(7b\right)\left(5b\right)$

$=12a^2+15ab-28ab-35b^2$

$=12a^2-13ab-35b^2$

15. $\left(2x+3y\right)^2=\left(2x\right)^2+2\left(2x\right)\left(3y\right)+\left(3y\right)^2$

$=4x^2+12xy+9y^2$

16. $\dfrac{-25x^{16}}{5x^4}=\dfrac{-25}{5}\cdot\dfrac{x^{16}}{x^4}=-5x^{16-4}$

$=-5x^{12}$

Check by multiplication:

$5x^4\left(-5x^{12}\right)=-25x^{4+12}=-25x^{16}$

17. $\dfrac{15x^4-10x^3+25x^2}{5x}$

$=\dfrac{15x^4}{5x}-\dfrac{10x^3}{5x}+\dfrac{25x^2}{5x}$

$=3x^3-2x^2+5x$

Check by multiplication:

$5x\left(3x^3-2x^2+5x\right)$

$=5x\left(3x^3\right)+5x\left(-2x^2\right)+5x\left(5x\right)$

$=15x^4-10x^3+25x^2$

18.

$$\begin{array}{r}x^2-2x+3\\2x+1\overline{)2x^3-3x^2+4x+4}\end{array}$$

$\underline{2x^3+\ x^2}$

$-4x^2+4x$

$\underline{-4x^2-2x}$

$6x+4$

$\underline{6x+3}$

1

$\dfrac{2x^3-3x^2+4x+4}{2x+1}=x^2-2x+3+\dfrac{1}{2x+1}$

Check by multiplication:

$\left(2x+1\right)\left(x^2-2x+3\right)+1$

$=\left[2x\left(x^2-2x+3\right)+1\left(x^2-2x+3\right)\right]+1$

$=\left(2x^3-4x^2+6x+x^2-2x+3\right)+1$

$=\left(2x^3-3x^2+4x+3\right)+1$

$=2x^3-3x^2+4x+4$

19. $10^{-2}=\dfrac{1}{10^2}=\dfrac{1}{100}$

20. $\dfrac{1}{4^{-3}} = 1 \cdot 4^3 = 4^3 = 64$

21. $\left(-3x^2\right)^3 = (-3)^3 \left(x^2\right)^3 = -27x^6$

22. $\dfrac{20x^3}{5x^8} = \dfrac{20}{5} \cdot \dfrac{x^3}{x^8} = 4x^{3-8} = 4x^{-5} = \dfrac{4}{x^5}$

23. $\left(-7x^{-8}\right)\left(3x^2\right) = -21x^{-8+2} = -\dfrac{21}{x^6}$

24. $\dfrac{\left(2y^3\right)^4}{y^8} = \dfrac{2^4\left(y^3\right)^4}{y^8} = \dfrac{16y^{12}}{y^8} = 16y^4$

25. $\left(5x^{-4}\right)^{-2} = 5^{-2}\left(x^{-4}\right)^{-2} = 5^{-2}x^8$

$\quad = \dfrac{x^8}{5^2} = \dfrac{x^8}{25}$

26. $\left(\dfrac{x^{10}}{x^5}\right)^{-3} = \left(x^{10-5}\right)^{-3} = \left(x^5\right)^{-3}$

$\quad = x^{-15} = \dfrac{1}{x^{15}}$

27. $3.7 \times 10^{-4} = 0.00037$

28. $7,600,000 = 7.6 \times 10^6$

29. $\left(4.1 \times 10^2\right)\left(3 \times 10^{-5}\right)$

$\quad = (4.1 \cdot 3)\left(10^2 \cdot 10^{-5}\right)$

$\quad = 12.3 \times 10^{-3}$

$\quad = 1.23 \times 10^{-2}$

30. $\dfrac{8.4 \times 10^6}{4 \times 10^{-2}} = \dfrac{8.4}{4} \times \dfrac{10^6}{10^{-2}}$

$\quad = 2.1 \times 10^{6-(-2)}$

$\quad = 2.1 \times 10^8$

31. $A = (x+8)(x+2)$

$\quad = x^2 + 2x + 8x + 16$

$\quad = x^2 + 10x + 16$

Cumulative Review (Chapters 1-6)

1. $(-7)(-5) \div (12 - 3) = (-7)(-5) \div 9$

$\qquad = 35 \div 9 = \dfrac{35}{9}$

2. $(3-7)^2 (9-11)^3 = (-4)^2 (-2)^3$

$\qquad = 16(-8) = -128$

3. $14,300 - (-750) = 14,300 + 750$

$\qquad = 15,050$

The difference in elevation between the plane and the submarine is 15,050 feet.

4. $2(x+3) + 2x = x + 4$

$\quad 2x + 6 + 2x = x + 4$

$\qquad 4x + 6 = x + 4$

$\qquad 3x + 6 = 4$

$\qquad 3x = -2$

$\qquad x = -\dfrac{2}{3}$

The solution set is $\left\{-\dfrac{2}{3}\right\}$.

5. $\dfrac{x}{5} - \dfrac{1}{3} = \dfrac{x}{10} - \dfrac{1}{2}$

To clear fractions, multiply by the LCD = 30.

$30\left(\dfrac{x}{5} - \dfrac{1}{3}\right) = 30\left(\dfrac{x}{10} - \dfrac{1}{2}\right)$

$30\left(\dfrac{x}{5}\right) - 30\left(\dfrac{1}{3}\right) = 30\left(\dfrac{x}{10}\right) - 30\left(\dfrac{1}{2}\right)$

$6x - 10 = 3x - 15$

$3x - 10 = -15$

$3x = -5$

$x = -\dfrac{5}{3}$

The solution set is $\left\{-\dfrac{5}{3}\right\}$.

6. Let $x =$ width of sign.
Then $3x - 2 =$ length of sign.

$$2x + 2(3x - 2) = 28$$
$$2x + 6x - 4 = 28$$
$$8x - 4 = 28$$
$$8x = 32$$
$$x = 4$$
$$3x - 2 = 3(4) - 2 = 10$$

The length of the sign is 10 feet and the width is 4 feet, so the dimensions are 10 feet by 4 feet.

7.
$$7 - 8x \le -6x - 5$$
$$7 - 8x + 6x \le -6x - 5 + 6x$$
$$-2x + 7 \le -5$$
$$-2x + 7 - 7 \le -5 - 7$$
$$-2x \le -12$$
$$\frac{-2x}{-2} \ge \frac{-12}{-2}$$
$$x \ge 6$$

$[6, \infty)$

8.

	Rate	×	Time	=	Distance
You	13		x		$13x$
Friend	11		x		$11x$

$$13x + 11x = 72$$
$$24x = 72$$
$$x = 3$$

It will take 3 hours to meet.

9. Let $x =$ the number of pounds of fertilizer needed to cover 26,000 square feet.

$$\frac{20 \text{ pounds}}{5000 \text{ square feet}} = \frac{x \text{ pounds}}{26,000 \text{ square feet}}$$

$$\frac{20}{5000} = \frac{x}{26,000}$$

$$5000x = 20(26,000)$$

$$5000x = 520,000$$

$$\frac{5000x}{5000} = \frac{520,000}{5000}$$

$$x = 104$$

To cover an area of 26,000 square feet, 104 pounds of fertilizer are needed.

$$\frac{104}{20} = 5.2$$

Since the fertilizer is sold in 20-pound bags and you cannot buy a fraction of a bag, 6 bags of fertilizer are needed.

10. $y = -\dfrac{2}{5}x + 2$

slope $= -\dfrac{2}{5} = \dfrac{-2}{5}$; y-intercept $= 2$

Plot $(0,2)$. Move 2 units *down* (since -2 is negative) and 5 units to the *right* to reach the point $(5,0)$. Draw a line through $(0,2)$ and $(5,0)$.

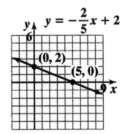

11. $x - 2y = 4$

x-intercept: 4
y-intercept: -2
checkpoint: $(-2, -3)$

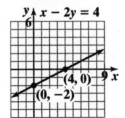

12.　$m = \dfrac{y_2 - y_1}{x_2 - x_1} = \dfrac{-4 - 2}{2 - (-3)} = \dfrac{-6}{5} = -\dfrac{6}{5}$

Because the slope is negative, the line is falling.

13.　$y - (-1) = -2(x - 3)$

$y + 1 = -2(x - 3)$　point-slope form

$y + 1 = -2x + 6$

$y = -2x + 5$　slope-intercept form

14.　$3x + 2y = 10$

$4x - 3y = -15$

Multiply the first equation by 3 and the second equation by 2:

$9x + 6y = 30$

$\underline{8x - 6y = -30}$

$17x = 0$

$x = 0$

Back-substitute $x = 0$ to find y:

$3(0) + 2y = 10$

$2y = 10$

$y = 5$

The solution set is $\{(0, 5)\}$.

15.　$2x + 3y = -6$

$y = 3x - 13$

Substitute the second equation in for y in the first equation:

$2x + 3y = -6$

$2x + 3(3x - 13) = -6$

$2x + 9x - 39 = -6$

$11x - 39 = -6$

$11x = 33$

$x = 3$

Back-substitute $x = 3$ to find y:

$y = 3x - 13 = 3(3) - 13 = -4$

The solution set is $\{(3, -4)\}$.

16.　Let y = total charge.

Let x = # of minutes.

Plan A:　$y = 0.05x + 15$

Plan B:　$y = 0.07x + 5$

To find when the plans are the same, substitute the second equation into the first equation:

$0.07x + 5 = 0.05x + 15$

$0.02x + 5 = 15$

$0.02x = 10$

$x = 500$

Back-substitute to find y:

$y = 0.07x + 5 = 0.07(500) + 5 = 40$

The plans will be the same for 500 minutes at $40 a plan.

17.　$2x + 5y \le 10$

$x - y \ge 4$

Graph $2x + 5y \le 10$:

Graph $2x + 5y = 10$ as a solid line using its x-intercept, 5 and y-intercept, 2.

Since $2(0) + 5(0) \le 10$ is true, shade the half-plane containing (0,0).

Graph $x - y \ge 4$:

Graph $x - y = 4$ as a solid line using its x-intercept, 4 and y-intercept, -4. Since $0 - 0 \ge 4$ is false, shade the half-plane *not* containing (0,0).

The solution set of the system is the intersection of the two shaded regions.

18.　$\left(9x^5 - 3x^3 + 2x - 7\right) - \left(6x^5 + 3x^3 - 7x - 9\right)$

$= \left(9x^5 - 3x^3 + 2x - 7\right) + \left(-6x^5 - 3x^3 + 7x + 9\right)$

$= \left(9x^5 - 6x^5\right) + \left(-3x^3 - 3x^3\right) + (2x + 7x) + (-7 + 9)$

$= 3x^5 - 6x^3 + 9x + 2$

19.

$$\begin{array}{r} x^2+2x+3 \\ x+1\overline{\smash{\big)}\,x^3+3x^2+5x+3} \end{array}$$

$$\underline{x^3+\ \ x^2}$$
$$2x^2+5x$$
$$\underline{2x^2+2x}$$
$$3x+3$$
$$\underline{3x+3}$$
$$0$$

$$\frac{x^3+3x^2+5x+3}{x+1}=x^2+2x+3$$

20. $\dfrac{\left(3x^2\right)^4}{x^{10}}=\dfrac{3^4\left(x^2\right)^4}{x^{10}}=\dfrac{81x^8}{x^{10}}$

$$=81x^{8-10}=81x^{-2}=\frac{81}{x^2}$$

Chapter 7
Factoring Polynomials

7.1 Check Points

1. a. $18x^3 = 3x^2 \cdot 6x$

   $15x^2 = 3x^2 \cdot 5$

   The GCF is $3x^2$.

   b. $-20x^2 = 4x^2 \cdot (-5)$

   $12x^4 = 4x^2 \cdot 3x^2$

   $40x^3 = 4x^2 \cdot 10x$

   The GCF is $4x^2$.

   c. $x^4y = x^2y \cdot x^2$

   $x^3y^2 = x^2y \cdot xy$

   $x^2y = x^2y$

   The GCF is x^2y.

2. $6x^2 + 18 = 6 \cdot x^2 + 6 \cdot 3 = 6(x^2 + 3)$

3. $25x^2 + 35x^3 = 5x^2 \cdot 5 + 5x^2 \cdot 7x = 5x^2(5 + 7x)$

4. $15x^5 + 12x^4 - 27x^3 = 3x^3 \cdot 5x^2 + 3x^3 \cdot 4x - 3x^3 \cdot 9$

   $\qquad\qquad\qquad\qquad = 3x^3(5x^2 + 4x - 9)$

5. $8x^3y^2 - 14x^2y + 2xy = 2xy \cdot 4x^2y - 2xy \cdot 7x + 2xy \cdot 1)$

   $\qquad\qquad\qquad\quad = 2xy \cdot (4x^2y - 7x + 1)$

6. a. $x^2 \overbrace{(x+1)}^{\text{GCF}} + 7 \overbrace{(x+1)}^{\text{GCF}} = (x+1)(x^2 + 7)$

   b. $x \overbrace{(y+4)}^{\text{GCF}} - 7 \overbrace{(y+4)}^{\text{GCF}} = (y+4)(x-7)$

7. $x^3 + 5x^2 + 2x + 10 = (x^3 + 5x^2) + (2x + 10)$

   $\qquad\qquad\qquad\qquad = x^2(x+5) + 2(x+5)$

   $\qquad\qquad\qquad\qquad = (x+5)(x^2 + 2)$

8. $xy + 3x - 5y - 15 = x(y+3) - 5(y+3)$

   $\qquad\qquad\qquad\quad = (y+3)(x-5)$

7.1 Exercise Set

1. The GCF of 4 and $8x$ is 4.

3. The GCF of $12x^2$ and $8x$ is $4x$.

5. The GCF of $-2x^4$ and $6x^3$ is $2x^3$.

7. The GCF of $9y^5, 18y^2$, and $-3y$ is $3y$.

9. The GCF of xy, xy^2, and xy^3 is xy.

11. The GCF of $16x^5y^4, 8x^6y^3$, and $20x^4y^5$ is $4x^4y^3$.

13. $8x + 8 = 8 \cdot x + 8 \cdot 1$
$= 8(x+1)$

15. $4y - 4 = 4 \cdot y - 4 \cdot 1$
$= 4(y-1)$

17. $5x + 30 = 5 \cdot x + 5 \cdot 6$
$= 5(x+6)$

19. $30x - 12 = 6 \cdot 5x - 6 \cdot 2$
$= 6(5x-2)$

21. $x^2 + 5x = x \cdot x + x \cdot 5$
$= x(x+5)$

23. $18y^2 + 12 = 6 \cdot 3y^2 + 6 \cdot 2$
$= 6(3y^2 + 2)$

25. $14x^3 + 21x^2 = 7x^2 \cdot 2x + 7x^2 \cdot 3$
$= 7x^2(2x+3)$

27. $13y^2 - 25y = y \cdot 13y - y \cdot 25$
$= y(13y - 25)$

29. $9y^4 + 27y^6 = 9y^4 \cdot 1 + 9y^4 \cdot 3y^2$
$= 9y^4(1 + 3y^2)$

31. $8x^2 - 4x^4 = 4x^2(2) - 4x^2(x^2)$
$= 4x^2(2 - x^2)$

33. $12y^2 + 16y - 8 = 4(3y^2) + 4(4y) - 4(2)$
$= 4(3y^2 + 4y - 2)$

35. $9x^4 + 18x^3 + 6x^2$
$= 3x^2(3x^2) + 3x^2(6x) + 3x^2(2)$
$= 3x^2(3x^2 + 6x + 2)$

37. $100y^5 - 50y^3 + 100y^2$
$= 50y^2(2y^3) - 50y^2(y) + 50y^2(2)$
$= 50y^2(2y^3 - y + 2)$

39. $10x - 20x^2 + 5x^3$
$= 5x(2) - 5x(4x) + 5x(x^2)$
$= 5x(2 - 4x + x^2)$

41. $11x^2 - 23$ cannot be factored because the two terms have no common factor other than 1.

43. $6x^3y^2 + 9xy = 3xy(2x^2 + y) + 3xy(3)$
$= 3xy(2x^2y + 3)$

45. $30x^2y^2 - 10xy^2 + 20xy$
$= 10xy(3xy^2) - 10xy(y) + 10xy(2)$
$= 10xy(3xy^2 - y + 2)$

47. $32x^3y^2 - 24x^3y - 16x^2y$
$= 8x^2y(4xy) - 8x^2y(3x) - 8x^2y(2)$
$= 8x^2y(4xy - 3x - 2)$

49. $x(x+5) + 3(x+5) = (x+5)(x+3)$

51. $x(x+2) - 4(x+2) = (x+2)(x-4)$

53. $x(y+6) - 7(y+6) = (y+6)(x-7)$

55. $3x(x+y) - (x+y)$
$= 3x(x+y) - 1(x+y)$
$= (x+y)(3x-1)$

57. $4x(3x+1)+3x+1$

$\quad = 4x(3x+1)+1(3x+1)$

$\quad = (3x+1)(4x+1)$

59. $7x^2(5x+4)+5x+4$

$\quad = 7x^2(5x+4)+1(5x+4)$

$\quad = (5x+4)(7x^2+1)$

61. $x^2+2x+4x+8 = (x^2+2x)+(4x+8)$

$\qquad\qquad\qquad = x(x+2)+4(x+2)$

$\qquad\qquad\qquad = (x+2)(x+4)$

63. $x^2+3x-5x-15 = (x^2+3x)+(-5x-15)$

$\qquad\qquad\qquad = x(x+3)-5(x+3)$

$\qquad\qquad\qquad = (x+3)(x-5)$

65. $x^3-2x^2+5x-10$

$\quad = (x^3-2x^2)+(5x-10)$

$\quad = x^2(x-2)+5(x-2)$

$\quad = (x-2)(x^2+5)$

67. $x^3-x^2+2x-2 = x^2(x-1)+2(x-1)$

$\qquad\qquad\qquad = (x-1)(x^2+2)$

69. $xy+5x+9y+45 = x(y+5)+9(y+5)$

$\qquad\qquad\qquad = (y+5)(x+9)$

71. $xy-x+5y-5 = x(y-1)+5(y-1)$

$\qquad\qquad\qquad = (y-1)(x+5)$

73. $3x^2-6xy+5xy-10y^2$

$\quad = 3x(x-2y)+5y(x-2y)$

$\quad = (x-2y)(3x+5y)$

75. $3x^3-2x^2-6x+4$

$\quad = x^2(3x-2)-2(3x-2)$

$\quad = (3x-2)(x^2-2)$

77. $x^2-ax-bx+ab = x(x-a)-b(x-a)$

$\qquad\qquad\qquad = (x-a)(x-b)$

79. $24x^3y^3z^3+30x^2y^2z+18x^2yz^2$

$\quad = 6x^2yz(4xy^2z^2)+6x^2yz(5y)+6x^2yz(3z)$

$\quad = 6x^2yz(4xy^2z^2+5y+3z)$

81. $x^3-4+3x^3y-12y = 1(x^3-4)+3y(x^3-4)$

$\qquad\qquad\qquad\qquad = (x^3-4)(1+3y)$

83. $4x^5(x+1)-6x^3(x+1)-8x^2(x+1)$

$\quad = 2x^2(x+1)\cdot 2x^3-2x^2(x+1)\cdot 3x-2x^2(x+1)\cdot 4$

$\quad = 2x^2(x+1)(2x^3-3x-4)$

85. $3x^5-3x^4+x^3-x^2+5x-5$

$\quad = (3x^5-3x^4)+(x^3-x^2)+(5x-5)$

$\quad = 3x^4(x-1)+x^2(x-1)+5(x-1)$

$\quad = (x-1)(3x^4+x^2+5)$

87. The area of the square is $6x\cdot 6x=36x^2$. The area of the circle is $\pi(2x)^2=\pi\cdot 4x^2=4\pi x^2$. So the shaded area is the area of the square minus the area of the circle, which is $36x^2-4\pi x^2=4x^2(9-\pi)$.

89. a. Use the formula, $64x-16x^2$, for the height of the debris above the ground. Substitute 3 for x.

$\quad 64x-16x^2 = 64(3)-16(3)^2$

$\quad = 192-16(9)=192-144=48$

Therefore, the height of the debris after 3 seconds is 48 feet.

b. $64x-16x^2 = 16x(4-x)$

c. Substitute 3 for x in the factored polynomial.

$\quad 16\cdot 3(4-3)=48(1)=48$

You do get the same answer as in part (a) but this does not prove your factorization is correct.

91. Use the formula for the area of a rectangle, $A = l \cdot w$. Substitute $5x^4 - 10x$ for A and $5x$ for w.

$$A = l \cdot w$$
$$5x^4 - 10x = l(5x)$$
$$\frac{5x^4 - 10x}{5x} = \frac{l(5x)}{5x}$$
$$\frac{5x(x^3 - 2)}{5x} = l$$
$$x^3 - 2 = l$$

The length, l, is $\left(x^3 - 2\right)$ units.

93. – 97. Answers will vary.

99. makes sense

101. does not make sense; Explanations will vary. Sample explanation: The power must be the greatest that is *common* for this variable.

103. false; Changes to make the statement true will vary. A sample change is: Since $\frac{3x}{3x} = 1$, it is necessary to write the 1.

105. false; Changes to make the statement true will vary. A sample change is: $a^2 + b^2$ is not factorable.

107. The polynomial will be
$$x + (x + 100) + (x + 200) + (x + 300)$$
$$= 4x + 600$$
$$= 4(x + 150)$$

109. Answers will vary. One example is $5x^2 + 10x - 4x - 8$.

111. The graphs do not coincide.

Factor by grouping.
$$x^2 - 2x + 5x - 10 = x(x - 2) + 5(x - 2)$$
$$= (x - 2)(x + 5)$$

Change the expression on the right side to $(x - 2)(x + 5)$.

113. $(x + 7)(x + 10) = x^2 + 10x + 7x + 70$
$$= x^2 + 17x + 70$$

114. $2x - y = -4$
$x - 3y = 3$
Graph both equations on the same axes.
$2x - y = -4$: x-intercept: -2; y-intercept: 4
$x - 3y = 3$: x-intercept: 3; y-intercept: -1

The lines intersect as $(-3, -2)$.

The solution set is $\{(-3, -2)\}$.

115. First, find the slope $m = \dfrac{5 - 2}{-4 - (-7)} = \dfrac{3}{3} = 1$

Write the point-slope equation using $m = 1$ and $(x_1, y_1) = (-7, 2)$.
$$y - y_1 = m(x - x_1)$$
$$y - 2 = 1[x - (-7)]$$
$$y - 2 = 1(x + 7)$$

Now rewrite this equation in slope-intercept form.
$$y - 2 = x + 7$$
$$y = x + 9$$

Note: If $(-4, 5)$ is used as $(x_1 y_1)$, the point-slope equation will be
$$y - 5 = 1[x - (-4)]$$
$$y - 5 = x + 4$$

This also leads to the slope-intercept equation $y = x + 9$.

116. $2 \times 4 = 8$ and $2 + 4 = 6$

117. $(-3)(-2) = 6$ and $(-3) + (-2) = -5$

118. $(-5)(7) = -35$ and $(-5) + 7 = 2$

7.2 Check Points

1. $x^2 + 5x + 6$

Factors of 6	6,1	−6,−1	2,3	−2,−3
Sum of Factors	7	−7	5	−5

The factors of 6 whose sum is 5 are 2 and 3.

Thus, $x^2 + 5x + 6 = (x+2)(x+3)$.

Check:

$(x+2)(x+3) = x^2 + 3x + 2x + 6$
$ = x^2 + 5x + 6$

2. $x^2 - 6x + 8$

Factors of 8	8,1	−8,−1	2,4	−2,−4
Sum of Factors	9	−9	6	−6

The factors of 8 whose sum is −6 are −2 and −4.

Thus, $x^2 - 6x + 8 = (x-2)(x-4)$.

Check:

$(x-2)(x-4) = x^2 - 4x - 2x + 8$
$ = x^2 - 6x + 8$

3. $x^2 + 3x - 10$

Factors of −10	−10,1	10,−1	−5,2	5,−2
Sum of Factors	−9	9	−3	3

The factors of −10 whose sum is 3 are 5 and −2.

Thus, $x^2 + 3x - 10 = (x+5)(x-2)$.

Check:

$(x+5)(x-2) = x^2 - 2x + 5x - 10$
$ = x^2 + 3x - 10$

4. The factors of −27 whose sum is −6 are −9 and 3.
   Thus, $y^2 - 6y - 27 = (y-9)(y+3)$.

5. No factor pair of −7 has a sum of 1.
   Thus, $x^2 + x - 7$ is prime.

6. The factors of 3 whose sum is −4 are −3 and −1.
   Thus, $x^2 - 4xy + 3y^2 = (x-3y)(x-y)$.

7. First factor out the common factor of $2x$.
   $2x^3 + 6x^2 - 56x = 2x(x^2 + 6x - 28)$
   Continue by factoring the trinomial.
   $2x^3 + 6x^2 - 56x = 2x(x^2 + 6x - 28)$
   $ = 2x(x-4)(x+7)$

7.2 Exercise Set

1. $x^2 + 7x + 6$

Factors of 6	6,1	−6,−1	3,2	−3,−2
Sum of Factors	7	−7	5	−5

The factors of 6 whose sum is 7 are 6 and 1.

Thus, $x^2 + 7x + 6 = (x+6)(x+1)$.

Check:

$(x+6)(x+1) = x^2 + 1x + 6x + 6$
$ = x^2 + 7x + 6$

3. $x^2 + 7x + 10 = (x+5)(x+2)$
   $5(2) = 10;\ 5+2 = 7$

5. $x^2 + 11x + 10 = (x+10)(x+1)$
   $10(1) = 10;\ 10+1 = 11$

7. $x^2 - 7x + 12 = (x-4)(x-3)$
   $-4(-3) = 12;\ -4 + -3 = -7$

9. $x^2 - 12x + 36 = (x-6)(x-6)$
   $-6(-6) = 36;\ -6 + -6 = -12$

11. $y^2 - 8y + 15 = (y-5)(y-3)$
    $-5(-3) = 15;\ -5 + -3 = -8$

13. $x^2 + 3x - 10 = (x+5)(x-2)$
    $5(-2) = -10;\ 5 + -2 = 3$

15. $y^2 + 10y - 39 = (y+13)(y-3)$
    $(13)(-3) = -39;\ 13 + -3 = 10$

17. $x^2 - 2x - 15 = (x-5)(x+3)$
    $(-5)(3) = -15;\ -5 + 3 = -2$

19. $x^2 - 2x - 8 = (x-4)(x+2)$
    $(-4)(2) = -8;\ -4 + 2 = -2$

21. $x^2 + 4x + 12$ is prime because there is no pair of integers whose product is 12 and whose sum is 4.

23. $y^2 - 16y + 48 = (y-4)(y-12)$
    $(-4)(-12) = 48;\ -4 + -12 = -16$

25. $x^2 - 3x + 6$ is prime because there is no pair of integers whose product is 6 and whose sum is -3.

27. $w^2 - 30w - 64 = (w - 32)(w + 2)$
$(-32)(2) = -64; \ -32 + 2 = -30$

29. $y^2 - 18y + 65 = (y - 5)(y - 13)$
$(-5)(-13) = 65; \ -5 + -13 = -18$

31. $r^2 + 12r + 27 = (r + 3)(r + 9)$
$(3)(9) = 27; \ 3 + 9 = 12$

33. $y^2 - 7y + 5$ is prime because there is no pair of integers whose product is 5 and whose sum is -7.

35. $x^2 + 7xy + 6y^2 = (x + 6y)(x + y)$
$(6)(1) = 6; \ 6 + 1 = 7$

37. $x^2 - 8xy + 15y^2 = (x - 3y)(x - 5y)$
$(-3)(-5) = 15; \ -3 + -5 = -8$

39. $x^2 - 3xy - 18y^2 = (x - 6y)(x + 3y)$
$(-6)(3) = -18; \ -6 + 3 = -3$

41. $a^2 - 18ab + 45b^2 = (a - 15b)(a - 3b)$
$(-15)(-3) = 45; \ -15 + -3 = -18$

43. $3x^2 + 15x + 18$
First factor out the GCF, 3. Then factor the resulting binomial.
$3x^2 + 15x + 18 = 3\left(x^2 + 5x + 6\right)$
$= 3(x + 2)(x + 3)$

45. $4y^2 - 4y - 8 = 4\left(y^2 - y - 2\right)$
$= 4(y - 2)(y + 1)$

47. $10x^2 - 40x - 600 = 10\left(x^2 - 4x - 60\right)$
$= 10(x - 10)(x + 6)$

49. $3x^2 - 33x + 54 = 3\left(x^2 - 11x + 18\right)$
$3(x - 2)(x - 9)$

51. $2r^3 + 6r^2 + 4r = 2r\left(r^2 + 3r + 2\right)$
$= 2r(r + 2)(r + 1)$

53. $4x^3 + 12x^2 - 72x = 4x\left(x^2 + 3x - 18\right)$
$= 4x(x + 6)(x - 3)$

55. $2r^3 + 8r^2 - 64r = 2r\left(r^2 + 4r - 32\right)$
$= 2r(r + 8)(r - 4)$

57. $y^4 + 2y^3 - 80y^2 = y^2\left(y^2 + 2y - 80\right)$
$= y^2(y + 10)(y - 8)$

59. $x^4 - 3x^3 - 10x^2 = x^2\left(x^2 - 3x - 10\right)$
$= x^2(x - 5)(x + 2)$

61. $2w^4 - 26w^3 - 96w^2$
$= 2w^2\left(w^2 - 13w - 48\right)$
$= 2w^2(w - 16)(w + 3)$

63. $15xy^2 + 45xy - 60x = 15x\left(y^2 + 3y - 4\right)$
$= 15x(y + 4)(y - 1)$

65. $x^5 + 3x^4y - 4x^3y^2 = x^3\left(x^2 + 3xy - 4y^2\right)$
$= x^3(x + 4y)(x - y)$

67. $2x^2y^2 - 32x^2yz + 30x^2z^2$
$= 2x^2\left(y^2 - 16yz + 15z^2\right)$
$= 2x^2(y - 15z)(y - z)$

69. $(a + b)x^2 + (a + b)x - 20(a + b)$
$= (a + b)\left(x^2 + x - 20\right)$
$= (a + b)(x + 5)(x - 4)$

71. $x^2 + 0.5x + 0.06 = (x + 0.2)(x + 0.3)$
$0.2(0.3) = 0.06; \ 0.2 + 0.3 = 0.5$

73. $x^2 - \dfrac{2}{5}x + \dfrac{1}{25} = \left(x - \dfrac{1}{5}\right)\left(x - \dfrac{1}{5}\right)$

$\dfrac{1}{5}\left(\dfrac{1}{5}\right) = \dfrac{1}{25}; \ -\dfrac{1}{5} + -\dfrac{1}{5} = -\dfrac{2}{5}$

75. $-x^2 - 3x + 40 = -\left(x^2 + 3x - 40\right)$

$\qquad\qquad\qquad = -(x+8)(x-5)$

$8(-5) = -40; \ 8 + -5 = 3$

77. a. $-16t^2 + 16t + 32 = -16\left(t^2 - t - 2\right)$

$\qquad\qquad\qquad\qquad = -16(t-2)(t+1)$

b. Substitute 2 for t in the original polynomial:

$-16t^2 + 16t + 32 = -16(2)^2 + 16(2) + 32$

$\qquad\qquad\qquad = -16(4) + 32 + 32$

$\qquad\qquad\qquad = -64 + 64$

$\qquad\qquad\qquad = 0$

Substitute 2 for t in the factored polynomial:

$-16(t-2)(t+1) = -16(2-2)(2+1)$

$\qquad\qquad\qquad = -16(0)(3)$

$\qquad\qquad\qquad = 0$

The answers are the same.
This answer means that after 2 seconds you hit the water.

79. – 81. Answers will vary.

83. does not make sense; Explanations will vary. Sample explanation: If the order of the terms is switched, the factors of an expression will not change.

85. does not make sense; Explanations will vary. Sample explanation: $x^2 + x + 1$ is prime.

87. false; Changes to make the statement true will vary. A sample change is: $x^2 + x + 20$ is prime.

89. true

91. In order for $x^2 + bx + 15$ to be factorable, b must be the sum of two integers that are positive factors of 15. The only positive factor pairs for 15 are $3 \cdot 5$ and $1 \cdot 15$. Since $3 + 5 = 8, 1 + 15 = 16,$ the possible values of b are 8 and 16.

93. Answers will vary. An example is $x^2 + 14x + 2.$

95. $x^3 + 3x^2 + 2x = x\left(x^2 + 3x + 2\right)$

$\qquad\qquad\qquad = x(x+1)(x+2)$

The trinomial represents the product of three consecutive integers.

97. The graphs coincide.

This verifies the factorization
$x^2 - 5x + 6 = (x-2)(x-3).$

99. The graphs do not coincide.

$x^2 - 2x + 1 = (x-1)(x-1)$
Change the polynomial on the right to
$(x-1)(x-1).$

101. $4(x-2) = 3x + 5$

$\qquad 4x - 8 = 3x + 5$

$\qquad\quad x - 8 = 5$

$\qquad\qquad x = 13$

The solution set is $\{13\}.$

102. Graph $6x - 5y = 30$ with a solid line. Since the test point (0,0) makes the inequality true, shade the half-plane that contains the test point.

103. $y = -\dfrac{1}{2}x + 2$

The y-intercept is 2. Find an additional point by using the slope. From the y-intercept, move down one unit and to the right 2 units. Draw the line through these points.

104. $(2x+3)(x-2) = 2x^2 - 4x + 3x - 6$

$$= 2x^2 - x - 6$$

105. $(3x+4)(3x+1) = 9x^2 + 3x + 12x + 4$

$$= 9x^2 + 15x + 4$$

106. $8x^2 - 2x - 20x + 5 = 2x(4x-1) - 5(4x-1)$

$$= (4x-1)(2x-5)$$

7.3 Check Points

1. Factor $5x^2 - 14x + 8$ by trial and error.

Step 1 $5x^2 - 14x + 8 = (5x \quad)(x \quad)$

Step 2 The number 8 has pairs of factors that are either both positive or both negative. Because the middle term, $-14x$, is negative, both factors must be negative.

Step 3

Possible Factors of $5x^2 - 14x + 8$	Sum of Outside and Inside Products
	required middle term
$(5x-4)(x-2)$	$-10x - 4x = -14x$
$(5x-2)(x-4)$	$-20x - 2x = -22x$
$(5x-1)(x-8)$	$-40x - x = -41x$
$(5x-8)(x-1)$	$-5x - 8x = -13x$

Check:

$(5x-4)(x-2) = 5x^2 - 10x - 4x + 8$

$$= 5x^2 - 14x + 8$$

Thus, $5x^2 - 14x + 8 = (5x-4)(x-2)$.

2. Factor $6x^2 + 19x - 7$ by trial and error.

Step 1 Find two First terms whose product is $6x^2$.

$$6x^2 + 19x - 7 = (6x \quad)(x \quad)$$

$$6x^2 + 19x - 7 = (3x \quad)(2x \quad)$$

Step 2 The last term, -7, has possible factorizations of $1(-7)$ and $-1(7)$.

Step 3

Possible Factors of $6x^2 + 19x - 7$	Sum of Outside and Inside Products
$(6x+1)(x-7)$	$-42x + x = -41x$
$(6x-7)(x+1)$	$6x - 7x = -x$
$(6x-1)(x+7)$	$42x - x = 41x$
$(6x+7)(x-1)$	$-6x + 7x = x$
$(3x+1)(2x-7)$	$-21x + 2x = -19x$
$(3x-7)(2x+1)$	$3x - 14x = -11x$
	required middle term
$(3x-1)(2x+7)$	$21x - 2x = 19x$
$(3x+7)(2x-1)$	$-3x + 14x = 11x$

Check:

$(3x-1)(2x+7) = 6x^2 + 21x - 2x - 7$

$$= 6x^2 + 19x - 7$$

Thus, $6x^2 + 19x - 7 = (3x-1)(2x+7)$

3. Factor $3x^2 - 13xy + 4y^2$ by trial and error.

Step 1 Find two First terms whose product is $2x^2$.

$$3x^2 - 13xy + 4y^2 = (3x \quad)(x \quad)$$

Step 2 The last term, $4y^2$, has pairs of factors that are either both positive or both negative. Because the middle term, $-13xy$, is negative, both factors must be negative. Thus the last term has possible factorizations of $-2y(-2y)$ or $-y(-4y)$.

Step 3

Possible Factors of $3x^2 - 13xy + 4y^2$	Sum of Outside and Inside Products
$(3x-4y)(x-y)$	$-3xy - 4xy = -7xy$
	required middle term
$(3x-y)(x-4y)$	$-12xy - xy = -13xy$
$(3x-2y)(x-2y)$	$-6xy - 2xy = -8xy$

Check:

$(3x-y)(x-4y) = 3x^2 - 12xy - xy + 4y^2$

$$= 3x^2 - 13xy + 4y^2$$

Thus, $3x^2 - 13xy + 4y^2 = (3x-y)(x-4y)$

4. Factor $3x^2 - x - 10$ by grouping.

$a = 3$ and $c = -10$, so $ac = 3(-10) = -30$.

The factors of -30 whose sum is -1 are 5 and -6.

$$3x^2 - x - 10 = 3x^2 + 5x - 6x - 10$$
$$= x(3x + 5) - 2(3x + 5)$$
$$= (3x + 5)(x - 2)$$

5. Factor $8x^2 - 10x + 3$ by grouping.

$a = 8$ and $c = 3$, so $ac = 8(3) = 24$.

The factors of 24 whose sum is -10 are -6 and -4.

$$8x^2 - 10x + 3 = 8x^2 - 4x - 6x + 3$$
$$= 4x(2x - 1) - 3(2x - 1)$$
$$= (2x - 1)(4x - 3)$$

6. First factor out the GCF.

$$5y^4 + 13y^3 + 6y^2 = y^2(5y^2 + 13y + 6)$$

Then factor the resulting trinomial.

$$5y^4 + 13y^3 + 6y^2 = y^2(5y^2 + 13y + 6)$$
$$= y^2(5y + 3)(y + 2)$$

7.3 Exercise Set

1. Factor $2x^2 + 5x + 3$ by trial and error.

Step 1 $2x^2 + 5x + 3 = (2x \quad)(x \quad)$

Step 2 The number 3 has pairs of factors that are either both positive or both negative. Because the middle term, $5x$, is positive, both factors must be positive. The only positive factorization is $(1)(3)$.

Step 3

Possible Factors of $2x^2 + 5x + 3$	Sum of Outside and Inside Products
$(2x + 1)(x + 3)$	$6x + x = 7x$
$(2x + 3)(x + 1)$	$2x + 3x = 5x$

Check:

$$(2x + 3)(x + 1) = 2x^2 + 2x + 3x + 3$$
$$= 2x^2 + 5x + 3$$

Thus, $2x^2 + 5x + 3 = (2x + 3)(x + 1)$.

3. Factor $3x^2 + 13x + 4$ by trial and error. The only possibility for the first terms is

$$(3x)(x) = 3x^2.$$

Because the middle term is positive and the last term is also positive, the possible factorizations of 4 are $(1)(4)$ and $(2)(2)$.

Possible Factors of $3x^2 + 13x + 4$	Sum of Outside and Inside Products
$(3x + 1)(x + 4)$	$12x + x = 13x$
$(3x + 4)(x + 1)$	$3x + 4x = 7x$
$(3x + 2)(x + 2)$	$6x + 2x = 8x$

Thus, $3x^2 + 13x + 4 = (3x + 1)(x + 4)$.

5. Factor $2x^2 + 11x + 12$ by grouping.

$a = 2$ and $c = 12$, so $ac = 2(12) = 24$.

The factors of 24 whose sum is 11 are 8 and 3.

$$2x^2 + 11x + 12 = 2x^2 + 8x + 3x + 12$$
$$= 2x(x + 4) + 3(x + 4)$$
$$= (x + 4)(2x + 3)$$

7. Factor $5y^2 - 16y + 3$ by trial and error. The first terms must be $5y$ and y. Because the middle term is negative, the factors of 3 must be -3 and -1.

Possible Factors of $5y^2 - 16y + 3$	Sum of Outside and Inside Products
$(5y - 1)(y - 3)$	$-15y - y = -16y$
$(5y - 3)(y - 1)$	$-5y - 3y = -8y$

Thus, $y^2 - 16y + 3 = (5y - 1)(y - 3)$.

9. Factor $3y^2 + y - 4$ by trial and error.

$$(3y + 1)(y - 4) = 3y^2 - 11y - 4$$
$$(3y - 1)(y + 4) = 3y^2 + 11y - 4$$
$$(3y + 4)(y - 1) = 3y^2 + y - 4$$
$$(3y - 4)(y + 1) = 3y^2 - y - 4$$
$$(3y + 2)(y - 2) = 3y^2 - 4y - 4$$
$$(3y - 2)(y + 2) = 3y^2 + 4y - 4$$

Thus, $3y^2 + y - 4 = (3y + 4)(y - 1)$.

11. Factor $3x^2 + 13x - 10$ by grouping.

$a = 3$ and $c = -10$, so $ac = -30$.

The factors of -30 whose sum is 13 are 15 and -2.

$3x^2 + 13x - 10 = 3x^2 + 15x - 2x - 10$

$\qquad = 3x(x + 5) - 2(x + 5)$

$\qquad = (x + 5)(3x - 2)$

13. Factor $3x^2 - 22x + 7$ by trial and error.

$(3x - 7)(x - 1) = 3x^2 - 10x + 7$

$(3x - 1)(x - 7) = 3x^2 - 22x + 7$

Thus, $3x^2 - 22x + 7 = (3x - 1)(x - 7)$.

15. Factor $5y^2 - 16y + 3$ by trial and error.

$(5y - 3)(y - 1) = 5y^2 - 8y + 3$

$(5y - 1)(y - 3) = 5y^2 - 16y + 3$

Thus, $5y^2 - 16y + 3 = (5y - 1)(y - 3)$.

17. Factor $3x^2 - 17x + 10$ by grouping.

$a = 3$ and $c = 10$, so $ac = 30$.

The factors of 30 whose sum is -17 are -15 and -2.

$3x^2 - 17x + 10 = 3x^2 - 15x - 2x + 10$

$\qquad = 3x(x - 5) - 2(x - 5)$

$\qquad = (x - 5)(3x - 2)$

19. Factor $6w^2 - 11w + 4$ by grouping.

$a = 6$ and $c = 4$, so $ac = 24$.

The factors of 24 whose sum is -11 are -3 and -8.

$6w^2 - 11w + 4 = 6w^2 - 3w - 8w + 4$

$\qquad = 3w(2w - 1) - 4(2w - 1)$

$\qquad = (2w - 1)(3w - 4)$

21. Factor $8x^2 + 33x + 4$ by grouping.

$a = 8$ and $c = 4$, so $ac = 32$.

The factors of 32 whose sum is 33 are 32 and 1.

$8x^2 + 33x + 4 = 8x^2 + 32x + x + 4$

$\qquad = 8x(x + 4) + 1(x + 4)$

$\qquad = (x + 4)(8x + 1)$

23. Factor $5x^2 + 33x - 14$ by trial and error.

$(5x - 7)(x + 2) = 5x^2 + 3x - 14$

$(5x + 7)(x - 2) = 5x^2 - 3x - 14$

$(5x - 2)(x + 7) = 5x^2 + 33x - 14$

Because the correct factorization has been found, there is no need to try additional possibilities.

Thus, $5x^2 + 33x - 14 = (5x - 2)(x + 7)$.

25. Factor $14y^2 + 15y - 9$ by trial and error. The sign in one factor must be positive and the other negative.

$(7y + 9)(2y - 1) = 14y^2 + 11y - 9$

$(7y + 1)(2y - 9) = 14y^2 - 61y - 9$

$(7y + 3)(2y - 3) = 14y^2 - 15y - 9$

$(7y - 3)(2y + 3) = 14y^2 + 15y - 9$

Thus, $14y^2 + 15y - 9 = (7y - 3)(2y + 3)$.

27. Factor $6x^2 - 7x + 3$ by trial and error. List all the possibilities in which both signs are negative.

$(6x - 1)(x - 3) = 6x^2 - 19x + 3$

$(6x - 3)(x - 1) = 6x^2 - 9x + 3$

$(3x - 1)(2x - 3) = 6x^2 - 11x + 3$

$(3x - 3)(2x - 1) = 6x^2 - 9x + 3$

None of these possibilities gives the required middle term, $-7x$, and there are no more possibilities to try, so $6x^2 - 7x + 3$ is prime.

29. Factor $25z^2 - 30z + 9$ by trial and error until the correct factorization is obtained. The signs in both factors must be negative.

$(5z - 1)(5z - 9) = 25z^2 - 50z + 9$

$(5z - 3)(5z - 3) = 25z^2 - 30z + 9$

Thus, $25z^2 - 30z + 9 = (5z - 3)(5z - 3)$.

31. Factor $15y^2 - y - 2$ by grouping.

$a = 15$ and $c = -2$, so $ac = -30$.

The factors of -30 whose sum is -1 are -6 and 5.

$15y^2 - y - 2 = 15y^2 - 6y + 5y - 2$

$\qquad = 3y(5y - 2) + 1(5y - 2)$

$\qquad = (5y - 2)(3y + 1)$

33. Factor $5x^2 + 2x + 9$ by trial and error. The signs in both factors must be positive.

$$(5x+3)(x+3) = 5x^2 + 18x + 9$$

$$(5x+9)(x+1) = 5x^2 + 14x + 9$$

$$(5x+1)(x+9) = 5x^2 + 46x + 9$$

None of these possibilities gives the required middle term, $2x$, and there are no more possibilities to try, so $5x^2 + 2x + 9$ is prime.

35. Factor $10y^2 + 43y - 9$ by grouping.

$a = 10$ and $c = -9$ so $ac = -90$.
The factors of -90 whose sum is 43 are 45 and -2.

$$10y^2 + 43y - 9 = 10y^2 + 45y - 2y - 9$$
$$= 5y(2y+9) - 1(2y+9)$$
$$= (2y+9)(5y-1)$$

37. Factor $8x^2 - 2x - 1$ by trial and error until the correct factorization is obtained. The sign must be negative in one factor and positive in the other.

$$(4x-1)(2x+1) = 8x^2 + 2x - 1$$

$$(4x+1)(2x-1) = 8x^2 - 2x - 1$$

Thus, $8x^2 - 2x - 1 = (4x+1)(2x-1)$.

39. Factor $9y^2 - 9y + 2$ by grouping.

$a = 9$ and $c = 2$, so $ac = 18$.
The factors of 18 whose sum is -9 are -3 and -6.

$$9y^2 - 9y + 2 = 9y^2 - 3y - 6y + 2$$
$$= 3y(3y-1) - 2(3y-1)$$
$$= (3y-1)(3y-2)$$

41. Factor $20x^2 + 27x - 8$ by grouping.
$a = 20$ and $c = -8$, so $ac = -160$.
The factors of -160 whose sum is 27 are -5 and 32.

$$20x^2 + 27x - 8 = 20x^2 - 5x + 32x - 8$$
$$= 5x(4x-1) + 8(4x-1)$$
$$= (4x-1)(5x+8)$$

43. $2x^2 + 3xy + y^2 = (2x+y)(x+y)$

45. Factor $3x^2 + 5xy + 2y^2$ by trial and error.

$$(3x+y)(x+2y) = 3x^2 + 7xy + 2y^2$$

$$(3x+2y)(x+y) = 3x^2 + 5xy + 2y^2$$

Thus, $3x^2 + 5xy + 2y^2 = (3x+2y)(x+y)$.

47. Factor $2x^2 - 9xy + 9y^2$ by trial and error until the correct factorization is obtained. The signs in both factors must be negative.

$$(2x-9y)(x-y) = 2x^2 - 11xy + 9y^2$$

$$(2x+9y)(x+y) = 2x^2 + 11xy + 9y^2$$

$$(2x-3y)(x-3y) = 2x^2 - 9xy + 9y^2$$

Thus, $2x^2 - 9xy + 9y^2 = (2x-3y)(x-3y)$.

49. Factor $6x^2 - 5xy - 6y^2$ by grouping.

$a = 6$ and $c = -6$, so $ac = -36$.
The factors of -36 whose sum is -5 are -9 and 4.

$$6x^2 - 5xy - 6y^2$$
$$= 6x^2 - 9xy + 4xy - 6y^2$$
$$= 3x(2x-3y) + 2y(2x-3y)$$
$$= (2x-3y)(3x+2y)$$

51. Factor $15x^2 + 11xy - 14y^2$ by grouping.
$a = 15$ and $c = -14$, so $ac = -210$.
The factors of -210 whose sum is 11 are 21 and -10.

$$15x^2 + 11xy - 14y^2$$
$$= 15x^2 + 21xy - 10xy - 14y^2$$
$$= 3x(5x+7y) - 2y(5x+7y)$$
$$= (5x+7y)(3x-2y)$$

53. Factor $2a^2 + 7ab + 5b^2$ by trial and error.
$$(2a+5b)(a+b) = 2a^2 + 7ab + 5b^2$$
$$(2a+b)(a+5b) = 2a^2 + 11ab + 5b^2$$
Thus, $2a^2 + 7ab + 5b^2 = (2a+5b)(a+b)$.

55. Factor $15a^2 - ab - 6b^2$ by grouping.

$a = 15$ and $c = -6$, so $ac = -90$.

The factors of -90 whose sum is -1 are 9 and -10.

$$15a^2 - ab - 6b^2 = 15a^2 + 9ab - 10ab - 6b^2$$
$$= 3a(5a + 3b) - 2b(5a + 3b)$$
$$= (5a + 3b)(3a - 2b)$$

57. Factor $12x^2 - 25xy + 12y^2$ by grouping.

$a = 12$ and $c = 12$, so $ac = 144$.

The factors of 144 whose sum is -25 are -9 and -16.

$$12x^2 - 25xy + 12y^2 = 12x^2 - 9xy - 16xy + 12y^2$$
$$= 3x(4x - 3y) - 4y(4x - 3y)$$
$$= (4x - 3y)(3x - 4y)$$

59. $4x^2 + 26x + 30$

First factor out the GCF, 2. Then factor the resulting trinomial by trial and error or grouping.

$$4x^2 + 26x + 30 = 2(2x^2 + 13x + 15)$$
$$= 2(2x + 3)(x + 5)$$

61. $9x^2 - 6x - 24$

First factor out the GCF, 3. Then factor the resulting trinomial by trial and error or grouping.

$$9x^2 - 6x - 24 = 3(3x^2 - 2x - 8)$$
$$= 3(3x + 4)(x - 2)$$

63. $4y^2 + 2y - 30 = 2(2y^2 + y - 15)$
$$= 2(2y - 5)(y + 3)$$

65. $9y^2 + 33y - 60 = 3(3y^2 + 11y - 20)$
$$= 3(3y - 4)(y + 5)$$

67. $3x^3 + 4x^2 + x$

First factor out the GCF, x. Then factor the resulting trinomial by trial and error or grouping.

$$3x^3 + 4x^2 + x = x(3x^2 + 4x + 1)$$
$$= x(3x + 1)(x + 1)$$

69. $2x^3 - 3x^2 - 5x = x(2x^2 - 3x - 5)$
$$= x(2x - 5)(x + 1)$$

71. $9y^3 - 39y^2 + 12y$

First factor out the GCF, $3y$. Then factor the resulting trinomial by trial and error or grouping.

$$9y^3 - 39y^2 + 12y = 3y(3y^2 - 13y + 4)$$
$$= 3y(3y - 1)(y - 4)$$

73. $60z^3 + 40z^2 + 5z = 5z(12z^2 + 8z + 1)$
$$= 5z(6z + 1)(2z + 1)$$

75. $15x^4 - 39x^3 + 18x^2 = 3x^2(5x^2 - 13x + 6)$
$$= 3x^2(5x - 3)(x - 2)$$

77. $10x^5 - 17x^4 + 3x^3 = x^3(10x^2 - 17x + 3)$
$$= x^3(2x - 3)(5x - 1)$$

79. $6x^2 - 3xy - 18y^2 = 3(2x^2 - xy - 6y^2)$
$$= 3(2x + 3y)(x - 2y)$$

81. $12x^2 + 10xy - 8y^2 = 2(6x^2 + 5xy - 4y^2)$
$$= 2(2x - y)(3x + 4y)$$

83. $8x^2y + 34xy - 84y = 2y(4x^2 + 17x - 42)$
$$= 2y(4x - 7)(x + 6)$$

85. $12a^2b - 46ab^2 + 14b^3 = 2b(6a^2 - 23ab + 7b^2)$
$$= 2b(2a - 7b)(3a - b)$$

87. $30(y + 1)x^2 + 10(y + 1)x - 20(y + 1)$
$$= 10(y + 1)(3x^2 + x - 2)$$
$$= 10(y + 1)(3x - 2)(x + 1)$$

89. $-32x^2y^4 + 20xy^4 + 12y^4$
$$= -4y^4(8x^2 - 5x - 3)$$
$$= -4y^4(8x + 3)(x - 1)$$

91. a. $2x^2 - 5x - 3 = (2x + 1)(x - 3)$

b. $2(y + 1)^2 - 5(y + 1) - 3$
$= \left[2(y + 1) + 1\right]\left[(y + 1) - 3\right]$
$= \left[2y + 2 + 1\right]\left[y + 1 - 3\right]$
$= (2y + 3)(y - 2)$

93.
$$\begin{array}{r} 3x^2 - 5x + 2 \\ x - 2 \overline{)3x^3 - 11x^2 + 12x - 4} \\ \underline{3x^3 - 6x^2} \\ -5x^2 + 12x \\ \underline{-5x^2 + 10x} \\ 2x - 4 \\ \underline{2x - 4} \\ 0 \end{array}$$

The quotient $3x^2 - 5x + 2$ factors into
$(3x - 2)(x - 1)$.
Thus, $3x^3 - 11x^2 + 12x - 4 = (x - 2)(3x - 2)(x - 1)$.

95. a. $x^2 + 3x + 2$

b. $(x + 2)(x + 1)$

c. Yes, the pieces are the same in both figures: one large square, three long rectangles, and two small squares. This geometric model illustrates the factorization:
$x^2 + 3x + 2 = (x + 2)(x + 1)$.

97. – 99. Answers will vary.

101. makes sense

103. does not make sense; Explanations will vary. Sample explanation: If a polynomial has a greatest common factor then it is not prime.

105. true

107. false; Changes to make the statement true will vary. A sample change is: The factorization of $4y^2 - 11y - 3$ is $(y - 3)(4y + 1)$.

109. $3x^2 + bx + 2$
The possible factorizations that will give $3x^2$ as the first term and 2 as the last term are:

$(3x + 1)(x + 2) = 3x^2 + 7x + 2$
$(3x + 2)(x + 1) = 3x^2 + 5x + 2$
$(3x - 1)(x - 2) = 3x^2 - 7x + 2$
$(3x - 2)(x - 1) = 3x^2 - 5x + 2$
The possible middle terms are
$5x, 7x, -5x$ and $-7x$, so $3x^2 + bx + 2$ can be factored if b is 5, 7, –5, or –7.

111. $3x^{10} - 4x^5 - 15$
Since $\left(x^5\right)^2 = x^{10}$, the first terms of the factors must be $3x^5$ and x^5 so the middle term will contain x^5. Use trial and error or grouping to obtain the correct factorization.
$3x^{10} - 4x^5 - 15 = \left(3x^5 + 5\right)\left(x^5 - 3\right)$

113. $4x - y = 105$
$x + 7y = -10$
Multiply the second equation by –4 and then add the equations.
$$\begin{array}{r} 4x - y = 105 \\ \underline{-4x - 28y = 40} \\ -29y = 145 \end{array}$$
$\dfrac{-29y}{-29} = \dfrac{145}{-29}$
$y = -5$
Back-substitute to find x.
$x + 7y = -10$
$x + 7(-5) = -10$
$x - 35 = -10$
$x = 25$
The solution set is $\{(25, -5)\}$.

114. $0.00086 = 8.6 \times 10^{-4}$

115. $8x - \dfrac{x}{6} = \dfrac{1}{6} - 8$
Multiply both sides by the LCD of 6.
$6\left(8x - \dfrac{x}{6}\right) = 6\left(\dfrac{1}{6} - 8\right)$
$48x - x = 1 - 48$
$47x = -47$
$x = -1$
The solution set is $\{-1\}$.

116. $(9x+10)(9x-10) = (9x)^2 - 10^2$
$$= 81x^2 - 100$$

117. $(4x+5y)^2 = (4x)^2 + 2(4x)(5y) + (5y)^2$
$$= 16x^2 + 40xy + 25y^2$$

118. $(x+2)(x^2 - 2x + 4)$
$$= x(x^2 - 2x + 4) + 2(x^2 - 2x + 4)$$
$$= x^3 - 2x^2 + 4x + 2x^2 - 4x + 8$$
$$= x^3 + 8$$

Mid-Chapter Check Point

1. The GCF is x^4.
$$x^5 + x^4 = x^4(x+1)$$

2. $x^2 + 7x - 18 = (x-2)(x+9)$

3. The GCF is x^2y. The polynomial in the parentheses is prime because there are no factors of 1 whose sum is -1.
$$x^2y^3 - x^2y^2 + x^2y = x^2y(y^2 - y + 1)$$

4. $x^2 - 2x + 4$ is prime because there are no factors of 4 whose sum is -2.

5. Factor $7x^2 - 22x + 3$ by grouping.
$a = 7$ and $c = 3$, so $ac = 21$.
The only factors of 21 whose sum is -22 are -21 and -1.
$$7x^2 - 22x + 3 = 7x^2 - 21x - x + 3$$
$$= 7x(x-3) - 1(x-3)$$
$$= (x-3)(7x-1)$$

6. Factor $x^3 + 5x^2 + 3x + 15$ by grouping.
$$x^3 + 5x^2 + 3x + 15 = (x^3 + 5x^2) + (3x + 15)$$
$$= x^2(x+5) + 3(x+5)$$
$$= (x+5)(x^2 + 3)$$

7. The GCF is x.
$$2x^3 - 11x^2 + 5x = x(2x^2 - 11x + 5)$$
$$= x(2x-1)(x-5)$$

8. Factor $xy - 7x - 4y + 28$ by grouping.
$$xy - 7x - 4y + 28 = (xy - 7x) + (-4y + 28)$$
$$= x(y-7) - 4(y-7)$$
$$= (y-7)(x-4)$$

9. Factor $x^2 - 17xy + 30y^2$ by trial and error. The only factors of 30 whose sum is -17 are -15 and -2.
$$x^2 - 17xy + 30y^2 = (x-15y)(x-2y)$$

10. Factor $25x^2 - 25x - 14$ by trial and error.
$$(5x-2)(5x+7) = 25x^2 + 25x - 14$$
$$(5x+2)(5x-7) = 25x^2 - 25x - 14$$
Because the correct factorization has been found, there is no need to try additional possibilities.
$$25x^2 - 25x - 14 = (5x+2)(5x-7).$$

11. The GCF is 2.
$$16x^2 - 70x + 24 = 2(8x^2 - 35x + 12)$$
Factor the polynomial in parentheses by grouping.
$a = 8$ and $c = 12$, so $ac = 96$.
The only factors of 96 whose sum is -35 are -32 and -3.
$$16x^2 - 70x + 24 = 2(8x^2 - 35x + 12)$$
$$= 2(8x^2 - 32x - 3x + 12)$$
$$= 2[8x(x-4) - 3(x-4)]$$
$$= 2(x-4)(8x-3)$$

12. Factor $3x^2 + 10xy + 7y^2$ by grouping.
$a = 3$ and $c = 7$, so $ac = 21$.
The only factors of 21 whose sum is 10 are 3 and 7.
$$3x^2 + 10xy + 7y^2 = 3x^2 + 3xy + 7xy + 7y^2$$
$$= 3x(x+y) + 7y(x+y)$$
$$= (x+y)(3x+7y)$$

7.4 Check Points

1. a. $x^2 - 81 = (x+9)(x-9)$

   b. $36x^2 - 25 = (6x+5)(6x-5)$

2. a. $25 - 4x^{10} = (5 + 2x^5)(5 - 2x^5)$

   b. $100x^2 - 9y^2 = (10x + 3y)(10x - 3y)$

3. a. $18x^3 - 2x = 2x(9x^2 - 1)$

   $= 2x(3x+1)(3x-1)$

   b. $72 - 18x^2 = 18(4 - x^2)$

   $= 18(2+x)(2-x)$

4. $81x^4 - 16 = (9x^2 + 4)(9x^2 - 4)$

   $= (9x^2 + 4)(3x+2)(3x-2)$

5. a. Notice that the trinomial fits the form $A^2 + 2AB + B^2$.

   Thus it factors as $(A+B)^2$.

   $x^2 + 14x + 49 = (x+7)^2$

   b. Notice that the trinomial fits the form $A^2 - 2AB + B^2$.

   Thus it factors as $(A-B)^2$.

   $x^2 - 6x + 9 = (x-3)^2$

   c. Notice that the trinomial fits the form $A^2 - 2AB + B^2$.

   Thus it factors as $(A-B)^2$.

   $16x^2 - 56x + 49 = (4x-7)^2$

6. Notice that the trinomial fits the form $A^2 + 2AB + B^2$.

   Thus it factors as $(A+B)^2$.

   $4x^2 + 12xy + 9y^2 = (2x+3y)^2$

7. Notice that the polynomial fits the form $A^3 + B^3$.

   Thus it factors as $(A+B)(A^2 - AB + B^2)$.

   $x^3 + 27 = x^3 + 3^3$

   $= (x+3)(x^2 - 3x + 3^2)$

   $= (x+3)(x^2 - 3x + 9)$

8. Notice that the polynomial fits the form $A^3 - B^3$.

   Thus it factors as $(A-B)(A^2 + AB + B^2)$.

   $1 - y^3 = 1^3 - y^3$

   $= (1-y)(1^2 + 1 \cdot y + y^2)$

   $= (1-y)(1 + y + y^2)$

9. Notice that the polynomial fits the form $A^3 + B^3$.

   Thus it factors as $(A+B)(A^2 - AB + B^2)$.

   $125x^3 + 8 = (5x)^3 + 2^3$

   $= (5x+2)\left[(5x)^2 - (5x)(2) + 2^2\right]$

   $= (5x+2)(25x^2 - 10x + 4)$

7.4 Exercise Set

1. $x^2 - 25 = x^2 - 5^2 = (x+5)(x-5)$

3. $y^2 - 1 = y^2 - 1^2 = (y+1)(y-1)$

5. $4x^2 - 9 = (2x)^2 - 3^2 = (2x+3)(2x-3)$

7. $25 - x^2 = 5^2 - x^2 = (5+x)(5-x)$

9. $1 - 49x^2 = 1^2 - (7x)^2 = (1+7x)(1-7x)$

11. $9 - 25y^2 = 3^2 - (5y)^2 = (3+5y)(3-5y)$

13. $x^4 - 9 = (x^2)^2 - 3^2 = (x^2+3)(x^2-3)$

15. $49y^4 - 16 = (7y^2)^2 - 4^2$

   $= (7y^2+4)(7y^2-4)$

17. $x^{10} - 9 = (x^5)^2 - 3^2 = (x^5+3)(x^5-3)$

19. $25x^2 - 16y^2 = (5x)^2 - (4y)^2$

   $= (5x+4y)(5x-4y)$

21. $x^4 - y^{10} = (x^2)^2 - (y^5)^2$

   $= (x^2+y^5)(x^2-y^5)$

23. $x^4 - 16 = \left(x^2\right)^2 - 4^2 = \left(x^2 + 4\right)\left(x^2 - 4\right)$

Because $x^2 - 4$ is also the difference of two squares, the factorization must be continued.

$x^4 - 16 = \left(x^2 + 4\right)\left(x^2 - 4\right)$

$= \left(x^2 + 4\right)\left(x^2 - 2^2\right)$

$= \left(x^2 + 4\right)(x+2)(x-2).$

25. $16x^4 - 81 = \left(4x^2\right)^2 - 9^2$

$= \left(4x^2 + 9\right)\left(4x^2 - 9\right)$

$= \left(4x^2 + 9\right)\left[\left(2x\right)^2 - 3^2\right]$

$= \left(4x^2 + 9\right)(2x+3)(2x-3)$

27. $2x^2 - 18 = 2\left(x^2 - 9\right) = 2(x+3)(x-3)$

29. $2x^3 - 72x = 2x\left(x^2 - 36\right)$

$= 2x(x+6)(x-6)$

31. $x^2 + 36$ is prime because it is the sum of two squares with no common factor other than 1.

33. $3x^3 + 27x = 3x\left(x^2 + 9\right)$

35. $18 - 2y^2 = 2\left(9 - y^2\right) = 2(3+y)(3-y)$

37. $3y^3 - 48y = 3y\left(y^2 - 16\right)$

$= 3y(y+4)(y-4)$

39. $18x^3 - 2x = 2x\left(9x^2 - 1\right)$

$= 2x(3x+1)(3x-1)$

41. $x^2 + 2x + 1 = x^2 + 2(1x) + 1^2$

$= (x+1)^2$

43. $x^2 - 14x + 49 = x^2 - 2(7x) + 7^2$

$= (x-7)^2$

45. $x^2 - 2x + 1 = x^2 - 2(1x) + 1^2$

$= (x-1)^2$

47. $x^2 + 22x + 121 = x^2 + 2(11x) + 11^2$

$= (x+11)^2$

49. $4x^2 + 4x + 1 = (2x)^2 + 2(2x) + 1^2$

$= (2x+1)^2$

51. $25y^2 - 10y + 1 = (5y)^2 - 2(5y) + 1^2$

$= (5y-1)^2$

53. $x^2 - 10x + 100$ is prime.

To be a perfect square trinomial, the middle term would have to be $2(-10x) = -20x$ rather than $-10x$.

55. $x^2 + 14xy + 49y^2 = x^2 + 2(7xy) + (7y)^2$

$= (x+7y)^2$

57. $x^2 - 12xy + 36y^2 = x^2 - 2(6xy) + (6y)^2$

$= (x-6y)^2$

59. $x^2 - 8xy + 64y^2$ is prime.

To be a perfect square trinomial, the middle term would have to be $2(-8xy) = -16xy$ rather than $-8xy$.

61. $16x^2 - 40xy + 25y^2$

$= (4x)^2 - 2(4x \cdot 5y) + (5y)^2$

$= (4x - 5y)^2$

63. $12x^2 - 12x + 3 = 3\left(4x^2 - 4x + 1\right)$

$= 3\left[(2x)^2 - 2(2x) + 1^2\right]$

$= 3(2x-1)^2$

65. $9x^3 + 6x^2 + x$

$\quad = x\left(9x^2 + 6x + 1\right)$

$\quad = x\left[(3x)^2 + 2(3x) + 1^2\right]$

$\quad = x(3x+1)^2$

67. $2y^2 - 4y + 2 = 2\left(y^2 - 2y + 1\right)$

$\qquad\qquad\quad = 2(y-1)^2$

69. $2y^3 + 28y^2 + 98y = 2y\left(y^2 + 14y + 49\right)$

$\qquad\qquad\qquad\quad = 2y(y+7)^2$

71. $x^3 + 1 = x^3 + 1^3$

$\qquad\quad = (x+1)\left(x^2 - x\cdot 1 + 1^2\right)$

$\qquad\quad = (x+1)\left(x^2 - x + 1\right)$

73. $x^3 - 27 = x^3 - 3^3$

$\qquad\qquad = (x-3)\left(x^2 + x\cdot 3 + 3^2\right)$

$\qquad\qquad = (x-3)\left(x^2 + 3x + 9\right)$

75. $8y^3 - 1 = (2y)^3 - 1^3$

$\qquad\qquad = (2y-1)\left[(2y)^2 + 2y\cdot 1 + 1\right]$

$\qquad\qquad = (2y-1)\left(4y^2 + 2y + 1\right)$

77. $27x^3 + 8 = (3x)^3 + 2^3$

$\qquad\qquad\; = (3x+2)\left[(3x)^2 - 3x\cdot 2 + 2^2\right]$

$\qquad\qquad\; = (3x+2)\left(9x^2 - 6x + 4\right)$

79. $x^3y^3 - 64 = (xy)^3 - 4^3$

$\qquad\qquad\quad = (xy-4)\left[(xy)^2 + xy\cdot 4 + 4^2\right]$

$\qquad\qquad\quad = (xy-4)\left(x^2y^2 + 4xy + 16\right)$

81. $27y^4 + 8y = y\left(27y^3 + 8\right)$

$\qquad\qquad\; = y\left[(3y)^3 + 2^3\right]$

$\qquad\qquad\; = y(3y+2)\left[(3y)^2 - 3y\cdot 2 + 2^2\right]$

$\qquad\qquad\; = y(3y+2)\left(9y^2 - 6y + 4\right)$

83. $54 - 16y^3 = 2\left(27 - 8y^3\right)$

$\qquad\qquad\quad = 2\left[3^3 - (2y)^3\right]$

$\qquad\qquad\quad = 2(3-2y)\left[3^2 + 3\cdot 2y + (2y)^2\right]$

$\qquad\qquad\quad = 2(3-2y)\left(9 + 6y + 4y^2\right)$

85. $64x^3 + 27y^3 = (4x)^3 + (3y)^3$

$\qquad\qquad\qquad = (4x+3y)\left[(4x)^2 - 4x\cdot 3y + (3y)^2\right]$

$\qquad\qquad\qquad = (4x+3y)\left(16x^2 - 12xy + 9y^2\right)$

87. $125x^3 - 64y^3 = (5x)^3 - (4y)^3$

$\qquad\qquad\qquad\; = (5x-4y)\left[(5x)^2 + 5x\cdot 4y + (4y)^2\right]$

$\qquad\qquad\qquad\; = (5x-4y)\left(25x^2 + 20xy + 16y^2\right)$

89. $25x^2 - \dfrac{4}{49} = (5x)^2 - \left(\dfrac{2}{7}\right)^2$

$\qquad\qquad\quad = \left(5x + \dfrac{2}{7}\right)\left(5x - \dfrac{2}{7}\right)$

91. $y^4 - \dfrac{y}{1000} = y\left(y^3 - \dfrac{1}{1000}\right)$

$\qquad\qquad\; = y\left[y^3 - \left(\dfrac{1}{10}\right)^3\right]$

$\qquad\qquad\; = y\left(y - \dfrac{1}{10}\right)\left[y^2 + y\cdot\dfrac{1}{10} + \left(\dfrac{1}{10}\right)^2\right]$

$\qquad\qquad\; = y\left(y - \dfrac{1}{10}\right)\left(y^2 + \dfrac{y}{10} + \dfrac{1}{100}\right)$

93. $0.25x - x^3 = x\left(0.25 - x^2\right)$

$$= x\left[\left(0.5\right)^2 - x^2\right]$$

$$= x\left(0.5 + x\right)\left(0.5 - x\right)$$

95. $\left(x+1\right)^2 - 25 = \left(x+1\right)^2 - 5^2$

$$= \left[\left(x+1\right)+5\right]\left[\left(x+1\right)-5\right]$$

$$= \left(x+6\right)\left(x-4\right)$$

97.

$$
\begin{array}{r}
x^2 + 2x + 1 \\
x-3\overline{\smash{\big)}\,x^3 - x^2 - 5x - 3} \\
\underline{x^3 - 3x^2} \\
2x^2 - 5x \\
\underline{2x^2 - 6x} \\
x - 3 \\
\underline{x - 3}
\end{array}
$$

The quotient $x^2 + 2x + 1$ factors further.

$x^2 + 2x + 1 = \left(x+1\right)^2$.

Thus, $x^3 - x^2 - 5x - 3 = \left(x-3\right)\left(x+1\right)^2$.

99. Area of outer square $= x^2$

Area of inner square $= 5^2 = 25$

Area of shaded region $= x^2 - 25 = \left(x+5\right)\left(x-5\right)$

101. Area of large square $= x^2$

Area of each small corner squares $= 2^2 = 4$

Area of four corner squares $= 4 \cdot 4 = 16$

Area of shaded region $= x^2 - 16$

$$= \left(x+4\right)\left(x-4\right)$$

103. – 105. Answers will vary.

107. does not make sense; Explanations will vary.
Sample explanation: The original expression has a common factor of 9.

$9x^2 - 36 = 9(x^2 - 4) = 9(x+2)(x-2)$

109. does not make sense; Explanations will vary.
Sample explanation: The second factor involves a subtraction. The commutative property does not apply to subtraction.

111. false; Changes to make the statement true will vary.
A sample change is: $x^2 + 25$ is prime.

113. false; Changes to make the statement true will vary.
A sample change is: $4x^2 + 36$ is a polynomial that is the sum of two squares. $4x^2 + 36$ factors into $4(x^2 + 9)$.

115. The error in the proof is in step 7 where you are asked to divide by $a - b = 0$.
Division by 0 is not permitted because division by zero is undefined.

117. $x^{2n} - 25y^{2n} = \left(x^n\right)^2 - \left(5y^n\right)^2$

$$= \left(x^n + 5y^n\right)\left(x^n - 5y^n\right)$$

119. $\left(x+3\right)^2 - 2\left(x+3\right) + 1$

$$= \left[\left(x+3\right) - 1\right]^2$$

$$= \left(x+2\right)^2$$

121. $64x^2 - 16x + k$

Let r be the number such that $r^2 = k$.

Then, $64x^2 - 16x + k = \left(8x\right)^2 - 2 \cdot 8x \cdot r + r^2$.

Comparing the middle terms, we see that

$-2 \cdot 8x \cdot r = -16x$

$\qquad -16xr = -16x$

$\qquad\quad r = 1$.

Therefore, $k = r^2 = 1^2 = 1$.

123. The graphs coincide.

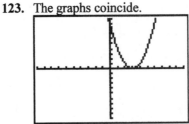

This verifies that $x^2 - 6x + 9 = \left(x-3\right)^2$.

125. The graphs do not coincide.

$$x^3 - 1 = x^3 - 1^3 = (x-1)\left(x^2 + x + 1\right)$$

The polynomial on the right side should be changed to $(x-1)\left(x^2 + x + 1\right)$.

126. $\left(2x^2 y^3\right)^4 \left(5xy^2\right)$

$= \left[2^4 \left(x^2\right)^4 \left(y^3\right)^4\right] \cdot \left(5xy^2\right)$

$= \left(16x^8 y^{12}\right)\left(5xy^2\right)$

$= (16 \cdot 5)\left(x^8 \cdot x^1\right)\left(y^{12} \cdot y^2\right)$

$= 80x^9 y^{14}$

127. $\left(10x^2 - 5x + 2\right) - \left(14x^2 - 5x - 1\right)$

$= \left(10x^2 - 5x + 2\right) + \left(-14x^2 + 5x + 1\right)$

$= \left(10x^2 - 14x^2\right) + (-5x + 5x) + (2+1)$

$= -4x^2 + 3$

128.
$$\begin{array}{r} 2x+5 \\ 3x-2 \overline{\smash{)}6x^2 + 11x - 10} \\ \underline{6x^2 - 4x} \\ 15x - 10 \\ \underline{15x - 10} \\ 0 \end{array}$$

$$\frac{6x^2 + 11x - 10}{3x - 2} = 2x + 5$$

129. $3x^3 - 75x = 3x(x^2 - 25) = 3x(x+5)(x-5)$

130. $2x^2 - 20x + 50 = 2(x^2 - 10x + 25) = 2(x-5)^2$

131. $x^3 - 2x^2 - x + 2 = x^2(x-2) - 1(x-2)$

$= (x-2)(x^2 - 1)$

$= (x-2)(x+1)(x-1)$

7.5 Check Points

1. $5x^4 - 45x^2 = 5x^2(x^2 - 9)$

$= 5x^2(x+3)(x-3)$

2. $4x^2 - 16x - 48 = 4(x^2 - 4x - 12)$

$= 4(x-6)(x+2)$

3. $4x^5 - 64x = 4x(x^4 - 16)$

$= 4x(x^2 + 4)(x^2 - 4)$

$= 4x(x^2 + 4)(x+2)(x-2)$

4. $x^3 - 4x^2 - 9x + 36 = x^2(x-4) - 9(x-4)$

$= (x-4)(x^2 - 9)$

$= (x-4)(x+3)(x-3)$

5. $3x^3 - 30x^2 + 75x = 3x(x^2 - 10x + 25)$

$= 3x(x-5)^2$

6. $2x^5 + 54x^2 = 2x^2(x^3 + 27)$

$= 2x^2(x+3)(x^2 - 3x + 9)$

7. $3x^4 y - 48y^5 = 3y(x^4 - 16y^4)$

$= 3y(x^2 + 4y^2)(x^2 - 4y^2)$

$= 3y(x^2 + 4y^2)(x+2y)(x-2y)$

8. $12x^3 + 36x^2 y + 27xy^2 = 3x(4x^2 + 12xy + 9y^2)$

$= 3x(2x+3y)^2$

7.5 Exercise Set

1. $5x^3 - 20x = 5x\left(x^2 - 4\right)$

$= 5x\left(x+2\right)\left(x-2\right)$

3. $7x^3 + 7x = 7x\left(x^2 + 1\right)$

5. $5x^2 - 5x - 30 = 5\left(x^2 - x - 6\right)$

$= 5\left(x+2\right)\left(x-3\right)$

7. $2x^4 - 162 = 2\left(x^4 - 81\right)$

$\qquad = 2\left(x^2 + 9\right)\left(x^2 - 9\right)$

$\qquad = 2\left(x^2 + 9\right)(x + 3)(x - 3)$

9. $x^3 + 2x^2 - 9x - 18 = \left(x^3 + 2x^2\right) + (-9x - 18)$

$\qquad = x^2(x + 2) - 9(x + 2)$

$\qquad = (x + 2)\left(x^2 - 9\right)$

$\qquad = (x + 2)(x + 3)(x - 3)$

11. $3x^3 - 24x^2 + 48x = 3x\left(x^2 - 8x + 16\right)$

$\qquad = 3x(x - 4)^2$

13. $2x^5 + 2x^2 = 2x^2\left(x^3 + 1\right)$

$\qquad = 2x^2(x + 1)\left(x^2 - x + 1\right)$

15. $6x^2 + 8x = 2x(3x + 4)$

17. $2y^2 - 2y - 112 = 2\left(y^2 - y - 56\right)$

$\qquad = 2(y - 8)(y + 7)$

19. $7y^4 + 14y^3 + 7y^2 = 7y^2\left(y^2 + 2y + 1\right)$

$\qquad = 7y^2(y + 1)^2$

21. $y^2 + 8y - 16$ is prime because there are no two integers whose product is -16 and whose sum is 8.

23. $16y^2 - 4y - 2 = 2\left(8y^2 - 2y - 1\right)$

$\qquad = 2(4y + 1)(2y - 1)$

25. $r^2 - 25r = r(r - 25)$

27. $4w^2 + 8w - 5 = (2w + 5)(2w - 1)$

29. $x^3 - 4x = x\left(x^2 - 4\right) = x(x + 2)(x - 2)$

31. $x^2 + 64$ is prime because it is the sum of two squares with no common factor other than 1.

33. $9y^2 + 13y + 4 = (9y + 4)(y + 1)$

35. $y^3 + 2y^2 - 4y - 8 = \left(y^3 + 2y^2\right) + (-4y - 8)$

$\qquad = y^2(y + 2) - 4(y + 2)$

$\qquad = (y + 2)\left(y^2 - 4\right)$

$\qquad = (y + 2)(y + 2)(y - 2)$

$\qquad = (y + 2)^2(y - 2)$

37. $16y^2 + 24y + 9 = (4y)^2 + 2(4y \cdot 3) + 3^2$

$\qquad = (4y + 3)^2$

39. $4y^3 - 28y^2 + 40y = 4y\left(y^2 - 7y + 10\right)$

$\qquad = 4y(y - 5)(y - 2)$

41. $y^5 - 81y = y\left(y^4 - 81\right)$

$\qquad = y\left(y^2 + 9\right)\left(y^2 - 9\right)$

$\qquad = y\left(y^2 + 9\right)(y + 3)(y - 3)$

43. $20a^4 - 45a^2 = 5a^2\left(4a^2 - 9\right)$

$\qquad = 5a^2(2a + 3)(2a - 3)$

45. $9x^4 + 18x^3 + 6x^2 = 3x^2(3x^2 + 6x + 2)$

47. $12y^2 - 11y + 2 = (4y - 1)(3y - 2)$

49. $9y^2 - 64 = (3y)^2 - 8^2$

$\qquad = (3y + 8)(3y - 8)$

51. $9y^2 + 64$ is prime because it is the sum of two squares with no common factor other than 1.

53. $2y^3 + 3y^2 - 50y - 75 = \left(2y^3 + 3y^2\right) + (-50y - 75)$

$\qquad = y^2(2y + 3) - 25(2y + 3)$

$\qquad = (2y + 3)\left(y^2 - 25\right)$

$\qquad = (2y + 3)(y + 5)(y - 5)$

55. $2r^3 + 30r^2 - 68r = 2r\left(r^2 + 15r - 34\right)$

$\qquad = 2r(r + 17)(r - 2)$

57. $8x^5 - 2x^3 = 2x^3 \left(4x^2 - 1\right)$

$\qquad = 2x^3 \left[(2x)^2 - 1^2\right]$

$\qquad = 2x^3 (2x+1)(2x-1)$

59. $3x^2 + 243 = 3\left(x^2 + 81\right)$

61. $x^4 + 8x = x\left(x^3 + 8\right)$

$\qquad = x\left(x^3 + 2^3\right)$

$\qquad = x(x+2)\left(x^2 - 2x + 4\right)$

63. $2y^5 - 2y^2 = 2y^2 \left(y^3 - 1\right)$

$\qquad = 2y^2 (y-1)\left(y^2 + y + 1\right)$

65. $6x^2 + 8xy = 2x(3x + 4y)$

67. $xy - 7x + 3y - 21 = (xy - 7x) + (3y - 21)$

$\qquad = x(y-7) + 3(y-7)$

$\qquad = (y-7)(x+3)$

69. $x^2 - 3xy - 4y^2 = (x - 4y)(x + y)$

71. $72a^3b^2 + 12a^2 - 24a^4b^2$

$\qquad = 12a^2 \left(6ab^2 + 1 - 2a^2b^2\right)$

73. $3a^2 + 27ab + 54b^2 = 3\left(a^2 + 9ab + 18b^2\right)$

$\qquad = 3(a + 6b)(a + 3b)$

75. $48x^4y - 3x^2y = 3x^2y\left(16x^2 - 1\right)$

$\qquad = 3x^2y(4x+1)(4x-1)$

77. $6a^2b + ab - 2b = b\left(6a^2 + a - 2\right)$

$\qquad = b(3a + 2)(2a - 1)$

79. $7x^5y - 7xy^5 = 7xy\left(x^4 - y^4\right)$

$\qquad = 7xy\left(x^2 + y^2\right)\left(x^2 - y^2\right)$

$\qquad = 7xy\left(x^2 + y^2\right)(x + y)(x - y)$

81. $10x^3y - 14x^2y^2 + 4xy^3 = 2xy\left(5x^2 - 7xy + 2y^2\right)$

$\qquad = 2xy(5x - 2y)(x - y)$

83. $2bx^2 + 44bx + 242b = 2b\left(x^2 + 22x + 121\right)$

$\qquad = 2b\left(x^2 + 2(11x) + 11^2\right)$

$\qquad = 2b(x + 11)^2$

85. $15a^2 + 11ab - 14b^2 = (5a + 7b)(3a - 2b)$

87. $36x^3y - 62x^2y^2 + 12xy^3$

$\qquad = 2xy\left(18x^2 - 31xy + 6y^2\right)$

$\qquad = 2xy(9x - 2y)(2x - 3y)$

89. $a^2y - b^2y - a^2x + b^2x$

$\qquad = \left(a^2y - b^2y\right) + \left(-a^2x + b^2x\right)$

$\qquad = y\left(a^2 - b^2\right) - x\left(a^2 - b^2\right)$

$\qquad = \left(a^2 - b^2\right)(y - x)$

$\qquad = (a + b)(a - b)(y - x)$

91. $9ax^3 + 15ax^2 - 14ax = ax\left(9x^2 + 15x - 14\right)$

$\qquad = ax(3x + 7)(3x - 2)$

93. $2x^4 + 6x^3y + 2x^2y^2 = 2x^2(x^2 + 3xy + y^2)$

95. $81x^4y - y^5 = y\left(81x^4 - y^4\right)$

$\qquad = y\left(9x^2 + y^2\right)\left(9x^2 - y^2\right)$

$\qquad = y\left(9x^2 + y^2\right)(3x + y)(3x - y)$

97. $10x^2(x+1) - 7x(x+1) - 6(x+1)$

$\qquad = (x+1)\left(10x^2 - 7x - 6\right)$

$\qquad = (x+1)(5x - 6)(2x + 1)$

99. $6x^4 + 35x^2 - 6 = \left(x^2 + 6\right)\left(6x^2 - 1\right)$

101. $(x-7)^2 - 4a^2 = (x-7)^2 - (2a)^2$

$\qquad = \left[(x-7)+2a\right]\left[(x-7)-2a\right]$

$\qquad = (x-7+2a)(x-7-2a)$

103. $x^2 + 8x + 16 - 25a^2$

$\qquad = \left(x^2 + 8x + 16\right) - (5a)^2$

$\qquad = (x+4)^2 - (5a)^2$

$\qquad = \left[(x+4)+5a\right]\left[(x+4)-5a\right]$

$\qquad = (x+4+5a)(x+4-5a)$

105. $y^7 + y = y\left(y^6 + 1\right) = y\left[\left(y^2\right)^3 + 1^3\right]$

$\qquad = y\left(y^2 + 1\right)\left(y^4 - y^2 + 1\right)$

107. $256 - 16t^2 = 16\left(16 - t^2\right)$

$\qquad = 16(4+t)(4-t)$

109. Area of outer circle $= \pi b^2$

Area of inner circle $= \pi a^2$

Area of shaded ring $= \pi b^2 - \pi a^2$

$\pi b^2 - \pi a^2 = \pi\left(b^2 - a^2\right)$

$\qquad = \pi(b+a)(b-a)$

111. Answers will vary.

113. makes sense

115. makes sense

117. false; Changes to make the statement true will vary. A sample change is: $x^2 - 9 = (x+3)(x-3)$ for any real number x.

119. false; Changes to make the statement true will vary. A sample change is: Some polynomials are completely factored after one step.

121. $3x^5 - 21x^3 - 54x = 3x\left(x^4 - 7x^2 - 18\right)$

$\qquad = 3x\left(x^2 + 2\right)\left(x^2 - 9\right)$

$\qquad = 3x\left(x^2 + 2\right)(x+3)(x-3)$

123. $4x^4 - 9x^2 + 5 = \left(4x^2 - 5\right)\left(x^2 - 1\right)$

$\qquad = \left(4x^2 - 5\right)(x+1)(x-1)$

125. $3x^{2n} - 27y^{2n} = 3\left(x^{2n} - 9y^{2n}\right)$

$\qquad = 3\left[\left(x^n\right)^2 - \left(3y^n\right)^2\right]$

$\qquad = 3\left(x^n + 3y^n\right)\left(x^n - 3y^n\right)$

127. The graphs do not coincide.

$3x^3 - 12x^2 - 15x = 3x\left(x^2 - 4x - 5\right)$

$\qquad = 3x(x-5)(x+1)$

Change the polynomial on the right side to $3x(x-5)(x+1)$.

129. The graphs coincide.

This verifies that the factorization $x^4 - 16 = \left(x^2 + 4\right)(x+2)(x-2)$ is correct.

131. $9x^2 - 16 = (3x)^2 - 4^2$

$\qquad = (3x+4)(3x-4)$

132. $5x - 2y = 10$

To find the x-intercept, let $y = 0$.

$$5x - 2(0) = 10$$
$$5x = 10$$
$$x = 2$$

To find the y-intercept, let $x = 0$.

$$5(0) - 2y = 10$$
$$-2y = 10$$
$$y = -5$$

Checkpoint: $(4, 5)$

133. Let $x =$ the measure of the first angle.

Then $3x =$ the measure of the second angle,

$x + 80 =$ the measure of the third angle.

$$x + 3x + (x + 80) = 180$$
$$5x + 80 = 180$$
$$5x = 100$$
$$x = 20$$

Measure of first angle $= x = 20°$

Measure of second angle $= 3x = 60°$

Measure of third angle $= x + 80 = 100°$

134. $(3x - 1)(x + 2) = \left(3 \cdot \dfrac{1}{3} - 1\right)\left(\dfrac{1}{3} + 2\right)$

$$= (1 - 1)\left(2\dfrac{1}{3}\right)$$
$$= (0)\left(2\dfrac{1}{3}\right)$$
$$= 0$$

135. $2x^2 + 7x - 4 = 2\left(\dfrac{1}{2}\right)^2 + 7\left(\dfrac{1}{2}\right) - 4$

$$= \dfrac{1}{2} + \dfrac{7}{2} - 4$$
$$= \dfrac{8}{2} - 4$$
$$= 4 - 4$$
$$= 0$$

136. $(x - 2)(x + 3) - 6 = x^2 + 3x - 2x - 6 - 6$

$$= x^2 + x - 12$$
$$= (x + 4)(x - 3)$$

7.6 Check Points

1. $(2x + 1)(x - 4) = 0$

$2x + 1 = 0$ or $x - 4 = 0$

$2x = -1$ $x = 4$

$$x = -\dfrac{1}{2}$$

The solution set is $\left\{-\dfrac{1}{2}, 4\right\}$.

2. $x^2 - 6x + 5 = 0$

$$(x - 1)(x - 5) = 0$$

$x - 1 = 0$ or $x - 5 = 0$

$x = 1$ $x = 5$

The solution set is $\{1, 5\}$.

3. $4x^2 = 2x$

$$4x^2 - 2x = 0$$
$$2x(2x - 1) = 0$$

$2x = 0$ or $2x - 1 = 0$

$x = 0$ $2x = 1$

$$x = \dfrac{1}{2}$$

The solution set is $\left\{0, \dfrac{1}{2}\right\}$.

4. $x^2 = 10x - 25$

$$x^2 - 10x + 25 = 0$$
$$(x - 5)^2 = 0$$

Because both factors are the same, it is only necessary to set one of them equal to zero.

$$x - 5 = 0$$
$$x = 5$$

The solution set is $\{5\}$.

5.
$$16x^2 = 25$$
$$16x^2 - 25 = 0$$
$$(4x+5)(4x-5) = 0$$

$$4x+5 = 0 \quad \text{or} \quad 4x-5 = 0$$
$$4x = -5 \qquad\qquad 4x = 5$$
$$x = -\frac{5}{4} \qquad\qquad x = \frac{5}{4}$$

The solution set is $\left\{-\frac{5}{4}, \frac{5}{4}\right\}$.

6. $(x-5)(x-2) = 28$

$$x^2 - 7x + 10 = 28$$
$$x^2 - 7x - 18 = 0$$
$$(x-9)(x+2) = 0$$
$$x-9 = 0 \quad \text{or} \quad x+2 = 0$$
$$x = 9 \qquad\qquad x = -2$$

The solution set is $\{-2, 9\}$.

7. $h = -16t^2 + 48t + 160$

$$192 = -16t^2 + 48t + 160$$
$$0 = -16t^2 + 48t - 32$$
$$0 = -16(t^2 - 3t + 2)$$
$$0 = -16(t-1)(t-2)$$
$$x-1 = 0 \quad \text{or} \quad x-2 = 0$$
$$x = 1 \qquad\qquad x = 2$$

The ball's height will be 192 feet at 1 second and 2 seconds after it is thrown.
This is represented on the graph by the points (1,192) and (2,192).

8. Let $x = $ the width of the sign.
Let $x+3 = $ the length of the sign.
The area of 54 square units can be represented as follows.

$$A = l \cdot w$$
$$54 = (x+3) \cdot x$$
$$54 = x^2 + 3x$$
$$0 = x^2 + 3x - 54$$
$$0 = (x-6)(x+9)$$
$$x-6 = 0 \quad \text{or} \quad x+9 = 0$$
$$x = 6 \qquad\qquad x = -9$$

Reject –9 because the width cannot be negative.
The width of the sign is 6 units and the length is 9 units.

7.6 Exercise Set

1. $x(x+7) = 0$
$$x = 0 \quad \text{or} \quad x+7 = 0$$
$$x = -7$$
The solution set is $\{-7, 0\}$.

3. $(x-6)(x+4) = 0$
$$x-6 = 0 \quad \text{or} \quad x+4 = 0$$
$$x = 6 \qquad\qquad x = -4$$
The solution set is $\{-4, 6\}$.

5. $(x-9)(5x+4) = 0$
$$x-9 = 0 \quad \text{or} \quad 5x+4 = 0$$
$$x = 9 \qquad\qquad 5x = -4$$
$$x = -\frac{4}{5}$$
The solution set is $\left\{-\frac{4}{5}, 9\right\}$.

7. $10(x-4)(2x+9) = 0$
$$x-4 = 0 \quad \text{or} \quad 2x+9 = 0$$
$$x = 4 \qquad\qquad 2x = -9$$
$$x = -\frac{9}{2}$$
The solution set is $\left\{-\frac{9}{2}, 4\right\}$.

9. $x^2 + 8x + 15 = 0$
$$(x+5)(x+3) = 0$$
$$x+5 = 0 \quad \text{or} \quad x+3 = 0$$
$$x = -5 \qquad\qquad x = -3$$
Check –5:
$$x^2 + 8x + 15 = 0$$
$$(-5)^2 + 8(-5) + 15 = 0$$
$$25 - 40 + 15 = 0$$
$$0 = 0 \text{ true}$$
Check –3:
$$x^2 + 8x + 15 = 0$$
$$(-3)^2 + 8(-3) + 15 = 0$$
$$9 - 24 + 15 = 0$$
$$0 = 0 \text{ true}$$
The solution set is $\{-5, -3\}$.

11. $x^2 - 2x - 15 = 0$

$(x+3)(x-5) = 0$

$x+3 = 0$ or $x-5 = 0$

    $x = -3$ $x = 5$

The solution set is $\{-3, 5\}$.

13. $x^2 - 4x = 21$

$x^2 - 4x - 21 = 0$

$(x+3)(x-7) = 0$

$x+3 = 0$ or $x-7 = 0$

    $x = -3$ $x = 7$

The solution set is $\{-3, 7\}$.

15. $x^2 + 9x = -8$

$x^2 + 9x + 8 = 0$

$(x+8)(x+1) = 0$

$x+8 = 0$ or $x+1 = 0$

    $x = -8$ $x = -1$

The solution set is $\{-8, -1\}$.

17. $x^2 + 4x = 0$

$x(x+4) = 0$

$x = 0$ or $x+4 = 0$

                $x = -4$

The solution set is $\{-4, 0\}$.

19. $x^2 - 5x = 0$

$x(x-5) = 0$

$x = 0$ or $x-5 = 0$

                $x = 5$

The solution set is $\{0, 5\}$.

21. $x^2 = 4x$

$x^2 - 4x = 0$

$x(x-4) = 0$

$x = 0$ or $x-4 = 0$

                $x = 4$

The solution set is $\{0, 4\}$.

23. $2x^2 = 5x$

$2x^2 - 5x = 0$

$x(2x-5) = 0$

$x = 0$ or $2x-5 = 0$

             $2x = 5$

              $x = \dfrac{5}{2}$

The solution set is $\left\{0, \dfrac{5}{2}\right\}$.

25. $3x^2 = -5x$

$3x^2 + 5x = 0$

$x(3x+5) = 0$

$x = 0$ or $3x+5 = 0$

             $3x = -5$

              $x = -\dfrac{5}{3}$

The solution set is $\left\{-\dfrac{5}{3}, 0\right\}$.

27. $x^2 + 4x + 4 = 0$

$(x-2)^2 = 0$

$x+2 = 0$

    $x = -2$

The solution set is $\{-2\}$.

29. $x^2 = 12x - 36$

$x^2 - 12x + 36 = 0$

$(x-6)^2 = 0$

$x-6 = 0$

    $x = 6$

The solution set is $\{6\}$.

31.
$$4x^2 = 12x - 9$$
$$4x^2 - 12x + 9 = 0$$
$$(2x - 3)^2 = 0$$
$$2x - 3 = 0$$
$$2x = 3$$
$$x = \frac{3}{2}$$

The solution set is $\left\{\dfrac{3}{2}\right\}$.

33.
$$2x^2 = 7x + 4$$
$$2x^2 - 7x - 4 = 0$$
$$(2x + 1)(x - 4) = 0$$
$$2x + 1 = 0 \quad \text{or} \quad x - 4 = 0$$
$$2x = -1 \qquad x = 4$$
$$x = -\frac{1}{2}$$

The solution set is $\left\{-\dfrac{1}{2}, 4\right\}$.

35.
$$5x^2 = 18 - x$$
$$5x^2 + x - 18 = 0$$
$$(5x - 9)(x + 2) = 0$$
$$5x - 9 = 0 \quad \text{or} \quad x + 2 = 0$$
$$5x = 9 \qquad x = -2$$
$$x = \frac{9}{5}$$

The solution set is $\left\{-2, \dfrac{9}{5}\right\}$.

37.
$$x^2 - 49 = 0$$
$$(x + 7)(x - 7) = 0$$
$$x + 7 = 0 \quad \text{or} \quad x - 7 = 0$$
$$x = -7 \qquad x = 7$$
The solution set is $\{-7, 7\}$.

39.
$$4x^2 - 25 = 0$$
$$(2x + 5)(2x - 5) = 0$$
$$2x + 5 = 0 \quad \text{or} \quad 2x - 5 = 0$$
$$2x = -5 \qquad 2x = 5$$
$$x = -\frac{5}{2} \qquad x = \frac{5}{2}$$
The solution set is $\left\{-\dfrac{5}{2}, \dfrac{5}{2}\right\}$.

41.
$$81x^2 = 25$$
$$81x^2 - 25 = 0$$
$$(9x + 5)(9x - 5) = 0$$
$$9x + 5 = 0 \quad \text{or} \quad 9x - 5 = 0$$
$$9x = -5 \qquad 9x = 5$$
$$x = -\frac{5}{9} \qquad x = \frac{5}{9}$$
The solution set is $\left\{-\dfrac{5}{9}, \dfrac{5}{9}\right\}$.

43.
$$x(x - 4) = 21$$
$$x^2 - 4x = 21$$
$$x^2 - 4x - 21 = 0$$
$$(x + 3)(x - 7) = 0$$
$$x + 3 = 0 \quad \text{or} \quad x - 7 = 0$$
$$x = -3 \qquad x = 7$$
The solution set is $\{-3, 7\}$.

45.
$$4x(x + 1) = 15$$
$$4x^2 + 4x = 15$$
$$4x^2 + 4x - 15 = 0$$
$$(2x + 5)(2x - 3) = 0$$
$$2x + 5 = 0 \quad \text{or} \quad 2x - 3 = 0$$
$$2x = -5 \qquad 2x = 3$$
$$x = -\frac{5}{2} \qquad x = \frac{3}{2}$$
The solution set is $\left\{-\dfrac{5}{2}, \dfrac{3}{2}\right\}$.

47. $(x-1)(x+4)=14$

$x^2+3x-4=14$

$x^2+3x-18=0$

$(x+6)(x-3)=0$

$x+6=0$ or $x-3=0$

$x=-6$ $x=3$

The solution set is $\{-6,3\}$.

49. $(x+1)(2x+5)=-1$

$2x^2+7x+5=-1$

$2x^2+7x+6=0$

$(2x+3)(x+2)=0$

$2x+3=0$ or $x+2=0$

$2x=-3$ $x=-2$

$x=-\dfrac{3}{2}$

The solution set is $\left\{-2,-\dfrac{3}{2}\right\}$.

51. $y(y+8)=16(y-1)$

$y^2+8y=16y-16$

$y^2-8y+16=0$

$(y-4)^2=0$

$y-4=0$

$y=4$

The solution set is $\{4\}$.

53. $4y^2+20y+25=0$

$(2y+5)^2=0$

$2y+5=0$

$2y=-5$

$y=-\dfrac{5}{2}$

The solution set is $\left\{-\dfrac{5}{2}\right\}$.

55. $64w^2=48w-9$

$64w^2-48w+9=0$

$(8w-3)^2=0$

$8w-3=0$

$8w=3$

$w=\dfrac{3}{8}$

The solution set is $\left\{\dfrac{3}{8}\right\}$.

57. $(x-4)(x^2+5x+6)=0$

$(x-4)(x+3)(x+2)=0$

$x-4=0$ or $x+3=0$ or $x+2=0$

$x=4$ $x=-3$ $x=-2$

The solution set is $\{-3,-2,4\}$.

59. $x^3-36x=0$

$x(x^2-36)=0$

$x(x+6)(x-6)=0$

$x=0$ or $x+6=0$ or $x-6=0$

$x=-6$ $x=6$

The solution set is $\{-6,0,6\}$.

61. $y^3+3y^2+2y=0$

$y(y^2+3y+2)=0$

$y(y+2)(y+1)=0$

$y=0$ or $y+2=0$ or $y+1=0$

$y=-2$ $y=-1$

The solution set is $\{-2,-1,0\}$.

63. $2(x-4)^2+x^2=x(x+50)-46x$

$2(x^2-8x+16)+x^2=x^2+50x-46x$

$2x^2-16x+32+x^2=x^2+4x$

$3x^2-16x+32=x^2+4x$

$2x^2-20x+32=0$

$2(x^2-10x+16)=0$

$2(x-8)(x-2)=0$

$x-8=0$ or $x-2=0$

$x=8$ $x=2$

The solution set is $\{2,8\}$.

65.
$$(x-2)^2 - 5(x-2) + 6 = 0$$
$$\left[(x-2)-3\right]\left[(x-2)-2\right] = 0$$
$$(x-5)(x-4) = 0$$
$$x-5 = 0 \quad \text{or} \quad x-4 = 0$$
$$x = 5 \qquad\qquad x = 4$$
The solution set is $\{4,5\}$.

67. $h = -16t^2 + 20t + 300$
Substitute 0 for h and solve for t.
$$0 = -16t^2 + 20t + 300$$
$$-16t^2 + 20t + 300 = 0$$
$$-4t\left(4t^2 - 5t - 75\right) = 0$$
$$-4t\left(4t + 15\right)(t - 5) = 0$$
$$-4t = 0 \text{ or } 4t + 15 = 0 \quad \text{or} \quad t - 5 = 0$$
$$t = 0 \qquad 4t = -15 \qquad\qquad t = 5$$
$$t = -\frac{15}{4} = -3.75$$
Reject $t = 0$ since this represents the time before the ball was thrown. Also discard $t = -3.75$ since time cannot be negative. The only solution that makes sense is 5. So it will take 5 seconds for the ball to hit the ground. Each tick mark represents one second.

69. Substitute 276 for h and solve for t.
$$276 = -16t^2 + 20t + 300$$
$$16t^2 - 20t - 24 = 0$$
$$4\left(4t^2 - 5t - 6\right) = 0$$
$$4(4t + 3)(t - 2) = 0$$
$$4t + 3 = 0 \qquad \text{or} \qquad t - 2 = 0$$
$$4t = -3 \qquad\qquad t = 2$$
$$t = -\frac{3}{4}$$
Reject $t = -\frac{3}{4}$ since time cannot be negative. The ball's height will be 276 feet 2 seconds after it is thrown. This corresponds to the point $(2, 276)$ on the graph.

71. $h = -16t^2 + 72t$
Substitute 32 for h and solve for t.
$$32 = -16t^2 + 72t$$
$$16t^2 - 72t + 32 = 0$$
$$8\left(2t^2 - 9t + 4\right) = 0$$
$$8(2t - 1)(t - 4) = 0$$
$$2t - 1 = 0 \quad \text{or} \quad t - 4 = 0$$
$$t = \frac{1}{2} \qquad\qquad t = 4$$
The debris will be 32 feet above the ground $\frac{1}{2}$ second after the explosion and 4 seconds after the explosion.

73. $S = 2x^2 - 12x + 82$
Substitute 72 for S and solve for x.
$$S = 2x^2 - 12x + 82$$
$$66 = 2x^2 - 12x + 82$$
$$0 = 2x^2 - 12x + 16$$
$$0 = 2(x^2 - 6x + 8)$$
$$0 = x^2 - 6x + 8$$
$$0 = (x - 2)(x - 4)$$
$$x - 2 = 0 \qquad \text{or} \qquad x - 4 = 0$$
$$x = 2 \qquad\qquad x = 4$$
International travelers spent \$66 billion 2 years and 4 years after 2000, or 2002 and 2004.

75. International travelers spent \$66 billion 2 years and 4 years after 2000. This corresponds to the point $(2, 66)$ and the point $(4, 66)$ on the graph.

77. $P = -10x^2 + 475x + 3500$
Substitute 7250 for P and solve for x.
$$7250 = -10x^2 + 475x + 3500$$
$$10x^2 - 475x + 3750 = 0$$
$$5\left(2x^2 - 95x + 750\right) = 0$$
$$5(x - 10)(2x - 75) = 0$$
$$x - 10 = 0 \quad \text{or} \quad 2x - 75 = 0$$
$$x = 10 \qquad\qquad 2x = 75$$
$$x = \frac{75}{2} \text{ or } 37.5$$
The alligator population will have increased to 7250 after 10 years. (Discard 37.5 because this value is outside of $0 \le x \le 12$.)

79. The solution in Exercise 77 corresponds to the point $(10, 7250)$ on the graph.

81. $N = \dfrac{t^2 - t}{2}$

Substitute 45 for N and solve for t.

$$45 = \frac{t^2 - t}{2}$$

$$2 \cdot 45 = 2\left(\frac{t^2 - t}{2}\right)$$

$$90 = t^2 - t$$

$$0 = t^2 - t - 90$$

$$0 = (t - 10)(t + 9)$$

$$t - 10 = 0 \quad \text{or} \quad t + 9 = 0$$

$$t = 10 \qquad\qquad t = -9$$

Reject $t = -9$ since the number of teams cannot be negative. If 45 games are scheduled, there are 10 teams in the league.

83. Let x = the width of the parking lot.
Then $x + 3$ = the length.

$$l \cdot w = A$$

$$(x + 3)(x) = 180$$

$$x^2 + 3x = 180$$

$$x^2 + 3x - 180 = 0$$

$$(x + 15)(x - 12) = 0$$

$$x + 15 = 0 \quad \text{or} \quad x - 12 = 0$$

$$x = -15 \qquad\qquad x = 12$$

Reject $x = -15$ since the width cannot be negative. Then $x = 12$ and $x + 3 = 15$, so the length is 15 yards and the width is 12 yards.

85. Use the formula for the area of a triangle where x is the base and $x + 1$ is the height.

$$\frac{1}{2}bh = A$$

$$\frac{1}{2}x(x + 1) = 15$$

$$2\left[\frac{1}{2}x(x + 1)\right] = 2 \cdot 15$$

$$x(x + 1) = 30$$

$$x^2 + x = 30$$

$$x^2 + x - 30 = 0$$

$$(x + 6)(x - 5) = 0$$

$$x + 6 = 0 \quad \text{or} \quad x - 5 = 0$$

$$x = -6 \qquad\qquad x = 5$$

Reject $x = -6$ since the length of the base cannot be negative. Then $x = 5$ and $x + 1 = 6$, so the base is 5 centimeters and the height is 6 centimeters.

87. a. Area of border

$$= \overbrace{(2x + 12)(2x + 10)}^{\text{Area of a large rectangle}} - \overbrace{10 \cdot 12}^{\substack{\text{Area of} \\ \text{flower bed}}}$$

$$= 4x^2 + 20x + 24x + 120 - 120$$

$$= 4x^2 + 44x$$

b. Find the width of the border for which the area of the border would be 168 square feet.

$$4x^2 + 44x = 168$$

$$4x^2 + 44x - 168 = 0$$

$$4\left(x^2 + 11x - 42\right) = 0$$

$$4(x + 14)(x - 3) = 0$$

$$x + 14 = 0 \quad \text{or} \quad x - 3 = 0$$

$$x = -14 \qquad\qquad x = 3$$

Reject $x = -14$ since the width of the border cannot be negative. You should prepare a strip that is 3 feet wide for the border.

89. Answers will vary.

91. does not make sense; Explanations will vary. Sample explanation: Though 4 cannot equal 0 and can therefore be ignored, $4x$ will equal 0 when $x = 0$ and so it cannot be ignored.

93. makes sense

95. false; Changes to make the statement true will vary. A sample change is: If $(x+3)(x-4)=0$, then $x+3=0$ or $x-4=0$.

97. false; Changes to make the statement true will vary. A sample change is: Some equations solved by factoring have more than 2 solutions and some have fewer than 2 solutions

99. If -3 and 5 are solutions of the quadratic equation, then $x-(-3)=x+3$ and $x-5$ must be factors of the polynomial on the left side when the quadratic equation is written in standard form.

$$(x+3)(x-5)=0$$
$$x^2-5x+3x-15=0$$
$$x^2-2x-15=0$$

Thus, $x^2-2x-15=0$ is a quadratic equation in standard form whose solutions are -3 and 5.

101. $3^{x^2-9x+20}=1$

Because $3^0=1$ (and there is no other power of 3 that is equal to 1), $x^2-9x+20=0$. Solve this equation.

$$x^2-9x+20=0$$
$$(x-4)(x-5)=0$$
$$x-4=0 \quad \text{or} \quad x-5=0$$
$$x=4 \qquad \qquad x=5$$

The solution set is $\{4,5\}$.

103. $y=x^2-x-2$

To match this equation with its graph, find the intercepts.
To find the y-intercept, let $x=0$ and solve for y.

$$y=0^2-0-2=-2$$

The y-intercept is -2.
To find the x intercepts (if any), let $y=0$ and solve for x.

$$0=x^2-x-2$$
$$0=(x+1)(x-2)$$

The x intercepts are -1 and 2.
The only graph with y-intercept -2 and x-intercepts -1 and 2 is graph, c, so this is the graph of $y=x^2-x-2$

105. $y=x^2-4$

To match this equation with its graph, find the intercepts.
To find the y-intercepts, let $x=0$ and solve for y.

$$y=0^2-4=-4$$

The y-intercept is -4.
To find the x-intercepts (if any), let $y=0$ and solve for x.

$$0=x^2-4$$
$$0=(x+2)(x-2)$$
$$x+2=0 \quad \text{or} \quad x-2=0$$
$$x=-2 \qquad \qquad x=2$$

The x-intercepts are -2 and 2.
The only graph with y-intercept -4 and x-intercepts -2 and 2 is graph d, so this is the graph of $y=x^2-4$.

107. $y=x^2+3x-4$

$$x^2+3x-4=0$$

Graph $y=x^2+3x-4$ and use the graph to find the x-intercepts.

The x-intercepts of $y=x^2+3x-4$ are -4 and 1, so the solution set of $x^2+3x-4=0$ is $\{-4,1\}$.
Check -4:

$$x^2+3x-4=0$$
$$(-4)^2+3(-4)-4=0$$
$$16-12-4=0$$
$$4-4=0$$
$$0=0, \text{ true}$$

Check 1:

$$x^2+3x-4=0$$
$$1^2+3(1)-4=0$$
$$1+3-4=0$$
$$4-4=0$$
$$0=0, \text{ true}$$

109. $y = (x-2)(x+3)-6$

$(x-2)(x+3)-6 = 0$

Graph $y = (x-2)(x-3)-6$ and use the graph to find the x-intercepts.

The x-intercepts of $y = (x-2)(x+3)-6$ are -4 and 3, so the solution set of $(x-2)(x+3)-6 = 0$ is $\{-4, 3\}$.

Check -4:

$(x-2)(x+3)-6 = 0$

$(-4-2)(-4+3)-6 = 0$

$(-6)(-1)-6 = 0$

$6-6 = 0$

$= 0$, true

Check 3:

$(x-2)(x+3)-6 = 0$

$(3-1)(3+3)-6 = 0$

$(1)(6)-6 = 0$

$6-6 = 0$

$0 = 0$, true

111. Answers will vary depending on the exercises chosen.

113. $y > -\dfrac{2}{3}x+1$

Graph $y = -\dfrac{2}{3}x+1$ as a dashed line using the slope

$-\dfrac{2}{3} = \dfrac{-2}{3}$ and y-intercept 1. (Plot (0,1) and move 2 units *down* and 3 units to the *right* to reach the point $(3, -1)$. Draw a line through (0,1) and $(3, -1)$.)

Use (0,0) as a test point. Since $0 > -\dfrac{2}{3}(0)+1$ is false, shade the half-plane *not* containing (0,0).

$y > -\dfrac{2}{3}x+1$

114. $\left(\dfrac{8x^4}{4x^7}\right)^2 = \left(\dfrac{8}{4}\cdot x^{4-7}\right) = \left(2x^{-3}\right)^2$

$= 2^2 \cdot \left(x^{-3}\right)^2 = 4x^{-6} = \dfrac{4}{x^6}$

115.
$5x + 28 = 6 - 6x$

$5x + 6x + 28 = 6 - 6x + 6x$

$11x + 28 = 6$

$11x + 28 - 28 = 6 - 28$

$11x = -22$

$\dfrac{11x}{11} = \dfrac{-22}{11}$

$x = -2$

The solution set is $\{-2\}$.

116. $\dfrac{250x}{100-x} = \dfrac{250(60)}{100-60} = \dfrac{15000}{40} = 375$

117. When x is replaced with 4, the denominator is 0. Division by zero is undefined.

$7x - 28 = 7(4) - 28 = 28 - 28 = 0$

118. $\dfrac{x^2 + 6x + 5}{x^2 - 25} = \dfrac{(x+5)(x+1)}{(x+5)(x-5)}$

$= \dfrac{\cancel{(x+5)}(x+1)}{\cancel{(x+5)}(x-5)}$

$= \dfrac{x+1}{x-5}$

Chapter 7 Review

1. $30x - 45 = 15(2x-3)$

2. $12x^3 + 16x^2 - 400x = 4x(3x^2 + 4x - 100)$

3. $30x^4y + 15x^3y + 5x^2y = 5x^2y(6x^2 + 3x + 1)$

4. $7(x+3) - 2(x+3) = (x+3)(7-2)$
$= (x+3)\cdot 5$ or $5(x+3)$

5. $7x^2(x+y) - (x+y) = 7x^2(x+y) - 1(x+y)$
$= (x+y)(7x^2 - 1)$

6. $x^3 + 3x^2 + 2x + 6 = \left(x^3 + 3x^2\right) + \left(2x + 6\right)$

$$= x^2\left(x + 3\right) + 2\left(x + 3\right)$$

$$= \left(x + 3\right)\left(x^2 + 2\right)$$

7. $xy + y + 4x + 4 = \left(xy + y\right) + \left(4x + 4\right)$

$$= y\left(x + 1\right) + 4\left(x + 1\right)$$

$$= \left(x + 1\right)\left(y + 4\right)$$

8. $x^3 + 5x + x^2 + 5 = \left(x^3 + 5x\right) + \left(x^2 + 5\right)$

$$= x\left(x^2 + 5\right) + 1\left(x^2 + 5\right)$$

$$= \left(x^2 + 5\right)\left(x + 1\right)$$

9. $xy + 4x - 2y - 8 = \left(xy + 4x\right) + \left(-2y - 8\right)$

$$= x\left(y + 4\right) - 2\left(y + 4\right)$$

$$= \left(y + 4\right)\left(x - 2\right)$$

10. $x^2 - 3x + 2 = \left(x - 2\right)\left(x - 1\right)$

11. $x^2 - x - 20 = \left(x - 5\right)\left(x + 4\right)$

12. $x^2 + 19x + 48 = \left(x + 3\right)\left(x + 16\right)$

13. $x^2 - 6xy + 8y^2 = \left(x - 4y\right)\left(x - 2y\right)$

14. $x^2 + 5x - 9$ is prime because there is no pair of integers whose product is −9 and whose sum is 5.

15. $x^2 + 16xy - 17y^2 = \left(x + 17y\right)\left(x - y\right)$

16. $3x^2 + 6x - 24 = 3\left(x^2 + 2x - 8\right)$

$$= 3\left(x + 4\right)\left(x - 2\right)$$

17. $3x^3 - 36x^2 + 33x = 3x\left(x^2 - 12x + 11\right)$

$$= 3x\left(x - 11\right)\left(x - 1\right)$$

18. Factor $3x^2 + 17x + 10$ by trial and error or by grouping. To factor by grouping, find two integers whose product is $ac = 3 \cdot 10 = 30$ and whose sum is $b = 17$. These integers are 15 and 2.

$3x^2 + 17x + 10 = 3x^2 + 15x + 2x + 10$

$$= 3x\left(x + 5\right) + 2\left(x + 5\right)$$

$$= \left(x + 5\right)\left(3x + 2\right)$$

19. Factor $5y^2 - 17y + 6$ by trial and error or by grouping. To factor by trial and error, start with the First terms, which must be $5y$ and y. Because the middle term is negative, the factors of 6 must both be negative. Try various combinations until the correct middle term is obtained.

$\left(5y - 1\right)\left(y - 6\right) = 5y^2 - 31y + 6$

$\left(5y - 6\right)\left(y - 1\right) = 5y^2 - 11y + 6$

$\left(5y - 3\right)\left(y - 2\right) = 5y^2 - 13y + 6$

$\left(5y - 2\right)\left(y - 3\right) = 5y^2 - 17y + 6$

Thus, $5y^2 - 17y + 6 = \left(5y - 2\right)\left(y - 3\right)$.

20. $4x^2 + 4x - 15 = \left(2x + 5\right)\left(2x - 3\right)$

21. Factor $5y^2 + 11y + 4$ by trial and error. The first terms must be $5y$ and y. Because the middle term is positive, the factors of 4 must both be positive. Try all the combinations.

$\left(5y + 2\right)\left(y + 2\right) = 5y^2 + 12y + 4$

$\left(5y + 4\right)\left(y + 1\right) = 5y^2 + 9y + 4$

$\left(5y + 1\right)\left(y + 4\right) = 5y^2 + 21y + 4$

None of these possibilities gives the required middle term, $11x$, and there are no more possibilities to try, so $5y^2 + 11y + 4$ is prime.

22. First factor out the GCF, 2. Then factor the resulting trinomial by trial and error or by grouping.

$8x^2 + 8x - 6 = 2\left(4x^2 + 4x - 3\right)$

$$= 2\left(2x + 3\right)\left(2x - 1\right)$$

23. $2x^3 + 7x^2 - 72x = x\left(2x^2 + 7x - 72\right)$

$$= x\left(2x - 9\right)\left(x + 8\right)$$

24. $12y^3 + 28y^2 + 8y = 4y\left(3y^2 + 7y + 2\right)$

$$= 4y\left(3y + 1\right)\left(y + 2\right)$$

25. $2x^2 - 7xy + 3y^2 = \left(2x - y\right)\left(x - 3y\right)$

26. $5x^2 - 6xy - 8y^2 = \left(5x + 4y\right)\left(x - 2y\right)$

27. $4x^2 - 1 = \left(2x\right)^2 - 1^2 = \left(2x + 1\right)\left(2x - 1\right)$

28. $81 - 100y^2 = 9^2 - (10y)^2$
$$= (9 + 10y)(9 - 10y)$$

29. $25a^2 - 49b^2 = (5a)^2 - (7b)^2$
$$= (5a + 7b)(5a - 7b)$$

30. $z^4 - 16 = (z^2)^2 - 4^2$
$$= (z^2 + 4)(z^2 - 4)$$
$$= (z^2 + 4)(z + 2)(z - 2)$$

31. $2x^2 - 18 = 2(x^2 - 9) = 2(x + 3)(x - 3)$

32. $x^2 + 1$ is prime because it is the sum of two squares with no common factor other than 1.

33. $9x^3 - x = x(9x^2 - 1) = x(3x + 1)(3x - 1)$

34. $18xy^2 - 8x = 2x(9y^2 - 4)$
$$= 2x(3y + 2)(3y - 2)$$

35. $x^2 + 22x + 121 = x^2 + 2(11x) + 11^2$
$$= (x + 11)^2$$

36. $x^2 - 16x + 64 = x^2 - 2(8 \cdot x) + 8^2$
$$= (x - 8)^2$$

37. $9y^2 + 48y + 64 = (3y)^2 + 2(3y \cdot 8) + 8^2$
$$= (3y + 8)^2$$

38. $16x^2 - 40x + 25 = (4x)^2 - 2(4x \cdot 5) + 5^2$
$$= (4x - 5)^2$$

39. $25x^2 + 15x + 9$ is prime.
Note that to be a perfect square trinomial, the middle term would have to be $2(5x \cdot 3) = 30x$.

40. $36x^2 + 60xy + 25y^2$
$$= (6x)^2 + 2(6x \cdot 5y) + (5y)^2$$
$$= (6x + 5y)^2$$

41. $25x^2 - 40xy + 16y^2$
$$= (5x)^2 - 2(5x \cdot 4y) + (4y)^2$$
$$= (5x - 4y)^2$$

42. $x^3 - 27 = x^3 - 3^2 = (x - 3)(x^2 + 3x + 9)$

43. $64x^3 + 1 = (4x)^3 + 1^3$
$$= (4x + 1)\left[(4x)^2 - 4x \cdot 1 + 1^2\right]$$
$$= (4x + 1)(16x^2 - 4x + 1)$$

44. $54x^3 - 16y^3$
$$= 2(27x^3 - 8y^3)$$
$$= 2\left[(3x)^3 - (2y)^3\right]$$
$$= 2(3x - 2y)\left[(3x)^2 + 3x \cdot 2y + (2y)^2\right]$$
$$= 2(3x - 2y)(9x^2 + 6xy + 4y^2)$$

45. $27x^3y + 8y = y(27x^3 + 8)$
$$= y\left[(3x)^3 + 2^3\right]$$
$$= y(3x + 2)\left[(3x)^2 - 3x \cdot 2 + 2^2\right]$$
$$= y(3x + 2)(9x^2 - 6x + 4)$$

46. Area of outer square = a^2
Area of inner square = $3^2 = 9$
Area of shaded region = $a^2 - 9$
$$= (a + 3)(a - 3)$$

47. Area of large square = a^2
Area of each small corner square = b^2
Area of four corner squares = $4b^2$
Area of shaded region = $a^2 - 4b^2$
$$= (a + 2b)(a - 2b)$$

48. Area on the left:

Area of large square = A^2
Area of each rectangle: $A \cdot 1 = A$
Area of two rectangles = $2A$
Area of small square = $1^2 = 1$
Area on the right:
Area of square = $(A+1)^2$
This geometric model illustrates the
factorization $A^2 + 2A - 1 = (A+1)^2$

49. $x^3 - 8x^2 + 7x = x(x^2 - 8x + 7) = x(x-7)(x-1)$

50. $10y^2 + 9y + 2 = (5y+2)(2y+1)$

51. $128 - 2y^2 = 2(64 - y^2) = 2(8+y)(8-y)$

52. $9x^2 + 6x + 1 = (3x)^2 + 2(3x) + 1^2 = (3x+1)^2$

53. $20x^7 - 36x^3 = 4x^3(5x^4 - 9)$

54. $x^3 - 3x^2 - 9x + 27$
$= (x^3 - 3x^2) + (-9x + 27)$
$= x^2(x-3) - 9(x-3)$
$= (x-3)(x^2 - 9)$
$= (x-3)(x+3)(x-3)$
or $(x-3)^2(x+3)$

55. $y^2 + 16$ is prime because it is the sum of two squares with no common factor other than 1.

56. $2x^3 + 19x^2 + 35x = x(2x^2 + 19x + 35)$
$= x(2x+5)(x+7)$

57. $3x^3 - 30x^2 + 75x = 3x(x^2 - 10x + 25)$
$= 3x(x-5)^2$

58. $3x^5 - 24x^2 = 3x^2(x^3 - 8)$
$= 3x^2(x^3 - 2^3)$
$= 3x^2(x-2)(x^2 + 2x + 4)$

59. $4y^4 - 36y^2 = 4y^2(y^2 - 9)$
$= 4y^2(y+3)(y-3)$

60. $5x^2 + 20x - 105 = 5(x^2 + 4x - 21)$
$= 5(x+7)(x-3)$

61. $9x^2 + 8x - 3$ is prime because there are no two integers whose product is $ac = -27$ and whose sum is 8.

62. $10x^5 - 44x^4 + 16x^3 = 2x^3(5x^2 - 22x + 8)$
$= 2x^3(5x-2)(x-4)$

63. $100y^2 - 49 = (10y)^2 - 7^2$
$= (10y+7)(10y-7)$

64. $9x^5 - 18x^4 = 9x^4(x-2)$

65. $x^4 - 1 = (x^2)^2 - 1^2$
$= (x^2+1)(x^2-1)$
$= (x^2+1)(x+1)(x-1)$

66. $2y^3 - 16 = 2(y^3 - 8)$
$= 2(y^3 - 2^3)$
$= 2(y-2)(y^2 + 2y + 2^2)$
$= 2(y-2)(y^2 + 2y + 4)$

67. $x^3 + 64 = x^3 + 4^3$
$= (x+4)(x^2 - 4x + 4^2)$
$= (x+4)(x^2 - 4x + 16)$

68. $6x^2 + 11x - 10 = (3x-2)(2x+5)$

69. $3x^4 - 12x^2 = 3x^2(x^2 - 4)$
$= 3x^2(x+2)(x-2)$

70. $x^2 - x - 90 = (x-10)(x+9)$

71. $25x^2 + 25xy + 6y^2 = (5x + 2y)(5x + 3y)$

72. $x^4 + 125x = x(x^3 + 125)$
$$= x(x^3 + 5^3)$$
$$= x(x+5)(x^2 - 5x + 5^2)$$
$$= x(x+5)(x^2 - 5x + 25)$$

73. $32y^3 + 32y^2 + 6y = 2y(16y^2 + 16y + 3)$
$$= 2y(4y+3)(4y+1)$$

74. $2y^2 - 16y + 32 = 2(y^2 - 8y + 16)$
$$= 2(y-4)^2$$

75. $x^2 - 2xy - 35y^2 = (x + 5y)(x - 7y)$

76. $x^2 + 7x + xy + 7y = x(x+7) + y(x+7)$
$$= (x+7)(x+y)$$

77. $9x^2 + 24xy + 16y^2$
$$= (3x)^2 + 2(3x \cdot 4y) + (4y)^2$$
$$= (3x + 4y)^2$$

78. $2x^4 y - 2x^2 y = 2x^2 y(x^2 - 1)$
$$= 2x^2 y(x+1)(x-1)$$

79. $100y^2 - 49z^2 = (10y)^2 - (7z)^2$
$$= (10y + 7z)(10y - 7z)$$

80. $x^2 + xy + y^2$ is prime.
Note that to be a perfect square trinomial, the middle term would have to be $2xy$.

81. $3x^4 y^2 - 12x^2 y^4 = 3x^2 y^2(x^2 - 4y^2)$
$$= 3x^2 y^2(x + 2y)(x - 2y)$$

82. $x(x - 12) = 0$
$x = 0$　or　$x - 12 = 0$
$$x = 12$$
The solution set is $\{0, 12\}$.

83. $3(x - 7)(4x + 9) = 0$
$x - 7 = 0$　or　$4x + 9 = 0$
$x = 7$　　　　$4x = -9$
$$x = -\frac{9}{4}$$
The solution set is $\left\{-\frac{9}{4}, 7\right\}$.

84. $x^2 + 5x - 14 = 0$
$(x + 7)(x - 2) = 0$
$x + 7 = 0$　or　$x - 2 = 0$
$x = -7$　　　$x = 2$
The solution set is $\{-7, 2\}$.

85. $5x^2 + 20x = 0$
$5x(x + 4) = 0$
$5x = 0$　or　$x + 4 = 0$
$x = 0$　　　$x = -4$
The solution set is $\{-4, 0\}$.

86. $2x^2 + 15x = 8$
$2x^2 + 15x - 8 = 0$
$(2x - 1)(x + 8) = 0$
$2x - 1 = 0$　or　$x + 8 = 0$
$2x = 1$　　　　$x = -8$
$$x = \frac{1}{2}$$
The solution set is $\left\{-8, \frac{1}{2}\right\}$.

87. $x(x - 4) = 32$
$x^2 - 4x = 32$
$x^2 - 4x - 32 = 0$
$(x + 4)(x - 8) = 0$
$x + 4 = 0$　or　$x - 8 = 0$
$x = -4$　　　$x = 8$
The solution set is $\{-4, 8\}$.

88. $(x+3)(x-2)=50$

$x^2+x-6=50$

$x^2+x-56=0$

$(x+8)(x-7)=0$

$x+8=0$ or $x-7=0$

$x=-8$ $x=7$

The solution set is $\{-8,7\}$.

89. $x^2=14x-49$

$x^2-14x+49=0$

$(x-7)^2=0$

$x-7=0$

$x=7$

The solution set is $\{7\}$.

90. $9x^2=100$

$9x^2-100=0$

$(3x+10)(3x-10)=0$

$3x+10=0$ or $3x-10=0$

$3x=-10$ $3x=10$

$x=-\dfrac{10}{3}$ $x=\dfrac{10}{3}$

The solution set is $\left\{-\dfrac{10}{3},\dfrac{10}{3}\right\}$.

91. $3x^2+21x+30=0$

$3\left(x^2+7x+10\right)=0$

$3(x+5)(x+2)=0$

$x+5=0$ or $x+2=0$

$x=-5$ $x=-2$

The solution set is $\{-5,-2\}$.

92. $3x^2=22x-7$

$3x^2-22x+7=0$

$(3x-1)(x-7)=0$

$3x-1=0$ or $x-7=0$

$3x=1$ $x=7$

$x=\dfrac{1}{3}$

The solution set is $\left\{\dfrac{1}{3},7\right\}$.

93. $h=-16t^2+16t+32$

Substitute 0 for h and solve for t.

$0=-16t^2+16t+32$

$16t^2-16t-32=0$

$16\left(t^2-t-2\right)=0$

$16(t+1)(t-2)=0$

$t+1=0$ or $t-2=0$

$t=-1$ $t=2$

Because time cannot be negative, reject the solution $t=-1$.

It will take you 2 seconds to hit the water.

94. Let x = the width of the sign.

Then $x+3$ = the length of the sign.

Use the formula for the area of a rectangle.

$l\cdot w=A$

$(x+3)(x)=40$

$x^2+3x=40$

$x^2+3x-40=0$

$(x+8)(x-5)=0$

$x+8=0$ or $x-5=0$

$x=-8$ $x=5$

A rectangle cannot have a negative length. Thus $x=$ 5, and $x+3=8$.

The length of the sign is 8 feet and the width is 5 feet.

95. Area of garden $=x(x-3)=88$

$x(x-3)=88$

$x^2-3x=88$

$x^2-3x-88=0$

$(x-11)(x+8)=0$

$x-11=0$ or $x+8=0$

$x=11$ $x=-8$

Because a length cannot be negative, reject $x=-8$. Each side of the square lot is 11 meters, that is, the dimensions of the square lot are 11 meters by 11 meters.

Chapter 7 Test

1. $x^2 - 9x + 18 = (x-3)(x-6)$

2. $x^2 - 14x + 49 = x^2 - 2(x \cdot 7) + 7^2$
$$= (x-7)^2$$

3. $15y^4 - 35y^3 + 10y^2 = 5y^2\left(3y^2 - 7y + 2\right)$
$$= 5y^2(3y-1)(y-2)$$

4. $x^3 + 2x^2 + 3x + 6 = \left(x^3 + 2x^2\right) + (3x+6)$
$$= x^2(x+2) + 3(x+2)$$
$$= (x+2)\left(x^2 + 3\right)$$

5. $x^2 - 9x = x(x-9)$

6. $x^3 + 6x^2 - 7x = x\left(x^2 + 6x - 7\right)$
$$= x(x+7)(x-1)$$

7. $14x^2 + 64x - 30 = 2\left(7x^2 + 32x - 15\right)$
$$= 2(7x-3)(x+5)$$

8. $25x^2 - 9 = (5x)^2 - 3^2$
$$= (5x+3)(5x-3)$$

9. $x^3 + 8 = x^3 + 2^3 = (x+2)\left(x^2 - 2x + 2^2\right)$
$$= (x+2)\left(x^2 - 2x + 4\right)$$

10. $x^2 - 4x - 21 = (x+3)(x-7)$

11. $x^2 + 4$ is prime.

12. $6y^3 + 9y^2 + 3y = 3y\left(2y^2 + 3y + 1\right)$
$$= 3y(2y+1)(y+1)$$

13. $4y^2 - 36 = 4\left(y^2 - 9\right) = 4(y+3)(y-3)$

14. $16x^2 + 48x + 36$
$$= 4\left(4x^2 + 12x + 9\right)$$
$$= 4\left[(2x)^2 + 2(2x \cdot 3) + 3^2\right]$$
$$= 4(2x+3)^2$$

15. $2x^4 - 32 = 2\left(x^4 - 16\right)$
$$= 2\left(x^2 + 4\right)\left(x^2 - 4\right)$$
$$= 2\left(x^2 + 4\right)(x+2)(x-2)$$

16. $36x^2 - 84x + 49 = (6x)^2 - 2(6x \cdot 7) + 7^2$
$$= (6x-7)^2$$

17. $7x^2 - 50x + 7 = (7x-1)(x-7)$

18. $x^3 + 2x^2 - 5x - 10$
$$= \left(x^3 + 2x^2\right) + (-5x - 10)$$
$$= x^2(x+2) - 5(x+2)$$
$$= (x+2)\left(x^2 - 5\right)$$

19. $12y^3 - 12y^2 - 45y = 3y\left(4y^2 - 4y - 15\right)$
$$= 3y(2y+3)(2y-5)$$

20. $y^3 - 125 = y^3 - 5^3$
$$= (y-5)\left(y^2 + 5y + 5^2\right)$$
$$= (y-5)\left(y^2 + 5y + 25\right)$$

21. $5x^2 - 5xy - 30y^2 = 5\left(x^2 - xy - 6y^2\right)$
$$= 5(x-3y)(x+2y)$$

22. $x^2 + 2x - 24 = 0$
$$(x+6)(x-4) = 0$$
$$x+6 = 0 \quad \text{or} \quad x-4 = 0$$
$$x = -6 \qquad x = 4$$
The solution set is $\{-6, 4\}$.

23. $3x^2 - 5x = 2$

$3x^2 - 5x - 2 = 0$

$(3x+1)(x-2) = 0$

$3x+1=0$ or $x-2=0$

$3x = -1$ $x = 2$

$x = -\dfrac{1}{3}$

The solution set is $\left\{-\dfrac{1}{3}, 2\right\}$.

24. $x(x-6) = 16$

$x^2 - 6x = 16$

$x^2 - 6x - 16 = 0$

$(x+2)(x-8) = 0$

$x+2=0$ or $x-8=0$

$x = -2$ $x = 8$

The solution set is $\{-2, 8\}$.

25. $6x^2 = 21x$

$6x^2 - 21x = 0$

$3x(2x-7) = 0$

$3x = 0$ or $2x - 7 = 0$

$x = 0$ $2x = 7$

$x = \dfrac{7}{2}$

The solution set is $\left\{0, \dfrac{7}{2}\right\}$.

26. $16x^2 = 81$

$16x^2 - 81 = 0$

$(4x+9)(4x-9) = 0$

$4x+9=0$ or $4x-9=0$

$4x = -9$ $4x = 9$

$x = -\dfrac{9}{4}$ $x = \dfrac{9}{4}$

The solution set is $\left\{-\dfrac{9}{4}, \dfrac{9}{4}\right\}$.

27. $(5x+4)(x-1) = 2$

$5x^2 - x - 4 = 2$

$5x^2 - x - 6 = 0$

$(5x-6)(x+1) = 0$

$5x-6=0$ or $x+1=0$

$5x = 6$ $x = -1$

$x = \dfrac{6}{5}$

The solution set is $\left\{-1, \dfrac{6}{5}\right\}$.

28.   Area of large square $= x^2$

Area of each small (corner) square $= 1^2 = 1$

Area of four corner squares $= 4 \cdot 1 = 4$

Area of shaded region $= x^2 - 4$

$\qquad\qquad = (x+2)(x-2)$

29. $h = -16t^2 + 80t + 96$

Substitute 0 for h and solve for t.

$0 = -16t^2 + 80t + 96$

$16t^2 - 80t - 96 = 0$

$16(t^2 - 5t - 6) = 0$

$16(t-6)(t+1) = 0$

$t-6=0$ or $t+1=0$

$t = 6$ $t = -1$

Since time cannot be negative, reject $t = -1$. The rocket will reach the ground after 6 seconds.

30.   Let $x =$ the width of the garden.

Then $x + 6 =$ the length of the garden.

$(x+6)(x) = 55$

$x^2 + 6x = 55$

$x^2 + 6x - 55 = 0$

$(x+11)(x-5) = 0$

$x+11=0$ or $x-5=0$

$x = -11$ $x = 5$

Since the width cannot be negative, reject $x = -11$. Then $x = 5$ and $x + 6 = 11$, so the width is 5 feet and the length is 11 feet.

Cumulative Review (Chapters 1-7)

1. $6[5+2(3-8)-3] = 6[5+2(-5)-3]$
$$= 6[5-10-3]$$
$$= 6(-8) = -48$$

2. $4(x-2) = 2(x-4)+3x$
$$4x-8 = 2x-8+3x$$
$$4x-8 = 5x-8$$
$$-x = 0$$
$$x = 0$$
The solution set is $\{0\}$.

3. $\dfrac{x}{2}-1 = \dfrac{x}{3}+1$
$$6\left(\dfrac{x}{2}-1\right) = 6\left(\dfrac{x}{3}+1\right)$$
$$3x-6 = 2x+6$$
$$x = 12$$
The solution set is $\{12\}$.

The solution is 12.

4. $5-5x > 2(5-x)+1$
$$5-5x > 10-2x+1$$
$$5-5x > 11-2x$$
$$5-5x+2x > 11-2x+2x$$
$$5-3x > 11$$
$$5-3x-5 > 11-5$$
$$-3x > 6$$
$$\dfrac{-3x}{-3} < \dfrac{6}{-3}$$
$$x < -2$$
$(-\infty, -2)$

```
<---+---+---)---+---+---+---+---+---+--->
 -5 -4 -3 -2 -1  0  1  2  3  4  5
```

5. Let x = the measure of each of the two base angles. Then $3x-10$ = the measure of the third angle.
$$x+x+(3x-10) = 180$$
$$5x-10 = 180$$
$$5x = 190$$
$$x = 38$$
$$3x-10 = 104$$
The measures of the three angles of the triangle are $38°$, $38°$, and $104°$.

6. Let x = the cost of the dinner before tax.
$$x+0.06x = 159$$
$$1.06x = 159$$
$$\dfrac{1.06x}{1.06} = \dfrac{159}{1.06}$$
$$x \approx 150$$
The cost of the dinner before tax was $150.

7. $y = -\dfrac{3}{5}x+3$

slope $= -\dfrac{3}{5} = \dfrac{-3}{5}$; y-intercept $= 3$

Plot $(0,3)$. From this point, move 3 units *down* (because -3 is negative) and 5 units to the *right* to reach the point $(5,0)$. Draw a line through $(0,3)$ and $(5,0)$.

8. First, find slope $m = \dfrac{1-(-4)}{3-2} = \dfrac{5}{1} = 5$.

Use the point $(2, -4)$ in the point-slope equation.
$$y-y_1 = m(x-x_1)$$
$$y-(-4) = 5(x-2)$$
$$y+4 = 5(x-2)$$
Rewrite this equation in slope-intercept form.
$$y+4 = 5x-10$$
$$y = 5x-14$$

9. $5x-6y > 30$

Graph $5x-6y = 30$ as a dashed line through $(6,0)$ and $(0, -5)$. Use $(0,0)$ as a test point. Since $0-0 > 30$ is false, shade the half-plane *not* containing $(0,0)$.

10. $5x + 2y = 13$

$y = 2x - 7$

The substitution method is a good choice for solving this system because the second equation is already solved for y.

Substitute $2x - 7$ for y in the first equation.

$$5x + 2y = 13$$
$$5x + 2(2x - 7) = 13$$
$$5x + 4x - 14 = 13$$
$$9x - 14 = 13$$
$$9x = 27$$
$$x = 3$$

Back-substitute into the second given equation.

$$y = 2x - 7$$
$$y = 2(3) - 7 = -1$$

The solution set is $\{(3, -1)\}$.

11. $2x + 3y = 5$

$3x - 2y = -4$

The addition method is a good choice for solving this system because both equations are written in the form $Ax + By = C$.

Multiply the first equation by 2 and the second equation by 3; then add the results.

$$\begin{array}{rcl} 4x + 6y &=& 10 \\ 9x - 6y &=& -12 \\ \hline 13x &=& -2 \end{array}$$

$$x = -\frac{2}{13}$$

Instead of back-substituting $-\dfrac{2}{13}$ and working with fractions, go back to the original system and eliminate x. Multiply the first equation by 3 and the second equation by -2; then add the results.

$$\begin{array}{rcl} 6x + 9y &=& 15 \\ -6x + 4y &=& 8 \\ \hline 13y &=& 23 \end{array}$$

$$y = \frac{23}{13}$$

The solution set is $\left\{ \left(-\dfrac{2}{13}, \dfrac{23}{13} \right) \right\}$.

12. $\dfrac{4}{5} - \dfrac{9}{8} = \dfrac{4}{5} \cdot \dfrac{8}{5} - \dfrac{9}{8} \cdot \dfrac{5}{5}$

$$= \frac{32}{40} - \frac{45}{40} = -\frac{13}{40}$$

13. $\dfrac{6x^5 - 3x^4 + 9x^2 + 27x}{3x}$

$$= \frac{6x^5}{3x} - \frac{3x^4}{3x} + \frac{9x^2}{3x} + \frac{27x}{3x}$$

$$= 2x^4 - x^3 + 3x + 9$$

14. $(3x - 5y)(2x + 9y)$

$$= 6x^2 + 27xy - 10xy - 45y^2$$

$$= 6x^2 + 17xy - 45y^2$$

15.

$$\require{enclose}
\begin{array}{r}
2x^2 + 5x - 3 \\
3x - 5 \enclose{longdiv}{6x^3 + 5x^2 - 34x + 13}
\end{array}$$

$$\begin{array}{r}
\underline{6x^3 - 10x^2} \\
15x^2 - 34x \\
\underline{15x^2 - 25x} \\
-9x + 13 \\
\underline{-9x + 15} \\
-2
\end{array}$$

$$\frac{6x^3 + 5x^2 - 34x + 13}{3x - 5} = 2x^2 + 5x - 3 + \frac{-2}{3x - 5}$$

$$\text{or } 2x^2 + 5x - 3 - \frac{2}{3x - 5}$$

16. $0.0071 = 7.1 \times 10^{-3}$

To write 0.0071 in scientific notation, move the decimal point 3 places to the right. Because the given number is between 0 and 1, the exponent will be negative.

17. Factor $3x^2 + 11x + 6$ by trial and error or by grouping. To Factor by grouping, find two integers whose product is $ac = 3 \cdot 6 = 18$ and whose sum is $b = 11$. These integers are 9 and 2.

$$3x^2 + 11x + 6 = 3x^2 + 9x + 2x + 6$$

$$= 3x(x + 3) + 2(x + 3)$$

$$= (x + 3)(3x + 2)$$

18. $y^5 - 16y = y(y^4 - 16)$

$$= y(y^2 + 4)(y^2 - 4)$$

$$= y(y^2 + 4)(y + 2)(y - 2)$$

19. $4x^2 + 12x + 9 = (2x)^2 + 2(2x \cdot 3) + 3x^2$
$$= (2x+3)^2$$

20. Let x = the width of the rectangle.
Then $x + 2$ = the length of the rectangle.
Use the formula for the area of a rectangle.

$$l \cdot w = A$$
$$(x+2)(x) = 24$$
$$x^2 + 2x = 24$$
$$x^2 + 2x - 24 = 0$$
$$(x+6)(x-4) = 0$$

$x + 6 = 0$ or $x - 4 = 0$

$\qquad x = -6 \qquad\qquad\qquad x = 4$

Reject -6 because the width cannot be negative.
$x = 4$ and $x + 2 = 6$.
The dimensions of the rectangle are 6 feet by 4 feet.

Chapter 8
Rational Expressions

8.1 Check Points

1. **a.** $\dfrac{7x-28}{8x-40}$

   Set the denominator equal to 0 and solve for x.

   $8x - 40 = 0$

   $\qquad 8x = 40$

   $\qquad x = 5$

   The rational expression is undefined for $x = 5$.

   b. $\dfrac{8x-40}{x^2+3x-28}$

   Set the denominator equal to 0 and solve for x.

   $x^2 + 3x - 28 = 0$

   $(x+7)(x-4) = 0$

   $x + 7 = 0 \quad \text{or} \quad x - 4 = 0$

   $\quad x = -7 \qquad\qquad x = 4$

   The rational expression is undefined for $x = -7$ and $x = 4$.

2. $\dfrac{7x+28}{21x} = \dfrac{7(x+4)}{7\cdot 3x} = \dfrac{x+4}{3x}$

3. $\dfrac{x^3-x^2}{7x-7} = \dfrac{x^2(x-1)}{7(x-1)} = \dfrac{x^2}{7}$

4. $\dfrac{x^2-1}{x^2+2x+1} = \dfrac{(x+1)(x-1)}{(x+1)^2} = \dfrac{\cancel{(x+1)}(x-1)}{\cancel{(x+1)}(x+1)} = \dfrac{x-1}{x+1}$

5. $\dfrac{9x^2-49}{28-12x} = \dfrac{(3x+7)(3x-7)}{4(7-3x)}$

   $\qquad = \dfrac{(3x+7)\,\overset{-1}{\cancel{(3x-7)}}}{4\cancel{(7-3x)}}$

   $\qquad = \dfrac{-(3x+7)}{4} \quad \text{or} \quad -\dfrac{3x+7}{4} \quad \text{or} \quad \dfrac{-3x-7}{4}$

8.1 Exercise Set

1. $\dfrac{5}{2x}$

   Set the denominator equal to 0 and solve for x.

   $2x = 0$

   $\quad x = 0$

   The rational expression is undefined for $x = 0$.

3. $\dfrac{x}{x-8}$

Set the denominator equal to 0 and solve for x.

$x - 8 = 0$

$x = 8$

The rational expression is undefined for $x = 8$.

5. $\dfrac{13}{5x-20}$

Set the denominator equal to 0 and solve for x.

$5x - 20 = 0$

$5x = 20$

$x = 4$

The rational expression is undefined for $x = 4$.

7. $\dfrac{x+3}{(x+9)(x-2)}$

Set the denominator equal to 0 and solve for x.

$(x+9)(x-2) = 0$

$x+9 = 0$ or $x-2 = 0$

$x = -9$ $x = 2$

The rational expression is undefined for $x = -9$ and $x = 2$.

9. $\dfrac{4x}{(3x-17)(x+3)}$

Set the denominator equal to 0 and solve for x.

$(3x-17)(x+3) = 0$

$3x-17 = 0$ or $x+3 = 0$

$3x = 17$ $x = -3$

$x = \dfrac{17}{3}$

The rational expression is undefined for $x = \dfrac{17}{3}$ and $x = -3$.

11. $\dfrac{x+5}{x^2+x-12}$

Set the denominator equal to 0 and solve for x.

$x^2 + x - 12 = 0$

$(x+4)(x-3) = 0$

$x+4 = 0$ or $x-3 = 0$

$x = -4$ $x = 3$

The rational expression is undefined for $x = -4$ and $x = 3$.

13. $\dfrac{x+5}{5}$

Because the denominator, 5, is not zero for any value of x, the rational expression is defined for all real numbers.

15. $\dfrac{y+3}{4y^2+y-3}$

Set the denominator equal to 0 and solve for x.

$4y^2 + y - 3 = 0$

$(y+1)(4y-3) = 0$

$y+1 = 0$ or $4y-3 = 0$

$y = -1$ $4y = 3$

$y = \dfrac{3}{4}$

The rational expression is undefined for $y = -1$ and $y = \dfrac{3}{4}$.

17. $\dfrac{y+5}{y^2-25}$

Set the denominator equal to 0 and solve for x.

$y^2 - 25 = 0$

$(y+5)(y-5) = 0$

$y+5 = 0$ or $y-5 = 0$

$y = -5$ $y = 5$

The rational expression is undefined for $y = -5$ and $y = 5$.

19. $\dfrac{5}{x^2+1}$

The smallest possible value of x^2 is 0, so $x^2 + 1 \geq 1$ for all real numbers of x. This means that there is no real number x for which $x^2 + 1 = 0$. Thus, the rational expression is defined for all real numbers.

21. $\dfrac{14x^2}{7x} = \dfrac{2 \cdot 7 \cdot x \cdot x}{7 \cdot x} = \dfrac{2x}{1} = 2x$

23. $\dfrac{5x-15}{25} = \dfrac{5(x-3)}{5 \cdot 5} = \dfrac{x-3}{5}$

25. $\dfrac{2x-8}{4x} = \dfrac{2(x-4)}{2 \cdot 2x} = \dfrac{x-4}{2x}$

27. $\dfrac{3}{3x-9} = \dfrac{3}{3(x-3)} = \dfrac{1}{x-3}$

29. $\dfrac{-15}{3x-9} = \dfrac{-15}{3(x-3)} = \dfrac{-5}{x-3}$ or $-\dfrac{5}{x-3}$

31. $\dfrac{3x+9}{x+3} = \dfrac{3(x+3)}{x+3} = \dfrac{3}{1} = 3$

33. $\dfrac{x+5}{x^2-25} = \dfrac{x+5}{(x+5)(x-5)} = \dfrac{1}{x-5}$

35. $\dfrac{2y-10}{3y-15} = \dfrac{2(y-5)}{3(y-5)} = \dfrac{2}{3}$

37. $\dfrac{x+1}{x^2-2x-3} = \dfrac{x+1}{(x+1)(x-3)} = \dfrac{1}{x-3}$

39. $\dfrac{4x-8}{x^2-4x+4} = \dfrac{4(x-2)}{(x-2)(x-2)} = \dfrac{4}{x-2}$

41. $\dfrac{y^2-3y+2}{y^2+7y-18} = \dfrac{(y-1)(y-2)}{(y+9)(y-2)} = \dfrac{y-1}{y+9}$

43. $\dfrac{2y^2-7y+3}{2y^2-5y+2} = \dfrac{(2y-1)(y-3)}{(2y-1)(y-2)} = \dfrac{y-3}{y-2}$

45. $\dfrac{2x+3}{2x+5}$

The numerator and denominator have no common factor (other than 1), so this rational expression cannot be simplified.

47. $\dfrac{x^2+12x+36}{x^2-36} = \dfrac{(x+6)(x+6)}{(x+6)(x-6)} = \dfrac{x+6}{x-6}$

49. $\dfrac{x^3-2x^2+x-2}{x-2} = \dfrac{x^2(x-2)+1(x-2)}{x-2}$
$$= \dfrac{(x-2)(x^2+1)}{x-2}$$
$$= x^2+1$$

51. $\dfrac{x^3-8}{x-2} = \dfrac{(x-2)(x^2+2x+4)}{x-2}$
$$= x^2+2x+4$$

53. $\dfrac{(x-4)^2}{x^2-16} = \dfrac{(x-4)(x-4)}{(x+4)(x-4)} = \dfrac{x-4}{x+4}$

55. $\dfrac{x}{x+1}$; The numerator and denominator have no common factor (other than 1), so this rational expression cannot be simplified.

57. $\dfrac{x+4}{x^2+16}$; The numerator and denominator are both prime polynomials. They have no common factor (other than 1), so this rational expression cannot be simplified.

59. $\dfrac{x-5}{5-x} = \dfrac{-1(5-x)}{5-x} = -1$

Notice that the numerator and denominator of the given rational expression are additive inverses.

61. The numerator and denominator of this rational expression are additive inverses, so $\dfrac{2x-3}{3-2x} = -1$.

63. $\dfrac{x-5}{x+5}$; The numerator and denominator have no common factor and they are not additive inverses, so this rational expression cannot be simplified.

65. $\dfrac{4x-6}{3-2x} = \dfrac{2(2x-3)}{3-2x} = \dfrac{-2(3-2x)}{3-2x} = -2$

67. $\dfrac{4-6x}{3x^2-2x} = \dfrac{2(2-3x)}{x(3x-2)}$
$$= \dfrac{-2(3x-2)}{x(3x-2)}$$
$$= -\dfrac{2}{x}$$

69. $\dfrac{x^2-1}{1-x} = \dfrac{(x+1)(x-1)}{1-x}$
$$= \dfrac{(x+1)\cdot-1(1-x)}{1-x}$$
$$= -1(x+1) = -x-1$$

71. $\dfrac{y^2-y-12}{4-y}=\dfrac{(y-4)(y+3)}{4-y}$

$\qquad=\dfrac{-1(4-y)(y+3)}{4-y}$

$\qquad=-1(y+3)=-y-3$

73. $\dfrac{x^2y-x^2}{x^3-x^3y}=\dfrac{x^2(y-1)}{x^3(1-y)}$

$\qquad=\dfrac{x^2\cdot-1(1-y)}{x^3(1-y)}$

$\qquad=-\dfrac{1}{x}$

75. $\dfrac{x^2+2xy-3y^2}{2x^2+5xy-3y^2}=\dfrac{(x-y)(x+3y)}{(2x-y)(x+3y)}$

$\qquad=\dfrac{x-y}{2x-y}$

77. $\dfrac{x^2-9x+18}{x^3-27}=\dfrac{(x-3)(x-6)}{(x-3)(x^2+3x+9)}$

$\qquad=\dfrac{x-6}{x^2+3x+9}$

79. $\dfrac{9-y^2}{y^2-3(2y-3)}=\dfrac{(3+y)(3-y)}{y^2-6y+9}$

$\quad=\dfrac{(3+y)(3-y)}{(y-3)(y-3)}=\dfrac{(3+y)\cdot-1(y-3)}{(y-3)(y-3)}$

$\quad=\dfrac{-1(3+y)}{y-3}$ or $\dfrac{3+y}{-1(y-3)}=\dfrac{3+y}{3-y}$

81. $\dfrac{xy+2y+3x+6}{x^2+5x+6}=\dfrac{y(x+2)+3(x+2)}{(x+2)(x+3)}$

$\quad=\dfrac{(x+2)(y+3)}{(x+2)(x+3)}=\dfrac{y+3}{x+3}$

83. $\dfrac{8x^2+4x+2}{1-8x^3}=\dfrac{2(4x^2+2x+1)}{(1-2x)(1+2x+4x^2)}$

$\qquad=\dfrac{2}{1-2x}$

85. $\dfrac{130x}{100-x}$

a. $x=40$:

$\dfrac{130x}{100-x}=\dfrac{130(40)}{100-40}$

$\qquad=\dfrac{5200}{60}$

$\qquad\approx86.67$

This means it costs about \$86.67 million to inoculate 40% of the population.

$x=80$:

$\dfrac{130x}{100-x}=\dfrac{130(80)}{100-80}$

$\qquad=\dfrac{10,400}{20}$

$\qquad=520$

This means it costs \$520 million to inoculate 80% of the population.

$x=90$:

$\dfrac{130x}{100-x}=\dfrac{130(90)}{100-90}$

$\qquad=\dfrac{11,700}{10}$

$\qquad=1170$

This means it costs \$1170 million (\$1,170,000,000) to inoculate 90% of the population.

b. Set the denominator equal to 0 and solve for x.
$100-x=0$

$\qquad100=x$

The rational expression is undefined for $x=100$.

c. The cost keeps rising as x approaches 100. No amount of money will be enough to inoculate 100% of the population.

87. $D=1000, A=8$

$\dfrac{DA}{A+12}=\dfrac{1000\cdot8}{8+12}$

$\qquad=\dfrac{8000}{20}=400$

The correct dosage for an 8-year old is 400 milligrams.

89. $C = \dfrac{100x + 100,000}{x}$

   a. $x = 500$

$$C = \frac{100(500) + 100,000}{500}$$

$$= \frac{150,000}{500} = 300$$

The cost per bicycle when manufacturing 500 bicycles is $300.

   b. $x = 4000$

$$C = \frac{100(4000) + 100,000}{4000}$$

$$= \frac{400,000 + 100,000}{4000}$$

$$= \frac{500,000}{4000} = 125$$

The cost per bicycle when manufacturing 4000 bicycles is $125.

   c. The cost per bicycle decreases as more bicycles are manufactured. One possible reason for this is that there could be fixed costs for equipment, so the more the equipment is used, the lower the cost per bicycle.

91. $y = \dfrac{5x}{x^2 + 1}; x = 3$

$$y = \frac{5 \cdot 3}{3^2 + 1} + \frac{15}{10} = 1.5$$

The equation indicates that the drug's concentration after 3 hours is 1.5 milligram per liter. This is represented on the graph by the point $(3, 1.5)$.

93. a. Substitute 4 for x in the model.

$$W = -82x^2 + 654x + 620$$

$$W = -82(4)^2 + 654(4) + 620$$

$$W = 1924$$

According to the model, women between the ages of 19 and 30 with this lifestyle need 1924 calories per day. This underestimates the actual value shown in the bar graph by 76 calories.

b. Substitute 4 for x in the model.

$$M = -96x^2 + 802x + 660$$

$$M = -96(4)^2 + 802(4) + 660$$

$$M = 2332$$

According to the model, men between the ages of 19 and 30 with this lifestyle need 2332 calories per day. This underestimates the actual value shown in the bar graph by 68 calories.

c. $\dfrac{W}{M} = \dfrac{-82x^2 + 654x + 620}{-96x^2 + 802x + 660}$

$$= \frac{2\left(-41x^2 + 327x + 310\right)}{2\left(-48x^2 + 401x + 330\right)}$$

$$= \frac{-41x^2 + 327x + 310}{-48x^2 + 401x + 330}$$

95. – 99. Answers will vary.

101. makes sense

103. does not make sense; Explanations will vary. Sample explanation: 1 makes the denominator equal to 0 and thus the expression is undefined at 1.

105. false; Changes to make the statement true will vary. A sample change is: 3 is not a factor of $x^2 + 3$.

107. false; Changes to make the statement true will vary. A sample change is: x is not a factor of the numerator or the denominator.

109. Answers will vary. The denominator should be $x + 4$ or contain a factor of $x + 4$.

111. The graphs coincide.

This verifies that the simplification $\dfrac{3x + 15}{x + 5} = 3, x \neq -5$, is correct. Notice the screen shows no y – value for $x = -5$.

113. The graphs do not coincide.

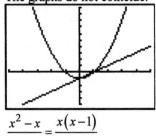

$$\frac{x^2 - x}{x} = \frac{x(x-1)}{x}$$
$$= x - 1, x \neq 0$$

Change the expression on the right from $x^2 - 1$ to $x - 1$.

115. $\dfrac{5}{6} \cdot \dfrac{9}{25} = \dfrac{\cancel{5}^{\,1}}{\cancel{6}_{\,2}} \cdot \dfrac{\cancel{9}^{\,3}}{\cancel{25}_{\,5}} = \dfrac{3}{10}$

116. $\dfrac{2}{3} \div 4 = \dfrac{2}{3} \cdot \dfrac{1}{4} = \dfrac{2}{12} = \dfrac{2 \cdot 1}{2 \cdot 6} = \dfrac{1}{6}$

117. $2x - 5y = -2$

$3x + 4y = 20$

Multiply the first equation by 3 and the second equation by -2; then add the results.

$\begin{array}{r} 6x - 15y = -6 \\ \underline{-6x - 8y = -40} \\ -23y = -46 \\ y = 2 \end{array}$

Back-substitute to find x.

$$2x - 5y = -2$$
$$2x - 5(2) = -2$$
$$2x - 10 = -2$$
$$2x = 8$$
$$x = 4$$

The solution set is $\{(4,2)\}$.

118. $\dfrac{2}{5} \cdot \dfrac{3}{7} = \dfrac{6}{35}$

119. $\dfrac{3}{4} \div \dfrac{1}{2} = \dfrac{3}{4} \cdot \dfrac{2}{1} = \dfrac{6}{4} = \dfrac{2 \cdot 3}{2 \cdot 2} = \dfrac{3}{2}$

120. $\dfrac{5}{4} \div \dfrac{15}{8} = \dfrac{5}{4} \cdot \dfrac{8}{15} = \dfrac{\cancel{5}^{\,1}}{\cancel{4}_{\,1}} \cdot \dfrac{\cancel{8}^{\,2}}{\cancel{15}_{\,3}} = \dfrac{2}{3}$

8.2 Check Points

1. $\dfrac{9}{x+4} \cdot \dfrac{x-5}{2} = \dfrac{9(x-5)}{(x+4)2} = \dfrac{9x-45}{2x+8}$

2. $\dfrac{x+4}{x-7} \cdot \dfrac{3x-21}{8x+32} = \dfrac{x+4}{x-7} \cdot \dfrac{3(x-7)}{8(x+4)}$

$$= \dfrac{\overset{1}{\cancel{x+4}}}{\cancel{x-7}} \cdot \dfrac{3\,\overset{1}{\cancel{(x-7)}}}{8\,\cancel{(x+4)}}$$

$$= \dfrac{3}{8}$$

3. $\dfrac{x-5}{x-2} \cdot \dfrac{x^2-4}{9x-45} = \dfrac{x-5}{x-2} \cdot \dfrac{(x+2)(x-2)}{9(x-5)}$

$$= \dfrac{\overset{1}{\cancel{x-5}}}{\cancel{x-2}} \cdot \dfrac{(x+2)\,\overset{1}{\cancel{(x-2)}}}{9\,\cancel{(x-5)}}$$

$$= \dfrac{x+2}{9}$$

4. $\dfrac{5x+5}{7x-7x^2} \cdot \dfrac{2x^2+x-3}{4x^2-9} = \dfrac{5(x+1)}{7x(1-x)} \cdot \dfrac{(2x+3)(x-1)}{(2x+3)(2x-3)}$

$$= \dfrac{5(x+1)}{7x\,\cancel{(1-x)}} \cdot \dfrac{\cancel{(2x+3)}\,\overset{-1}{\cancel{(x-1)}}}{\cancel{(2x+3)}(2x-3)}$$

$$= \dfrac{-5(x+1)}{7x(2x-3)} \quad \text{or} \quad -\dfrac{5(x+1)}{7x(2x-3)}$$

5. $(x+3) \div \dfrac{x-4}{x+7} = \dfrac{x+3}{1} \cdot \dfrac{x+7}{x-4}$

$$= \dfrac{(x+3)(x+7)}{x-4}$$

6. $\dfrac{x^2+5x+6}{x^2-25} \div \dfrac{x+2}{x+5} = \dfrac{x^2+5x+6}{x^2-25} \cdot \dfrac{x+5}{x+2}$

$$= \dfrac{(x+3)(x+2)}{(x+5)(x-5)} \cdot \dfrac{x+5}{x+2}$$

$$= \dfrac{(x+3)\,\cancel{(x+2)}}{\cancel{(x+5)}(x-5)} \cdot \dfrac{\cancel{x+5}}{\cancel{x+2}}$$

$$= \dfrac{x+3}{x-5}$$

7. $\dfrac{y^2+3y+2}{y^2+1} \div \left(5y^2+10y\right) = \dfrac{y^2+3y+2}{y^2+1} \div \dfrac{5y^2+10y}{1}$

$$= \dfrac{y^2+3y+2}{y^2+1} \cdot \dfrac{1}{5y^2+10y}$$

$$= \dfrac{(y+2)(y+1)}{y^2+1} \cdot \dfrac{1}{5y(y+2)}$$

$$= \dfrac{\cancel{(y+2)}(y+1)}{y^2+1} \cdot \dfrac{1}{5y\cancel{(y+2)}}$$

$$= \dfrac{y+1}{5y(y^2+1)}$$

8.2 Exercise Set

1. $\dfrac{4}{x+3} \cdot \dfrac{x-5}{9} = \dfrac{4(x-5)}{(x+3)9} = \dfrac{4x-20}{9x+27}$

3. $\dfrac{x}{3} \cdot \dfrac{12}{x+5} = \dfrac{3 \cdot 4x}{3(x+5)} = \dfrac{4x}{x+5}$

5. $\dfrac{3}{x} \cdot \dfrac{4x}{15} = \dfrac{3 \cdot 4x}{3 \cdot 5x} = \dfrac{4}{5}$

7. $\dfrac{x-3}{x+5} \cdot \dfrac{4x+20}{9x-27} = \dfrac{x-3}{x+5} \cdot \dfrac{4(x+5)}{9(x-3)} = \dfrac{4}{9}$

9. $\dfrac{x^2+9x+14}{x+7} \cdot \dfrac{1}{x+2} = \dfrac{(x+7)(x+2) \cdot 1}{(x+7)(x+2)} = 1$

11. $\dfrac{x^2-25}{x^2-3x-10} \cdot \dfrac{x+2}{x} = \dfrac{(x+5)(x-5)}{(x+2)(x-5)} \cdot \dfrac{(x+2)}{x}$

$$= \dfrac{x+5}{x}$$

13. $\dfrac{4y+30}{y^2-3y} \cdot \dfrac{y-3}{2y+15} = \dfrac{2(2y+15)}{y(y-3)} \cdot \dfrac{(y-3)}{(2y+15)}$

$$= \dfrac{2}{y}$$

15. $\dfrac{y^2-7y-30}{y^2-6y-40}\cdot\dfrac{2y^2+5y+2}{2y^2+7y+3}$

$=\dfrac{(y+3)(y-10)}{(y+4)(y-10)}\cdot\dfrac{(2y+1)(y+2)}{(2y+1)(y+3)}$

$=\dfrac{y+2}{y+4}$

17. $\left(y^2-9\right)\cdot\dfrac{4}{y-3}=\dfrac{y^2-9}{1}\cdot\dfrac{4}{y-3}$

$=\dfrac{(y+3)(y-3)}{1}\cdot\dfrac{4}{y-3}$

$=4(y+3)$ or $4y+12$

19. $\dfrac{x^2-5x+6}{x^2-2x-3}\cdot\dfrac{x^2-1}{x^2-4}$

$=\dfrac{(x-2)(x-3)}{(x+1)(x-3)}\cdot\dfrac{(x+1)(x-1)}{(x+2)(x-2)}$

$=\dfrac{x-1}{x+2}$

21. $\dfrac{x^3-8}{x^2-4}\cdot\dfrac{x+2}{3x}$

$=\dfrac{(x-2)\left(x^2+2x+4\right)}{(x+2)(x-2)}\cdot\dfrac{(x+2)}{3x}$

$=\dfrac{x^2+2x+4}{3x}$

23. $\dfrac{(x-2)^3}{(x-1)^3}\cdot\dfrac{x^2-2x+1}{x^2-4x+4}$

$=\dfrac{(x-2)^3}{(x-1)^3}\cdot\dfrac{(x-1)^2}{(x-2)^2}$

$=\dfrac{x-2}{x-1}$

25. $\dfrac{6x+2}{x^2-1}\cdot\dfrac{1-x}{3x^2+x}$

$=\dfrac{2(3x+1)}{(x+1)(x-1)}\cdot\dfrac{(1-x)}{x(3x+1)}$

$=\dfrac{2(3x+1)}{(x+1)(x-1)}\cdot\dfrac{-1(x-1)}{x(3x+1)}$

$=\dfrac{-2}{x(x+1)}$ or $-\dfrac{2}{x(x+1)}$

27. $\dfrac{25-y^2}{y^2-2y-35}\cdot\dfrac{y^2-8y-20}{y^2-3y-10}$

$=\dfrac{(5+y)(5-y)}{(y+5)(y-7)}\cdot\dfrac{(y-10)(y+2)}{(y-5)(y+2)}$

$=\dfrac{-(y-10)}{y-7}$ or $-\dfrac{y-10}{y-7}$

29. $\dfrac{x^2-y^2}{x}\cdot\dfrac{x^2+xy}{x+y}$

$=\dfrac{(x+y)(x-y)}{x}\cdot\dfrac{x(x+y)}{(x+y)}$

$=(x-y)(x+y)$ or x^2-y^2

31. $\dfrac{x^2+2xy+y^2}{x^2-2xy+y^2}\cdot\dfrac{4x-4y}{3x+3y}$

$=\dfrac{(x+y)(x+y)}{(x-y)(x-y)}\cdot\dfrac{4(x-y)}{3(x+y)}$

$=\dfrac{4(x+y)}{3(x-y)}$

33. $\dfrac{x}{7}\div\dfrac{5}{3}=\dfrac{x}{7}\cdot\dfrac{3}{5}=\dfrac{3x}{35}$

35. $\dfrac{3}{x}\div\dfrac{12}{x}=\dfrac{3}{x}\cdot\dfrac{x}{12}=\dfrac{1}{4}$

37. $\dfrac{15}{x}\div\dfrac{3}{2x}=\dfrac{15}{x}\cdot\dfrac{2x}{3}=10$

39. $\dfrac{x+1}{3}\div\dfrac{3x+3}{7}=\dfrac{x+1}{3}\cdot\dfrac{7}{3x+3}$

$=\dfrac{x+1}{3}\cdot\dfrac{7}{3(x+1)}$

$=\dfrac{7}{9}$

41. $\dfrac{7}{x-5}\div\dfrac{28}{3x-15}=\dfrac{7}{x-5}\cdot\dfrac{3x-15}{28}$

$=\dfrac{7}{(x-5)}\cdot\dfrac{3(x-5)}{7\cdot4}$

$=\dfrac{3}{4}$

334

43.
$$\frac{x^2-4}{x} \div \frac{x+2}{x-2} = \frac{x^2-4}{x} \cdot \frac{x-2}{x+2}$$
$$= \frac{(x+2)(x-2)}{x} \cdot \frac{x-2}{x+2}$$
$$= \frac{(x-2)^2}{x}$$

45.
$$\left(y^2-16\right) \div \frac{y^2+3y-4}{y^2+4}$$
$$= \frac{y^2-16}{1} \cdot \frac{y^2+4}{y^2+3y-4}$$
$$= \frac{(y+4)(y-4)}{1} \cdot \frac{y^2+4}{(y+4)(y-1)}$$
$$= \frac{(y-4)\left(y^2+4\right)}{y-1}$$

47.
$$\frac{y^2-y}{15} \div \frac{y-1}{5} = \frac{y^2-y}{15} \cdot \frac{5}{y-1}$$
$$= \frac{y(y-1)}{15} \cdot \frac{5}{(y-1)}$$
$$= \frac{y}{3}$$

49.
$$\frac{4x^2+10}{x-3} \div \frac{6x^2+15}{x^2-9}$$
$$= \frac{4x^2+10}{x-3} \cdot \frac{x^2-9}{6x^2+15}$$
$$= \frac{2\left(2x^2+5\right)}{(x-3)} \cdot \frac{(x+3)(x-3)}{3\left(2x^2+5\right)}$$
$$= \frac{2(x+3)}{3} \quad \text{or} \quad \frac{2x+6}{3}$$

51.
$$\frac{x^2-25}{2x-2} \div \frac{x^2+10x+25}{x^2+4x-5}$$
$$= \frac{x^2-25}{2x-2} \cdot \frac{x^2+4x-5}{x^2+10x+25}$$
$$= \frac{(x+5)(x-5)}{2(x-1)} \cdot \frac{(x+5)(x-1)}{(x+5)(x+5)}$$
$$= \frac{x-5}{2}$$

53.
$$\frac{y^3+y}{y^2-y} \div \frac{y^3-y^2}{y^2-2y+1}$$
$$= \frac{y^3+y}{y^2-y} \cdot \frac{y^2-2y+1}{y^3-y^2}$$
$$= \frac{y\left(y^2+1\right)}{y(y-1)} \cdot \frac{(y-1)(y-1)}{y^2(y-1)}$$
$$= \frac{y^2+1}{y^2}$$

55.
$$\frac{y^2+5y+4}{y^2+12y+32} \div \frac{y^2-12y+35}{y^2+3y-40}$$
$$= \frac{y^2+5y+4}{y^2+12y+32} \cdot \frac{y^2+3y-40}{y^2-12y+35}$$
$$= \frac{(y+4)(y+1)}{(y+4)(y+8)} \cdot \frac{(y+8)(y-5)}{(y-7)(y-5)}$$
$$= \frac{y+1}{y-7}$$

57.
$$\frac{2y^2-128}{y^2+16y+64} \div \frac{y^2-6y-16}{3y^2+30y+48}$$
$$= \frac{2y^2-128}{y^2+16y+64} \cdot \frac{3y^2+30y+48}{y^2-6y-16}$$
$$= \frac{2\left(y^2-64\right)}{(y+8)(y+8)} \cdot \frac{3\left(y^2+10y+16\right)}{(y+2)(y-8)}$$
$$= \frac{2(y+8)(y-8)}{(y+8)(y+8)} \cdot \frac{3(y+2)(y+8)}{(y+2)(y-8)}$$
$$= 6$$

59.
$$\frac{2x+2y}{3} \div \frac{x^2-y^2}{x-y}$$
$$= \frac{2x+2y}{3} \cdot \frac{x-y}{x^2-y^2}$$
$$= \frac{2(x+y)}{3} \cdot \frac{x-y}{(x+y)(x-y)}$$
$$= \frac{2}{3}$$

61. $\dfrac{x^2-y^2}{8x^2-16xy+8y^2} \div \dfrac{4x-4y}{x+y}$

$\qquad = \dfrac{x^2-y^2}{8x^2-16xy+8y^2} \cdot \dfrac{x+y}{4x-4y}$

$\qquad = \dfrac{(x+y)(x-y)}{8\left(x^2-2xy+y^2\right)} \cdot \dfrac{x+y}{4(x-y)}$

$\qquad = \dfrac{(x+y)(x-y)}{8(x-y)(x-y)} \cdot \dfrac{x+y}{4(x-y)}$

$\qquad = \dfrac{(x+y)^2}{32(x-y)^2}$

63. $\dfrac{xy-y^2}{x^2+2x+1} \div \dfrac{2x^2+xy-3y^2}{2x^2+5xy+3y^2}$

$\qquad = \dfrac{xy-y^2}{x^2+2x+1} \cdot \dfrac{2x^2+5xy+3y^2}{2x^2+xy-3y^2}$

$\qquad = \dfrac{y(x-y)}{(x+1)(x+1)} \cdot \dfrac{(2x+3y)(x+y)}{(2x+3y)(x-y)}$

$\qquad = \dfrac{y(x+y)}{(x+1)^2}$

65. $\left(\dfrac{y-2}{y^2-9y+18} \cdot \dfrac{y^2-4y-12}{y+2}\right) \div \dfrac{y^2-4}{y^2+5y+6} = \left(\dfrac{y-2}{y^2-9y+18} \cdot \dfrac{y^2-4y-12}{y+2}\right) \cdot \dfrac{y^2+5y+6}{y^2-4}$

$\qquad = \left(\dfrac{y-2}{(y-6)(y-3)} \cdot \dfrac{(y-6)(y+2)}{y+2}\right) \cdot \dfrac{(y+2)(y+3)}{(y+2)(y-2)} = \left(\dfrac{y-2}{y-3}\right) \cdot \dfrac{y+3}{y-2} = \dfrac{y+3}{y-3}$

67. $\dfrac{3x^2+3x-60}{2x-8} \div \left(\dfrac{30x^2}{x^2-7x+10} \cdot \dfrac{x^3+3x^2-10x}{25x^3}\right)$

$\qquad = \dfrac{3x^2+3x-60}{2x-8} \div \left(\dfrac{30x^2}{(x-2)(x-5)} \cdot \dfrac{x\left(x^2+3x-10\right)}{25x^3}\right)$

$\qquad = \dfrac{3\left(x^2+x-20\right)}{2x-8} \div \left(\dfrac{30x^2}{(x-2)(x-5)} \cdot \dfrac{x(x+5)(x-2)}{25x^3}\right)$

$\qquad = \dfrac{3(x+5)(x-4)}{2(x-4)} \div \dfrac{6(x+5)}{5(x-5)} = \dfrac{3(x+5)(x-4)}{2(x-4)} \cdot \dfrac{5(x-5)}{6(x+5)} = \dfrac{5(x-5)}{4}$

69. $\dfrac{x^2+xz+xy+yz}{x-y} \div \dfrac{x+z}{x+y} = \dfrac{x(x+z)+y(x+z)}{x-y} \cdot \dfrac{x+y}{x+z} = \dfrac{(x+z)(x+y)}{x-y} \cdot \dfrac{x+y}{x+z} = \dfrac{(x+y)^2}{x-y}$

71.
$$\frac{3xy+ay+3xb+ab}{9x^2-a^2}\div\frac{y^3+b^3}{6x-2a}=\frac{3xy+ay+3xb+ab}{9x^2-a^2}\cdot\frac{6x-2a}{y^3+b^3}$$

$$=\frac{y(3x+a)+b(3x+a)}{(3x+a)(3x-a)}\cdot\frac{2(3x-a)}{(y+b)(y^2-by+b^2)}$$

$$=\frac{(3x+a)(y+b)}{(3x+a)(3x-a)}\cdot\frac{2(3x-a)}{(y+b)(y^2-by+b^2)}$$

$$=\frac{2}{y^2-by+b^2}$$

73. $A=l\cdot w$

$$A=\frac{x+1}{x^2+2x}\cdot\frac{x^2-4}{x^2-1}$$

$$=\frac{x+1}{x(x+2)}\cdot\frac{(x+2)(x-2)}{(x+1)(x-1)}$$

$$=\frac{\cancel{x+1}}{x\cancel{(x+2)}}\cdot\frac{\cancel{(x+2)}(x-2)}{\cancel{(x+1)}(x-1)}$$

$$=\frac{x-2}{x(x-1)}\text{ in.}^2$$

75. $A=\dfrac{1}{2}\cdot b\cdot h$

$$A=\frac{1}{2}\cdot\frac{18x}{x^2+3x+2}\cdot\frac{x+1}{3}$$

$$=\frac{1}{2}\cdot\frac{2\cdot3\cdot3x}{(x+2)(x+1)}\cdot\frac{x+1}{3}$$

$$=\frac{1}{\cancel{2}}\cdot\frac{\cancel{2}\cdot\cancel{3}\cdot3x}{(x+2)\cancel{(x+1)}}\cdot\frac{\cancel{x+1}}{\cancel{3}}$$

$$=\frac{3x}{x+2}\text{ in.}^2$$

77. – 79. Answers will vary.

81. makes sense

83. makes sense

85. true

87. false; Changes to make the statement true will vary. A sample change is: The quotient of two rational expressions can be found by inverting the divisor and then multiplying .

89. $-\dfrac{1}{2x-3} \div \dfrac{?}{?} = \dfrac{1}{3}$

The numerator of the unknown rational expression must contain a factor of -3. The denominator of the unknown rational expression must contain a factor of $(2x-3)$. Therefore, the simplest pair of polynomials that will work are -3 in the numerator and $2x-3$ in the denominator, to give the rational expression $\dfrac{-3}{2x-3}$.

Check:

$$-\dfrac{1}{2x-3} \div \dfrac{-3}{2x-3} = -\dfrac{1}{2x-3} \cdot \dfrac{2x-3}{-3} = \dfrac{1}{3}$$

91. The graph coincides.

This verifies that $\dfrac{x^3+x}{3x} \cdot \dfrac{6x}{x+1} = 2x$.

93. The graphs do not coincide.

$$\dfrac{x^2-9}{x+4} \div \dfrac{x-3}{x+4} = \dfrac{x^2-9}{x+4} \cdot \dfrac{x+4}{x-3}$$
$$= \dfrac{(x+3)(x-3)}{(x+4)} \cdot \dfrac{(x+4)}{(x-3)}$$
$$= x+3$$

Change the expression on the right from $(x-3)$ to $(x+3)$.

95. $2x+3 < 3(x-5)$
$2x+3 < 3x-15$
$-x+3 < -15$
$-x < -18$
$x > 18$
$(18, \infty)$

96. $3x^2-15x-42 = 3\left(x^2-5x-14\right)$
$\qquad\qquad\qquad = 3(x-7)(x+2)$

97. $\qquad x(2x+9) = 5$
$\qquad 2x^2+9x = 5$
$\qquad 2x^2+9x-5 = 0$
$\qquad (2x-1)(x+5) = 0$
$\qquad 2x-1=0 \ \text{ or } \ x+5=0$
$\qquad\quad 2x=1 \qquad\qquad x=-5$
$\qquad\qquad x = \dfrac{1}{2}$

The solution set is $\left\{-5, \dfrac{1}{2}\right\}$.

98. $\dfrac{7}{9} - \dfrac{1}{9} = \dfrac{6}{9} = \dfrac{2}{3}$

99. $\dfrac{2x}{3} + \dfrac{x}{3} = \dfrac{3x}{3} = x$

100. $\dfrac{x^2-6x+9}{x^2-9} = \dfrac{(x-3)^2}{(x+3)(x-3)}$
$\qquad\qquad\qquad = \dfrac{(x-3)(x-3)}{(x+3)(x-3)} = \dfrac{x-3}{x+3}$

8.3 Check Points

1. $\dfrac{3x-2}{5} + \dfrac{2x+12}{5} = \dfrac{3x-2+2x+12}{5}$
$\qquad\qquad\qquad\qquad = \dfrac{5x+10}{5}$
$\qquad\qquad\qquad\qquad = \dfrac{\overset{1}{\cancel{5}}(x+2)}{\underset{1}{\cancel{5}}}$
$\qquad\qquad\qquad\qquad = x+2$

2. $\dfrac{x^2}{x^2-25} + \dfrac{25-10x}{x^2-25} = \dfrac{x^2-10x+25}{x^2-25}$
$\qquad\qquad\qquad\qquad\quad = \dfrac{(x-5)^2}{(x+5)(x-5)}$
$\qquad\qquad\qquad\qquad\quad = \dfrac{(x-5)\cancel{(x-5)}}{(x+5)\cancel{(x-5)}}$
$\qquad\qquad\qquad\qquad\quad = \dfrac{x-5}{x+5}$

3. a. $\dfrac{4x+5}{x+7} - \dfrac{x}{x+7} = \dfrac{4x+5-x}{x+7} = \dfrac{3x+5}{x+7}$

b. $\dfrac{3x^2+4x}{x-1} - \dfrac{11x-4}{x-1} = \dfrac{3x^2+4x-(11x-4)}{x-1}$

$\qquad\qquad = \dfrac{3x^2+4x-11x+4}{x-1}$

$\qquad\qquad = \dfrac{3x^2-7x+4}{x-1}$

$\qquad\qquad = \dfrac{(3x-4)(x-1)}{x-1}$

$\qquad\qquad = 3x-4$

4.

$\dfrac{y^2+3y-6}{y^2-5y+4} - \dfrac{4y-4-2y^2}{y^2-5y+4} = \dfrac{y^2+3y-6-(4y-4-2y^2)}{y^2-5y+4}$

$\qquad = \dfrac{y^2+3y-6-4y+4+2y^2}{y^2-5y+4}$

$\qquad = \dfrac{3y^2-y-2}{y^2-5y+4}$

$\qquad = \dfrac{(3y+2)(y-1)}{(y-4)(y-1)}$

$\qquad = \dfrac{3y+2}{y-4}$

5. $\dfrac{x^2}{x-7} + \dfrac{4x+21}{7-x} = \dfrac{x^2}{x-7} + \dfrac{(-1)}{(-1)} \cdot \dfrac{4x+21}{7-x}$

$\qquad\qquad = \dfrac{x^2}{x-7} + \dfrac{-4x-21}{x-7}$

$\qquad\qquad = \dfrac{x^2-4x-21}{x-7}$

$\qquad\qquad = \dfrac{(x+3)(x-7)}{x-7}$

$\qquad\qquad = x+3$

6. $\dfrac{7x-x^2}{x^2-2x-9} - \dfrac{5x-3x^2}{9+2x-x^2}$

$\qquad = \dfrac{7x-x^2}{x^2-2x-9} - \dfrac{3x^2-5x}{x^2-2x-9}$

$\qquad = \dfrac{7x-x^2-(3x^2-5x)}{x^2-2x-9}$

$\qquad = \dfrac{7x-x^2-3x^2+5x}{x^2-2x-9}$

$\qquad = \dfrac{-4x^2+12x}{x^2-2x-9}$

8.3 Exercise Set

1. $\dfrac{7x}{13} + \dfrac{2x}{13} = \dfrac{9x}{13}$

3. $\dfrac{8x}{15} + \dfrac{x}{15} = \dfrac{9x}{15} = \dfrac{3x}{5}$

5. $\dfrac{x-3}{12} + \dfrac{5x+21}{12} = \dfrac{6x+18}{12}$

$\qquad\qquad = \dfrac{6(x+3)}{12}$

$\qquad\qquad = \dfrac{x+3}{2}$

7. $\dfrac{4}{x} + \dfrac{2}{x} = \dfrac{6}{x}$

9. $\dfrac{8}{9x} + \dfrac{13}{9x} = \dfrac{21}{9x} = \dfrac{7}{3x}$

11. $\dfrac{5}{x+3} + \dfrac{4}{x+3} = \dfrac{9}{x+3}$

13. $\dfrac{x}{x-3} + \dfrac{4x+5}{x-3} = \dfrac{5x+5}{x-3}$

15. $\dfrac{4x+1}{6x+5} + \dfrac{8x+9}{6x+5} = \dfrac{12x+10}{6x+5}$

$\qquad\qquad = \dfrac{2(6x+5)}{6x+5} = 2$

17. $\dfrac{y^2+7y}{y^2-5y}+\dfrac{y^2-4y}{y^2-5y}=\dfrac{y^2+7y+y^2-4y}{y^2-5y}$

$\qquad\qquad =\dfrac{2y^2+3y}{y^2-5y}$

$\qquad\qquad =\dfrac{y(2y+3)}{y(y-5)}$

$\qquad\qquad =\dfrac{2y+3}{y-5}$

19. $\dfrac{4y-1}{5y^2}+\dfrac{3y+1}{5y^2}=\dfrac{4y-1+3y+1}{5y^2}$

$\qquad\qquad =\dfrac{7y}{5y^2}=\dfrac{7}{5y}$

21. $\dfrac{x^2-2}{x^2+x-2}+\dfrac{2x-x^2}{x^2+x-2}$

$\qquad =\dfrac{x^2-2+2x-x^2}{x^2+x-2}$

$\qquad =\dfrac{2x-2}{x^2+x-2}=\dfrac{2(x-1)}{(x+2)(x-1)}=\dfrac{2}{x+2}$

23. $\dfrac{x^2-4x}{x^2-x-6}+\dfrac{4x-4}{x^2-x-6}$

$\qquad =\dfrac{x^2-4x+4x-4}{x^2-x-6}$

$\qquad =\dfrac{x^2-4}{x^2-x-6}=\dfrac{(x+2)(x-2)}{(x-3)(x+2)}=\dfrac{x-2}{x-3}$

25. $\dfrac{3x}{5x-4}-\dfrac{4}{5x-4}=\dfrac{3x-4}{5x-4}$

27. $\dfrac{4x}{4x-3}-\dfrac{3}{4x-3}=\dfrac{4x-3}{4x-3}=1$

29. $\dfrac{14y}{7y+2}-\dfrac{7y-2}{7y+2}=\dfrac{14y-(7y-2)}{7y+2}$

$\qquad\qquad =\dfrac{14y-7y+2}{7y+2}$

$\qquad\qquad =\dfrac{7y+2}{7y+2}=1$

31. $\dfrac{3x+1}{4x-2}-\dfrac{x+1}{4x-2}=\dfrac{(3x+1)-(x+1)}{4x-2}$

$\qquad\qquad =\dfrac{3x+1-x-1}{4x-2}$

$\qquad\qquad =\dfrac{2x}{4x-2}$

$\qquad\qquad =\dfrac{2x}{2(2x-1)}$

$\qquad\qquad =\dfrac{x}{2x-1}$

33. $\dfrac{3y^2-1}{3y^3}-\dfrac{6y^2-1}{3y^3}$

$\qquad =\dfrac{(3y^2-1)-(6y^2-1)}{3y^3}$

$\qquad =\dfrac{3y^2-1-6y^2+1}{3y^3}=\dfrac{-3y^2}{3y^3}=-\dfrac{1}{y}$

35. $\dfrac{4y^2+5}{9y^2-64}-\dfrac{y^2-y+29}{9y^2-64}$

$\qquad =\dfrac{(4y^2+5)-(y^2-y+29)}{9y^2-64}$

$\qquad =\dfrac{4y^2+5-y^2+y-29}{9y^2-64}$

$\qquad =\dfrac{3y^2+y-24}{9y^2-64}$

$\qquad =\dfrac{(3y-8)(y+3)}{(3y+8)(3y-8)}=\dfrac{y+3}{3y+8}$

37. $\dfrac{6y^2+y}{2y^2-9y+9}-\dfrac{2y+9}{2y^2-9y+9}-\dfrac{4y-3}{2y^2-9y+9}$

$=\dfrac{\left(6y^2+y\right)-(2y+9)-(4y-3)}{2y^2-9y+9}$

$=\dfrac{6y^2+y-2y-9-4y+3}{2y^2-9y+9}$

$=\dfrac{6y^2-5y-6}{2y^2-9y+9}$

$=\dfrac{(2y-3)(3y+2)}{(2y-3)(y-3)}$

$=\dfrac{3y+2}{y-3}$

39. $\dfrac{4}{x-3}+\dfrac{2}{3-x}=\dfrac{4}{x-3}+\dfrac{(-1)}{(-1)}\cdot\dfrac{2}{3-x}$

$=\dfrac{4}{x-3}+\dfrac{-2}{x-3}$

$=\dfrac{2}{x-3}$

41. $\dfrac{6x+7}{x-6}+\dfrac{3x}{6-x}=\dfrac{6x+7}{x-6}+\dfrac{(-1)}{(-1)}\cdot\dfrac{3x}{6-x}$

$=\dfrac{6x+7}{x-6}+\dfrac{-3x}{x-6}$

$=\dfrac{3x+7}{x-6}$

43. $\dfrac{5x-2}{3x-4}+\dfrac{2x-3}{4-3x}=\dfrac{5x-2}{3x-4}+\dfrac{(-1)}{(-1)}\cdot\dfrac{2x-3}{4-3x}$

$=\dfrac{5x-2}{3x-4}+\dfrac{-2x+3}{3x-4}$

$=\dfrac{5x-2-2x+3}{3x-4}$

$=\dfrac{3x+1}{3x-4}$

45. $\dfrac{x^2}{x-2}+\dfrac{4}{2-x}=\dfrac{x^2}{x-2}+\dfrac{(-1)}{(-1)}\cdot\dfrac{4}{2-x}$

$=\dfrac{x^2}{x-2}+\dfrac{-4}{x-2}$

$=\dfrac{x^2-4}{x-2}$

$=\dfrac{(x+2)(x-2)}{x-2}$

$=x+2$

47. $\dfrac{y-3}{y^2-25}+\dfrac{y-3}{25-y^2}$

$=\dfrac{y-3}{y^2-25}+\dfrac{(-1)}{(-1)}\cdot\dfrac{y-3}{25-y^2}$

$=\dfrac{y-3}{y^2-25}+\dfrac{-y+3}{y^2-25}$

$=\dfrac{y-3-y+3}{y^2-25}=\dfrac{0}{y^2-25}=0$

49. $\dfrac{6}{x-1}-\dfrac{5}{1-x}=\dfrac{6}{x-1}-\dfrac{(-1)}{(-1)}\cdot\dfrac{5}{1-x}$

$=\dfrac{6}{x-1}-\dfrac{-5}{x-1}$

$=\dfrac{6+5}{x-1}=\dfrac{11}{x-1}$

51. $\dfrac{10}{x+3}-\dfrac{2}{-x-3}=\dfrac{10}{x+3}-\dfrac{(-1)}{(-1)}\cdot\dfrac{2}{-x-3}$

$=\dfrac{10}{x+3}-\dfrac{-2}{x+3}$

$=\dfrac{10+2}{x+3}=\dfrac{12}{x+3}$

53. $\dfrac{y}{y-1}-\dfrac{1}{1-y}=\dfrac{y}{y-1}-\dfrac{(-1)}{(-1)}\cdot\dfrac{1}{1-y}$

$=\dfrac{y}{y-1}-\dfrac{-1}{y-1}$

$=\dfrac{y+1}{y-1}$

55. $\dfrac{3-x}{x-7} - \dfrac{2x-5}{7-x} = \dfrac{3-x}{x-7} - \dfrac{(-1)}{(-1)} \cdot \dfrac{2x-5}{7-x}$

$\qquad = \dfrac{3-x}{x-7} - \dfrac{-2x+5}{x-7}$

$\qquad = \dfrac{(3-x)-(-2x+5)}{x-7}$

$\qquad = \dfrac{3-x+2x-5}{x-7}$

$\qquad = \dfrac{x-2}{x-7}$

57. $\dfrac{x-2}{x^2-25} - \dfrac{x-2}{25-x^2}$

$\qquad = \dfrac{x-2}{x^2-25} - \dfrac{(-1)}{(-1)} \cdot \dfrac{x-2}{25-x^2}$

$\qquad = \dfrac{x-2}{x^2-25} - \dfrac{-x+2}{x^2-25}$

$\qquad = \dfrac{(x-2)-(-x+2)}{x^2-25}$

$\qquad = \dfrac{x-2+x-2}{x^2-25} = \dfrac{2x-4}{x^2-25}$

59. $\dfrac{x}{x-y} + \dfrac{y}{y-x} = \dfrac{x}{x-y} + \dfrac{(-1)}{(-1)} \cdot \dfrac{y}{y-x}$

$\qquad = \dfrac{x}{x-y} + \dfrac{-y}{x-y}$

$\qquad = \dfrac{x-y}{x-y} = 1$

61. $\dfrac{2x}{x^2-y^2} + \dfrac{2y}{y^2-x^2}$

$\qquad = \dfrac{2x}{x^2-y^2} + \dfrac{(-1)}{(-1)} \cdot \dfrac{2y}{y^2-x^2}$

$\qquad = \dfrac{2x}{x^2-y^2} + \dfrac{-2y}{x^2-y^2}$

$\qquad = \dfrac{2x-2y}{x^2-y^2} = \dfrac{2(x-y)}{(x+y)(x-y)} = \dfrac{2}{x+y}$

63. $\dfrac{x^2-2}{x^2+6x-7} + \dfrac{19-4x}{7-6x-x^2}$

$\qquad = \dfrac{x^2-2}{x^2+6x-7} + \dfrac{(-1)}{(-1)} \cdot \dfrac{19-4x}{7-6x-x^2}$

$\qquad = \dfrac{x^2-2}{x^2+6x-7} + \dfrac{-19+4x}{-7+6x+x^2}$

$\qquad = \dfrac{x^2-2}{x^2+6x-7} + \dfrac{-19+4x}{x^2+6x-7}$

$\qquad = \dfrac{x^2-2-19+4x}{x^2+6x-7}$

$\qquad = \dfrac{x^2+4x-21}{x^2+6x-7}$

$\qquad = \dfrac{(x+7)(x-3)}{(x+7)(x-1)} = \dfrac{x-3}{x-1}$

65.

$\dfrac{6b^2-10b}{16b^2-48b+27} + \dfrac{7b^2-20b}{16b^2-48b+27} - \dfrac{6b-3b^2}{16b^2-48b+27}$

$\qquad = \dfrac{6b^2-10b+7b^2-20b-6b+3b^2}{16b^2-48b+27}$

$\qquad = \dfrac{16b^2-36b}{16b^2-48b+27} = \dfrac{4b(4b-9)}{(4b-9)(4b-3)}$

$\qquad = \dfrac{4b}{4b-3}$

67. $\dfrac{2y}{y-5} - \left(\dfrac{2}{y-5} + \dfrac{y-2}{y-5} \right)$

$\qquad = \dfrac{2y}{y-5} - \left(\dfrac{2+y-2}{y-5} \right) = \dfrac{2y}{y-5} - \dfrac{y}{y-5}$

$\qquad = \dfrac{y}{y-5}$

69. $\dfrac{b}{ac+ad-bc-bd}-\dfrac{a}{ac+ad-bc-bd}$

$=\dfrac{b-a}{ac+ad-bc-bd}$

$=\dfrac{b-a}{a(c+d)-b(c+d)}$

$=\dfrac{b-a}{(c+d)(a-b)}=\dfrac{(-1)}{(-1)}\cdot\dfrac{b-a}{(c+d)(a-b)}$

$=\dfrac{a-b}{-(c+d)(a-b)}=\dfrac{-1}{c+d}\ \text{ or }\ -\dfrac{1}{c+d}$

71. $\dfrac{(y-3)(y+2)}{(y+1)(y-4)}-\dfrac{(y+2)(y+3)}{(y+1)(4-y)}-\dfrac{(y+5)(y-1)}{(y+1)(4-y)}=\dfrac{y^2-y-6}{(y+1)(y-4)}-\dfrac{y^2+5y+6}{(y+1)(4-y)}-\dfrac{y^2+4y-5}{(y+1)(4-y)}$

$=\dfrac{y^2-y-6}{(y+1)(y-4)}-\dfrac{(-1)}{(-1)}\cdot\dfrac{y^2+5y+6}{(y+1)(4-y)}-\dfrac{(-1)}{(-1)}\cdot\dfrac{y^2+4y-5}{(y+1)(4-y)}$

$=\dfrac{y^2-y-6}{(y+1)(y-4)}+\dfrac{y^2+5y+6}{(y+1)(y-4)}+\dfrac{y^2+4y-5}{(y+1)(y-4)}=\dfrac{y^2-y-6+y^2+5y+6+y^2+4y-5}{(y+1)(y-4)}$

$=\dfrac{3y^2+8y-5}{(y+1)(y-4)}$

73. a. $\dfrac{L+60W}{L}-\dfrac{L-40W}{L}$

$=\dfrac{(L+60W)-(L-40W)}{L}$

$=\dfrac{L+60W-L+40W}{L}$

$=\dfrac{100W}{L}$

b. $\dfrac{100W}{L}$; $W=5, L=6$

$\dfrac{100W}{L}=\dfrac{100\cdot5}{6}\approx 83.3$

Since this value is over 80, the skull is round.

75. $P=2L+2W$

$=2\left(\dfrac{5x+10}{x+3}\right)+2\left(\dfrac{5}{x+3}\right)$

$=\dfrac{10x+20}{x+3}+\dfrac{10}{x+3}$

$=\dfrac{10x+30}{x+3}=\dfrac{10(x+3)}{x+3}=10$

The perimeter is 10 meters.

77. – 79. Answers will vary.

81. does not make sense; Explanations will vary.

Sample explanation: $\dfrac{3x+1}{4}+\dfrac{x+2}{4}=\dfrac{4x+3}{4}$ and

$4x+3$ is not divisible by 4.

83. makes sense

85. false; Changes to make the statement true will vary. A sample change is: You do not add the common denominators. You just keep the common denominator in your answer.

87. false; Changes to make the statement true will vary. A sample change is: Some such rational expressions cannot be simplified.

89. $\left(\dfrac{3x-1}{x^2+5x-6}-\dfrac{2x-7}{x^2+5x-6}\right)\div\dfrac{x+2}{x^2-1}$

$=\left(\dfrac{(3x-1)-(2x-7)}{x^2+5x-6}\right)\div\dfrac{x+2}{x^2-1}$

$=\dfrac{3x-1-2x+7}{x^2+5x-6}\div\dfrac{x+2}{x^2-1}$

$=\dfrac{x+6}{x^2+5x-6}\div\dfrac{x+2}{x^2-1}$

$=\dfrac{x+6}{x^2+5x-6}\cdot\dfrac{x^2-1}{x+2}$

$=\dfrac{(x+6)}{(x+6)(x-1)}\cdot\dfrac{(x+1)(x-1)}{(x+2)}$

$=\dfrac{x+1}{x+2}$

91. $\dfrac{2x}{x+3}+\dfrac{?}{x+3}=\dfrac{4x+1}{x+3}$

The sum of numerators on the left side must be $4x+1$, so the missing expression is $2x+1$.

Check:

$\dfrac{2x}{x+3}+\dfrac{2x+1}{x+3}=\dfrac{2x+2x+1}{x+3}$

$=\dfrac{4x+1}{x+3}$

93. $\dfrac{6}{x-2}+\dfrac{?}{2-x}=\dfrac{13}{x-2}$

$\dfrac{6}{x-2}+\dfrac{(-1)}{(-1)}\cdot\dfrac{?}{2-x}=\dfrac{13}{x-2}$

$\dfrac{6}{x-2}+\dfrac{(-1)?}{x-2}=\dfrac{13}{x-2}$

Since $6+7=13$, the opposite of the missing expression must be 7, so the missing expression is -7.

Check:

$\dfrac{6}{x-2}+\dfrac{-7}{2-x}=\dfrac{6}{x-2}+\dfrac{(-1)\cdot-7}{(-1)(2-x)}$

$=\dfrac{6}{x-2}+\dfrac{7}{x-2}=\dfrac{13}{x-2}$

95. $\dfrac{3x}{x-5}+\dfrac{?}{5-x}=\dfrac{7x+1}{x-5}$

$\dfrac{3x}{x-5}+\dfrac{(-1)}{(-1)}\cdot\dfrac{?}{5-x}=\dfrac{7x+1}{x-5}$

$\dfrac{3x}{x-5}+\dfrac{(-1)?}{x-5}=\dfrac{7x+1}{x-5}$

Since $3x+(4x+1)=7x+1$, the opposite of the missing expression must be $4x+1$, so the missing expression is $-4x-1$.

Check:

$\dfrac{3x}{x-5}+\dfrac{-4x-1}{5-x}=\dfrac{3x}{x-5}+\dfrac{4x+1}{x-5}$

$=\dfrac{7x+1}{x-5}$

97. The graphs do not coincide.

$$\frac{x^2+4x+3}{x+2}-\frac{5x+9}{x+2}$$

$$=\frac{\left(x^2+4x+3\right)-\left(5x+9\right)}{x+2}$$

$$=\frac{x^2+4x+3-5x-9}{x+2}$$

$$=\frac{x^2-x-6}{x+2}$$

$$=\frac{(x+2)(x-3)}{x+2}$$

$$=x-3$$

Change $x-2$ to $x-3$.

99. $\dfrac{13}{15}-\dfrac{8}{45}=\dfrac{13}{15}\cdot\dfrac{3}{3}-\dfrac{8}{45}$

$$=\frac{39}{45}-\frac{8}{45}=\frac{31}{45}$$

100. $81x^4-1=\left(9x^2+1\right)\left(9x^2-1\right)$

$$=\left(9x^2+1\right)(3x+1)(3x-1)$$

101.

$$\begin{array}{r} 3x^2-7x-5 \\ x+3\overline{)3x^3+2x^2-26x-15} \\ \underline{3x^3+9x^2} \\ -7x^2-26x \\ \underline{-7x^2-21x} \\ -5x-15 \\ \underline{-5x-15} \\ 0 \end{array}$$

$$\frac{3x^3+2x^2-26x-15}{x+3}=3x^2-7x-5$$

102. $\dfrac{1}{2}+\dfrac{2}{3}=\dfrac{3}{6}+\dfrac{4}{6}=\dfrac{7}{6}$

103. $\dfrac{1}{8}-\dfrac{5}{6}=\dfrac{3}{24}-\dfrac{20}{24}=-\dfrac{17}{24}$

104. $\dfrac{(y+2)y-2\cdot4}{4y(y+4)}=\dfrac{y^2+2y-8}{4y(y+4)}$

$$=\frac{(y+4)(y-2)}{4y(y+4)}$$

$$=\frac{y-2}{4y}$$

8.4 Check Points

1. $\dfrac{3}{10x^2}$ and $\dfrac{7}{15x}$

$$10x^2=2\cdot5x^2$$

$$15x=3\cdot5x$$

$$\text{LCD}=2\cdot3\cdot5\cdot x^2=30x^2$$

2. $\dfrac{2}{x+3}$ and $\dfrac{4}{x-3}$

$$x+3=1(x+3)$$

$$x-3=1(x-3)$$

$$\text{LCD}=(x+3)(x-3)$$

3. $\dfrac{9}{7x^2+28x}$ and $\dfrac{11}{x^2+8x+16}$

$$7x^2+28x=7x(x+4)$$

$$x^2+8x+16=(x+4)^2$$

$$\text{LCD}=7x(x+4)^2$$

4. $\dfrac{3}{10x^2}+\dfrac{7}{15x}$

$$\text{LCD}=30x^2$$

$$\frac{3}{10x^2}+\frac{7}{15x}=\frac{3}{3}\cdot\frac{3}{10x^2}+\frac{2x}{2x}\cdot\frac{7}{15x}$$

$$=\frac{9}{30x^2}+\frac{14x}{30x^2}$$

$$=\frac{9+14x}{30x^2}$$

5. $\dfrac{2}{x+3}+\dfrac{4}{x-3}$

LCD $=(x+3)(x-3)$

$$\dfrac{2}{x+3}+\dfrac{4}{x-3}=\dfrac{x-3}{x-3}\cdot\dfrac{2}{x+3}+\dfrac{x+3}{x+3}\cdot\dfrac{4}{x-3}$$

$$=\dfrac{2x-6}{(x+3)(x-3)}+\dfrac{4x+12}{(x+3)(x-3)}$$

$$=\dfrac{2x-6+4x+12}{(x+3)(x-3)}$$

$$=\dfrac{6x+6}{(x+3)(x-3)}$$

6. $\dfrac{x}{x+5}-1$

LCD $=x+5$

$$\dfrac{x}{x+5}-1=\dfrac{x}{x+5}-\dfrac{x+5}{x+5}$$

$$=\dfrac{x-(x+5)}{x+5}$$

$$=\dfrac{x-x-5}{x+5}$$

$$=\dfrac{-5}{x+5}\ \text{ or }\ -\dfrac{5}{x+5}$$

7. $\dfrac{5}{y^2-5y}-\dfrac{y}{5y-25}=\dfrac{5}{y(y-5)}-\dfrac{y}{5(y-5)}$

LCD $=5y(y-5)$

$$\dfrac{5}{y^2-5y}-\dfrac{y}{5y-25}=\dfrac{5}{y(y-5)}-\dfrac{y}{5(y-5)}$$

$$=\dfrac{5}{5}\cdot\dfrac{5}{y(y-5)}-\dfrac{y}{y}\cdot\dfrac{y}{5(y-5)}$$

$$=\dfrac{25}{5y(y-5)}-\dfrac{y^2}{5y(y-5)}$$

$$=\dfrac{25-y^2}{5y(y-5)}$$

$$=\dfrac{(5+y)(5-y)}{5y(y-5)}$$

$$=\dfrac{(5+y)\overset{-1}{\cancel{(5-y)}}}{5y\underset{1}{\cancel{(y-5)}}}$$

$$=-\dfrac{5+y}{5y}$$

8. $\dfrac{4x}{x^2-25}+\dfrac{3}{5-x}=\dfrac{4x}{(x+5)(x-5)}+\dfrac{3}{5-x}$

LCD $=(x+5)(x-5)$

$$\dfrac{4x}{x^2-25}+\dfrac{3}{5-x}=\dfrac{4x}{(x+5)(x-5)}+\dfrac{3}{5-x}$$

$$=\dfrac{4x}{(x+5)(x-5)}+\dfrac{-1(x+5)}{-1(x+5)}\cdot\dfrac{3}{5-x}$$

$$=\dfrac{4x}{(x+5)(x-5)}+\dfrac{-1(x+5)\cdot3}{(x+5)(x-5)}$$

$$=\dfrac{4x}{(x+5)(x-5)}+\dfrac{-3x-15}{(x+5)(x-5)}$$

$$=\dfrac{4x-3x-15}{(x+5)(x-5)}$$

$$=\dfrac{x-15}{(x+5)(x-5)}$$

8.4 Exercise Set

1. $\dfrac{7}{15x^2}$ and $\dfrac{13}{24x}$

$15x^2=3\cdot5x^2$

$24x=2^3\cdot3x$

LCD $=2^3\cdot3\cdot5x^2=120x^2$

3. $\dfrac{8}{15x^2}$ and $\dfrac{5}{6x^5}$

$15x^2=3\cdot5x^2$

$6x^5=2\cdot3x^5$

LCD $=2\cdot3\cdot5\cdot x^5=30x^5$

5. $\dfrac{4}{x-3}$ and $\dfrac{7}{x+1}$

LCD $=(x-3)(x+1)$

7. $\dfrac{5}{7(y+2)}$ and $\dfrac{10}{y}$

LCD $=7y(y+2)$

9. $\dfrac{17}{x+4}$ and $\dfrac{18}{x^2-16}$

$x+4=1(x+4)$

$x^2-16=(x+4)(x-4)$

LCD $=(x+4)(x-4)$

11. $\dfrac{8}{y^2-9}$ and $\dfrac{14}{y(y+3)}$

$$y^2-9=(y+3)(y-3)$$
$$y(y+3)=y(y+3)$$
$$\text{LCD}=y(y+3)(y-3)$$

13. $\dfrac{7}{y^2-1}$ and $\dfrac{y}{y^2-2y+1}$

$$y^2-1=(y+1)(y-1)$$
$$y^2-2y+1=(y-1)(y-1)$$
$$\text{LCD}=(y+1)(y-1)(y-1)$$

15. $\dfrac{3}{x^2-x-20}$ and $\dfrac{x}{2x^2+7x-4}$

$$x^2-x-20=(x-5)(x+4)$$
$$2x^2+7x-4=(2x-1)(x+4)$$
$$\text{LCD}=(x-5)(x+4)(2x-1)$$

17. $\dfrac{3}{x}+\dfrac{5}{x^2}$

$$\text{LCD}=x^2$$
$$\frac{3}{x}+\frac{5}{x^2}=\frac{3}{x}\cdot\frac{x}{x}+\frac{5}{x^2}=\frac{3x+5}{x^2}$$

19. $\dfrac{2}{9x}+\dfrac{11}{6x}$

$$\text{LCD}=18x$$
$$\frac{2}{9x}+\frac{11}{6x}=\frac{2}{9x}\cdot\frac{2}{2}+\frac{11}{6x}\cdot\frac{3}{3}$$
$$=\frac{4}{18x}+\frac{33}{18x}=\frac{37}{18x}$$

21. $\dfrac{4}{x}+\dfrac{7}{2x^2}$

$$\text{LCD}=2x^2$$
$$\frac{4}{x}+\frac{7}{2x^2}=\frac{4}{x}\cdot\frac{2x}{2x}+\frac{7}{2x^2}=\frac{8x}{2x^2}+\frac{7}{2x^2}$$
$$=\frac{8x+7}{2x^2}$$

23. $6+\dfrac{1}{x}$

$$\text{LCD}=x$$
$$6+\frac{1}{x}=\frac{6}{1}\cdot\frac{x}{x}+\frac{1}{x}=\frac{6x}{x}+\frac{1}{x}=\frac{6x+1}{x}$$

25. $\dfrac{2}{x}+9$

$$\text{LCD}=x$$
$$\frac{2}{x}+9=\frac{2}{x}+\frac{9}{1}\cdot\frac{x}{x}=\frac{2}{x}+\frac{9x}{x}=\frac{2+9x}{x}$$

27. $\dfrac{x-1}{6}+\dfrac{x+2}{3}$

$$\text{LCD}=6$$
$$\frac{x-1}{6}+\frac{x+2}{3}=\frac{x-1}{6}+\frac{(x+2)}{3}\cdot\frac{2}{2}$$
$$=\frac{x-1}{6}+\frac{2x+4}{6}=\frac{3x+3}{6}=\frac{3(x+1)}{6}$$
$$=\frac{x+1}{2}$$

29. $\dfrac{4}{x}+\dfrac{3}{x-5}$

$$\text{LCD}=x(x-5)$$
$$\frac{4}{x}+\frac{3}{x-5}=\frac{4(x-5)}{x(x-5)}+\frac{3}{x-5}\cdot\frac{x}{x}$$
$$=\frac{4(x-5)}{x(x-5)}+\frac{3x}{x(x-5)}$$
$$=\frac{4x-20+3x}{x(x-5)}$$
$$=\frac{7x-20}{x(x-5)}$$

31. $\dfrac{2}{x-1}+\dfrac{3}{x+2}$

$$\text{LCD}=(x-1)(x+2)$$
$$\frac{2}{x-1}+\frac{3}{x+2}$$
$$=\frac{2(x+2)}{(x-1)(x+2)}+\frac{3(x-1)}{(x-1)(x+2)}$$
$$=\frac{2x+4+3x-3}{(x-1)(x+2)}$$
$$=\frac{5x+1}{(x-1)(x+2)}$$

33. $\dfrac{2}{y+5}+\dfrac{3}{4y}$

LCD $= 4y(y+5)$

$$\dfrac{2}{y+5}+\dfrac{3}{4y}=\dfrac{2(4y)}{(4y)(y+5)}+\dfrac{3(y+5)}{4y(y+5)}$$

$$=\dfrac{2(4y)+3(y+5)}{4y(y+5)}$$

$$=\dfrac{8y+3y+15}{4y(y+5)}$$

$$=\dfrac{11y+15}{4y(y+5)}$$

35. $\dfrac{x}{x+7}-1$

LCD $= x+7$

$$\dfrac{x}{x+7}-1=\dfrac{x}{x+7}-\dfrac{x+7}{x+7}$$

$$=\dfrac{x-(x+7)}{x+7}$$

$$=\dfrac{x-x-7}{x+7}$$

$$=\dfrac{-7}{x+7}\ \text{or}\ -\dfrac{7}{x+7}$$

37. $\dfrac{7}{x+5}-\dfrac{4}{x-5}$

LCD $= (x+5)(x-5)$

$$\dfrac{7}{x+5}-\dfrac{4}{x-5}$$

$$=\dfrac{7(x-5)}{(x+5)(x-5)}-\dfrac{4(x+5)}{(x+5)(x-5)}$$

$$=\dfrac{7(x-5)-4(x+5)}{(x+5)(x-5)}$$

$$=\dfrac{7x-35-4x-20}{(x+5)(x-5)}$$

$$=\dfrac{3x-55}{(x+5)(x-5)}$$

39. $\dfrac{2x}{x^2-16}+\dfrac{x}{x-4}$

$x^2-16=(x+4)(x-4)$

$x-4=1(x-4)$

LCD $= (x+4)(x-4)$

$$\dfrac{2x}{x^2-16}+\dfrac{x}{x-4}$$

$$=\dfrac{2x}{(x+4)(x-4)}+\dfrac{x}{x-4}$$

$$=\dfrac{2x}{(x+4)(x-4)}+\dfrac{x(x+4)}{(x+4)(x-4)}$$

$$=\dfrac{2x+x(x+4)}{(x+4)(x-4)}$$

$$=\dfrac{2x+x^2+4x}{(x+4)(x-4)}$$

$$=\dfrac{x^2+6x}{(x+4)(x-4)}$$

41. $\dfrac{5y}{y^2-9}-\dfrac{4}{y+3}$

LCD $= (y+3)(y-3)$

$$\dfrac{5y}{y^2-9}-\dfrac{4}{y+3}$$

$$=\dfrac{5y}{(y+3)(y-3)}-\dfrac{4}{y+3}$$

$$=\dfrac{5y}{(y+3)(y-3)}-\dfrac{4(y-3)}{(y+3)(y-3)}$$

$$=\dfrac{5y-4(y-3)}{(y+3)(y-3)}$$

$$=\dfrac{5y-4y+12}{(y+3)(y-3)}$$

$$=\dfrac{y+12}{(y+3)(y-3)}$$

43. $\dfrac{7}{x-1} - \dfrac{3}{(x-1)(x-1)}$

LCD $= (x-1)(x-1)$

$\dfrac{7}{x-1} - \dfrac{3}{(x-1)(x-1)}$

$= \dfrac{7(x-1)}{(x-1)(x-1)} - \dfrac{3}{(x-1)(x-1)}$

$= \dfrac{7x-7-3}{(x-1)(x-1)}$

$= \dfrac{7x-10}{(x-1)(x-1)}$ or $\dfrac{7x-10}{(x-1)^2}$

45. $\dfrac{3y}{4y-20} + \dfrac{9y}{6y-30}$

$4y-20 = 4(y-5)$

$6y-30 = 6(y-5)$

LCD $= 12(y-5)$

$\dfrac{3y}{4y-20} + \dfrac{9y}{6y-30}$

$= \dfrac{4y}{4(y-5)} + \dfrac{9y}{6(y-5)}$

$= \dfrac{4y}{4(y-5)} \cdot \dfrac{3}{3} + \dfrac{9y}{6(y-5)} \cdot \dfrac{2}{2}$

$= \dfrac{12y}{12(y-5)} + \dfrac{18y}{12(y-5)}$

$= \dfrac{9y+18y}{12(y-5)} = \dfrac{27y}{12(y-5)}$

$= \dfrac{9y}{4(y-5)}$

47. $\dfrac{y+4}{y} - \dfrac{y}{y+4}$

LCD $= y(y+4)$

$\dfrac{y+4}{y} - \dfrac{y}{y+4}$

$= \dfrac{(y+4)(y+4)}{y(y+4)} - \dfrac{y \cdot y}{y(y+4)}$

$= \dfrac{y^2+8y+16-y^2}{y(y+4)}$

$= \dfrac{8y+16}{y(y+4)}$

49. $\dfrac{2x+9}{x^2-7x+12} = \dfrac{2}{x-3}$

$x^2-7x+12 = (x-3)(x-4)$

$x-3 = 1(x-3)$

LCD $= (x-3)(x-4)$

$\dfrac{2x+9}{x^2-7x+12} - \dfrac{2}{x-3}$

$= \dfrac{2x+9}{(x-3)(x-4)} - \dfrac{2}{x-3}$

$= \dfrac{2x+9}{(x-3)(x-4)} - \dfrac{2(x-4)}{(x-3)(x-4)}$

$= \dfrac{2x+9-2(x-4)}{(x-3)(x-4)}$

$= \dfrac{2x+9-2x+8}{(x-3)(x-4)}$

$= \dfrac{17}{(x-3)(x-4)}$

51. $\dfrac{3}{x^2-1} + \dfrac{4}{(x+1)^2}$

$x^2-1 = (x+1)(x-1)$

$(x+1)^2 = (x+1)(x+1)$

LCD $= (x+1)(x+1)(x-1)$

$\dfrac{3}{x^2-1} + \dfrac{4}{(x+1)^2}$

$= \dfrac{3}{(x+1)(x-1)} + \dfrac{4}{(x+1)(x+1)}$

$= \dfrac{3(x+1)}{(x+1)(x+1)(x-1)} + \dfrac{4(x-1)}{(x+1)(x+1)(x-1)}$

$= \dfrac{3(x+1)+4(x-1)}{(x+1)(x+1)(x-1)}$

$= \dfrac{3x+3+4x-4}{(x+1)(x+1)(x-1)}$

$= \dfrac{7x-1}{(x+1)(x+1)(x-1)}$

53. $\dfrac{3x}{x^2+3x-10}-\dfrac{2x}{x^2+x-6}$

$x^2+3x-10=(x-2)(x+5)$

$x^2+x-6=(x+3)(x-2)$

$\text{LCD}=(x+3)(x-2)(x+5)$

$\dfrac{3x}{x^2+3x-10}-\dfrac{2x}{x^2+x-6}$

$=\dfrac{3x}{(x-2)(x+5)}-\dfrac{2x}{(x+3)(x-2)}$

$=\dfrac{3x(x+3)}{(x+3)(x-2)(x+5)}-\dfrac{2x(x+5)}{(x+3)(x-2)(x+5)}$

$=\dfrac{3x(x+3)-2x(x+5)}{(x+3)(x-2)(x+5)}$

$=\dfrac{3x^2+9x-2x^2-10x}{(x+3)(x-2)(x+5)}$

$=\dfrac{x^2-x}{(x+3)(x-2)(x+5)}$

55. $\dfrac{y}{y^2+2y+1}+\dfrac{4}{y^2+5y+4}$

$y^2+2y+1=(y+1)(y+1)$

$y^2+5y+4=(y+4)(y+1)$

$\text{LCD}=(y+4)(y+1)(y+1)$

$\dfrac{y}{y^2+2y+1}+\dfrac{4}{y^2+5y+4}$

$=\dfrac{y}{(y+1)(y+1)}+\dfrac{4}{(y+4)(y+1)}$

$=\dfrac{y(y+4)}{(y+4)(y+1)(y+1)}+\dfrac{4(y+1)}{(y+4)(y+1)(y+1)}$

$=\dfrac{y(y+4)+4(y+1)}{(y+4)(y+1)(y+1)}$

$=\dfrac{y^2+4y+4y+4}{(y+4)(y+1)(y+1)}$

$=\dfrac{y^2+8y+4}{(y+4)(y+1)(y+1)}$

57. $\dfrac{x-5}{x+3}+\dfrac{x+3}{x-5}$

$\text{LCD}=(x+3)(x-5)$

$\dfrac{x-5}{x+3}+\dfrac{x+3}{x-5}$

$=\dfrac{(x-5)(x-5)}{(x+3)(x-5)}+\dfrac{(x+3)(x+3)}{(x-5)(x+3)}$

$=\dfrac{(x-5)(x-5)+(x+3)(x+3)}{(x+3)(x-5)}$

$=\dfrac{\left(x^2-10x+25\right)+\left(x^2+6x+9\right)}{(x+3)(x-5)}$

$=\dfrac{2x^2-4x+34}{(x+3)(x-5)}$

59. $\dfrac{5}{2y^2-2y}-\dfrac{3}{2y-2}$

$2y^2-2y=2y(y-1)$

$2y-2=2(y-1)$

$\text{LCD}=2y(y-1)$

$\dfrac{5}{2y^2-2y}-\dfrac{3}{2y-2}$

$=\dfrac{5}{2y(y-1)}-\dfrac{3}{2(y-1)}$

$=\dfrac{5}{2y(y-1)}-\dfrac{3\cdot y}{2y(y-1)}$

$=\dfrac{5-3y}{2y(y-1)}$

61. $\dfrac{4x+3}{x^2-9} - \dfrac{x+1}{x-3}$

$\text{LCD} = (x+3)(x-3)$

$\dfrac{4x+3}{x^2-9} - \dfrac{x+1}{x-3}$

$= \dfrac{4x+3}{(x+3)(x-3)} - \dfrac{(x+1)(x+3)}{(x+3)(x-3)}$

$= \dfrac{(4x+3)-(x+1)(x+3)}{(x+3)(x-3)}$

$= \dfrac{(4x+3)-\left(x^2+4x+3\right)}{(x+3)(x-3)}$

$= \dfrac{4x+3-x^2-4x-3}{(x+3)(x-3)}$

$= \dfrac{-x^2}{(x+3)(x-3)} = -\dfrac{x^2}{(x+3)(x-3)}$

63. $\dfrac{y^2-39}{y^2+3y-10} - \dfrac{y-7}{y-2}$

$y^2+3y-10 = (y-2)(y+5)$

$y-2 = 1(y-2)$

$\text{LCD} = (y-2)(y+5)$

$\dfrac{y^2-39}{y^2+3y-10} - \dfrac{y-7}{y-2}$

$= \dfrac{y^2-39}{(y-2)(y+5)} - \dfrac{y-7}{y-2}$

$= \dfrac{y^2-39}{(y-2)(y+5)} - \dfrac{(y-7)(y+5)}{(y-2)(y+5)}$

$= \dfrac{\left(y^2-39\right)-(y-7)(y+5)}{(y-2)(y+5)}$

$= \dfrac{\left(y^2-39\right)-\left(y^2-2y-35\right)}{(y-2)(y+5)}$

$= \dfrac{y^2-39-y^2+2y+35}{(y-2)(y+5)}$

$= \dfrac{2y-4}{(y-2)(y+5)} = \dfrac{2(y-2)}{(y-2)(y+5)}$

$= \dfrac{2}{y+5}$

65. $4 + \dfrac{1}{x-3}$

$\text{LCD} = x-3$

$4 + \dfrac{1}{x-3} = \dfrac{4(x-3)}{x-3} + \dfrac{1}{x-3}$

$= \dfrac{4(x-3)+1}{x-3}$

$= \dfrac{4x-12+1}{x-3}$

$= \dfrac{4x-11}{x-3}$

67. $3 - \dfrac{3y}{y+1}$

$\text{LCD} = y+1$

$3 - \dfrac{3y}{y+1} = \dfrac{3(y+1)}{y+1} - \dfrac{3y}{y+1}$

$= \dfrac{3(y+1)-3y}{y+1}$

$= \dfrac{3y+3-3y}{y+1}$

$= \dfrac{3}{y+1}$

69. $\dfrac{9x+3}{x^2-x-6} + \dfrac{x}{3-x}$

$x^2-x-6 = (x-3)(x+2)$

$3-x = -1(x-3)$

$\text{LCD} = (x-3)(x+2)$

$\dfrac{9x+3}{x^2-x-6} + \dfrac{x}{3-x}$

$= \dfrac{9x+3}{(x-3)(x+2)} + \dfrac{(-1)}{(-1)} \cdot \dfrac{x}{3-x}$

$= \dfrac{9x+3}{(x-3)(x+2)} + \dfrac{-x}{x-3}$

$= \dfrac{9x+3}{(x-3)(x+2)} + \dfrac{-x(x+2)}{(x-3)(x+2)}$

$= \dfrac{9x+3-x(x+2)}{(x-3)(x+2)}$

$= \dfrac{9x+3-x^2-2x}{(x-3)(x+2)}$

$= \dfrac{-x^2+7x+3}{(x-3)(x+2)}$

71. $\dfrac{x+3}{x^2+x-2}-\dfrac{2}{x^2-1}$

$x^2+x-2=(x-1)(x+2)$

$x^2-1=(x+1)(x-1)$

LCD $=(x+1)(x-1)(x+2)$

$\dfrac{x+3}{x^2+x-2}-\dfrac{2}{x^2-1}$

$=\dfrac{x+3}{(x-1)(x+2)}-\dfrac{2}{(x+1)(x-1)}$

$=\dfrac{(x+3)(x+1)}{(x+1)(x-1)(x+2)}$

$-\dfrac{2(x+2)}{(x+1)(x-1)(x+2)}$

$=\dfrac{(x+3)(x+1)-2(x+2)}{(x+1)(x-1)(x+2)}$

$=\dfrac{x^2+4x+3-2x-4}{(x+1)(x-1)(x+2)}$

$=\dfrac{x^2+2x-1}{(x+1)(x-1)(x+2)}$

73. $\dfrac{y+3}{5y^2}-\dfrac{y-5}{15y}$

LCD $=15y^2$

$\dfrac{y+3}{5y^2}-\dfrac{y-5}{15y}$

$=\dfrac{(y+3)(3)}{5y^2(3)}-\dfrac{(y-5)(y)}{15y(y)}$

$=\dfrac{(3y+9)-\left(y^2-5y\right)}{15y^2}$

$=\dfrac{3y+9-y^2+5y}{15y^2}$

$=\dfrac{-y^2+8y+9}{15y^2}$

75. $\dfrac{x+3}{3x+6}+\dfrac{x}{4-x^2}$

$3x+6=3(x+2)$

$4-x^2=(2+x)(2-x)$

Note that $-1(2-x)=x-2$

LCD $=3(x+2)(x-2)$

$\dfrac{x+3}{3x+6}+\dfrac{x}{4-x^2}$

$=\dfrac{x+3}{3(x+2)}+\dfrac{x}{(2+x)(2-x)}$

$=\dfrac{x+3}{3(x+2)}+\dfrac{(-1)}{(-1)}\cdot\dfrac{x}{(2+x)(2-x)}$

$=\dfrac{x+3}{3(x+2)}+\dfrac{-x}{(x+2)(x-2)}$

$=\dfrac{(x+3)(x-2)}{3(x+2)(x-2)}+\dfrac{-x(3)}{3(x+2)(x-2)}$

$=\dfrac{x^2+x-6-3x}{3(x+2)(x-2)}$

$=\dfrac{x^2-2x-6}{3(x+2)(x-2)}$

77. $\dfrac{y}{y^2-1}+\dfrac{2y}{y-y^2}$

$y^2-1=(y+1)(y-1)$

$y-y^2=y(1-y)$

Note that $-1(1-y)=y-1$

LCD $=y(y+1)(y-1)$

$\dfrac{y}{y^2-1}+\dfrac{2y}{y-y^2}$

$=\dfrac{y}{(y+1)(y-1)}+\dfrac{2y}{y(1-y)}$

$=\dfrac{y}{(y+1)(y-1)}+\dfrac{(-1)}{(-1)}\dfrac{2y}{y(1-y)}$

$=\dfrac{y}{(y+1)(y-1)}+\dfrac{-2y}{y(y-1)}$

$=\dfrac{y\cdot y}{y(y+1)(y-1)}+\dfrac{-2y(y+1)}{y(y+1)(y-1)}$

$=\dfrac{y^2-2y(y+1)}{y(y+1)(y-1)}=\dfrac{y^2-2y^2-2y}{y(y+1)(y-1)}$

$=\dfrac{-y^2-2y}{y(y+1)(y-1)}=\dfrac{-y(y+2)}{y(y+1)(y-1)}$

$=\dfrac{-1(y+2)}{(y+1)(y-1)}=\dfrac{-y-2}{(y+1)(y-1)}$

79. $\dfrac{x-1}{x}+\dfrac{y+1}{y}$

LCD $= xy$

$\dfrac{x-1}{x}+\dfrac{y+1}{y}$

$=\dfrac{(x-1)(y)}{xy}+\dfrac{(y+1)(x)}{xy}$

$=\dfrac{xy-y+xy+x}{xy}$

$=\dfrac{x+2xy-y}{xy}$

81. $\dfrac{3x}{x^2-y^2}-\dfrac{2}{y-x}$

$x^2-y^2=(x+y)(x-y)$

Note that $y-x=-1(x-y)$

LCD $=(x+y)(x-y)$

$\dfrac{3x}{x^2-y^2}-\dfrac{2}{y-x}$

$=\dfrac{3x}{(x+y)(x-y)}-\dfrac{(-1)}{(-1)}\cdot\dfrac{2}{y-x}$

$=\dfrac{3x}{(x+y)(x-y)}-\dfrac{-2}{x-y}$

$=\dfrac{3x}{(x+y)(x-y)}-\dfrac{-2(x+y)}{(x+y)(x-y)}$

$=\dfrac{3x+2(x+y)}{(x+y)(x-y)}=\dfrac{3x+2x+2y}{(x+y)(x-y)}$

$=\dfrac{5x+2y}{(x+y)(x-y)}$

83. $\dfrac{x+6}{x^2-4}-\dfrac{x+3}{x+2}+\dfrac{x-3}{x-2}$

LCD $=(x+2)(x-2)$

$\dfrac{x+6}{x^2-4}-\dfrac{x+3}{x+2}+\dfrac{x-3}{x-2}=\dfrac{x+6}{(x+2)(x-2)}-\dfrac{x+3}{x+2}+\dfrac{x-3}{x-2}$

$=\dfrac{x+6}{(x+2)(x-2)}-\dfrac{(x+3)(x-2)}{(x+2)(x-2)}+\dfrac{(x-3)(x+2)}{(x-2)(x+2)}$

$=\dfrac{x+6-(x+3)(x-2)+(x-3)(x+2)}{(x+2)(x-2)}=\dfrac{x+6-\left(x^2+x-6\right)+\left(x^2-x-6\right)}{(x+2)(x-2)}$

$=\dfrac{x+6-x^2-x+6+x^2-x-6}{(x+2)(x-2)}=\dfrac{-x+6}{(x+2)(x-2)}$

85. $\dfrac{5}{x^2-25}+\dfrac{4}{x^2-11x+30}-\dfrac{3}{x^2-x-30}$

$x^2-25=(x+5)(x-5)$

$x^2-11x+30=(x-6)(x-5)$

$x^2-x-30=(x-6)(x+5)$

$\text{LCD}=(x+5)(x-5)(x-6)$

$\dfrac{5}{x^2-25}+\dfrac{4}{x^2-11x+30}-\dfrac{3}{x^2-x-30}$

$=\dfrac{5}{(x+5)(x-5)}+\dfrac{4}{(x-6)(x-5)}-\dfrac{3}{(x-6)(x+5)}$

$=\dfrac{5(x-6)}{(x+5)(x-5)(x-6)}+\dfrac{4(x+5)}{(x-6)(x-5)(x+5)}-\dfrac{3(x-5)}{(x-6)(x+5)(x-5)}$

$=\dfrac{5(x-6)+4(x+5)-3(x-5)}{(x+5)(x-5)(x-6)}=\dfrac{5x-30+4x+20-3x+15}{(x+5)(x-5)(x-6)}$

$=\dfrac{6x+5}{(x+5)(x-5)(x-6)}$

87. $\dfrac{x+6}{x^3-27}-\dfrac{x}{x^3+3x^2+9x}$

$x^3-27=(x-3)\left(x^2+3x+9\right)$

$x^3+3x^2+9x=x\left(x^2+3x+9\right)$

$\text{LCD}=x(x-3)\left(x^2+3x+9\right)$

$\dfrac{x+6}{x^3-27}-\dfrac{x}{x^3+3x^2+9x}=\dfrac{x+6}{(x-3)\left(x^2+3x+9\right)}-\dfrac{x}{x\left(x^2+3x+9\right)}$

$=\dfrac{(x+6)x}{(x-3)\left(x^2+3x+9\right)x}-\dfrac{x(x-3)}{x\left(x^2+3x+9\right)(x-3)}$

$=\dfrac{x(x+6)-x(x-3)}{x(x-3)\left(x^2+3x+9\right)}=\dfrac{x^2+6x-x^2+3x}{x(x-3)\left(x^2+3x+9\right)}$

$=\dfrac{9x}{x(x-3)\left(x^2+3x+9\right)}=\dfrac{9}{(x-3)\left(x^2+3x+9\right)}$

89. $\dfrac{9y+3}{y^2-y-6}+\dfrac{y}{3-y}+\dfrac{y-1}{y+2}$

$y^2-y-6=(y-3)(y+2)$

$3-y=-1(y-3)$

$y+2=1(y+2)$

LCD $=(y-3)(y+2)$

$\dfrac{9y+3}{y^2-y-6}+\dfrac{y}{3-y}+\dfrac{y-1}{y+2}=\dfrac{9y+3}{(y-3)(y+2)}+\dfrac{y}{-1(y-3)}+\dfrac{y-1}{y+2}$

$=\dfrac{9y+3}{(y-3)(y+2)}+\dfrac{-y(y+2)}{(y-3)(y+2)}+\dfrac{(y-1)(y-3)}{(y+2)(y-3)}$

$=\dfrac{9y+3+-y(y+2)+(y-1)(y-3)}{(y-3)(y+2)}=\dfrac{9y+3-y^2-2y+y^2-4y+3}{(y-3)(y+2)}$

$=\dfrac{3y+6}{(y-3)(y+2)}=\dfrac{3(y+2)}{(y-3)(y+2)}=\dfrac{3}{y-3}$

91. $\dfrac{3}{x^2+4xy+3y^2}-\dfrac{5}{x^2-2xy-3y^2}+\dfrac{2}{x^2-9y^2}$

$x^2+4xy+3y^2=(x+y)(x+3y)$

$x^2-2xy-3y^2=(x-3y)(x+y)$

$x^2-9y^2=(x+3y)(x-3y)$

LCD $=(x+y)(x+3y)(x-3y)$

$\dfrac{3}{x^2+4xy+3y^2}-\dfrac{5}{x^2-2xy-3y^2}+\dfrac{2}{x^2-9y^2}$

$=\dfrac{3}{(x+y)(x+3y)}-\dfrac{5}{(x-3y)(x+y)}+\dfrac{2}{(x+3y)(x-3y)}$

$=\dfrac{3(x-3y)}{(x+y)(x+3y)(x-3y)}-\dfrac{5(x+3y)}{(x-3y)(x+y)(x+3y)}+\dfrac{2(x+y)}{(x+3y)(x-3y)(x+y)}$

$=\dfrac{3(x-3y)-5(x+3y)+2(x+y)}{(x+y)(x+3y)(x-3y)}=\dfrac{3x-9y-5x-15y+2x+2y}{(x+y)(x+3y)(x-3y)}$

$=\dfrac{-22y}{(x+y)(x+3y)(x-3y)}$

93. Young's Rule: $C = \dfrac{DA}{A+12}$

$A = 8$;

$C = \dfrac{D \cdot 8}{8+12} = \dfrac{8D}{20} = \dfrac{2D}{5}$

$A = 3$;

$C = \dfrac{D \cdot 3}{3+12} = \dfrac{3D}{15} = \dfrac{D}{5}$

Difference:

$\dfrac{2D}{5} - \dfrac{D}{5} = \dfrac{D}{5}$

The difference in dosages for an 8-year-old child and a 3-year-old child is $\dfrac{D}{5}$. This means that an 8-year-old should be given $\dfrac{1}{5}$ of the adult dosage more than a 3-year-old.

95. Young's Rule: $C = \dfrac{DA}{A+12}$

Cowling's Rule: $C = \dfrac{D(A+1)}{24}$

For $A = 12$, Young's Rule gives

$C = \dfrac{D \cdot 12}{12+12} = \dfrac{12D}{24} = \dfrac{D}{2}$ and Cowling's Rule gives

$C = \dfrac{D(12+1)}{24} = \dfrac{13D}{24}$.

The difference between the dosages given by Cowling's Rule and Young's Rule is

$\dfrac{13D}{24} - \dfrac{12D}{24} = \dfrac{D}{24}$.

This means that Cowling's Rule says to give a 12-year-old $\dfrac{1}{24}$ of the adult dose more than Young's Rule says the dosage should be.

97. No, because the graphs cross, neither formula gives a consistently smaller dosage.

99. The difference in dosage is greatest at 5 years. This is where the graphs are farthest apart.

101. $P = 2L + 2W$

$= 2\left(\dfrac{x}{x+3}\right) + 2\left(\dfrac{x}{x-4}\right)$

$= \dfrac{2x}{x+3} + \dfrac{2x}{x+4}$

$= \dfrac{2x(x+4)}{(x+3)(x+4)} + \dfrac{2x(x+3)}{(x+3)(x+4)}$

$= \dfrac{2x^2 + 8x + 2x^2 + 6x}{(x+3)(x+4)}$

$= \dfrac{4x^2 + 14x}{(x+3)(x+4)}$

103. Answers will vary.

105. Explanations will vary. The right side of the equation should be charged from $\dfrac{3}{x+5}$ to $\dfrac{5+2x}{5x}$.

107. Answers will vary.

109. makes sense

111. does not make sense; Explanations will vary. Sample explanation: It is acceptable to leave the numerator in factored form.

113. false; Changes to make the statement true will vary. A sample change is: The LCD is $x(x-1)$ or $x^2 - x$.

115. true

117. $\left(\dfrac{1}{x+h} - \dfrac{1}{x}\right) \div h$

$= \left(\dfrac{1(x)}{(x+h)(x)} - \dfrac{1(x+h)}{x(x+h)}\right) \div h$

$= \left(\dfrac{x - (x+h)}{x(x+h)}\right) \div h$

$= \left(\dfrac{x - x - h}{x(x+h)}\right) \div h = \dfrac{-h}{x(x+h)} \div h$

$= \dfrac{-h}{x(x+h)} \cdot \dfrac{1}{h} = \dfrac{-1}{x(x+h)}$

119. $\dfrac{4}{x-2} - \dfrac{?}{?} = \dfrac{2x+8}{(x-2)(x+1)}$

The missing rational expression must have $(x+1)$ as a factor in its denominator or as the complete denominator. Let $y =$ the numerator of the missing rational expression.

$$\dfrac{4}{x-2} - \dfrac{y}{x+1} = \dfrac{2x+8}{(x-2)(x+1)}$$

Then, $\dfrac{4(x+1) - y(x-2)}{(x-2)(x+1)} - \dfrac{2x+8}{(x-2)(x+1)}$

So $4x+4-yx+2y = 2x+8$, which implies that $4x - yx = 2x$ and $4 + 2y = 8$. Both of these equations give $y = 2$. Thus, the missing rational expression is $\dfrac{2}{x+1}$.

120. $(3x+5)(2x-7)$

$= 6x^2 - 21x + 10x - 35$

$= 6x^2 - 11x - 35$

121. $3x - y < 3$

Graph $3x - y = 3$ as a dashed line using the x-intercept, 1, and the y-intercept -3. Use $(9,0)$ as a test point. Since $3 \cdot 0 - 9 < 3$ is a true statement, shade the half-plane including $(0,0)$.

$3x - y < 3$

122. First find the slope $m = \dfrac{0-(-4)}{1-(-3)} = \dfrac{4}{4} = 1$

Use $m = 1$ and $(x_1, y_1) = (1,0)$ in the point-slope form and simplify to find the slope-intercept form.

$y - y_1 = m(x - x_1)$

$y - 0 = 1(x - 1)$

$y = x - 1$

123. a. $\dfrac{1}{3} + \dfrac{2}{5} = \dfrac{1 \cdot 5}{3 \cdot 5} + \dfrac{2 \cdot 3}{5 \cdot 3} = \dfrac{5}{15} + \dfrac{6}{15} = \dfrac{11}{15}$

b. $\dfrac{2}{5} - \dfrac{1}{3} = \dfrac{2 \cdot 3}{5 \cdot 3} - \dfrac{1 \cdot 5}{3 \cdot 5} = \dfrac{6}{15} - \dfrac{5}{15} = \dfrac{1}{15}$

c. $\left(\dfrac{1}{3} + \dfrac{2}{5}\right) \div \left(\dfrac{2}{5} - \dfrac{1}{3}\right) = \dfrac{11}{15} \div \dfrac{1}{15} = \dfrac{11}{15} \cdot \dfrac{15}{1} = 11$

124. a. $\dfrac{1}{x} + \dfrac{1}{y} = \dfrac{1 \cdot y}{x \cdot y} + \dfrac{1 \cdot x}{y \cdot x} = \dfrac{y}{xy} + \dfrac{x}{xy} = \dfrac{y+x}{xy}$

b. $\dfrac{1}{xy} \div \left(\dfrac{1}{x} + \dfrac{1}{y}\right) = \dfrac{1}{xy} \div \left(\dfrac{y+x}{xy}\right)$

$= \dfrac{1}{xy} \cdot \dfrac{xy}{y+x}$

$= \dfrac{1}{y+x}$

125. $xy\left(\dfrac{1}{x} + \dfrac{1}{y}\right) = \dfrac{xy}{x} + \dfrac{xy}{y} = y + x$

Mid-Chapter Check Point

1. $\dfrac{x^2 - 4}{x^2 - 2x - 8}$

$x^2 - 2x - 8 = 0$

$(x-4)(x+2) = 0$

$x - 4 = 0$ or $x + 2 = 0$

$x = 4$ $x = -2$

The rational expression is undefined for $x = 4$ and $x = -2$.

2. $\dfrac{3x^2 - 7x + 2}{6x^2 + x - 1} = \dfrac{(3x-1)(x-2)}{(3x-1)(2x+1)}$

$= \dfrac{x-2}{2x+1}$

3. $\dfrac{9-3y}{y^2 - 5y + 6} = \dfrac{3(3-y)}{(y-3)(y-2)}$

$= \dfrac{-3(y-3)}{(y-3)(y-2)} = \dfrac{-3}{y-2}$

4. $\dfrac{16w^3 - 24w^2}{8w^4 - 12w^3} = \dfrac{8w^2(2w-3)}{4w^3(2w-3)} = \dfrac{2}{w}$

5. $\dfrac{7x-3}{x^2+3x-4}-\dfrac{3x+1}{x^2+3x-4}=\dfrac{7x-3-3x-1}{(x-1)(x+4)}$

$\qquad =\dfrac{4x-4}{(x-1)(x+4)}=\dfrac{4(x-1)}{(x-1)(x+4)}$

$\qquad =\dfrac{4}{x+4}$

6. $\dfrac{x+2}{2x-4}\cdot\dfrac{8}{x^2-4}$

$\qquad =\dfrac{x+2}{2(x-2)}\cdot\dfrac{8}{(x+2)(x-2)}$

$\qquad =\dfrac{4}{(x-2)(x-2)}$ or $\dfrac{4}{(x-2)^2}$

7. $1+\dfrac{7}{x-2}=\dfrac{x-2}{x-2}+\dfrac{7}{x-2}=\dfrac{x+5}{x-2}$

8. $\dfrac{2x^2+x-1}{2x^2-7x+3}\div\dfrac{x^2-3x-4}{x^2-x-6}$

$\qquad =\dfrac{2x^2+x-1}{2x^2-7x+3}\cdot\dfrac{x^2-x-6}{x^2-3x-4}$

$\qquad =\dfrac{(2x-1)(x+1)}{(2x-1)(x-3)}\cdot\dfrac{(x-3)(x+2)}{(x-4)(x+1)}$

$\qquad =\dfrac{x+2}{x-4}$

9. $\dfrac{1}{x^2+2x-3}+\dfrac{1}{x^2+5x+6}$

$\qquad x^2+2x-3=(x+3)(x-1)$

$\qquad x^2+5x+6=(x+2)(x+3)$

$\qquad \text{LCD}=(x+3)(x-1)(x+2)$

$\qquad \dfrac{1}{x^2+2x-3}+\dfrac{1}{x^2+5x+6}=\dfrac{1}{(x+3)(x-1)}+\dfrac{1}{(x+2)(x+3)}$

$\qquad =\dfrac{1(x+2)}{(x+3)(x-1)(x+2)}+\dfrac{1(x-1)}{(x+2)(x+3)(x-1)}$

$\qquad =\dfrac{x+2+x-1}{(x+3)(x-1)(x+2)}=\dfrac{2x+1}{(x+3)(x-1)(x+2)}$

10. $\dfrac{17}{x-5}+\dfrac{x+8}{5-x}$

Note: $5-x=-1(x-5)$

LCD $=x-5$

$\dfrac{17}{x-5}+\dfrac{-1(x+8)}{-1(5-x)}=\dfrac{17}{x-5}+\dfrac{-x-8}{x-5}=\dfrac{17-x-8}{x-5}=\dfrac{9-x}{x-5}$

11. $\dfrac{4y^2-1}{9y-3y^2}\cdot\dfrac{y^2-7y+12}{2y^2-7y-4}=\dfrac{(2y+1)(2y-1)}{3y(3-y)}\cdot\dfrac{(y-4)(y-3)}{(2y+1)(y-4)}$

$=\dfrac{-1(2y+1)(2y-1)}{-1\cdot3y(3-y)}\cdot\dfrac{(y-4)(y-3)}{(2y+1)(y-4)}=\dfrac{-1(2y+1)(2y-1)}{3y(y-3)}\cdot\dfrac{(y-4)(y-3)}{(2y+1)(y-4)}$

$=\dfrac{-(2y-1)}{3y}=\dfrac{-2y+1}{3y}$

12. $\dfrac{y}{y+1}-\dfrac{2y}{y+2}$

LCD $=(y+1)(y+2)$

$\dfrac{y(y+2)}{(y+1)(y+2)}-\dfrac{2y(y+1)}{(y+2)(y+1)}=\dfrac{y^2+2y-2y^2-2y}{(y+1)(y+2)}=\dfrac{-y^2}{(y+1)(y+2)}$

13. $\dfrac{w^2+6w+5}{7w^2-63}\div\dfrac{w^2+10w+25}{7w+21}=\dfrac{w^2+6w+5}{7w^2-63}\cdot\dfrac{7w+21}{w^2+10w+25}$

$=\dfrac{(w+5)(w+1)}{7(w^2-9)}\cdot\dfrac{7(w+3)}{(w+5)(w+5)}=\dfrac{(w+5)(w+1)}{7(w+3)(w-3)}\cdot\dfrac{7(w+3)}{(w+5)(w+5)}=\dfrac{w+1}{(w-3)(w+5)}$

14. $\dfrac{2z}{z^2-9}-\dfrac{5}{z^2+4z+3}$

$z^2-9=(z+3)(z-3)$

$z^2+4z+3=(z+3)(z+1)$

LCD $=(z+3)(z-3)(z+1)$

$\dfrac{2z}{z^2-9}-\dfrac{5}{z^2+4z+3}=\dfrac{2z}{(z+3)(z-3)}-\dfrac{5}{(z+3)(z+1)}$

$=\dfrac{2z(z+1)}{(z+3)(z-3)(z+1)}-\dfrac{5(z-3)}{(z+3)(z+1)(z-3)}=\dfrac{2z^2+2z-5z+15}{(z+3)(z-3)(z+1)}=\dfrac{2z^2-3z+15}{(z+3)(z-3)(z+1)}$

15. $\dfrac{z+2}{3z-1}+\dfrac{5}{(3z-1)^2}$

LCD $=(3z-1)(3z-1)$

$\dfrac{(z+2)(3z-1)}{(3z-1)(3z-1)}+\dfrac{5}{(3z-1)^2}=\dfrac{3z^2+5z-2+5}{(3z-1)^2}=\dfrac{3z^2+5z+3}{(3z-1)^2}$

16. $\dfrac{8}{x^2+4x-21}+\dfrac{3}{x+7}$

$x^2+4x-21=(x+7)(x-3)$

$x+7=1(x+7)$

LCD $=(x+7)(x-3)$

$\dfrac{8}{x^2+4x-21}+\dfrac{3}{x+7}$

$=\dfrac{8}{(x+7)(x-3)}+\dfrac{3}{x+7}$

$=\dfrac{8}{(x+7)(x-3)}+\dfrac{3(x-3)}{(x+7)(x-3)}$

$=\dfrac{8+3x-9}{(x+7)(x-3)}=\dfrac{3x-1}{(x+7)(x-3)}$

17. $\dfrac{x^4-27x}{x^2-9}\cdot\dfrac{x+3}{x^2+3x+9}$

$=\dfrac{x\left(x^3-27\right)}{(x+3)(x-3)}\cdot\dfrac{x+3}{x^2+3x+9}$

$=\dfrac{x(x-3)\left(x^2+3x+9\right)}{(x+3)(x-3)}\cdot\dfrac{x+3}{x^2+3x+9}$

$=\dfrac{x}{1}=x$

18. $\dfrac{x-1}{x^2-x-2}-\dfrac{x+2}{x^2+4x+3}$

$x^2-x-2=(x-2)(x+1)$

$x^2+4x+3=(x+3)(x+1)$

LCD $=(x-2)(x+1)(x+3)$

$\dfrac{x-1}{x^2-x-2}-\dfrac{x+2}{x^2+4x+3}$

$=\dfrac{x-1}{(x-2)(x+1)}-\dfrac{x+2}{(x+1)(x+3)}$

$=\dfrac{(x-1)(x+3)}{(x-2)(x+1)(x+3)}-\dfrac{(x+2)(x-2)}{(x+1)(x+3)(x-2)}$

$=\dfrac{x^2+2x-3-\left(x^2-4\right)}{(x-2)(x+1)(x+3)}$

$=\dfrac{x^2+2x-3-x^2+4}{(x-2)(x+1)(x+3)}$

$=\dfrac{2x+1}{(x-2)(x+1)(x+3)}$

19. $\dfrac{x^2-2xy+y^2}{x+y}\div\dfrac{x^2-xy}{5x+5y}$

$=\dfrac{x^2-2xy+y^2}{x+y}\cdot\dfrac{5x+5y}{x^2-xy}$

$=\dfrac{(x-y)(x-y)}{x+y}\cdot\dfrac{5(x+y)}{x(x-y)}$

$=\dfrac{5(x-y)}{x}=\dfrac{5x-5y}{x}$

20. $\dfrac{5}{x+5}+\dfrac{x}{x-4}-\dfrac{11x-8}{x^2+x-20}$

$x^2+x-20=(x+5)(x-4)$

LCD $=(x+5)(x-4)$

$\dfrac{5}{x+5}+\dfrac{x}{x-4}-\dfrac{11x-8}{x^2+x-20}$

$=\dfrac{5}{x+5}+\dfrac{x}{x-4}-\dfrac{11x-8}{(x+5)(x-4)}$

$=\dfrac{5(x-4)}{(x+5)(x-4)}+\dfrac{x(x+5)}{(x-4)(x+5)}$

$\qquad-\dfrac{11x-8}{(x+5)(x-4)}$

$=\dfrac{5x-20+x^2+5x-11x+8}{(x+5)(x-4)}$

$=\dfrac{x^2-x-12}{(x+5)(x-4)}=\dfrac{(x+3)(x-4)}{(x+5)(x-4)}$

$=\dfrac{x+3}{x+5}$

8.5 Check Points

1. $\dfrac{\dfrac{1}{4}+\dfrac{2}{3}}{\dfrac{2}{3}-\dfrac{1}{4}}$

Add to get a single rational expression in the numerator.

$$\frac{1}{4}+\frac{2}{3}=\frac{3}{12}+\frac{8}{12}=\frac{11}{12}$$

Subtract to get a single rational expression in the denominator.

$$\frac{2}{3}-\frac{1}{4}=\frac{8}{12}-\frac{3}{12}=\frac{5}{12}$$

Perform the division indicated by the fraction bar. Invert and multiply.

$$\frac{\dfrac{1}{4}+\dfrac{2}{3}}{\dfrac{2}{3}-\dfrac{1}{4}}=\frac{\dfrac{11}{12}}{\dfrac{5}{12}}=\frac{11}{12}\cdot\frac{12}{5}=\frac{11}{5}$$

2. $\dfrac{2-\dfrac{1}{x}}{2+\dfrac{1}{x}}$

Subtract to get a single rational expression in the numerator.

$$2-\frac{1}{x}=\frac{2x}{x}-\frac{1}{x}=\frac{2x-1}{x}$$

Add to get a single rational expression in the denominator.

$$2+\frac{1}{x}=\frac{2x}{x}+\frac{1}{x}=\frac{2x+1}{x}$$

Perform the division indicated by the fraction bar. Invert and multiply.

$$\frac{2-\dfrac{1}{x}}{2+\dfrac{1}{x}}=\frac{2x-1}{2x+1}$$

3. $\dfrac{\dfrac{1}{x}-\dfrac{1}{y}}{\dfrac{1}{xy}}$

Subtract to get a single rational expression in the numerator.

$$\frac{1}{x}-\frac{1}{y}=\frac{y}{xy}-\frac{x}{xy}=\frac{y-x}{xy}$$

Perform the division indicated by the fraction bar. Invert and multiply.

$$\frac{\dfrac{y-x}{xy}}{\dfrac{1}{xy}}=\frac{y-x}{xy}\cdot\frac{xy}{1}=y-x$$

4. $\dfrac{\dfrac{1}{4}+\dfrac{2}{3}}{\dfrac{2}{3}-\dfrac{1}{4}}$

Multiply the numerator and the denominator by the LCD of 12.

$$\dfrac{\dfrac{1}{4}+\dfrac{2}{3}}{\dfrac{2}{3}-\dfrac{1}{4}}=\dfrac{12\left(\dfrac{1}{4}+\dfrac{2}{3}\right)}{12\left(\dfrac{2}{3}-\dfrac{1}{4}\right)}=\dfrac{12\cdot\dfrac{1}{4}+12\cdot\dfrac{2}{3}}{12\cdot\dfrac{2}{3}-12\cdot\dfrac{1}{4}}=\dfrac{3+8}{8-3}=\dfrac{11}{5}$$

5. $\dfrac{2-\dfrac{1}{x}}{2+\dfrac{1}{x}}$

Multiply the numerator and the denominator by the LCD of x.

$$\dfrac{2-\dfrac{1}{x}}{2+\dfrac{1}{x}}=\dfrac{x\left(2-\dfrac{1}{x}\right)}{x\left(2+\dfrac{1}{x}\right)}=\dfrac{x\cdot2-x\cdot\dfrac{1}{x}}{x\cdot2+x\cdot\dfrac{1}{x}}=\dfrac{2x-1}{2x+1}$$

6. $\dfrac{\dfrac{1}{x}-\dfrac{1}{y}}{\dfrac{1}{xy}}$

Multiply the numerator and the denominator by the LCD of xy.

$$\dfrac{\dfrac{1}{x}-\dfrac{1}{y}}{\dfrac{1}{xy}}=\dfrac{xy\left(\dfrac{1}{x}-\dfrac{1}{y}\right)}{xy\left(\dfrac{1}{xy}\right)}=\dfrac{xy\cdot\dfrac{1}{x}-xy\cdot\dfrac{1}{y}}{xy\cdot\dfrac{1}{xy}}=\dfrac{y-x}{1}=y-x$$

8.5 Exercise Set

1. $\dfrac{\dfrac{1}{2}+\dfrac{1}{4}}{\dfrac{1}{2}+\dfrac{1}{3}}$

Add to get a single rational expression in the numerator.

$$\dfrac{1}{2}+\dfrac{1}{4}=\dfrac{2}{4}+\dfrac{1}{4}=\dfrac{3}{4}$$

Add to get a single rational expression in the denominator.

$$\dfrac{1}{2}+\dfrac{1}{3}=\dfrac{3}{6}+\dfrac{2}{6}=\dfrac{5}{6}$$

Perform the division indicated by the fraction bar. Invert and multiply.

$$\dfrac{\dfrac{1}{2}+\dfrac{1}{4}}{\dfrac{1}{2}+\dfrac{1}{3}}=\dfrac{\dfrac{3}{4}}{\dfrac{5}{6}}=\dfrac{3}{4}\cdot\dfrac{6}{5}=\dfrac{9}{10}$$

3. $\dfrac{5+\dfrac{2}{5}}{7-\dfrac{1}{10}} = \dfrac{\dfrac{25}{5}+\dfrac{2}{5}}{\dfrac{70}{10}-\dfrac{1}{10}}$

$= \dfrac{\dfrac{27}{5}}{\dfrac{69}{10}} = \dfrac{27}{5}\cdot\dfrac{10}{69} = \dfrac{9\cdot3\cdot2\cdot5}{5\cdot3\cdot23} = \dfrac{18}{23}$

5. $\dfrac{\dfrac{2}{5}-\dfrac{1}{3}}{\dfrac{2}{3}-\dfrac{3}{4}}$

LCD = 60

$\dfrac{\dfrac{2}{5}-\dfrac{1}{3}}{\dfrac{2}{3}-\dfrac{3}{4}} = \dfrac{60\cdot\left(\dfrac{2}{5}-\dfrac{1}{3}\right)}{60\cdot\left(\dfrac{2}{3}-\dfrac{3}{4}\right)}$

$= \dfrac{60\cdot\dfrac{2}{5}-60\cdot\dfrac{1}{3}}{60\cdot\dfrac{2}{3}-60\cdot\dfrac{3}{4}}$

$= \dfrac{24-20}{40-45} = \dfrac{4}{-5} = -\dfrac{4}{5}$

7. $\dfrac{\dfrac{3}{4}-x}{\dfrac{3}{4}+x} = \dfrac{\dfrac{3}{4}-\dfrac{4x}{4}}{\dfrac{3}{4}+\dfrac{4x}{4}}$

$= \dfrac{\dfrac{3-4x}{4}}{\dfrac{3+4x}{4}}$

$= \dfrac{3-4x}{4}\cdot\dfrac{4}{3+4x} = \dfrac{3-4x}{3+4x}$

9. $\dfrac{7-\dfrac{2}{x}}{5+\dfrac{1}{x}} = \dfrac{\dfrac{7x-2}{x}}{\dfrac{5x+1}{x}} = \dfrac{7x-2}{x}\cdot\dfrac{x}{5x+1} = \dfrac{7x-2}{5x+1}$

11. $\dfrac{2+\dfrac{3}{y}}{1-\dfrac{7}{y}} = \dfrac{\dfrac{2y+3}{y}}{\dfrac{y-7}{y}}$

$= \dfrac{2y+3}{y}\cdot\dfrac{y}{y-7} = \dfrac{2y+3}{y-7}$

13. $\dfrac{\dfrac{1}{y}-\dfrac{3}{2}}{\dfrac{1}{y}+\dfrac{3}{4}} = \dfrac{\dfrac{2-3y}{2y}}{\dfrac{4+3y}{4y}}$

$= \dfrac{2-3y}{2y}\cdot\dfrac{4y}{4+3y}$

$= \dfrac{2(2-3y)}{4+3y} = \dfrac{4-6y}{4+3y}$

15. $\dfrac{\dfrac{x}{5}-\dfrac{5}{x}}{\dfrac{1}{5}+\dfrac{1}{x}}$

LCD = $5x$

$\dfrac{\dfrac{x}{5}-\dfrac{5}{x}}{\dfrac{1}{5}+\dfrac{1}{x}} = \dfrac{5x\cdot\left(\dfrac{x}{5}-\dfrac{5}{x}\right)}{5x\cdot\left(\dfrac{1}{5}+\dfrac{1}{x}\right)}$

$= \dfrac{5x\cdot\dfrac{x}{5}-5x\cdot\dfrac{5}{x}}{5x\cdot\dfrac{1}{5}+5x\cdot\dfrac{1}{x}}$

$= \dfrac{x^2-25}{x+5}$

$= \dfrac{(x+5)(x-5)}{x+5} = x-5$

17. $\dfrac{1+\dfrac{1}{x}}{1-\dfrac{1}{x^2}} = \dfrac{\dfrac{x+1}{x}}{\dfrac{x^2-1}{x^2}}$

$= \dfrac{x+1}{x}\cdot\dfrac{x^2}{x^2-1}$

$= \dfrac{x+1}{x}\cdot\dfrac{x^2}{(x+1)(x-1)}$

$= \dfrac{x}{x-1}$

19. $\dfrac{\dfrac{1}{7}-\dfrac{1}{y}}{\dfrac{7-y}{7}}$

LCD $= 7y$

$$\dfrac{\dfrac{1}{7}-\dfrac{1}{y}}{\dfrac{7-y}{7}}=\dfrac{7y\left(\dfrac{1}{7}-\dfrac{1}{y}\right)}{7y\left(\dfrac{7-y}{7}\right)}$$

$$=\dfrac{7y\left(\dfrac{1}{7}\right)-7y\left(\dfrac{1}{y}\right)}{7y\left(\dfrac{7-y}{7}\right)}$$

$$=\dfrac{y-7}{y(7-y)}$$

$$=\dfrac{-1(7-y)}{y(7-y)}=-\dfrac{1}{y}$$

21. $\dfrac{x+\dfrac{2}{y}}{\dfrac{x}{y}}=\dfrac{\dfrac{xy+2}{y}}{\dfrac{x}{y}}=\dfrac{xy+2}{y}\cdot\dfrac{y}{x}=\dfrac{xy+2}{x}$

23. $\dfrac{\dfrac{1}{x}+\dfrac{1}{y}}{xy}$

LCD $= xy$

$$\dfrac{\dfrac{1}{x}+\dfrac{1}{y}}{xy}=\dfrac{xy\left(\dfrac{1}{x}+\dfrac{1}{y}\right)}{xy(xy)}=\dfrac{y+x}{x^2y^2}$$

25. $\dfrac{\dfrac{x}{y}+\dfrac{1}{x}}{\dfrac{y}{x}+\dfrac{1}{x}}=\dfrac{\dfrac{x^2+y}{xy}}{\dfrac{y+1}{x}}=\dfrac{x^2+y}{xy}\cdot\dfrac{x}{y+1}$

$$=\dfrac{x^2+y}{y(y+1)}$$

27. $\dfrac{\dfrac{1}{y}+\dfrac{2}{y^2}}{\dfrac{2}{y}+1}$

LCD $= y^2$

$$\dfrac{\dfrac{1}{y}+\dfrac{2}{y^2}}{\dfrac{2}{y}+1}=\dfrac{y^2\left(\dfrac{1}{y}+\dfrac{2}{y^2}\right)}{y^2\left(\dfrac{2}{y}+1\right)}$$

$$=\dfrac{y^2\left(\dfrac{1}{y}\right)+y^2\left(\dfrac{2}{y^2}\right)}{y^2\left(\dfrac{2}{y}\right)+y^2(1)}$$

$$=\dfrac{y+2}{2y+y^2}$$

$$=\dfrac{(y+2)}{y(2+y)}=\dfrac{1}{y}$$

29. $\dfrac{\dfrac{12}{x^2}-\dfrac{3}{x}}{\dfrac{15}{x}-\dfrac{9}{x^2}}=\dfrac{\dfrac{12}{x^2}-\dfrac{3x}{x^2}}{\dfrac{15x}{x^2}-\dfrac{9}{x^2}}=\dfrac{\dfrac{12-3x}{x^2}}{\dfrac{15x-9}{x^2}}$

$$=\dfrac{12-3x}{x^2}\cdot\dfrac{x^2}{15x-9}=\dfrac{12-3x}{15x-9}$$

$$=\dfrac{3(4-x)}{3(5x-3)}=\dfrac{4-x}{5x-3}$$

31. $\dfrac{2+\dfrac{6}{y}}{1-\dfrac{9}{y^2}}$

LCD $= y^2$

$$\dfrac{2+\dfrac{6}{y}}{1-\dfrac{9}{y^2}}=\dfrac{y^2\left(2+\dfrac{6}{y}\right)}{y^2\left(1-\dfrac{9}{y^2}\right)}$$

$$=\dfrac{2y^2+6y}{y^2-9}$$

$$=\dfrac{2y(y+3)}{(y+3)(y-3)}=\dfrac{2y}{y-3}$$

33. $\dfrac{\dfrac{1}{x+2}}{1+\dfrac{1}{x+2}}$

LCD $= x+2$

$$\frac{\dfrac{1}{x+2}}{1+\dfrac{1}{x+2}} = \frac{(x+2)\left(\dfrac{1}{x+2}\right)}{(x+2)\left(1+\dfrac{1}{x+2}\right)}$$

$$= \frac{1}{x+2+1} = \frac{1}{x+3}$$

35. $\dfrac{x-5+\dfrac{3}{x}}{x-7+\dfrac{2}{x}}$

LCD $= x$

$$\frac{x-5+\dfrac{3}{x}}{x-7+\dfrac{2}{x}} = \frac{x\left(x-5+\dfrac{3}{x}\right)}{x\left(x-7+\dfrac{2}{x}\right)}$$

$$= \frac{x^2-5x+3}{x^2-7x+2}$$

37. $\dfrac{\dfrac{3}{xy^2}+\dfrac{2}{x^2y}}{\dfrac{1}{x^2y}+\dfrac{2}{xy^3}} = \dfrac{\dfrac{3x}{x^2y^2}+\dfrac{2y}{x^2y^2}}{\dfrac{y^2}{x^2y^3}+\dfrac{2x}{x^2y^3}}$

$$= \frac{\dfrac{3x+2y}{x^2y^2}}{\dfrac{y^2+2x}{x^2y^3}}$$

$$= \frac{3x+2y}{x^2y^2}\cdot\frac{x^2y^3}{y^2+2x}$$

$$= \frac{3x+2y}{x^2y^2}\cdot\frac{x^2y^3}{y^2+2x}$$

$$= \frac{(3x+2y)(y)}{y^2+2x}$$

$$= \frac{3xy+2y^2}{y^2+2x}$$

39. $\dfrac{\dfrac{3}{x+1}-\dfrac{3}{x-1}}{\dfrac{5}{x^2-1}}$

$=\dfrac{\dfrac{3(x-1)-3(x+1)}{(x+1)(x-1)}}{\dfrac{5}{x^2-1}}$

$=\dfrac{\dfrac{3x-3-3x-3}{(x+1)(x-1)}}{\dfrac{5}{x^2-1}}$

$=\dfrac{\dfrac{-6}{(x+1)(x-1)}}{\dfrac{5}{x^2-1}}$

$=\dfrac{-6}{(x+1)(x-1)}\cdot\dfrac{x^2-1}{5}$

$=\dfrac{-6}{(x+1)(x-1)}\cdot\dfrac{(x+1)(x-1)}{5}$

$=-\dfrac{6}{5}$

41. $\dfrac{\dfrac{6}{x^2+2x-15}-\dfrac{1}{x-3}}{\dfrac{1}{x+5}+1}=\dfrac{\dfrac{6}{(x+5)(x-3)}-\dfrac{1}{x-3}}{\dfrac{1}{x+5}+1}$

LCD $=(x+5)(x-3)$

$\dfrac{\dfrac{6}{(x+5)(x-3)}-\dfrac{1}{x-3}}{\dfrac{1}{x+5}+1}=\dfrac{(x+5)(x-3)\left[\dfrac{6}{(x+5)(x-3)}-\dfrac{1}{x-3}\right]}{(x+5)(x-3)\left[\dfrac{1}{x+5}+1\right]}$

$=\dfrac{6-(x+5)}{x-3+(x+5)(x-3)}=\dfrac{6-x-5}{x-3+x^2+2x-15}=\dfrac{-x+1}{x^2+3x-18}=\dfrac{1-x}{(x-3)(x+6)}$

43. $\dfrac{y^{-1}-(y+5)^{-1}}{5}=\dfrac{\dfrac{1}{y}-\dfrac{1}{y+5}}{5}$

LCD $=y(y+5)$

$\dfrac{\dfrac{1}{y}-\dfrac{1}{y+5}}{5}=\dfrac{y(y+5)\left(\dfrac{1}{y}-\dfrac{1}{y+5}\right)}{y(y+5)(5)}=\dfrac{y+5-y}{5y(y+5)}=\dfrac{5}{5y(y+5)}=\dfrac{1}{y(y+5)}$

45.　$\dfrac{1}{1-\dfrac{1}{x}}-1=\dfrac{x(1)}{x\left(1-\dfrac{1}{x}\right)}-1=\dfrac{x}{x-1}-1=\dfrac{x}{x-1}-\dfrac{x-1}{x-1}=\dfrac{x-x+1}{x-1}=\dfrac{1}{x-1}$

47.　$\dfrac{1}{1+\dfrac{1}{1+\dfrac{1}{x}}}=\dfrac{1}{1+\dfrac{x(1)}{x\left(1+\dfrac{1}{x}\right)}}=\dfrac{1}{1+\dfrac{x}{x+1}}=\dfrac{(x+1)(1)}{(x+1)\left(1+\dfrac{x}{x+1}\right)}=\dfrac{x+1}{x+1+x}=\dfrac{x+1}{2x+1}$

49.　$\dfrac{2d}{\dfrac{d}{r_1}+\dfrac{d}{r_2}}$

LCD $= r_1 r_2$

$\dfrac{2d}{\dfrac{d}{r_1}+\dfrac{d}{r_2}}=\dfrac{r_1 r_2(2d)}{r_1 r_2\left(\dfrac{d}{r_1}+\dfrac{d}{r_2}\right)}$

$=\dfrac{2r_1 r_2 d}{r_2 d+r_1 d}$

$=\dfrac{2r_1 r_2 d}{d(r_2+r_1)}=\dfrac{2r_1 r_2}{r_2+r_1}$

If $r_1=40$ and $r_2=30$, the value of this expression will be $\dfrac{2\cdot40\cdot30}{30+40}=\dfrac{2400}{70}=34\dfrac{2}{7}$.

Your average speed will be $34\dfrac{2}{7}$ miles per hour.

51.　a.　$\dfrac{\dfrac{11}{10}+\dfrac{4}{x}+\dfrac{104}{x^2}}{\dfrac{6}{5}+\dfrac{23}{x}+\dfrac{219}{x^2}}=\dfrac{10x^2\left(\dfrac{11}{10}+\dfrac{4}{x}+\dfrac{104}{x^2}\right)}{10x^2\left(\dfrac{6}{5}+\dfrac{23}{x}+\dfrac{219}{x^2}\right)}$

$=\dfrac{10x^2\cdot\dfrac{11}{10}+10x^2\cdot\dfrac{4}{x}+10x^2\cdot\dfrac{104}{x^2}}{10x^2\cdot\dfrac{6}{5}+10x^2\cdot\dfrac{23}{x}+10x^2\cdot\dfrac{219}{x^2}}$

$=\dfrac{11x^2+40x+1040}{12x^2+230x+2190}$

b.　According to the data in the bar graph, $\dfrac{1707.2}{2708.7}$ or about 63% was spent on human resources in 2006.

c.　$\dfrac{11x^2+40x+1040}{12x^2+230x+2190}=\dfrac{11(36)^2+40(36)+1040}{12(36)^2+230(36)+2190}\approx 0.64$

According to the model about 64% was spent on human resources in 2006.
This overestimates the actual percent by 1%.

53. – 55.　Answers will vary.

57.　makes sense

59. does not make sense; Explanations will vary. Sample explanation: The expression simplifies to $\dfrac{x+y}{x-y}$.

61. true

63. false; Changes to make the statement true will vary. A sample change is: All complex rational expressions can simplified by both methods.

65.
$$\frac{2y}{2+\dfrac{2}{y}}+\frac{y}{1+\dfrac{1}{y}}=\frac{y}{y}\left(\frac{2y}{2+\dfrac{2}{y}}\right)+\frac{y}{y}\left(\frac{y}{1+\dfrac{1}{y}}\right)$$

$$=\frac{2y^2}{2y+2}+\frac{y^2}{y+1}=\frac{2y^2}{2(y+1)}+\frac{y^2}{y+1}$$

$$=\frac{y^2}{y+1}+\frac{y^2}{y+1}=\frac{2y^2}{y+1}$$

67. The graphs coincide.

69. The graphs do not coincide.

$$\frac{\dfrac{1}{x}+\dfrac{1}{3}}{\dfrac{1}{3x}}=\frac{3x\left(\dfrac{1}{x}+\dfrac{1}{3}\right)}{3x\left(\dfrac{1}{3x}\right)}=\frac{3+x}{1}=3+x$$

Therefore, $x+\dfrac{1}{3}$ should be $3+x$.

70.
$$2x^3-20x^2+50x$$
$$=2x\left(x^2-10x+25\right)$$
$$=2x(x-5)^2$$

71.
$$2-3(x-2)=5(x+5)-1$$
$$2-3x+6=5x+25-1$$
$$8-3x=5x+24$$
$$8-3x-5x=5x+24-5x$$
$$8-8x=24$$
$$8-8x-8=24-8$$
$$-8x=16$$
$$\frac{-8x}{-8}=\frac{16}{-8}$$
$$x=-2$$
The solution set is $\{-2\}$.

72.
$$(x+y)\left(x^2-xy+y^2\right)$$
$$=x\left(x^2-xy+y^2\right)+y\left(x^2-xy+y^2\right)$$
$$=x^3-x^2y+xy^2+x^2y-xy^2+y^3$$
$$=x^3+y^3$$

73.
$$\frac{x}{3}+\frac{x}{2}=\frac{5}{6}$$
$$6\left(\frac{x}{3}+\frac{x}{2}\right)=6\left(\frac{5}{6}\right)$$
$$\frac{6x}{3}+\frac{6x}{2}=\frac{6\cdot5}{6}$$
$$2x+3x=5$$
$$5x=5$$
$$x=1$$
The solution set is $\{1\}$.

74.
$$\frac{2x}{3} = \frac{14}{3} - \frac{x}{2}$$

$$6\left(\frac{2x}{3}\right) = 6\left(\frac{14}{3} - \frac{x}{2}\right)$$

$$\frac{6 \cdot 2x}{3} = \frac{6 \cdot 14}{3} - \frac{6 \cdot x}{2}$$

$$4x = 28 - 3x$$

$$7x = 28$$

$$x = 4$$

The solution set is $\{4\}$.

75.
$$2x^2 + 2 = 5x$$

$$2x^2 - 5x + 2 = 0$$

$$(2x - 1)(x - 2) = 0$$

$$2x - 1 = 0 \quad \text{or} \quad x - 2 = 0$$

$$2x = 1 \qquad\qquad x = 2$$

$$x = \frac{1}{2}$$

The solution set is $\left\{\frac{1}{2}, 2\right\}$.

8.6 Check Points

1. $\dfrac{x}{6} = \dfrac{1}{6} + \dfrac{x}{8}$

The LCD is 24.

$$\frac{x}{6} = \frac{1}{6} + \frac{x}{8}$$

$$24\left(\frac{x}{6}\right) = 24\left(\frac{1}{6} + \frac{x}{8}\right)$$

$$24 \cdot \frac{x}{6} = 24 \cdot \frac{1}{6} + 24 \cdot \frac{x}{8}$$

$$4x = 4 + 3x$$

$$x = 4$$

The solution set is $\{4\}$.

Check:

$$\frac{x}{6} = \frac{1}{6} + \frac{x}{8}$$

$$\frac{4}{6} = \frac{1}{6} + \frac{4}{8}$$

$$\frac{16}{24} = \frac{4}{24} + \frac{12}{24}$$

$$\frac{16}{24} = \frac{16}{24}$$

2. $\dfrac{5}{2x} = \dfrac{17}{18} - \dfrac{1}{3x}$

The restriction is $x \neq 0$.

The LCD is $18x$.

$$\frac{5}{2x} = \frac{17}{18} - \frac{1}{3x}$$

$$18x\left(\frac{5}{2x}\right) = 18x\left(\frac{17}{18} - \frac{1}{3x}\right)$$

$$18x \cdot \frac{5}{2x} = 18x \cdot \frac{17}{18} - 18x \cdot \frac{1}{3x}$$

$$45 = 17x - 6$$

$$51 = 17x$$

$$3 = x$$

The solution set is $\{3\}$.

3. $x + \dfrac{6}{x} = -5$

The restriction is $x \neq 0$.

The LCD is x.

$$x + \frac{6}{x} = -5$$

$$x\left(x + \frac{6}{x}\right) = x(-5)$$

$$x \cdot x + x \cdot \frac{6}{x} = -5x$$

$$x^2 + 6 = -5x$$

$$x^2 + 5x + 6 = 0$$

$$(x + 3)(x + 2) = 0$$

$$x + 3 = 0 \quad \text{or} \quad x + 2 = 0$$

$$x = -3 \qquad\qquad x = -2$$

The solution set is $\{-3, -2\}$.

4.
$$\frac{11}{x^2-25}+\frac{4}{x+5}=\frac{3}{x-5}$$

$$\frac{11}{(x+5)(x-5)}+\frac{4}{x+5}=\frac{3}{x-5}$$

The restrictions are $x \neq -5$ and $x \neq 5$.

The LCD is $(x+5)(x-5)$.

$$\frac{11}{(x+5)(x-5)}+\frac{4}{x+5}=\frac{3}{x-5}$$

$$(x+5)(x-5)\left(\frac{11}{(x+5)(x-5)}+\frac{4}{x+5}\right)=(x+5)(x-5)\left(\frac{3}{x-5}\right)$$

$$\frac{11(x+5)(x-5)}{(x+5)(x-5)}+\frac{4(x+5)(x-5)}{x+5}=\frac{3(x+5)(x-5)}{x-5}$$

$$11+4(x-5)=3(x+5)$$

$$11+4x-20=3x+15$$

$$4x-9=3x+15$$

$$x-9=15$$

$$x=24$$

The solution set is $\{24\}$.

5.
$$\frac{x}{x-3}=\frac{3}{x-3}+9$$

The restriction is $x \neq 3$.

The LCD is $x-3$.

$$\frac{x}{x-3}=\frac{3}{x-3}+9$$

$$(x-3)\left(\frac{x}{x-3}\right)=(x-3)\left(\frac{3}{x-3}+9\right)$$

$$\frac{x(x-3)}{x-3}=\frac{3(x-3)}{x-3}+9(x-3)$$

$$x=3+9(x-3)$$

$$x=3+9x-27$$

$$x=9x-24$$

$$-8x=-24$$

$$x=3$$

The proposed solution, 3, is not a solution because of the restriction $x \neq 3$.

The solution set is $\{\ \}$.

6. $y = \dfrac{250x}{100 - x}$

The restriction is $x \neq 100$.

$$750 = \dfrac{250x}{100 - x}$$

$$(100 - x)(750) = (100 - x)\left(\dfrac{250x}{100 - x}\right)$$

$$75,000 - 750x = 250x$$

$$75,000 = 1000x$$

$$75 = x$$

If government funding is increased to $750 million, then 75% of pollutants can be removed.

8.6 Exercise Set

1. $\dfrac{x}{3} = \dfrac{x}{2} - 2$

There are no restrictions on the variable because the variable does not appear in any denominator.
The LCD is 6.

$$\dfrac{x}{3} = \dfrac{x}{2} - 2$$

$$6\left(\dfrac{x}{3}\right) = 6\left(\dfrac{x}{2} - 2\right)$$

$$6 \cdot \dfrac{x}{3} = 6 \cdot \dfrac{x}{2} - 6 \cdot 2$$

$$2x = 3x - 12$$

$$0 = x - 12$$

$$12 = x$$

The solution set is $\{12\}$.

3. $\dfrac{4x}{3} = \dfrac{x}{18} - \dfrac{x}{6}$

There are no restrictions.
The LCD is 18.

$$\dfrac{4x}{3} = \dfrac{x}{18} - \dfrac{x}{6}$$

$$18\left(\dfrac{4x}{3}\right) = 18\left(\dfrac{x}{18} - \dfrac{x}{6}\right)$$

$$18 \cdot \dfrac{4x}{3} = 18 \cdot \dfrac{x}{18} - 18 \cdot \dfrac{x}{6}$$

$$24x = x - 3x$$

$$24x = -2x$$

$$26x = 0$$

$$x = 0$$

The solution set is $\{0\}$.

5. $2 - \dfrac{8}{x} = 6$

The restriction is $x \neq 0$.
The LCD is x.

$$2 - \dfrac{8}{x} = 6$$

$$x\left(2 - \dfrac{8}{x}\right) = x \cdot 6$$

$$x \cdot 2 - x \cdot \dfrac{8}{x} = x \cdot 6$$

$$2x - 8 = 6x$$

$$-8 = 4x$$

$$-2 = x$$

The solution set is $\{-2\}$.

7. $\dfrac{2}{x} + \dfrac{1}{3} = \dfrac{4}{x}$

The restriction is $x \neq 0$.
The LCD is $3x$.

$$\dfrac{2}{x} + \dfrac{1}{3} = \dfrac{4}{x}$$

$$3x\left(\dfrac{2}{x} + \dfrac{1}{3}\right) = 3x\left(\dfrac{4}{x}\right)$$

$$3x \cdot \dfrac{2}{x} + 3x \cdot \dfrac{1}{3} = 3x \cdot \dfrac{4}{x}$$

$$6 + x = 12$$

$$x = 6$$

The solution set is $\{6\}$.

9. $\dfrac{2}{x} + 3 = \dfrac{5}{2x} + \dfrac{13}{4}$

The restriction is $x \neq 0$
The LCD is $4x$.

$$\dfrac{2}{x} + 3 = \dfrac{5}{2x} + \dfrac{13}{4}$$

$$4x\left(\dfrac{2}{x} + 3\right) = 4x\left(\dfrac{5}{2x} + \dfrac{13}{4}\right)$$

$$8 + 12x = 10 + 13x$$

$$8 = 10 + x$$

$$-2 = x$$

The solution set is $\{-2\}$.

11. $\dfrac{2}{3x}+\dfrac{1}{4}=\dfrac{11}{6x}-\dfrac{1}{3}$

The restriction is $x \neq 0$.

The LCD is $12x$.

$$\dfrac{2}{3x}+\dfrac{1}{4}=\dfrac{11}{6x}-\dfrac{1}{3}$$

$$12x\left(\dfrac{2}{3x}+\dfrac{1}{4}\right)=12x\left(\dfrac{11}{6x}-\dfrac{1}{3}\right)$$

$$8+3x=22-4x$$

$$8+7x=22$$

$$7x=14$$

$$x=2$$

The solution set is $\{2\}$.

13. $\dfrac{6}{x+3}=\dfrac{4}{x-3}$

Restrictions: $x \neq -3, x \neq 3$

LCD $=(x+3)(x-3)$

$$\dfrac{6}{x+3}=\dfrac{4}{x-3}$$

$$(x+3)(x-3)\cdot\dfrac{6}{x+3}=(x+3)(x-3)\cdot\dfrac{4}{x-3}$$

$$(x-3)\cdot 6=(x+3)\cdot 4$$

$$6x-18=4x+12$$

$$2x-18=12$$

$$2x=30$$

$$x=15$$

The solution set is $\{15\}$.

15. $\dfrac{x-2}{2x}+1=\dfrac{x+1}{x}$

Restriction: $x \neq 0$

LCD $=2x$.

$$\dfrac{x-2}{2x}+1=\dfrac{x+1}{x}$$

$$2x\left(\dfrac{x-2}{2x}+1\right)=2x\left(\dfrac{x+1}{x}\right)$$

$$x-2+2x=2(x+1)$$

$$3x-2=2x+2$$

$$x-2=2$$

$$x=4$$

The solution set is $\{4\}$.

17. $x+\dfrac{6}{x}=-7$

Restriction: $x \neq 0$

LCD $=x$

$$x+\dfrac{6}{x}=-7$$

$$x\left(x+\dfrac{6}{x}\right)=x(-7)$$

$$x^2+6=-7x$$

$$x^2+7x+6=0$$

$$(x+6)(x+1)=0$$

$$x+6=0 \quad \text{or} \quad x+1=0$$

$$x=-6 \qquad\qquad x=-1$$

The solution set is $\{-6,-1\}$.

19. $\dfrac{x}{5}-\dfrac{5}{x}=0$

Restriction: $x \neq 0$

LCD $=5x$

$$\dfrac{x}{5}-\dfrac{5}{x}=0$$

$$5x\left(\dfrac{x}{5}-\dfrac{5}{x}\right)=5x\cdot 0$$

$$5x\cdot\dfrac{x}{5}-5x\cdot\dfrac{5}{x}=0$$

$$x^2-25=0$$

$$(x+5)(x-5)=0$$

$$x+5=0 \quad \text{or} \quad x-5=0$$

$$x=-5 \qquad\qquad x=5$$

The solution set is $\{-5,5\}$.

21. $x+\dfrac{3}{x}=\dfrac{12}{x}$

Restriction: $x \neq 0$

LCD $=x$

$$x+\dfrac{3}{x}=\dfrac{12}{x}$$

$$x\left(x+\dfrac{3}{x}\right)=x\left(\dfrac{12}{x}\right)$$

$$x^2+3=12$$

$$x^2-9=0$$

$$(x+3)(x-3)=0$$

$$x+3=0 \quad \text{or} \quad x-3=0$$

$$x=-3 \qquad\qquad x=3$$

The solution set is $\{-3,3\}$.

23. $\dfrac{4}{y} - \dfrac{y}{2} = \dfrac{7}{2}$

Restrictions: $y \neq 0$

LCD = $2y$

$$\dfrac{4}{y} - \dfrac{y}{2} = \dfrac{7}{2}$$

$$2y\left(\dfrac{4}{y} - \dfrac{y}{2}\right) = 2y\left(\dfrac{7}{2}\right)$$

$$8 - y^2 = 7y$$

$$0 = y^2 + 7y - 8$$

$$0 = (y+8)(y-1)$$

$y+8 = 0$　or　$y-1 = 0$

$y = -8$　　　　$y = 1$

The solution set is $\{-8, 1\}$.

25. $\dfrac{x-4}{x} = \dfrac{15}{x+4}$

Restrictions: $x \neq 0, x \neq -4$

LCD = $x(x+4)$

$$\dfrac{x-4}{x} = \dfrac{15}{x+4}$$

$$x(x+4)\left(\dfrac{x-4}{x}\right) = x(x+4)\left(\dfrac{15}{x+4}\right)$$

$$(x+4)(x-4) = x \cdot 15$$

$$x^2 - 16 = 15x$$

$$x^2 - 15x - 16 = 0$$

$$(x+1)(x-16) = 0$$

$x+1 = 0$　or　$x-16 = 0$

$x = -1$　　　　$x = 16$

The solution set is $\{-1, 16\}$.

27. $\dfrac{2}{x^2 - 1} = \dfrac{4}{x+1}$

$$\dfrac{2}{(x+1)(x-1)} = \dfrac{4}{x+1}$$

Restrictions: $x \neq -1, x \neq 1$

LCD = $(x+1)(x-1)$

$$\dfrac{2}{(x+1)(x-1)} = \dfrac{4}{x+1}$$

$$(x+1)(x-1)\dfrac{2}{(x+1)(x-1)} = (x+1)(x-1)\dfrac{4}{x+1}$$

$$2 = 4(x-1)$$

$$2 = 4x - 4$$

$$6 = 4x$$

$$\dfrac{6}{4} = x$$

$$\dfrac{3}{2} = x$$

The solution set is $\left\{\dfrac{3}{2}\right\}$.

29. $\dfrac{1}{x-1} + 5 = \dfrac{11}{x-1}$

Restriction: $x \neq 1$

LCD = $x-1$

$$\dfrac{1}{x-1} + 5 = \dfrac{11}{x-1}$$

$$(x-1)\left(\dfrac{1}{x-1} + 5\right) = (x-1)\left(\dfrac{11}{x-1}\right)$$

$$1 + (x-1) \cdot 5 = 11$$

$$1 + 5x - 5 = 11$$

$$5x - 4 = 11$$

$$5x = 15$$

$$x = 3$$

The solution set is $\{3\}$.

31. $\dfrac{8y}{y+1} = 4 - \dfrac{8}{y+1}$

Restriction: $y \neq -1$

LCD $= y+1$

$$\dfrac{8y}{y+1} = 4 - \dfrac{8}{y+1}$$

$$(y+1)\left(\dfrac{8y}{y+1}\right) = (y+1)\left(4 - \dfrac{8}{y+1}\right)$$

$$8y = (y+1)\cdot 4 - 8$$

$$8y = 4y+4-8$$

$$8y = 4y-4$$

$$4y = -4$$

$$y = -1$$

The proposed solution, -1, is *not* a solution because of the restriction $x \neq -1$. Notice that -1 makes two of the denominators zero in the original equation. Therefore, the equation has no solution. The solution set is $\{\ \}$.

33. $\dfrac{3}{x-1} + \dfrac{8}{x} = 3$

Restrictions: $x \neq 1, x \neq 0$

LCD $= x(x-1)$

$$\dfrac{3}{x-1} + \dfrac{8}{x} = 3$$

$$x(x-1)\left(\dfrac{3}{x-1} + \dfrac{8}{x}\right) = x(x-1)\cdot 3$$

$$x(x-1)\left(\dfrac{3}{x-1} + \dfrac{8}{x}\right) = 3x(x-1)$$

$$3x + 8(x-1) = 3x^2 - 3x$$

$$3x + 8x - 8 = 3x^2 - 3x$$

$$11x - 8 = 3x^2 - 3x$$

$$0 = 3x^2 - 14x + 8$$

$$0 = (3x-2)(x-4)$$

$3x-2 = 0 \quad$ or $x-4 = 0$

$\quad 3x = 2 \qquad\qquad x = 4$

$\quad x = \dfrac{2}{3}$

The solution set is $\left\{\dfrac{2}{3}, 4\right\}$.

35. $\dfrac{3y}{y-4} - 5 = \dfrac{12}{y-4}$

Restriction: $y \neq 4$

LCD $= y-4$

$$\dfrac{3y}{y-4} - 5 = \dfrac{12}{y-4}$$

$$(y-4)\left(\dfrac{3y}{y-4} - 5\right) = (y-4)\left(\dfrac{12}{y-4}\right)$$

$$3y - 5(y-4) = 12$$

$$3y - 5y + 20 = 12$$

$$-2y + 20 = 12$$

$$-2y = -8$$

$$y = 4$$

The proposed solution, 4, is *not* a solution because of the restriction $y \neq 4$. Therefore, this equation has no solution. The solution set is $\{\ \}$.

37. $\dfrac{1}{x} + \dfrac{1}{x-3} = \dfrac{x-2}{x-3}$

Restrictions: $x \neq 0, x \neq 3$

LCD $= x(x-3)$

$$\dfrac{1}{x} + \dfrac{1}{x-3} = \dfrac{x-2}{x-3}$$

$$x(x-3)\left(\dfrac{1}{x} + \dfrac{1}{x-3}\right) = x(x-3)\cdot\dfrac{x-2}{x-3}$$

$$x - 3 + x = x(x-2)$$

$$2x - 3 = x^2 - 2x$$

$$0 = x^2 - 4x + 3$$

$$0 = (x-3)(x-1)$$

$x-3 = 0 \quad$ or $x-1 = 0$

$\quad x = 3 \qquad\qquad x = 1$

The proposed solution 3 is *not* a solution because of the restriction $x \neq 3$.

The solution set is $\{1\}$.

39. $\dfrac{x+1}{3x+9} + \dfrac{x}{2x+6} = \dfrac{2}{4x+12}$

To find any restrictions and the LCD, factor the denominators.

$\dfrac{x+1}{3(x+3)} + \dfrac{x}{2(x+3)} = \dfrac{2}{4(x+3)}$

Restriction: $x \neq -3$

LCD $= 12(x+3)$

$12(x+3)\left[\dfrac{x+1}{3(x+3)} + \dfrac{x}{2(x+3)} \right] = 12(x+3)\left[\dfrac{2}{4(x+3)} \right]$

$$4(x+1) + 6x = 6$$
$$4x + 4 + 6x = 6$$
$$10x + 4 = 6$$
$$10x = 2$$
$$x = \dfrac{2}{10}$$
$$x = \dfrac{1}{5}$$

The solution set is $\left\{ \dfrac{1}{5}. \right\}$.

41. $\dfrac{4y}{y^2 - 25} + \dfrac{2}{y-5} = \dfrac{1}{y+5}$

To find any restrictions and the LCD, factor the first denominator.

$\dfrac{4y}{(y+5)(y-5)} + \dfrac{2}{y-5} = \dfrac{1}{y+5}$

Restrictions: $y \neq -5, y \neq 5$

LCD $= (y+5)(y-5)$

$(y+5)(y-5)\left[\dfrac{4y}{(y+5)(y-5)} + \dfrac{2}{y-5} \right] = (y+5)(y-5) \cdot \dfrac{1}{y+5}$

$$4y + 2(y+5) = y - 5$$
$$4y + 2y + 10 = y - 5$$
$$6y + 10 = y - 5$$
$$5y + 10 = -5$$
$$5y = -15$$
$$y = -3$$

The solution set is $\{-3\}$.

43. $\dfrac{1}{x-4} - \dfrac{5}{x+2} = \dfrac{6}{x^2 - 2x - 8}$

Factor the last denominator.

$\dfrac{1}{x-4} - \dfrac{5}{x+2} = \dfrac{6}{(x-4)(x+2)}$

Restrictions: $x \neq 4, x \neq -2$

LCD $= (x-4)(x+2)$

$(x-4)(x+2)\left[\dfrac{1}{x-4} - \dfrac{5}{x+2}\right] = (x-4)(x+2)\left[\dfrac{6}{(x-4)(x+2)}\right]$

$(x+2) \cdot 1 - (x-4) \cdot 5 = 6$

$x + 2 - 5x + 20 = 6$

$-4x + 22 = 6$

$-4x = -16$

$x = 4$

The proposed solution 4 is *not* a solution because of the restriction $x \neq 4$. Therefore, the given equation has no solution. The solution set is $\{\ \}$.

45. $\dfrac{2}{x+3} - \dfrac{2x+3}{x-1} = \dfrac{6x-5}{x^2 + 2x - 3}$

Factor the denominators.

$\dfrac{2}{x+3} - \dfrac{2x+3}{x-1} = \dfrac{6x-5}{(x+3)(x-1)}$

Restrictions: $x \neq -3, x \neq 1$

LCD $= (x+3)(x-1)$

$(x+3)(x-1)\left[\dfrac{2}{x+3} - \dfrac{2x+3}{x-1}\right] = (x+3)(x-1)\left[\dfrac{6x-5}{(x+3)(x-1)}\right]$

$(x-1) \cdot 2 - (x+3)(2x+3) = 6x - 5$

$2x - 2 - \left(2x^2 + 9x + 9\right) = 6x - 5$

$2x - 2 - 2x^2 - 9x - 9 = 6x - 5$

$-2x^2 - 7x - 11 = 6x - 5$

$0 = 2x^2 + 13x + 6$

$0 = (x+6)(2x+1)$

$x + 6 = 0 \quad \text{or} \quad 2x + 1 = 0$

$x = -6 \qquad 2x = -1$

$x = -\dfrac{1}{2}$

The solution set is $\left\{-6, -\dfrac{1}{2}\right\}$.

47. Solve $\dfrac{x^2-10}{x^2-x-20}=1+\dfrac{7}{x-5}-\dfrac{1}{2}$.

Factor the first denominator.

$$\frac{x^2-10}{(x-5)(x+4)}=1+\frac{7}{x-5}-\frac{1}{2}.$$

Restrictions: $x\neq 5, x\neq -4$

LCD $=(x-5)(x+4)$

$$(x-5)(x+4)\left(\frac{x^2-10}{(x-5)(x+4)}\right)=(x-5)(x+4)\cdot 1+(x-5)(x+4)\left(\frac{7}{x-5}\right)$$

$$x^2-10=(x-5)(x+4)+(x+4)\cdot 7$$

$$x^2-10=x^2-x-20+7x+28$$

$$x^2-10=x^2+6x+8$$

$$-10=6x+8$$

$$-18=6x$$

$$-3=x$$

The solution set is $\{-3\}$.

49. Simplify $\dfrac{x^2-10}{x^2-x-20}-1-\dfrac{7}{x-5}$.

Factor the first denominator.

$$\frac{x^2-10}{(x-5)(x+4)}-1-\frac{7}{x-5}$$

LCD $=(x-5)(x+4)$

$$\frac{x^2-10}{(x-5)(x+4)}-\frac{(x-5)(x+4)}{(x-5)(x+4)}-\frac{7(x+4)}{(x-5)(x+4)}=\frac{x^2-10-(x-5)(x+4)-7(x+4)}{(x-5)(x+4)}$$

$$=\frac{x^2-10-\left(x^2-x-20\right)-7x-28}{(x-5)(x+4)}$$

$$=\frac{x^2-10-x^2+x+20-7x-28}{(x-5)(x+4)}$$

$$=\frac{-6x-18}{(x-5)(x+4)}$$

51. Solve $5y^{-2} + 1 = 6y^{-1}$

$$\frac{5}{y^2} + 1 = \frac{6}{y}$$

Restrictions: $y \neq 0$

$\text{LCD} = y^2$

$$y^2\left(\frac{5}{y^2} + 1\right) = y^2\left(\frac{6}{y}\right)$$

$$y^2 \cdot \frac{5}{y^2} + y^2 \cdot 1 = 6y$$

$$5 + y^2 = 6y$$

$$y^2 - 6y + 5 = 0$$

$$(y-5)(y-1) = 0$$

$$y - 5 = 0 \quad \text{or} \quad y - 1 = 0$$

$$y = 5 \qquad\qquad y = 1$$

The solution set is $\{1, 5\}$.

53. Solve $\dfrac{3}{y+1} - \dfrac{1}{1-y} = \dfrac{10}{y^2-1}$.

Factor the denominators.

$$\frac{3}{y+1} - \frac{(-1)\cdot 1}{(-1)(1-y)} = \frac{10}{(y+1)(y-1)}$$

$$\frac{3}{y+1} - \frac{-1}{y-1} = \frac{10}{(y+1)(y-1)}$$

$$\frac{3}{y+1} + \frac{1}{y-1} = \frac{10}{(y+1)(y-1)}$$

Restrictions: $y \neq -1, y \neq 1$

$\text{LCD} = (y+1)(y-1)$

$$(y+1)(y-1)\left(\frac{3}{y+1} + \frac{1}{y-1}\right) = (y+1)(y-1)\left(\frac{10}{(y+1)(y-1)}\right)$$

$$(y-1)\cdot 3 + (y+1)\cdot 1 = 10$$

$$3y - 3 + y + 1 = 10$$

$$4y - 2 = 10$$

$$4y = 12$$

$$y = 3$$

The solution set is $\{3\}$.

55. $C = \dfrac{400x + 500{,}000}{x}; C = 450$

$450 = \dfrac{400x + 500{,}000}{x}$

LCD $= x$

$x \cdot 450 = x\left(\dfrac{400x + 500{,}000}{x}\right)$

$450x = 400x + 500{,}000$

$50x = 500{,}000$

$x = 10{,}000$

At an average cost of $450 per wheelchair, 10,000 wheelchairs can be produced.

57. $C = \dfrac{2x}{100 - x}; C = 2$

$2 = \dfrac{2x}{100 - x}$

LCD $= 100 - x$

$(100 - x) \cdot 2 = (100 - x) \cdot \dfrac{2x}{100 - x}$

$200 - 2x = 2x$

$200 = 4x$

$50 = x$

For $2 million, 50% of the contaminants can be removed.

59. $C = \dfrac{DA}{A + 12}; C = 300, D = 1000$

$300 = \dfrac{1000A}{A + 12}$

LCD $= A + 12$

$(A + 12) \cdot 300 = (A + 12)\left(\dfrac{1000A}{A + 12}\right)$

$300A + 3600 = 1000A$

$3600 = 700A$

$\dfrac{3600}{700} = A$

$A = \dfrac{36}{7} \approx 5.14$

To the nearest year, the child is 5 years old.

61. $C = \dfrac{10{,}000}{x} + 3x; C = 350$

$350 = \dfrac{10{,}000}{x} + 3x$

LCD $= x$

$x \cdot 350 = x\left(\dfrac{10{,}000}{x} + 3x\right)$

$350x = 10{,}000 + 3x^2$

$0 = 3x^2 - 350x + 10{,}000$

$0 = (3x - 200)(x - 50)$

$3x - 200 = 0 \quad \text{or} \quad x - 50 = 0$

$3x = 200 \qquad\qquad x = 50$

$x = \dfrac{200}{3}$

$= 66\dfrac{2}{3} \approx 67$

For yearly inventory costs to be $350, the owner should order either 50 or approximately 67 cases. These solutions correspond to the points $(50, 350)$ and $\left(66\dfrac{2}{3}, 350\right)$ on the graph.

63. – 67. Answers will vary.

69. makes sense

71. does not make sense; Explanations will vary. Sample explanation: If all potential solutions make any of the denominators of the rational equation equal to zero, then the equation will have no solution.

73. true

75. false; Changes to make the statement true will vary. A sample change is: You could begin by multiplying both sides by the LCD, $3x$.

77. $f = \dfrac{f_1 f_2}{f_1 + f_2}$ for f_2

$f = \dfrac{f_1 f_2}{f_1 + f_2}$

Multiply both sides by the LCD, $f_1 + f_2$.

$(f_1 + f_2) \cdot f = (f_1 + f_2)\left(\dfrac{f_1 f_2}{f_1 + f_2}\right)$

$f f_1 + f f_2 = f_1 f_2$

Get all terms containing f_2 on one side and all terms not containing f_2 on the other side.

$f f_2 - f_1 f_2 = -f_1 f$

Factor out the common factor f_2 on the left side.

$f_2 (f - f_1) = -f_1 f$

Divide both sides by $f - f_1$.

$\dfrac{f_2 (f - f_1)}{f - f_1} = \dfrac{-f_1 f}{f - f_1}$

$f_2 = \dfrac{-f_1 f}{f - f_1}$ or $\dfrac{f f_1}{f_1 - f}$

79. $\left(\dfrac{x+1}{x+7}\right)^2 \div \left(\dfrac{x+1}{x+7}\right)^4 = 0$

$\left(\dfrac{x+1}{x+7}\right)^2 \cdot \left(\dfrac{x+7}{x+1}\right)^4 = 0$

$\dfrac{(x+1)^2}{(x+7)^2} \cdot \dfrac{(x+7)^4}{(x+1)^4} = 0$

Restrictions: $x \neq -7, x \neq -1$

$\dfrac{(x+7)^2}{(x+1)^2} = 0$

Multiply both sides by $(x+1)^2$.

$(x+1)^2 \left[\dfrac{(x+7)^2}{(x+1)^2}\right] = (x+1)^2 \cdot 0$

$(x+7)^2 = 0$

$x + 7 = 0$

$x = -7$

The proposed solution, -7, is *not* a solution of the original equation because it is on the list of restrictions. Therefore, the given equation has no solution. The solution set is $\{\ \}$.

81. $\dfrac{x}{2} + \dfrac{x}{4} = 6$

The solution set is $\{8\}$.

Check $x = 8$:

$\dfrac{8}{2} + \dfrac{8}{4} = 6$

$4 + 2 = 6$

$6 = 6$ true

83. $x + \dfrac{6}{x} = -5$

The solution set is $\{-3, -2\}$.

Check -3:

$x + \dfrac{6}{x} = -5$

$-3 + \dfrac{6}{-3} = -5$

$-3 + (-2) = -5$

$-5 = -5$, true

Check -2:

$x + \dfrac{6}{x} = -5$

$-2 + \dfrac{6}{-2} = -5$

$-2 + (-3) = -5$

$-5 = -5$, true

84. $x^4 + 2x^3 - 3x - 6$

Factor by grouping.

$x^4 + 2x^3 - 3x - 6$

$= \left(x^4 + 2x^3\right) + \left(-3x - 6\right)$

$= x^3 (x + 2) - 3(x + 2)$

$= (x + 2)\left(x^3 - 3\right)$

85. $\left(3x^2\right)\left(-4x^{-10}\right)$

$= \left(3 \cdot -4\right)\left(x^2 \cdot x^{-10}\right) = -12x^{2+(-10)}$

$= -12x^{-8} = -\dfrac{12}{x^8}$

86. $-5\left[4(x-2)-3\right] = -5\left[4x-8-3\right]$

$= -5\left[4x-11\right]$

$= -20x + 55$

87.

$$\dfrac{15}{8+x} = \dfrac{9}{8-x}$$

$$(8+x)(8-x)\dfrac{15}{8+x} = (8+x)(8-x)\dfrac{9}{8-x}$$

$$15(8-x) = 9(8+x)$$

$$120 - 15x = 72 + 9x$$

$$-24x = -48$$

$$x = 2$$

The solution set is $\{2\}$.

88. In 1 hour you can complete $\dfrac{1}{5}$ of the job.

In 3 hours you can complete $\dfrac{3}{5}$ of the job.

In x hours you can complete $\dfrac{x}{5}$ of the job.

89. a. $y = \dfrac{k}{x}$

$12 = \dfrac{k}{8}$

$12 \cdot 8 = k$

$96 = k$

b. $y = \dfrac{k}{x}$

$y = \dfrac{96}{x}$

c. $y = \dfrac{96}{x}$

$y = \dfrac{96}{3}$

$y = 32$

8.7 Check Points

1. Let x = the rate of the current.
   Then $3 + x$ = the canoe's rate with the current.
   and $3 - x$ = the canoe's rate against the current.

	Distance	Rate	Time $= \dfrac{\text{Distance}}{\text{Rate}}$
With the current	10	$3 + x$	$\dfrac{10}{3 + x}$
Against the current	2	$3 - x$	$\dfrac{2}{3 - x}$

   $$\frac{10}{3 + x} = \frac{2}{3 - x}$$

   Use the cross-products principle to solve this equation.

   $$\frac{10}{3 + x} = \frac{2}{3 - x}$$
   $$10(3 - x) = 2(3 + x)$$
   $$30 - 10x = 6 + 2x$$
   $$30 - 12x = 6$$
   $$-12x = -24$$
   $$x = 2$$

   The rate of the current is 2 miles per hour.

2. Let x = the number of hours for both people to paint a house together.

	Fractional part of job completed in 1 hour	Time working together	Fractional part of job completed in x hours
First person	$\dfrac{1}{8}$	x	$\dfrac{x}{8}$
Second person	$\dfrac{1}{4}$	x	$\dfrac{x}{4}$

   Working together, the two people can complete the whole job, so $\dfrac{x}{8} + \dfrac{x}{4} = 1$.

   Multiply both sides by the LCD, 8.

   $$8\left(\frac{x}{8} + \frac{x}{4}\right) = 8 \cdot 1$$
   $$x + 2x = 8$$
   $$3x = 8$$
   $$x = \frac{8}{3}$$
   $$x = 2\frac{2}{3}$$

   It will take $2\frac{2}{3}$ hours (or 2 hours 40 minutes) if the work together.

3. $\dfrac{3}{8} = \dfrac{12}{x}$

$3x = 8 \cdot 12$

$3x = 96$

$x = 32$

The missing length is 32 inches.

4. $\dfrac{h}{2} = \dfrac{56}{3.5}$

$3.5h = 2 \cdot 56$

$3.5h = 112$

$h = \dfrac{112}{3.5}$

$h = 32$

The height of the tower is 32 yards.

5. *Step 1* Write an equation. $W = kt$

Step 2 Use the given values to find k.
Substitute 30 for W and 5 for t.

$W = kt$

$30 = k \cdot 5$

$6 = k$

Step 3 Substitute the value of k into the equation
$W = 6t$

Step 4 Answer the problem's question. Substitute 8 for t and solve for W.
$W = 6t$

$W = 6 \cdot 8$

$W = 48$

A shower lasting 8 minutes will use 48 gallons of water.

6. *Step 1* Write an equation. $P = \dfrac{k}{V}$

Step 2 Use the given values to find k.
Substitute 12 for P and 8 for V.

$P = \dfrac{k}{V}$

$12 = \dfrac{k}{8}$

$12 \cdot 8 = k$

$96 = k$

Step 3 Substitute the value of k into the equation

$P = \dfrac{96}{V}$

Step 4 Answer the problem's question. Substitute 20 for V and solve for P.

$P = \dfrac{96}{V}$

$P = \dfrac{96}{20}$

$P = 4.8$

If the sample expands to a volume of 20 cubic inches, the new pressure of the gas will be 4.8 pounds per square inch.

8.7 Exercise Set

1. The times are equal, so $\dfrac{10}{x} = \dfrac{15}{x+3}$

To solve this equation, multiply both sides by the LCD, $x(x+3)$.

$$x(x+3) \cdot \dfrac{10}{x} = x(x+3) \cdot \dfrac{15}{x+3}$$
$$10(x+3) = 15x$$
$$10x + 30 = 15x$$
$$30 = 5x$$
$$6 = x$$

If $x = 6, x + 3 = 9$.

Note: The equation $\dfrac{10}{x} = \dfrac{15}{x+3}$ is a proportion, so it can also be solved by using the cross-products principle.

$$10(x+3) = 15x$$

This allows you to skip the first step of the solution process shown above.
The walking rate is 6 miles per hour and the car's rate is 9 miles per hour.

3. Let x = the jogger's rate running uphill.
Then $x + 4$ = the jogger's rate running downhill.

	Distance	Rate	Time = $\dfrac{\text{Distance}}{\text{Rate}}$
Cycling	5	$x+4$	$\dfrac{5}{x+4}$
Walking	3	x	$\dfrac{3}{x}$

The times are equal, so $\dfrac{5}{x+4} = \dfrac{3}{x}$.

Use the cross-products principle to solve this equation.
$$5x = 3(x+4)$$
$$5x = 3x + 12$$
$$2x = 12$$
$$x = 6$$

If $x = 6, x + 4 = 10$.
The jogger runs 10 miles per hour downhill and 6 miles per hour uphill.

5. Let x = the rate of the current.
Then $15 + x$ = the boat's rate with the current.
and $15 - x$ = the boat's rate against the current.

	Distance	Rate	Time $= \dfrac{\text{Distance}}{\text{Rate}}$
With the current	20	$15 + x$	$\dfrac{20}{15 + x}$
Against the current	10	$15 - x$	$\dfrac{10}{15 - x}$

$$\frac{20}{15 + x} = \frac{10}{15 - x}$$

Use the cross-products principle to solve this equation.

$$20(15 - x) = 10(15 + x)$$
$$300 - 20x = 150 + 10x$$
$$300 = 150 + 30x$$
$$150 = 30x$$
$$5 = x$$

The rate of the current is 5 miles per hour.

7. Let x = walking rate.
Then $2x$ = jogging rate.

	Distance	Rate	Time $= \dfrac{\text{Distance}}{\text{Rate}}$
Walking	2	x	$\dfrac{2}{x}$
Jogging	2	$2x$	$\dfrac{2}{2x}$

The total time is 1 hour, so

$$\frac{2}{x} + \frac{2}{2x} = 1$$
$$\frac{2}{x} + \frac{1}{x} = 1.$$

To solve this equation, multiply both sides by the LCD, x.

$$x\left(\frac{2}{x} + \frac{1}{x}\right) = x \cdot 1$$
$$2 + 1 = x$$
$$3 = x$$

If $x = 3$, $2x = 6$.
The walking rate is 3 miles per hour and the jogging rate is 6 miles per hour.

9. Let x = the boat's average rate in still water.
   Then $x+2$ = the boat's rate with the current (downstream).
   and $x-2$ = the boat's rate against the current (upstream).

	Distance	Rate	Time $= \dfrac{\text{Distance}}{\text{Rate}}$
Downstream	6	$x+2$	$\dfrac{6}{x+2}$
Upstream	4	$x-2$	$\dfrac{4}{x-2}$

The times are equal so solve the following equation.

$$\frac{6}{x+2} = \frac{4}{x-2}$$
$$6(x-2) = 4(x+2)$$
$$6x-12 = 4x+8$$
$$2x-12 = 8$$
$$2x = 20$$
$$x = 10$$

The boat's average rate in still water is 10 miles per hour.

11. Let x = the time in minutes, for both people to shovel the driveway together.

	Fractional part of job completed in 1 minute	Time working together	Fractional part of job completed in x minutes
You	$\dfrac{1}{20}$	x	$\dfrac{x}{20}$
Your brother	$\dfrac{1}{15}$	x	$\dfrac{x}{15}$

Working together, you and your brother complete the whole job, so $\dfrac{x}{20} + \dfrac{x}{15} = 1$.

Multiply both sides by the LCD, 60.

$$60\left(\frac{x}{20} + \frac{x}{15}\right) = 60 \cdot 1$$
$$3x + 4x = 60$$
$$7x = 60$$
$$x = \frac{60}{7} \approx 8.6$$

It will take about 8.6 minutes, which is enough time.

13. Let x = the time, in hours, for both teams to clean the streets working together.

	Fractional part of job completed in 1 hour	Time working together	Fractional part of job completed in x hours
First team	$\dfrac{1}{400}$	x	$\dfrac{x}{400}$
Second team	$\dfrac{1}{300}$	x	$\dfrac{x}{300}$

Working together, the two teams complete one whole job, so $\dfrac{x}{400}+\dfrac{x}{300}=1$.

Multiply both sides by the LCD, 1200.

$$1200\left(\frac{x}{400}+\frac{x}{300}\right)=1200\cdot 1$$
$$3x+4x=1200$$
$$7x=1200$$
$$x=\frac{1200}{7}\approx 171.4$$

It will take about 171.4 hours for both teams to clean the streets working together. One week is $7\cdot 24 = 168$ hours, so even if both crews work 24 hours a day, there is not enough time.

15. Let x = the time, in hours, for both pipes to fill in the pool.

	Fractional part of job completed in 1 hour	Time working together	Fractional part of job completed in x hours
First pipe	$\dfrac{1}{4}$	x	$\dfrac{x}{4}$
Second pipe	$\dfrac{1}{6}$	x	$\dfrac{x}{6}$

$$\frac{x}{4}+\frac{x}{6}=1$$
$$12\left(\frac{x}{4}+\frac{x}{6}\right)=12\cdot 1$$
$$3x+2x=12$$
$$5x=12$$
$$x=\frac{12}{5}=2.4$$

Using both pipes, it will take 2.4 hours or 2 hours 24 minutes to fill the pool.

17. $\dfrac{18}{9}=\dfrac{10}{x}$

$18x=9\cdot 10$

$18x=90$

$x=5$

The length of the side marked x is 5 inches.

19. $\dfrac{10}{30} = \dfrac{x}{18}$

$30x = 10 \cdot 18$

$30x = 180$

$x = 6$

The length of the side marked x is 6 meters.

21. $\dfrac{20}{15} = \dfrac{x}{12}$

$15x = 12 \cdot 20$

$15x = 240$

$x = 16$

The length of the side marked x is 16 inches.

23. $\dfrac{8}{6} = \dfrac{x}{12}$

$6x = 8 \cdot 12$

$6x = 96$

$x = 16$

The tree is 16 feet tall.

25. $g = kh$

27. $w = \dfrac{k}{v}$

29. $y = kx$

To find k, substitute 80 for y and 4 for x.

$80 = k \cdot 4$

$20 = k$

The constant of variation is 20.

31. $W = \dfrac{k}{r}$

To find k, substitute 600 for W and 10 for r.

$600 = \dfrac{k}{10}$

$600 \cdot 10 = \dfrac{k}{10} \cdot 10$

$6000 = k$

The constant of variation is 6000.

33. *Step 1* Write an equation. $y = kx$

Step 2 Use the given values to find k.

Substitute 35 for y and 5 for x.

$35 = k \cdot 5$

$7 = k$

Step 3 Substitute the value of k into the equation

$y = 7k$

Step 4 Answer the question. Substitute 12 for x and solve for y.

$y = 7 \cdot 12 = 84$

35. *Step 1* $y = \dfrac{k}{x}$

Step 2 Substitute 10 for y and 5 for x.

$10 = \dfrac{k}{5}$

$50 = k$

Step 3 $y = \dfrac{50}{x}$

Step 4 Substitute 2 for x and solve for y.

$y = \dfrac{50}{2}$

$y = 25$

37. **a.** $G = kW$

   b. $G = 0.02W$

   c. $G = 0.02(52) = 1.04$

   Your fingernails would grow 1.04 inches in one year.

39. *Step 1* Write an equation. $C = kM$

Step 2 Use the given values to find k.

$400 = k \cdot 3000$

$\dfrac{400}{3000} = k$

$\dfrac{2}{15} = k$

Step 3 Substitute the value of k into the equation.

$C = \dfrac{2}{15}M$

Step 4 Answer the problem's question. Substitute 450 for M and solve for C.

$C = \dfrac{2}{15}(450) = 60$

The cost of a 450-mile trip is $60.

41. Let s = speed.
Then M = Mach number.
Step 1 $s = kM$
Step 2 To find k, substitute 1502.2 for s and 2.03 for M.
$$1502.2 = k \cdot 2.03$$
$$\frac{150.2}{2.03} = k$$
$$740 = k$$
Step 3 Substitute 740 for k.
$$s = 740M$$
Step 4 Substitute 3.3 for M and solve for s.
$$s = 740(3.3) = 2442$$
The speed of the Blackbird is 2442 miles per hour.

43. Let t = driving time.
Let r = driving rate.
Step 1 $t = \dfrac{k}{r}$
Step 2 $1.5 = \dfrac{k}{20}$
$$1.5 \cdot 20 = \frac{k}{20} \cdot 20$$
$$30 = k$$
Step 3 $t = \dfrac{30}{r}$
Step 4 $t = \dfrac{30}{60} = 0.5$
The trip would take 0.5 hour (or 30 minutes) at an average rate of 60 miles per hour.

45. Let V = volume and P = pressure.
Step 1 $V = \dfrac{k}{P}$
Step 2 $32 = \dfrac{k}{8}$
$$256 = k$$
Step 3 $V = \dfrac{256}{P}$
Step 4 $40 = \dfrac{256}{P}$
$$40P = 256$$
$$P = 6.4$$
When the volume is 40 cubic centimeters, the pressure is 6.4 pounds per square centimeter.

47. Let n = the number of pens.
Then p = the price per pen.
Step 1 $n = \dfrac{k}{p}$
Step 2 To find k, substitute 4000 for n and 1.50 for p.
$$4000 = \frac{k}{1.50}$$
$$4000 \cdot 1.50 = \frac{k}{1.50} \cdot 150$$
$$6000 = k$$
Step 3 $n = \dfrac{6000}{p}$
Step 4 Substitute 1.20 for p and solve for n.
$$n = \frac{6000}{1.20} = 5000$$
There will be 5000 pens sold at $1.20 each.

49. – 61. Answers will vary.

63. does not make sense; Explanations will vary.
Sample explanation: In the same amount of time, you will go further with the current than against it.

65. makes sense

67. Let x = the usual average rate.

Then $x - 15$ = the average rate, in miles per hour, of the bus in the snowstorm.

	Distance	Rate	Time $= \dfrac{\text{Distance}}{\text{Rate}}$
Usual conditions	60	x	$\dfrac{60}{x}$
Snowstorm conditions	60	$x - 15$	$\dfrac{60}{x - 15}$

Since the time during the snowstorm is 2 hours longer than the usual time, solve the following equation.

$$\frac{60}{x} + 2 = \frac{60}{x - 15}$$

Multiply both sides of the equation by the LCD, $x(x - 15)$

$$x(x-15)\left(\frac{60}{x} + 2\right) = x(x-15)\left(\frac{60}{x-15}\right)$$

$$(x-15) \cdot 60 + x(x-15) \cdot 2 = 60x$$

$$60x - 900 + 2x^2 - 30x = 60x$$

$$2x^2 + 30x - 900 = 60x$$

$$2x^2 - 30x - 900 = 0$$

$$x^2 - 15x - 450 = 0$$

$$(x-30)(x+15) = 0$$

$$x - 30 = 0 \quad \text{or} \quad x + 15 = 0$$

$$x = 30 \qquad\quad x = -15$$

Since the rate cannot be negative, the solution is 30. Therefore, the usual average rate of the bus is 30 miles per hour.

69. Let x = the time, in hours, it takes to prepare one report working together.

	Fractional part of job completed in 1 hour	Time working together	Fractional part of job completed in x hours
Ben	$\dfrac{1}{3}$	x	$\dfrac{x}{3}$
Shane	$\dfrac{1}{4.2} = \dfrac{10}{42} = \dfrac{5}{21}$	x	$\dfrac{5x}{21}$

Working together, Ben and Shane prepare one report, so $\dfrac{x}{3} + \dfrac{5x}{21} = 1$

To solve this equation, multiply both sides by the LCD, 21.

$$21 \cdot \left(\frac{x}{3} + \frac{5x}{21}\right) = 21 \cdot 1$$

$$7x + 5x = 21$$

$$12x = 21$$

$$x = \frac{21}{12} = 1.75$$

Ben and Shane can prepare one report in 1.75 hours. Multiply this by four to determine how many hours it takes to prepare four reports. $4(1.75) = 7$. Therefore, working together Ben and Shane can prepare four reports in 7 hours.

71. Let $x =$ time, in hours, to fill empty swimming pool.

	Fractional part of job completed in 1 hour	Time working together	Fractional part of job completed in x hours
Normal filling of pool	$\dfrac{1}{2}$	x	$\dfrac{x}{2}$
Leak	$-\dfrac{1}{10}$	x	$-\dfrac{x}{10}$

The situation can be modeled by the equation $\dfrac{x}{2} - \dfrac{x}{10} = 1$.

Multiply both sides of the equation by the LCD, 20.

$$20 \cdot \left(\frac{x}{2} - \frac{x}{10} \right) = 20 \cdot 1$$
$$10x - 2x = 20$$
$$8x = 20$$
$$x = 2.5$$

It will take 2.5 hours to fill the empty swimming pool.

73. Let $x =$ lower interest rate and $x + 1 =$ higher interest rate.

	Principal	Interest rate	Interest earned
Investment at higher interest rate	$\dfrac{200}{x+1}$	$x+1$	200
Investment at lower interest rate	$\dfrac{175}{x}$	x	175

Since the principal is the same at each rate, solve the following equation.

$$\frac{200}{x+1} = \frac{175}{x}$$
$$200x = 175(x+1)$$
$$200x = 175x + 175$$
$$25x = 175$$
$$x = 7$$

Therefore, the lower interest rate is 7% and the higher interest rate is 8%.

74. $25x^2 - 81 = (5x)^2 - 9^2$
$\qquad\qquad\quad = (5x+9)(5x-9)$

75. $x^2 - 12x + 36 = 0$
$\qquad (x-6)^2 = 0$
$\qquad\quad x - 6 = 0$
$\qquad\qquad\quad x = 6$

The solution set is $\{6\}$.

76. $y = -\dfrac{2}{3}x + 4$

slope $= -\dfrac{2}{3} = \dfrac{-2}{3}$

y-intercept $= 4$

Plot (0,4). From this point, move 2 units *down* and 3 units to the *right* to reach the point (3,2). Draw a line through (0,4) and (3,2).

77. $\sqrt{x-1} = \sqrt{17-1} = \sqrt{16} = 4$

78. $4\sqrt{x} + 30 = 4\sqrt{25} + 30 = 4 \cdot 5 + 30 = 20 + 30 = 50$

79. $(-2)^5 - (-1)^3 = (-1)^5 \cdot 2^5 - (-1)^3$
$\qquad\qquad = -1 \cdot 32 - (-1)$
$\qquad\qquad = -32 + 1$
$\qquad\qquad = -31$

Chapter 8 Review

1. $\dfrac{5x}{6x - 24}$

Set the denominator equal to 0 and solve for x.
$6x - 24 = 0$
$\qquad 6x = 24$
$\qquad\ x = 4$

The rational expression is undefined for $x = 4$.

2. $\dfrac{x+3}{(x-2)(x+5)}$

Set the denominator equal to 0 and solve for x.
$(x-2)(x+5) = 0$
$x - 2 = 0$ or $x + 5 = 0$
$\quad x = 2 \qquad\quad x = -5$

The rational expression is undefined for $x = 2$ and $x = -5$.

3. $\dfrac{x^2 + 3}{x^2 - 3x + 2}$

$x^2 - 3x + 2 = 0$
$(x-1)(x-2) = 0$
$x - 1 = 0$ or $x - 2 = 0$
$\quad x = 1 \qquad\quad x = 2$

The rational expression is undefined for $x = 1$ and $x = 2$.

4. $\dfrac{7}{x^2 + 81}$

The smallest possible value of x^2 is 0, so

$x^2 + 81 \geq 81$ for all real numbers x. This means that there is no real number for x for which

$x^2 + 81 = 0$. Thus, the rational expression is defined for all real numbers.

5. $\dfrac{16x^2}{12x} = \dfrac{4 \cdot 4 \cdot x \cdot x}{4 \cdot 3 \cdot x} = \dfrac{4x}{3}$

6. $\dfrac{x^2 - 4}{x - 2} = \dfrac{(x+2)(x-2)}{(x-2)} = x + 2$

7. $\dfrac{x^3 + 2x^2}{x + 2} = \dfrac{x^2(x+2)}{(x+2)} = x^2$

8. $\dfrac{x^2 + 3x - 18}{x^2 - 36} = \dfrac{(x+6)(x-3)}{(x+6)(x-6)}$
$\qquad\qquad\qquad = \dfrac{x-3}{x-6}$

9. $\dfrac{x^2 - 4x - 5}{x^2 + 8x + 7} = \dfrac{(x+1)(x-5)}{(x+1)(x+7)}$
$\qquad\qquad\qquad = \dfrac{x-5}{x+7}$

10. $\dfrac{y^2 + 2y}{y^2 + 4y + 4} = \dfrac{y(y+2)}{(y+2)(y+2)}$
$\qquad\qquad\qquad = \dfrac{y}{y+2}$

11. $\dfrac{x^2}{x^2 + 4}$

The numerator and denominator have no common factor, so this rational expression cannot be simplified.

12. $\dfrac{2x^2 - 18y^2}{3y - x} = \dfrac{2\left(x^2 - 9y^2\right)}{3y - x}$

$\qquad = \dfrac{2(x+3y)(x-3y)}{(3y-x)}$

$\qquad = \dfrac{2(x+3y)(-1)(3y-x)}{(3y-x)}$

$\qquad = -2(x+3y) \text{ or } -2x - 6y$

13. $\dfrac{x^2 - 4}{12x} \cdot \dfrac{3x}{x+2} = \dfrac{(x+2)(x-2)}{12x} \cdot \dfrac{3x}{(x+2)}$

$\qquad\qquad = \dfrac{x-2}{4}$

14. $\dfrac{5x+5}{6} \cdot \dfrac{3x}{x^2 + x} = \dfrac{5(x+1)}{6} \cdot \dfrac{3x}{x(x+1)}$

$\qquad\qquad\quad = \dfrac{5}{2}$

15. $\dfrac{x^2 + 6x + 9}{x^2 - 4} \cdot \dfrac{x-2}{x+3}$

$\qquad = \dfrac{(x+3)(x+3)}{(x+2)(x-2)} \cdot \dfrac{x-2}{x+3}$

$\qquad = \dfrac{x+3}{x+2}$

16. $\dfrac{y^2 - 2y + 1}{y^2 - 1} \cdot \dfrac{2y^2 + y - 1}{5y - 5}$

$\qquad = \dfrac{(y-1)(y-1)}{(y+1)(y-1)} \cdot \dfrac{(2y-1)(y+1)}{5(y-1)}$

$\qquad = \dfrac{2y-1}{5}$

17. $\dfrac{2y^2 + y - 3}{4y^2 - 9} \cdot \dfrac{3y+3}{5y - 5y^2}$

$\qquad = \dfrac{(2y+3)(y-1)}{(2y+3)(2y-3)} \cdot \dfrac{3(y+1)}{5y(1-y)}$

$\qquad = \dfrac{-3(y+1)}{5y(2y-3)} \text{ or } -\dfrac{3(y+1)}{5y(2y-3)}$

18. $\dfrac{x^2 + x - 2}{10} \div \dfrac{2x+4}{5}$

$\qquad = \dfrac{x^2 + x - 2}{10} \cdot \dfrac{5}{2x+4}$

$\qquad = \dfrac{(x-1)(x+2)}{10} \cdot \dfrac{5}{2(x+2)}$

$\qquad = \dfrac{x-1}{4}$

19. $\dfrac{6x+2}{x^2 - 1} \div \dfrac{3x^2 + x}{x - 1}$

$\qquad = \dfrac{6x+2}{x^2 - 1} \cdot \dfrac{x-1}{3x^2 + x}$

$\qquad = \dfrac{2(3x+1)}{(x+1)(x-1)} \cdot \dfrac{(x-1)}{x(3x+1)}$

$\qquad = \dfrac{2}{x(x+1)}$

20. $\dfrac{1}{y^2 + 8y + 15} \div \dfrac{7}{y+5}$

$\qquad = \dfrac{1}{y^2 + 8y + 15} \cdot \dfrac{y+5}{7}$

$\qquad = \dfrac{1}{(y+3)(y+5)} \cdot \dfrac{(y+5)}{7}$

$\qquad = \dfrac{1}{7(y+3)}$

21. $\dfrac{y^2 + y - 42}{y - 3} \div \dfrac{y+7}{(y-3)^2}$

$\qquad = \dfrac{y^2 + y - 42}{y - 3} \cdot \dfrac{(y-3)^2}{y+7}$

$\qquad = \dfrac{(y+7)(y-6)}{(y-3)} \cdot \dfrac{(y-3)(y-3)}{y+7}$

$\qquad = (y-6)(y-3) \text{ or } y^2 - 9y + 18$

22. $\dfrac{8x+8y}{x^2} \div \dfrac{x^2-y^2}{x^2}$

$= \dfrac{8x+8y}{x^2} \cdot \dfrac{x^2}{x^2-y^2}$

$= \dfrac{8(x+y)}{x^2} \cdot \dfrac{x^2}{(x+y)(x-y)}$

$= \dfrac{8}{x-y}$

23. $\dfrac{4x}{x+5} + \dfrac{20}{x+5} = \dfrac{4x+20}{x+5} = \dfrac{4(x+5)}{x+5} = 4$

24. $\dfrac{8x-5}{3x-1} + \dfrac{4x+1}{3x-1} = \dfrac{8x-5+4x+1}{3x-1}$

$= \dfrac{12x-4}{3x-1}$

$= \dfrac{4(3x-1)}{3x-1} = 4$

25. $\dfrac{3x^2+2x}{x-1} - \dfrac{10x-5}{x-1}$

$= \dfrac{(3x^2+2x)-(10x-5)}{x-1}$

$= \dfrac{3x^2+2x-10x+5}{x-1}$

$= \dfrac{3x^2-8x+5}{x-1}$

$= \dfrac{(3x-5)(x-1)}{x-1}$

$= 3x-5$

26. $\dfrac{6y^2-4y}{2y-3} - \dfrac{12-3y}{2y-3}$

$= \dfrac{(6y^2-4y)-(12-3y)}{2y-3}$

$= \dfrac{6y^2-4y-12+3y}{2y-3}$

$= \dfrac{6y^2-y-12}{2y-3}$

$= \dfrac{(2y-3)(3y+4)}{2y-3}$

$= 3y+4$

27. $\dfrac{x}{x-2} + \dfrac{x-4}{2-x} = \dfrac{x}{x-2} + \dfrac{(-1)}{(-1)} \cdot \dfrac{x-4}{x-2}$

$= \dfrac{x}{x-2} + \dfrac{-x+4}{x-2}$

$= \dfrac{x-x+4}{x-2} = \dfrac{4}{x-2}$

28. $\dfrac{x+5}{x-3} - \dfrac{x}{3-x} = \dfrac{x+5}{x-3} - \dfrac{(-1)}{(-1)} \cdot \dfrac{x}{3-x}$

$= \dfrac{x+5}{x-3} + \dfrac{x}{x-3}$

$= \dfrac{x+5+x}{x-3} = \dfrac{2x+5}{x-5}$

29. $\dfrac{7}{9x^3}$ and $\dfrac{5}{12x}$

$9x^3 = 3^2 x^3$

$12x = 2^2 \cdot 3x$

$\text{LCD} = 2^2 \cdot 3^2 \cdot x^3 = 36x^3$

30. $\dfrac{3}{x^2(x-1)}$ and $\dfrac{11}{x(x-1)^2}$

$\text{LCD} = x^2(x-1)^2$

31. $\dfrac{x}{x^2+4x+3}$ and $\dfrac{17}{x^2+10x+21}$

$x^2+4x+3 = (x+3)(x+1)$

$x^2+10x+21 = (x+3)(x+7)$

$\text{LCD} = (x+3)(x+1)(x+7)$

32. $\dfrac{7}{3x} + \dfrac{5}{2x^2}$

$\text{LCD} = 6x^2$

$\dfrac{7}{3x} + \dfrac{6}{2x^2} = \dfrac{7}{3x} \cdot \dfrac{2x}{2x} + \dfrac{5}{2x^2} \cdot \dfrac{3}{3}$

$= \dfrac{14x+15}{6x^2}$

33. $\dfrac{5}{x+1}+\dfrac{2}{x}$

$LCD = x(x+1)$

$\dfrac{5}{x+1}+\dfrac{2}{x}=\dfrac{5x}{x(x+1)}+\dfrac{2(x+1)}{x(x+1)}$

$\qquad=\dfrac{5x+2(x+1)}{x(x+1)}=\dfrac{5x+2x+2}{x(x+1)}$

$\qquad=\dfrac{7x+2}{x(x+1)}$

34. $\dfrac{7}{x+3}+\dfrac{4}{(x+3)^2}$

$LCD = (x+3)^2$ or $(x+3)(x+3)$

$\dfrac{7}{x+3}+\dfrac{4}{(x+3)^2}$

$=\dfrac{7}{x+3}+\dfrac{4}{(x+3)(x+3)}$

$=\dfrac{7(x+3)}{(x+3)(x+3)}+\dfrac{4}{(x+3)(x+3)}$

$=\dfrac{7(x+3)+4}{(x+3)(x+3)}=\dfrac{7x+21+4}{(x+3)(x+3)}$

$=\dfrac{7x+25}{(x+3)(x+3)}$ or $\dfrac{7x+25}{(x+3)^2}$

35. $\dfrac{6y}{y^2-4}-\dfrac{3}{y+2}$

$y^2-4=(y+2)(y-2)$

$y+2=1(y+2)$

$LCD = (y+2)(y-2)$

$\dfrac{6y}{y^2-4}-\dfrac{3}{y+2}$

$=\dfrac{6y}{(y+2)(y-2)}-\dfrac{3}{y+2}$

$=\dfrac{6y}{(y+2)(y-2)}-\dfrac{3(y-2)}{(y+2)(y-2)}$

$=\dfrac{6y-3(y-2)}{(y+2)(y-2)}=\dfrac{6y-3y+6}{(y+2)(y-2)}$

$=\dfrac{3y+6}{(y+2)(y-2)}=\dfrac{3(y+2)}{(y+2)(y-2)}$

$=\dfrac{3}{y-2}$

36. $\dfrac{y-1}{y^2-2y+1}-\dfrac{y+1}{y-1}$

$=\dfrac{y-1}{(y-1)(y-1)}-\dfrac{y+1}{y-1}$

$=\dfrac{1}{y-1}-\dfrac{y+1}{y-1}$

$=\dfrac{1-(y+1)}{y-1}=\dfrac{1-y-1}{y-1}$

$=\dfrac{-y}{y-1}$ or $-\dfrac{y}{y-1}$

37. $\dfrac{x+y}{y} - \dfrac{y-x}{x}$

LCD $= xy$

$\dfrac{x+y}{y} - \dfrac{y-x}{x} = \dfrac{(x+y)}{y} \cdot \dfrac{x}{x} - \dfrac{(x-y)}{x} \cdot \dfrac{y}{y}$

$\phantom{\dfrac{x+y}{y} - \dfrac{y-x}{x}} = \dfrac{x^2+xy}{xy} - \dfrac{xy-y^2}{xy}$

$\phantom{\dfrac{x+y}{y} - \dfrac{y-x}{x}} = \dfrac{\left(x^2+xy\right) - \left(xy - y^2\right)}{xy}$

$\phantom{\dfrac{x+y}{y} - \dfrac{y-x}{x}} = \dfrac{x^2 + xy - xy + y^2}{xy}$

$\phantom{\dfrac{x+y}{y} - \dfrac{y-x}{x}} = \dfrac{x^2 + y^2}{xy}$

38. $\dfrac{2x}{x^2+2x+1} + \dfrac{x}{x^2-1}$

$x^2 + 2x + 1 = (x+1)(x+1)$

$x^2 - 1 = (x+1)(x-1)$

LCD $= (x+1)(x+1)(x-1)$

$\dfrac{2x}{x^2+2x+1} + \dfrac{x}{x^2-1}$

$= \dfrac{2x}{(x+1)(x+1)} + \dfrac{x}{(x+1)(x-1)}$

$= \dfrac{2x(x-1)}{(x+1)(x+1)(x-1)} + \dfrac{x(x+1)}{(x+1)(x-1)(x+1)}$

$= \dfrac{2x(x-1) + x(x+1)}{(x+1)(x+1)(x-1)}$

$= \dfrac{2x^2 - 2x + x^2 + x}{(x+1)(x+1)(x-1)}$

$= \dfrac{3x^2 - x}{(x+1)(x+1)(x-1)}$

39. $\dfrac{5x}{x+1} - \dfrac{2x}{1-x^2}$

$x + 1 = 1(x+1)$

$1 - x^2 = -1\left(x^2 - 1\right) = -(x+1)(x-1)$

LCD $= (x+1)(x-1)$

$\dfrac{5x}{x+1} - \dfrac{2x}{1-x^2}$

$= \dfrac{5x}{x+1} - \dfrac{(-1)}{(-1)} \cdot \dfrac{2x}{1-x^2} = \dfrac{5x}{x+1} - \dfrac{-2x}{x^2-1}$

$= \dfrac{5x(x-1)}{(x+1)(x-1)} - \dfrac{-2x}{(x+1)(x-1)}$

$= \dfrac{5x(x-1) + 2x}{(x+1)(x-1)} = \dfrac{5x^2 - 5x + 2x}{(x+1)(x-1)}$

$= \dfrac{5x^2 - 3x}{(x+1)(x-1)}$

40. $\dfrac{4}{x^2-x-6} - \dfrac{4}{x^2-4}$

$x^2 - x - 6 = (x+2)(x-3)$

$x^2 - 4 = (x+2)(x-2)$

LCD $= (x+2)(x-3)(x-2)$

$\dfrac{4}{x^2-x-6} - \dfrac{4}{x^2-4}$

$= \dfrac{4}{(x+2)(x-3)} - \dfrac{4}{(x+2)(x-2)}$

$= \dfrac{4(x-2)}{(x+2)(x-3)(x-2)} - \dfrac{4(x-3)}{(x+2)(x-3)(x-2)}$

$= \dfrac{4(x-2) - 4(x-3)}{(x+2)(x-3)(x-2)}$

$= \dfrac{4x - 8 - 4x + 12}{(x+2)(x-3)(x-2)}$

$= \dfrac{4}{(x+2)(x-3)(x-2)}$

41. $\dfrac{7}{x+3}+2$

LCD $= x+3$

$\dfrac{7}{x+3}+2 = \dfrac{7}{x+3}+\dfrac{2(x+3)}{x+3}$

$\qquad = \dfrac{7+2(x+3)}{x+3}$

$\qquad = \dfrac{7+2x+6}{x+3}$

$\qquad = \dfrac{2x+13}{x+3}$

42. $\dfrac{2y-5}{6y+9}-\dfrac{4}{2y^2+3y}$

$6y+9 = 3(2y+3)$

$2y^2+3y = y(2y+3)$

LCD $= 3y(2y+3)$

$\dfrac{2y-5}{6y+9}-\dfrac{4}{2y^2+3y}$

$= \dfrac{2y-5}{3(2y+3)}-\dfrac{4}{y(2y+3)}$

$= \dfrac{(2y-5)(y)}{3(2y+3)(y)}-\dfrac{4(3)}{y(2y+3)(3)}$

$= \dfrac{2y^2-5y-12}{3y(2y+3)} = \dfrac{(2y+3)(y-4)}{3y(2y+3)}$

$= \dfrac{y-4}{3y}$

43. $\dfrac{\frac{1}{2}+\frac{3}{8}}{\frac{3}{4}-\frac{1}{2}} = \dfrac{\frac{4}{8}+\frac{3}{8}}{\frac{3}{4}-\frac{2}{4}} = \dfrac{\frac{7}{8}}{\frac{1}{4}} = \dfrac{7}{8}\cdot\dfrac{4}{1} = \dfrac{7}{2}$

44. $\dfrac{\frac{1}{x}}{1-\frac{1}{x}}$

LCD $= x$

$\dfrac{\frac{1}{x}}{1-\frac{1}{x}} = \dfrac{x}{x}\cdot\dfrac{\left(\frac{1}{x}\right)}{\left(1-\frac{1}{x}\right)}$

$= \dfrac{x\cdot\frac{1}{x}}{x\cdot 1-x\cdot\frac{1}{x}} = \dfrac{1}{x-1}$

45. $\dfrac{\frac{1}{x}+\frac{1}{y}}{\frac{1}{xy}}$

LCD $= xy$

$\dfrac{\frac{1}{x}+\frac{1}{y}}{\frac{1}{xy}} = \dfrac{xy}{xy}\cdot\dfrac{\left(\frac{1}{x}+\frac{1}{y}\right)}{\left(\frac{1}{xy}\right)}$

$= \dfrac{xy\cdot\frac{1}{x}+xy\cdot\frac{1}{y}}{xy\cdot\frac{1}{xy}}$

$= \dfrac{y+x}{1} = y+x \text{ or } x+y$

46. $\dfrac{\frac{1}{x}-\frac{1}{2}}{\frac{1}{3}-\frac{x}{6}} = \dfrac{\frac{2}{2x}-\frac{x}{2x}}{\frac{2}{6}-\frac{x}{6}} = \dfrac{\frac{2-x}{2x}}{\frac{2-x}{6}}$

$= \dfrac{2-x}{2x}\cdot\dfrac{6}{2-x} = \dfrac{3}{x}$

47. $\dfrac{3+\frac{12}{x}}{1-\frac{16}{x^2}}$

LCD $= x^2$

$\dfrac{3+\frac{12}{x}}{1-\frac{16}{x^2}} = \dfrac{x^2}{x^2}\cdot\dfrac{\left(3+\frac{12}{x}\right)}{\left(1-\frac{16}{x^2}\right)}$

$= \dfrac{x^2\cdot 3+x^2\cdot\frac{12}{x}}{x^2\cdot 1-x^2\cdot\frac{16}{x^2}} = \dfrac{3x^2+12x}{x^2-16}$

$= \dfrac{3x(x+4)}{(x+4)(x-4)} = \dfrac{3x}{x-4}$

48. $\dfrac{3}{x} - \dfrac{1}{6} = \dfrac{1}{x}$

The restriction is $x \neq 0$.
The LCD is $6x$.

$$\dfrac{3}{x} - \dfrac{1}{6} = \dfrac{1}{x}$$

$$6x\left(\dfrac{3}{x} - \dfrac{1}{6}\right) = 6x\left(\dfrac{1}{x}\right)$$

$$6x \cdot \dfrac{3}{x} - 6x \cdot \dfrac{1}{6} = 6x \cdot \dfrac{1}{x}$$

$$18 - x = 6$$

$$-x = -12$$

$$x = 12$$

The solution set is $\{12\}$.

49. $\dfrac{3}{4x} = \dfrac{1}{x} + \dfrac{1}{4}$

The restriction is $x \neq 0$.
The LCD is $4x$.

$$\dfrac{3}{4x} = \dfrac{1}{x} + \dfrac{1}{4}$$

$$4x\left(\dfrac{3}{4x}\right) = 4x\left(\dfrac{1}{x} + \dfrac{1}{4}\right)$$

$$3 = 4 + x$$

$$-1 = x$$

The solution set is $\{-1\}$.

50. $x + 5 = \dfrac{6}{x}$

The restriction is $x \neq 0$.
The LCD is x.

$$x + 5 = \dfrac{6}{x}$$

$$x(x+5) = x\left(\dfrac{6}{x}\right)$$

$$x^2 + 5x = 6$$

$$x^2 + 5x - 6 = 0$$

$$(x+6)(x-1) = 0$$

$$x + 6 = 0 \quad \text{or} \quad x - 1 = 0$$

$$x = -6 \qquad x = 1$$

The solution set is $\{-6, 1\}$.

51. $4 - \dfrac{x}{x+5} = \dfrac{5}{x+5}$

The restriction is $x \neq -5$.

The LCD is $x+5$.

$$(x+5)\left(4 - \frac{x}{x+5}\right) = (x+5)\left(\frac{5}{x+5}\right)$$

$$(x+5)\cdot 4 - (x+5)\left(\frac{x}{x+5}\right) = (x+5)\left(\frac{5}{x+5}\right)$$

$$4x + 20 - x = 5$$

$$3x + 20 = 5$$

$$3x = -15$$

$$x = -5$$

The only proposed solution, -5, is *not* a solution because of the restriction $x \neq -5$. Notice that -5 makes two of the denominators zero in the original equation. The solution set is $\{\ \}$.

52. $\dfrac{2}{x-3} = \dfrac{4}{x+3} + \dfrac{8}{x^2 - 9}$

To find any restrictions and the LCD, all denominators should be written in factored form.

$$\frac{2}{x-3} = \frac{4}{x+3} + \frac{8}{(x+3)(x-3)}$$

Restrictions: $x \neq 3, x \neq -3$

LCD $= (x+3)(x-3)$

$$(x+3)(x-3)\cdot\frac{2}{x-3} = (x+3)(x-3)\left(\frac{4}{x+3} + \frac{8}{(x+3)(x-3)}\right)$$

$$2(x+3) = 4(x-3) + 8$$

$$2x + 6 = 4x - 12 + 8$$

$$2x + 6 = 4x - 4$$

$$6 = 2x - 4$$

$$10 = 2x$$

$$5 = x$$

The solution set is $\{5\}$.

53. $\dfrac{2}{x} = \dfrac{2}{3} + \dfrac{x}{6}$

Restriction: $x \neq 0$

LCD $= 6x$

$$6x\left(\frac{2}{x}\right) = 6x\left(\frac{2}{3} + \frac{x}{6}\right)$$

$$12 = 4x + x^2$$

$$0 = x^2 + 4x - 12$$

$$0 = (x+6)(x-2)$$

$$x + 6 = 0 \quad \text{or} \quad x - 2 = 0$$

$$x = -6 \qquad\qquad x = 2$$

The solution set is $\{-6, 2\}$.

54. $\dfrac{13}{y-1} - 3 = \dfrac{1}{y-1}$

Restriction: $y \neq 1$

LCD $= y-1$

$$(y-1)\left(\dfrac{13}{y-1} - 3\right) = (y-1)\left(\dfrac{1}{y-1}\right)$$

$$13 - 3(y-1) = 1$$
$$13 - 3y + 3 = 1$$
$$16 - 3y = 1$$
$$-3y = -15$$
$$y = 5$$

The solution set is $\{5\}$.

55. $\dfrac{1}{x+3} - \dfrac{1}{x-1} = \dfrac{x+1}{x^2 + 2x - 3}$

$$\dfrac{1}{x+3} - \dfrac{1}{x-1} = \dfrac{x+1}{(x+3)(x-1)}$$

Restrictions: $x \neq -3, x \neq 1$

LCD $= (x+3)(x-1)$

$$(x+3)(x-1)\left[\dfrac{1}{x+3} - \dfrac{1}{x-1}\right] = (x+3)(x-1)\cdot\left[\dfrac{x+1}{(x+3)(x-1)}\right]$$

$$(x-1) - (x+3) = x+1$$
$$x - 1 - x - 3 = x + 1$$
$$-4 = x + 1$$
$$-5 = x$$

The solution set is $\{-5\}$.

56.

$$P = \dfrac{250(3t+5)}{t+25}$$

$$125 = \dfrac{250(3t+5)}{t+25}$$

$$125(t+25) = \dfrac{250(3t+5)}{t+25}\cdot(t+25)$$

$$125t + 3125 = 250(3t+5)$$
$$125t + 3125 = 750t + 1250$$
$$3125 = 625t + 1250$$
$$1875 = 625t$$
$$3 = t$$

It will take 3 years for the population to reach 125 elk.

57.

$$S = \frac{C}{1-r}$$

$$200 = \frac{140}{1-r}$$

$$200(1-r) = \frac{140}{1-r} \cdot 1 - r$$

$$200 - 200r = 140$$

$$-200r = -60$$

$$r = \frac{-60}{-200} = \frac{3}{10} = 30\%$$

The markup is 30%.

58. Let x = the rate of the current. Then $20 + x$ = the rate of the boat with the current and $20 - x$ = the rate of the boat against the current.

	Distance	Rate	Time $= \dfrac{\text{Distance}}{\text{Rate}}$
Downstream	72	$20 + x$	$\dfrac{72}{20+x}$
Upstream	48	$20 - x$	$\dfrac{48}{20-x}$

The times are equal, so

$$\frac{72}{20+x} = \frac{48}{20-x}$$

$$72(20-x) = 48(20+x)$$

$$1440 - 72x = 960 + 48x$$

$$1440 = 960 + 120x$$

$$480 = 120x$$

$$4 = x$$

The rate of the current is 4 miles per hour

59. Let x = the rate of the slower car. Then $x + 10$ = the rate of the faster car.

	Distance	Rate	Time $= \dfrac{\text{Distance}}{\text{Rate}}$
Slow car	60	x	$\dfrac{60}{x}$
Faster Car	90	$x + 10$	$\dfrac{90}{x+10}$

$$\frac{60}{x} = \frac{90}{x+10}$$

$$60(x+10) = 90x$$

$$60x + 600 = 90x$$

$$600 = 30x$$

$$20 = x$$

If $x = 20$, $x + 10 = 30$.

The rate of the slower car is 20 miles per hour and the rate of the faster car is 30 miles per hour.

60. Let x = the time, in hours, for both people to paint the fence together.

	Fractional part of job completed in 1 hour	Time working together	Fractional part of job completed in x hours
Painter	$\dfrac{1}{6}$	x	$\dfrac{x}{6}$
Apprentice	$\dfrac{1}{12}$	x	$\dfrac{x}{12}$

Working together, the two people complete one whole job, so $\dfrac{x}{6} + \dfrac{x}{12} = 1$.

Multiply both sides by the LCD, 12.

$$12\left(\frac{x}{6} + \frac{x}{12}\right) = 12 \cdot 1$$
$$2x + x = 12$$
$$3x = 12$$
$$x = 4$$

It would take them 4 hours to paint the fence working together.

61. $\dfrac{8}{4} = \dfrac{10}{x}$

$8x = 40$

$x = 5$

The length of the side marked with an x is 5 feet.

62. Write a proportion relating the corresponding sides of the large and small triangle. Notice that the length of the base of the larger triangle is 9 ft + 6ft = 15 ft.

$$\frac{x}{5} = \frac{15}{6}$$
$$6x = 5 \cdot 15$$
$$6x = 75$$
$$x = \frac{75}{6} = 12.5$$

The height of the lamppost is 12.5 feet.

63. Let b = electric bill (in dollars).

Then e = number of kilowatts of electricity used.

Step 1 $b = ke$

Step 2 To find k, substitute 98 for b and 1400 for e.

$$98 = k \cdot 1400$$
$$\frac{98}{1400} = k$$
$$0.07 = k$$

Step 3 $b = 0.07e$

Step 4 Substitute 2200 for e and solve for b.

$$b = 0.07(2200) = 154$$

The bill is $154 for 2200 kilowatts of electricity.

64. *Step 1* $\;t = \dfrac{k}{r}$

Step 2 To find k, substitute k, substitute 4 for t and 50 for r.

$$4 = \frac{k}{50}$$
$$200 = k$$

Step 3 $\;t = \dfrac{200}{r}$

Step 4 Substitute 40 for r and solve for t.

$$t = \frac{200}{40} = 5$$

At 40 miles per hour, the trip will take 5 hours.

Chapter 8 Test

1. $\dfrac{x+7}{x^2 + 5x - 36}$

Set the denominator equal to 0 and solve for x.

$$x^2 + 5x - 36 = 0$$
$$(x+9)(x-4) = 0$$
$$x + 9 = 0 \quad \text{or} \quad x - 4 = 0$$
$$x = -9 \qquad \quad x = 4$$

The rational expression is undefined for $x = -9$ and $x = 4$.

2. $\dfrac{x^2 + 2x - 3}{x^2 - 3x + 2} = \dfrac{(x-1)(x+3)}{(x-1)(x-2)} = \dfrac{x+3}{x-2}$

3. $\dfrac{4x^2 - 20x}{x^2 - 4x - 5} = \dfrac{4x(x-5)}{(x+1)(x-5)} = \dfrac{4x}{x+1}$

4. $\dfrac{x^2 - 16}{10} \cdot \dfrac{5}{x+4} = \dfrac{(x+4)(x-4)}{10} \cdot \dfrac{5}{(x+4)}$

$$= \dfrac{x-4}{2}$$

5. $\dfrac{x^2 - 7x + 12}{x^2 - 4x} \cdot \dfrac{x^2}{x^2 - 9}$

$$= \dfrac{(x-3)(x-4)}{x(x-4)} \cdot \dfrac{x^2}{(x+3)(x-3)}$$

$$= \dfrac{x}{x+3}$$

6. $\dfrac{2x+8}{x-3} \div \dfrac{x^2 + 5x + 4}{x^2 - 9}$

$$= \dfrac{2x+8}{x-3} \cdot \dfrac{x^2 - 9}{x^2 + 5x + 4}$$

$$= \dfrac{2(x+4)}{(x-3)} \cdot \dfrac{(x+3)(x-3)}{(x+4)(x+1)}$$

$$= \dfrac{2(x+3)}{x+1} = \dfrac{2x+6}{x+1}$$

7. $\dfrac{5y+5}{(y-3)^2} \div \dfrac{y^2 - 1}{y-3}$

$$= \dfrac{5y+5}{(y-3)^2} \cdot \dfrac{y-3}{y^2 - 1}$$

$$= \dfrac{5(y+1)}{(y-3)(y-3)} \cdot \dfrac{(y-3)}{(y+1)(y-1)}$$

$$= \dfrac{5}{(y-3)(y-1)}$$

8. $\dfrac{2y^2 + 5}{y+3} + \dfrac{6y-5}{y+3}$

$$= \dfrac{\left(2y^2 + 5\right) + (6y - 5)}{y+3}$$

$$= \dfrac{2y^2 + 5 + 6y - 5}{y+3}$$

$$= \dfrac{2y^2 + 6y}{y+3}$$

$$= \dfrac{2y(y+3)}{y+3} = 2y$$

9. $\dfrac{y^2-2y+3}{y^2+7y+12}-\dfrac{y^2-4y-5}{y^2+7y+12}$

$=\dfrac{\left(y^2-2y+3\right)-\left(y^2-4y-5\right)}{y^2+7y+12}$

$=\dfrac{y^2-2y+3-y^2+4y+5}{y^2+7y+12}$

$=\dfrac{2y+8}{y^2+7y+12}$

$=\dfrac{2(y+4)}{(y+3)(y+4)}$

$=\dfrac{2}{y+3}$

10. $\dfrac{x}{x+3}+\dfrac{5}{x-3}$

LCD $=(x+3)(x-3)$

$\dfrac{x}{x+3}+\dfrac{5}{x-3}$

$=\dfrac{x(x-3)}{(x+3)(x-3)}+\dfrac{5(x+3)}{(x+3)(x-3)}$

$=\dfrac{x(x-3)+5(x+3)}{(x+3)(x-3)}$

$=\dfrac{x^2-3x+5x+15}{(x+3)(x-3)}$

$=\dfrac{x^2+2x+15}{(x+3)(x-3)}$

11. $\dfrac{2}{x^2-4x+3}+\dfrac{6}{x^2+x-2}$

$x^2-4x+3=(x-1)(x-3)$

$x^2+x-2=(x-1)(x+2)$

LCD $=(x-1)(x-3)(x+2)$

$\dfrac{2}{x^2-4x+3}+\dfrac{6}{x^2+x-2}$

$=\dfrac{2}{(x-1)(x-3)}+\dfrac{6}{(x-1)(x+2)}$

$=\dfrac{2(x+2)}{(x-1)(x-3)(x+2)}$

$\quad+\dfrac{6(x-3)}{(x-1)(x-3)(x+2)}$

$=\dfrac{2(x+2)+6(x-3)}{(x-1)(x-3)(x+2)}$

$=\dfrac{2x+4+6x-18}{(x-1)(x-3)(x+2)}$

$=\dfrac{8x-14}{(x-1)(x-3)(x+2)}$

12. $\dfrac{4}{x-3}+\dfrac{x+5}{3-x}$

$3-x=-1(x-3)$

LCD $=x-3$

$\dfrac{4}{x-3}+\dfrac{x+5}{3-x}$

$=\dfrac{4}{x-3}+\dfrac{(-1)}{(-1)}\cdot\dfrac{(x+5)}{(3-x)}$

$=\dfrac{4}{x-3}+\dfrac{-x-5}{x-3}$

$=\dfrac{4-x-5}{x-3}=\dfrac{-x-1}{x-3}$

13. $1+\dfrac{3}{x-1}$

LCD $=x-1$

$1+\dfrac{3}{x-1}=\dfrac{1(x-1)}{x-1}+\dfrac{3}{x-1}$

$\qquad =\dfrac{x-1+3}{x-1}=\dfrac{x+2}{x-1}$

14. $\dfrac{2x+3}{x^2-7x+12}-\dfrac{2}{x-3}$

$x^2-7x+12=(x-3)(x-4)$

$x-3=1(x-3)$

LCD $=(x-3)(x-4)$

$\dfrac{2x+3}{x^2-7x+12}-\dfrac{2}{x-3}$

$=\dfrac{2x+3}{(x-3)(x-4)}-\dfrac{2(x-4)}{(x-3)(x-4)}$

$=\dfrac{2x+3-2(x-4)}{(x-3)(x-4)}$

$=\dfrac{2x+3-2x+8}{(x-3)(x-4)}$

$=\dfrac{11}{(x-3)(x-4)}$

15. $\dfrac{8y}{y^2-16}-\dfrac{4}{y-4}$

$y^2-16=(y+4)(y-4)$

$y-4=1(y-4)$

LCD $=(y+4)(y-4)$

$\dfrac{8y}{y^2-16}-\dfrac{4}{y-4}$

$=\dfrac{8y}{(y+4)(y-4)}-\dfrac{4}{y-4}$

$=\dfrac{8y}{(y+4)(y-4)}-\dfrac{4(y+4)}{(y+4)(y-4)}$

$=\dfrac{8y-4(y+4)}{(y+4)(y-4)}$

$=\dfrac{8y-4y-16}{(y+4)(y-4)}$

$=\dfrac{4y-16}{(y+4)(y-4)}$

$=\dfrac{4(y-4)}{(y+4)(y-4)}$

$=\dfrac{4}{y+4}$

16. $\dfrac{(x-y)^2}{x+y}\div\dfrac{x^2-xy}{3x+3y}$

$=\dfrac{(x-y)^2}{x+y}\cdot\dfrac{3x+3y}{x^2-xy}$

$=\dfrac{(x-y)(x-y)}{(x+y)}\cdot\dfrac{3(x+y)}{x(x-y)}$

$=\dfrac{3(x-y)}{x}=\dfrac{3x-3y}{x}$

17. $\dfrac{5+\dfrac{5}{x}}{2+\dfrac{1}{x}}=\dfrac{\dfrac{5x}{x}+\dfrac{5}{x}}{\dfrac{2x}{x}+\dfrac{1}{x}}=\dfrac{\dfrac{5x+5}{x}}{\dfrac{2x+1}{x}}$

$=\dfrac{5x+5}{x}\cdot\dfrac{x}{2x+1}$

$=\dfrac{5x+5}{2x+1}$

18. $\dfrac{\dfrac{1}{x}-\dfrac{1}{y}}{\dfrac{1}{x}}$

LCD $=xy$

$\dfrac{\dfrac{1}{x}-\dfrac{1}{y}}{\dfrac{1}{x}}=\dfrac{xy}{xy}\cdot\dfrac{\left(\dfrac{1}{x}-\dfrac{1}{y}\right)}{\left(\dfrac{1}{x}\right)}$

$=\dfrac{xy\cdot\dfrac{1}{x}-xy\cdot\dfrac{1}{y}}{xy\cdot\dfrac{1}{x}}$

$=\dfrac{y-x}{y}$

19. $\dfrac{5}{x}+\dfrac{2}{3}=2-\dfrac{2}{x}-\dfrac{1}{6}$

Restriction: $x \neq 0$

LCD $= 6x$

$6x\left(\dfrac{5}{x}+\dfrac{2}{3}\right)=6x\left(2-\dfrac{2}{x}-\dfrac{1}{6}\right)$

$6x\cdot\dfrac{5}{x}+6x\cdot\dfrac{2}{3}=6x\cdot 2-6x\cdot\dfrac{2}{x}-6x\cdot\dfrac{1}{6}$

$30+4x=12x-12-x$

$30+4x=11x-12$

$\qquad 30=7x-12$

$\qquad 42=7x$

$\qquad 6=x$

The solution set is $\{6\}$.

20. $\dfrac{3}{y+5}-1=\dfrac{4-y}{2y+10}$

$\dfrac{3}{y+5}-1=\dfrac{4-y}{2(y+5)}$

Restriction: $y \neq -5$

LCD $= 2(y+5)$

$2(y+5)\left(\dfrac{3}{y+5}-1\right)=2(y+5)\left[\dfrac{4-y}{2(y+5)}\right]$

$\qquad 6-2(y+5)=4-y$

$\qquad 6-2y-10=4-y$

$\qquad -4-2y=4-y$

$\qquad\qquad -4=4+y$

$\qquad\qquad -8=y$

The solution set is $\{-8\}$.

21. $\dfrac{2}{x-1} = \dfrac{3}{x^2-1} + 1$

$\dfrac{2}{x-1} = \dfrac{3}{(x+1)(x-1)} + 1$

Restrictions: $x \neq 1, x \neq -1$

LCD $= (x+1)(x-1)$

$(x+1)(x-1)\left(\dfrac{2}{x-1}\right) = (x+1)(x-1)\left[\dfrac{3}{(x+1)(x-1)} + 1\right]$

$$2(x+1) = 3 + (x+1)(x-1)$$
$$2x + 2 = 3 + x^2 - 1$$
$$2x + 2 = 2 + x^2$$
$$0 = x^2 - 2x$$
$$0 = x(x-2)$$
$$x = 0 \ \text{ or } \ x - 2 = 0$$
$$x = 2$$

The solution set is $\{0, 2\}$.

22. Let x = the rate of the current.

Then $30 + x$ = the rate of the boat with the current and $30 - x$ = the rate of the boat against the current.

	Distance	Rate	Time $= \dfrac{\text{Distance}}{\text{Rate}}$
Downstream	16	$30 + x$	$\dfrac{16}{30+x}$
Upstream	14	$30 - x$	$\dfrac{14}{30-x}$

$\dfrac{16}{30+x} = \dfrac{14}{30-x}$

$16(30-x) = 14(30+x)$

$480 - 16x = 420 + 14x$

$480 = 420 + 30x$

$60 = 30x$

$2 = x$

The rate of the current is 2 miles per hour.

23. Let x = the time (in minutes) for both pipes to fill the hot tub.

$\dfrac{x}{20} + \dfrac{x}{30} = 1$

LCD $= 60$

$60\left(\dfrac{x}{20} + \dfrac{x}{30}\right) = 60 \cdot 1$

$3x + 2x = 60$

$5x = 60$

$x = 12$

It will take 12 minutes for both pipes to fill the hot tub.

24. $\dfrac{10}{4} = \dfrac{8}{x}$

$10x = 8 \cdot 4$

$10x = 32$

$x = 3.2$

The length of the side marked with an x is 3.2 inches.

25. Let C = the current (in amperes).
Then R = the resistance (in ohms).

Step 1 $C = \dfrac{k}{R}$

Step 2 To find k, substitute 42 for C and 5 for R.

$42 = \dfrac{k}{5}$

$42 \cdot 5 = \dfrac{k}{5} \cdot 5$

$210 = k$

Step 3 $C = \dfrac{210}{R}$

Step 4 Substitute 4 for R and solve for C.

$C = \dfrac{210}{4} = 52.5$

When the resistance is 4 ohms, the current is 52.5 amperes.

Cumulative Review (Chapters 1-8)

1. $2(x-3) + 5x = 8(x-1)$

$2x - 6 + 5x = 8x - 8$

$7x - 6 = 8x - 8$

$-6 = x - 8$

$2 = x$

The solution set is $\{2\}$.

2. $-3(2x-4) > 2(6x-12)$

$-6x + 12 > 12x - 24$

$-18x + 12 > -24$

$-18x > -36$

$\dfrac{-18x}{-18} < \dfrac{-36}{-18}$

$x < 2$

$(-\infty, 2)$

3. $x^2 + 3x = 18$

$x^2 + 3x - 18 = 0$

$(x + 6)(x - 3) = 0$

$x + 6 = 0$ or $x - 3 = 0$

$x = -6$ $x = 3$

The solution set is $\{-6, 3\}$.

4. $\dfrac{2x}{x^2 - 4} + \dfrac{1}{x - 2} = \dfrac{2}{x + 2}$

$$x^2 - 4 = (x + 2)(x - 2)$$

Restrictions: $x \neq 2, x \neq -2$

LCD $= (x + 2)(x - 2)$

$$(x + 2)(x - 2)\left[\frac{2x}{(x + 2)(x - 2)} + \frac{1}{x - 2}\right] = (x + 2)(x - 2) \cdot \frac{2}{x + 2}$$

$$2x + (x + 2) = 2(x - 2)$$

$$3x + 2 = 2x - 4$$

$$x = -6$$

The solution set is $\{-6\}$.

5. $y = 2x - 3$

$x + 2y = 9$

To solve this system by the substitution method, substitute $2x - 3$ for y in the second equation.

$x + 2y = 9$

$x + 2(2x - 3) = 9$

$x + 4x - 6 = 9$

$5x - 6 = 9$

$5x = 15$

$x = 3$

Back-substitute 3 for x into the first equation.

$y = 2x - 3$

$y = 2 \cdot 3 - 3 = 3$

The solution set is $\{(3, 3)\}$.

6. $3x + 2y = -2$

$-4x + 5y = 18$

To solve this system by the addition method, multiply the first equation by 4 and the second equation by 3.
Then add the equations.

$12x + \ 8y = -8$

$\underline{-12x + 15y = 54}$

$\qquad 23y = 46$

$\qquad y = 2$

Back-substitute 2 for y in the first equation of the original system.

$3x + 2y = -2$

$3x + 2(2) = -2$

$3x + 4 = -2$

$3x = -6$

$x = -2$

The solution set is $\{(-2, 2)\}$.

7. $3x - 2y = 6$

x-intercept: 2
y-intercept: -3
checkpoint: $(4, 3)$
Draw a line through $(2, 0)$, $(0, -3)$ and $(4, 3)$.

$3x - 2y = 6$

8. $y > -2x + 3$

Graph $y = -2x + 3$ as a dashed line using its slope,

$-2 = \dfrac{-2}{1}$, and its y-intercept, 3. Use $(0, 0)$ as a test point. Because $0 > 2 \cdot 0 + 3$ is false, shade the half-plane *not* containing $(0, 0)$.

$y > -2x + 3$

9. $y = -3$

The graph is a horizontal line with y-intercept -3.

$y = -3$

10. $-21 - 16 - 3(2 - 8) = -21 - 16 - 3(-6)$

$\qquad = -21 - 16 + 18$

$\qquad = -37 + 18 = -19$

11. $\left(\dfrac{4x^5}{2x^2}\right)^3 = \left(2x^3\right)^3 = 2^3 \cdot \left(x^3\right)^3 = 8x^9$

12. $\dfrac{\dfrac{1}{x} - 2}{4 - \dfrac{1}{x}}$

$LCD = x$

$\dfrac{\dfrac{1}{x} - 2}{4 - \dfrac{1}{x}} = \dfrac{x\left(\dfrac{1}{x} - 2\right)}{x\left(4 - \dfrac{1}{x}\right)}$

$\qquad = \dfrac{x \cdot \dfrac{1}{x} - x \cdot 2}{x \cdot 4 - x \cdot \dfrac{1}{x}}$

$\qquad = \dfrac{1 - 2x}{4x - 1}$

13. $4x^2 - 13x + 3$

Factor by trial and error. Try various combinations until the correct one is found.

$4x^2 - 13x + 3 = (4x - 1)(x - 3)$

14. $4x^2 - 20x + 25 = (2x)^2 - 2(2x \cdot 5) + 5^2$

$\qquad = (2x - 5)^2$

15. $3x^2 - 75 = 3\left(x^2 - 25\right)$

$\qquad = 3(x + 5)(x - 5)$

16. $\left(4x^2 - 3x + 2\right) - \left(5x^2 - 7x - 6\right)$

$\qquad = \left(4x^2 - 3x + 2\right) + \left(-5x^2 + 7x + 6\right)$

$\qquad = -x^2 + 4x + 8$

17. $\dfrac{-8x^6 + 12x^4 - 4x^2}{4x^2} = \dfrac{-8x^6}{4x^2} + \dfrac{12x^4}{4x^2} - \dfrac{4x^2}{4x^2}$

$\qquad\qquad\qquad\qquad = -2x^4 + 3x^2 - 1$

18. $\dfrac{x+6}{x-2} + \dfrac{2x+1}{x+3}$

$\quad$ LCD $= \left(x-2\right)\left(x+3\right)$

$\quad \dfrac{x+6}{x-2} + \dfrac{2x+1}{x+3}$

$\quad = \dfrac{\left(x+6\right)\left(x+3\right)}{\left(x-2\right)\left(x+3\right)} + \dfrac{\left(2x+1\right)\left(x-2\right)}{\left(x-2\right)\left(x+3\right)}$

$\quad = \dfrac{\left(x+6\right)\left(x+3\right) + \left(2x+1\right)\left(x-2\right)}{\left(x-2\right)\left(x+3\right)}$

$\quad = \dfrac{x^2 + 9x + 18 + 2x^2 - 3x - 2}{\left(x-2\right)\left(x+3\right)}$

$\quad = \dfrac{3x^2 + 6x + 16}{\left(x-2\right)\left(x+3\right)}$

19. Let $x =$ the amount invested at 5%.
Then $4000 - x =$ the amount invested at 9%.

$0.05x + 0.09\left(4000 - x\right) = 311$

$\qquad 0.05x + 360 - 0.09x = 311$

$\qquad\qquad -0.04x + 360 = 311$

$\qquad\qquad\qquad -0.04x = -49$

$\qquad\qquad\qquad\qquad x = \dfrac{-49}{-0.04}$

$\qquad\qquad\qquad\qquad x = 1225$

If $x = 1225$, then $4000 - x = 2775$.
$1225 was invested at 5% and $2775 at 9%.

20. Let $x =$ the length of the shorter piece.
Then $3x =$ the length of the larger piece.

$\qquad x + 3x = 68$

$\qquad\quad 4x = 68$

$\qquad\quad\ x = 17$

If $x = 17$, then $3x = 51$.
The lengths of the pieces are 17 inches and 51 inches.

Chapter 9
Roots and Radicals

9.1 Check Points

1. a. $\sqrt{81} = 9$
    The principal square root of 81 is 9.

    b. $-\sqrt{9} = -3$
    The negative square root of 9 is -3.

    c. $\sqrt{\dfrac{1}{25}} = \dfrac{1}{5}$ because $\left(\dfrac{1}{5}\right)^2 = \dfrac{1}{25}$.

    d. $\sqrt{36+64} = \sqrt{100} = 10$

    e. $\sqrt{36} + \sqrt{64} = 6 + 8 = 14$

2. $E = \dfrac{w}{20\sqrt{a}}$

    $E = \dfrac{20}{20\sqrt{4}} = \dfrac{1}{2}$

    The surface evaporation is $\dfrac{1}{2}$ of an inch on this day.

3. $P = 3.32\sqrt{t} + 68.6$

    $P = 3.32\sqrt{15} + 68.6 \approx 81.5$
    According to the model, 81.5% completed high school in 1995.
    This underestimates the actual percentage shown in the figure by 0.2%.

4. a. $\sqrt[3]{1} = 1$ because $1^3 = 1$.

    b. $\sqrt[3]{-27} = -3$ because $(-3)^3 = -27$.

    c. $\sqrt[3]{\dfrac{1}{125}} = \dfrac{1}{5}$ because $\left(\dfrac{1}{5}\right)^3 = \dfrac{1}{125}$.

5. a. $\sqrt[4]{81} = 3$ because $3^4 = 81$.

    b. $\sqrt[4]{-81}$ is not a real number because the index, 4, is even and the radicand, -81, is negative.

    c. $-\sqrt[4]{81} = -3$ because $\sqrt[4]{81} = 3$.

    d. $\sqrt[5]{-\dfrac{1}{32}} = -\dfrac{1}{2}$ because $\left(-\dfrac{1}{2}\right)^5 = -\dfrac{1}{32}$.

9.1 Exercise Set

1. $\sqrt{36} = 6$
    The principal square root of 36 is 6.

3. $-\sqrt{36} = -6$
    The negative square root of 36 is -6.

5. $\sqrt{-36}$ is not a real number.
    There is no real number whose square is -36.

7. $\sqrt{\dfrac{1}{9}} = \dfrac{1}{3}$ because $\left(\dfrac{1}{3}\right)^2 = \dfrac{1}{9}$.

9. $\sqrt{\dfrac{1}{100}} = \dfrac{1}{10}$ because $\left(\dfrac{1}{10}\right)^2 = \dfrac{1}{100}$.

11. $-\sqrt{\dfrac{1}{36}} = -\dfrac{1}{6}$ because $\sqrt{\dfrac{1}{36}} = \dfrac{1}{6}$.

13. $\sqrt{-\dfrac{1}{36}}$ is not a real number.

15. $\sqrt{0.04} = 0.2$ because $(0.2)^2 = 0.04$ and 0.2 is positive.

17. $\sqrt{33-8} = \sqrt{25} = 5$

19. $\sqrt{2 \cdot 32} = \sqrt{64} = 8$

21. $\sqrt{144+25} = \sqrt{169} = 13$

23. $\sqrt{144} + \sqrt{25} = 12 + 5 = 17$

25. $\sqrt{25-144} = \sqrt{-119}$ which is not a real number.

27.

x	$y = \sqrt{x-1}$	(x, y)
1	$y = \sqrt{1-1} = 0$	$(1, 0)$
2	$y = \sqrt{2-1} = 1$	$(2, 1)$
5	$y = \sqrt{5-1} = 2$	$(5, 2)$
10	$y = \sqrt{10-1} = 3$	$(10, 3)$
17	$y = \sqrt{17-1} = 4$	$(17, 4)$

29. Answers will vary. The graph in exercise 27 is shaped like $y = \sqrt{x}$, but shifted 1 unit to the right.

31. $\sqrt{7} \approx 2.646$

33. $\sqrt{23} \approx 4.796$

35. $-\sqrt{65} \approx -8.062$

37. $12 + \sqrt{11} \approx 15.317$

39. $\dfrac{12 + \sqrt{11}}{2} \approx 7.658$

41. $\dfrac{-5 + \sqrt{321}}{6} \approx 2.153$

43. $\sqrt{13 - 5} = \sqrt{8} \approx 2.828$

45. $\sqrt{5 - 13} = \sqrt{-8}$, which is not a real number.

47. $\sqrt[3]{64} = 4$ because $4^3 = 64$.

49. $\sqrt[3]{-27} = -3$ because $(-3)^3 = -27$.

51. $-\sqrt[3]{8} = -2$ because $(2)^3 = 8$.

53. $\sqrt[3]{\dfrac{1}{125}} = \dfrac{1}{5}$ because $\left(\dfrac{1}{5}\right)^3 = \dfrac{1}{125}$.

55. $\sqrt[3]{-1000} = -10$ because $(-10)^3 = -1000$.

57. $\sqrt[4]{1} = 1$ because $1^4 = 1$.

59. $\sqrt[4]{16} = 2$ because $2^4 = 16$.

61. $-\sqrt[4]{16} = -2$ because $(2)^4 = 16$

63. $\sqrt[4]{-16}$ is not a real number because the index, 4, is even and the radicand, -16, is negative.

65. $\sqrt[5]{-1} = -1$ because $(-1)^5 = -1$.

67. $\sqrt[6]{-1}$ is not a real number because the index, 6, is even and the radicand, -1, is negative.

69. $-\sqrt[4]{256} = -4$ because $\sqrt[4]{256} = 4$.

71. $\sqrt[6]{64} = 2$ because $2^6 = 64$.

73. $-\sqrt[5]{32} = -2$ because $\sqrt[5]{32} = 2$.

75. $\sqrt{2x}$ yields a real number if $2x \geq 0$
$$x \geq 0.$$

77. $\sqrt{x-2}$ yields a real number if $x - 2 \geq 0$
$$x \geq 2.$$

79. $\sqrt{2-x}$ yields a real number if $2 - x \geq 0$
$$-x \geq -2$$
$$x \leq 2.$$

81. $\sqrt{x^2 + 2}$ yields a real number for all real numbers x since $x^2 + 2$ is always positive.

83. $\sqrt{12 - 2x}$ yields a real number if $12 - 2x \geq 0$
$$-2x \geq -12$$
$$x \leq 6.$$

85. $v = 4\sqrt{r}; \; r = 9$
$$v = 4\sqrt{9} = 4 \cdot 3 = 12$$
The maximum velocity is 12 miles per hour.

87. $v = \sqrt{20L} = \sqrt{20 \cdot 245} = \sqrt{4900} = 70$
The motorist was traveling 70 miles per hour, so she was speeding.

89. a. At birth we have $x = 0$.

$$y = 2.9\sqrt{x} + 36$$
$$= 2.9\sqrt{0} + 36$$
$$= 2.9(0) + 36$$
$$= 36$$

According to the model, the head circumference at birth is 36 cm.

b. At 9 months we have $x = 9$.

$$y = 2.9\sqrt{x} + 36$$
$$= 2.9\sqrt{9} + 36$$
$$= 2.9(3) + 36$$
$$= 44.7$$

According to the model, the head circumference at 9 months is 44.7 cm.

c. At 14 months we have $x = 14$.

$$y = 2.9\sqrt{x} + 36$$
$$= 2.9\sqrt{14} + 36$$
$$\approx 46.9$$

According to the model, the head circumference at 14 months is roughly 46.9 cm.

d. The model describes healthy children.

91. a. $y = a\sqrt{x} + b$
$$21 = a\sqrt{0} + b$$
$$21 = b$$

Therefore, $y = a\sqrt{x} + 21$.

b. $y = a\sqrt{x} + 21$
$$72 = a\sqrt{6} + 21$$
$$51 = a\sqrt{6}$$
$$\frac{51}{\sqrt{6}} = a$$
$$20.8 \approx a$$

Therefore, $y = 20.8\sqrt{x} + 21$.

c. In 2004, we have $x = 5$.

$$y = 20.8\sqrt{5} + 21 \approx 67.5$$

According to the model, 67.5% of email was spam in 2004.
This underestimates the actual value shown in the bar graph by 0.5%.

d. In 2011, we have $x = 12$.

$$y = 20.8\sqrt{12} + 21 \approx 93.1$$

According to the model, 93.1% of email will be spam in 2011.

93. – 97. Answers will vary.

99. does not make sense; Explanations will vary.
Sample explanation: $-\sqrt{9} = -3$ and -3 is a real number.

101. makes sense

103. false; Changes to make the statement true will vary.
A sample change is: $\sqrt{9} + \sqrt{16} = 3 + 4 = 7$.

105. false; Changes to make the statement true will vary.
A sample change is: $\sqrt[3]{-27} = \sqrt[3]{(-3)^3} = -3$. The expression is a real number.

107. $\sqrt{\sqrt[3]{64}} = \sqrt{4} = 2$

109. $\sqrt{\sqrt{16}} - \sqrt[3]{\sqrt{64}} = \sqrt{4} - \sqrt[3]{8}$
$$= 2 - 2$$
$$= 0$$

111. $y_1 = \sqrt{x}$
$$y_2 = \sqrt{x+4}$$
$$y_3 = \sqrt{x-3}$$

All three graphs are increasing and have a range of $y \geq 0$. The graphs of y_2 and y_3 look like the graph of y_1 but are shifted left 4 units and shifted right 3 units, respectively.

113. $4x - 5y = 20$

$-5y = -4x + 20$

$y = \dfrac{4}{5}x - 4$

x-intercept: 5
y-intercept: -4
checkpoint: $(-5, -8)$

114. $2(x-3) > 4x + 10$

$2x - 6 > 4x + 10$

$-2x - 6 > 10$

$-2x > 16$

$x < -8$

$(-\infty, 8)$

$-10\ -9\ -8\ -7\ -6\ -5\ -4\ -3\ -2\ -1\quad 0$

115. $\dfrac{1}{x^2 - 17x + 30} \div \dfrac{1}{x^2 + 7x - 18}$

$= \dfrac{1}{x^2 - 17x + 30} \cdot \dfrac{x^2 + 7x - 18}{1}$

$= \dfrac{1}{(x-15)(x-2)} \cdot \dfrac{(x+9)(x-2)}{1}$

$= \dfrac{x+9}{x-15}$

116. a. $\sqrt{25} \cdot \sqrt{4} = 5 \cdot 2 = 10$

b. $\sqrt{25 \cdot 4} = \sqrt{100} = 10$

c. $\sqrt{25} \cdot \sqrt{4} = \sqrt{25 \cdot 4}$

117. a. $\sqrt{500} \approx 22.361$

b. $10\sqrt{5} \approx 22.361$

c. $\sqrt{500} = 10\sqrt{5}$

118. a. $\dfrac{\sqrt{64}}{\sqrt{4}} = \dfrac{8}{2} = 4$

b. $\sqrt{\dfrac{64}{4}} = \sqrt{16} = 4$

c. $\dfrac{\sqrt{64}}{\sqrt{4}} = \sqrt{\dfrac{64}{4}}$

9.2 Check Points

1. a. $\sqrt{3} \cdot \sqrt{10} = \sqrt{3 \cdot 10} = \sqrt{30}$

b. $\sqrt{2x} \cdot \sqrt{13y} = \sqrt{2x \cdot 13y} = \sqrt{26xy}$

c. $\sqrt{5} \cdot \sqrt{5} = \sqrt{25} = 5$

d. $\sqrt{\dfrac{3}{2}} \cdot \sqrt{\dfrac{5}{11}} = \sqrt{\dfrac{3}{2} \cdot \dfrac{5}{11}} = \sqrt{\dfrac{15}{22}}$

2. a. $\sqrt{12} = \sqrt{4 \cdot 3} = \sqrt{4}\sqrt{3} = 2\sqrt{3}$

b. $\sqrt{60} = \sqrt{4 \cdot 15} = \sqrt{4}\sqrt{15} = 2\sqrt{15}$

c. $\sqrt{55}$ cannot be simplified because it has no perfect square factors other than 1.

3. $\sqrt{40x^{16}} = \sqrt{4x^{16} \cdot 10} = 2x^8\sqrt{10}$

4. $\sqrt{27x^9} = \sqrt{9x^8 \cdot 3x} = 3x^4\sqrt{3x}$

5. $\sqrt{15x^6} \cdot \sqrt{3x^7} = \sqrt{15x^6 \cdot 3x^7}$

$= \sqrt{45x^{13}}$

$= \sqrt{9x^{12} \cdot 5x}$

$= 3x^6\sqrt{5x}$

6. a. $\sqrt{\dfrac{49}{25}} = \dfrac{\sqrt{49}}{\sqrt{25}} = \dfrac{7}{5}$

b. $\dfrac{\sqrt{48x^5}}{\sqrt{3x}} = \sqrt{\dfrac{48x^5}{3x}} = \sqrt{16x^4} = 4x^2$

7. a. $\sqrt[3]{40} = \sqrt[3]{8 \cdot 5} = 2\sqrt[3]{5}$

b. $\sqrt[5]{8} \cdot \sqrt[5]{8} = \sqrt[5]{64} = \sqrt[5]{32 \cdot 2} = \sqrt[5]{32} \cdot \sqrt[5]{2} = 2\sqrt[5]{2}$

c. $\sqrt[3]{\dfrac{125}{27}} = \dfrac{5}{3}$

9.2 Exercise Set

1. $\sqrt{2} \cdot \sqrt{7} = \sqrt{2 \cdot 7} = \sqrt{14}$

3. $\sqrt{3x} \cdot \sqrt{5y} = \sqrt{3x \cdot 5y} = \sqrt{15xy}$

5. $\sqrt{5} \cdot \sqrt{5} = \sqrt{25} = 5$

7. $\sqrt{\dfrac{2}{3}} \cdot \sqrt{\dfrac{5}{7}} = \sqrt{\dfrac{2}{3} \cdot \dfrac{5}{7}} = \sqrt{\dfrac{10}{21}}$

9. $\sqrt{0.1x} \cdot \sqrt{5y} = \sqrt{0.5xy}$

11. $\sqrt{\dfrac{1}{5}a} \cdot \sqrt{\dfrac{1}{5}b} = \sqrt{\dfrac{1}{25}ab} = \sqrt{\dfrac{1}{25}} \cdot \sqrt{ab}$
$= \dfrac{1}{5}\sqrt{ab}$

13. $\sqrt{\dfrac{2x}{9}} \cdot \sqrt{\dfrac{9}{2}} = \sqrt{\dfrac{2x \cdot 9}{9 \cdot 2}} = \sqrt{\dfrac{18x}{18}} = \sqrt{x}$

15. $\sqrt{50} = \sqrt{25 \cdot 2} = \sqrt{25}\sqrt{2} = 5\sqrt{2}$

17. $\sqrt{45} = \sqrt{9 \cdot 5} = \sqrt{9}\sqrt{5} = 3\sqrt{5}$

19. $\sqrt{200} = \sqrt{100 \cdot 2} = \sqrt{100}\sqrt{2} = 10\sqrt{2}$

21. $\sqrt{75x} = \sqrt{25 \cdot 3x} = \sqrt{25}\sqrt{3x} = 5\sqrt{3x}$

23. $\sqrt{9x} = \sqrt{9}\sqrt{x} = 3\sqrt{x}$

25. $\sqrt{35}$ cannot be simplified because 35 has no perfect square factors other than 1.

27. $\sqrt{y^2} = y$

29. $\sqrt{64x^2} = 8x$

31. $\sqrt{11x^2} = \sqrt{x^2}\sqrt{11} = x\sqrt{11}$

33. $\sqrt{8x^2} = \sqrt{4x^2}\sqrt{2} = 2x\sqrt{2}$

35. $\sqrt{x^{20}} = x^{10}$ because $\left(x^{10}\right)^2 = x^{20}.$

37. $\sqrt{25y^{10}} = 5y^5$

39. $\sqrt{20x^6} = \sqrt{4x^6}\sqrt{5} = 2x^3\sqrt{5}$

41. $\sqrt{72y^{100}} = \sqrt{36y^{100}}\sqrt{2} = 6y^{50}\sqrt{2}$

43. $\sqrt{x^3} = \sqrt{x^2}\sqrt{x} = x\sqrt{x}$

45. $\sqrt{x^7} = \sqrt{x^6}\sqrt{x} = x^3\sqrt{x}$

47. $\sqrt{y^{17}} = \sqrt{y^{16}}\sqrt{y} = y^8\sqrt{y}$

49. $\sqrt{25x^5} = \sqrt{25x^4}\sqrt{x} = 5x^2\sqrt{x}$

51. $\sqrt{8x^{17}} = \sqrt{4x^{16}}\sqrt{2x} = 2x^8\sqrt{2x}$

53. $\sqrt{90y^{19}} = \sqrt{9y^{18}}\sqrt{10y} = 3y^9\sqrt{10y}$

55. $\sqrt{3} \cdot \sqrt{15} = \sqrt{45} = \sqrt{9}\sqrt{5} = 3\sqrt{5}$

57. $\sqrt{5x} \cdot \sqrt{10y} = \sqrt{50xy} = \sqrt{25}\sqrt{2xy}$
$= 5\sqrt{2xy}$

59. $\sqrt{12x} \cdot \sqrt{3x} = \sqrt{36x^2} = 6x$

61. $\sqrt{15x^2} \cdot \sqrt{3x} = \sqrt{45x^3} = \sqrt{9x^2}\sqrt{5x}$
$= 3x\sqrt{5x}$

63. $\sqrt{15x^4} \cdot \sqrt{5x^9} = \sqrt{75x^{13}}$
$= \sqrt{25x^{12}}\sqrt{3x} = 5x^6\sqrt{3x}$

65. $\sqrt{7x} \cdot \sqrt{3y} = \sqrt{21xy}$

67. $\sqrt{50xy} \cdot \sqrt{4xy^2} = \sqrt{200x^2y^3}$
$= \sqrt{100x^2y^2}\sqrt{2y} = 10xy\sqrt{2y}$

69. $\sqrt{\dfrac{49}{16}} = \dfrac{\sqrt{49}}{\sqrt{16}} = \dfrac{7}{4}$

71. $\sqrt{\dfrac{3}{4}} = \dfrac{\sqrt{3}}{\sqrt{4}} = \dfrac{\sqrt{3}}{2}$

73. $\sqrt{\dfrac{x^2}{36}} = \dfrac{\sqrt{x^2}}{6} = \dfrac{x}{6}$

75. $\sqrt{\dfrac{7}{x^4}} = \dfrac{\sqrt{7}}{\sqrt{x^4}} = \dfrac{\sqrt{7}}{x^2}$

77. $\sqrt{\dfrac{72}{y^{20}}} = \dfrac{\sqrt{72}}{\sqrt{y^{20}}} = \dfrac{\sqrt{36}\sqrt{2}}{y^{10}} = \dfrac{6\sqrt{2}}{y^{10}}$

79. $\dfrac{\sqrt{54}}{\sqrt{6}} = \sqrt{\dfrac{54}{6}} = \sqrt{9} = 3$

81. $\dfrac{\sqrt{24}}{\sqrt{3}} = \sqrt{\dfrac{24}{3}} = \sqrt{8} = \sqrt{4}\sqrt{2} = 2\sqrt{2}$

83. $\dfrac{\sqrt{75}}{\sqrt{15}} = \sqrt{\dfrac{75}{15}} = \sqrt{5}$

85. $\dfrac{\sqrt{48x}}{\sqrt{3x}} = \sqrt{\dfrac{48x}{3x}} = \sqrt{16} = 4$

87. $\dfrac{\sqrt{32x^3}}{\sqrt{8x}} = \sqrt{\dfrac{32x^3}{8x}} = \sqrt{4x^2} = 2x$

89. $\dfrac{\sqrt{150x^4}}{\sqrt{3x}} = \sqrt{\dfrac{150x^4}{3x}} = \sqrt{50x^3}$
$\qquad = \sqrt{25x^2}\sqrt{2x} = 5x\sqrt{2x}$

91. $\dfrac{\sqrt{400x^{10}}}{\sqrt{10x^3}} = \sqrt{\dfrac{400x^{10}}{10x^3}} = \sqrt{40x^7}$
$\qquad = \sqrt{4x^6}\sqrt{10x} = 2x^3\sqrt{10x}$

93. $\sqrt[3]{16} = \sqrt[3]{8\cdot 2} = \sqrt[3]{8}\cdot\sqrt[3]{2} = 2\sqrt[3]{2}$

95. $\sqrt[3]{54} = \sqrt[3]{27\cdot 2} = \sqrt[3]{27}\cdot\sqrt[3]{2} = 3\sqrt[3]{2}$

97. $\sqrt[4]{32} = \sqrt[4]{16\cdot 2} = \sqrt[4]{16}\cdot\sqrt[4]{2} = 2\sqrt[4]{2}$

99. $\sqrt[3]{4}\cdot\sqrt[3]{2} = \sqrt[3]{8} = 2$

101. $\sqrt[3]{9}\cdot\sqrt[3]{6} = \sqrt[3]{54} = \sqrt[3]{27}\sqrt[3]{2} = 3\sqrt[3]{2}$

103. $\sqrt[4]{4}\cdot\sqrt[4]{8} = \sqrt[4]{32} = \sqrt[4]{16}\cdot\sqrt[4]{2} = 2\sqrt[4]{2}$

105. $\sqrt[3]{\dfrac{27}{8}} = \dfrac{\sqrt[3]{27}}{\sqrt[3]{8}} = \dfrac{3}{2}$

107. $\sqrt[3]{\dfrac{3}{8}} = \dfrac{\sqrt[3]{3}}{\sqrt[3]{8}} = \dfrac{\sqrt[3]{3}}{2}$

109. $\sqrt{90(x+4)^3} = \sqrt{9(x+4)^2}\cdot\sqrt{10(x+4)}$
$\qquad\qquad = 3(x+4)\sqrt{10(x+4)}$

111. $\sqrt{x^2-6x+9} = \sqrt{(x-3)^2} = x-3$

113. $\sqrt{2^{43}x^{104}y^{13}} = \sqrt{2^{42}x^{104}y^{12}}\cdot\sqrt{2y}$
$\qquad\qquad = 2^{21}x^{52}y^6\sqrt{2y}$

115. $\sqrt[3]{24x^5} = \sqrt[3]{8x^3}\cdot\sqrt[3]{3x^2}$
$\qquad\qquad = 2x\sqrt[3]{3x^2}$

117. $A = l\cdot w$
$\qquad = \sqrt{15}\cdot\sqrt{5} = \sqrt{75}$
$\qquad = \sqrt{25}\sqrt{3} = 5\sqrt{3}$
The area is $5\sqrt{3}$ square feet.

118. $A = l\cdot w$
$\qquad = \sqrt{6}\cdot\sqrt{3} = \sqrt{18}$
$\qquad = \sqrt{9}\sqrt{2} = 3\sqrt{2}$
The area is $3\sqrt{2}$ square feet.

119. a. $A = \dfrac{\sqrt{h}\cdot\sqrt{w}}{56}$

$\qquad A = \dfrac{\sqrt{68}\cdot\sqrt{200}}{56}$

$\qquad = \dfrac{\sqrt{4\cdot 17}\cdot\sqrt{100\cdot 2}}{56}$

$\qquad = \dfrac{2\sqrt{17}\cdot 10\sqrt{2}}{56}$

$\qquad = \dfrac{20\sqrt{34}}{56}$

$\qquad = \dfrac{5\sqrt{34}}{14}$

The surface area is $\dfrac{5\sqrt{34}}{14}$ square meters.

b. $\dfrac{5\sqrt{34}}{14} \approx 2.08$

The surface area is approximately 2.08 square meters.

121. – 127. Answers will vary.

129. makes sense

131. makes sense

133. false; Changes to make the statement true will vary.

A sample change is: $\sqrt{y^9} = \sqrt{y^8 y} = y^4\sqrt{y}$.

135. false; Changes to make the statement true will vary.

A sample change is: $\sqrt{2} \cdot \sqrt{8} = \sqrt{16} = 4$.

137. $\sqrt{15x^{\square}} \cdot \sqrt{\square x^5} = 3x^3\sqrt{10x}$

Because

$x^2 \cdot x^5 = x^7$ and $\sqrt{x^7} = \sqrt{x^6}\sqrt{x} = x^3\sqrt{x}$, the missing exponent in the first radical is 2. Because $\sqrt{15} \cdot \sqrt{6} = \sqrt{90} = \sqrt{9}\sqrt{10} = 3\sqrt{10}$ the missing coefficient in the second radical is 6.

139. The graphs coincide.

This verifies that $\sqrt{x^4} = x^2$.

141. The graphs coincide.

This verifies that $\sqrt{x^3} = x\sqrt{x}$.

142. $4x + 3y = 18$

$5x - 9y = 48$

To solve this system by the addition method, multiply the first equation by 3 and add the result to the second equation.

$12x + 9y = 54$

$\underline{5x - 9y = 48}$

$17x = 102$

$x = 6$

Back-substitute into the first equation of the original system.

$4x + 3y = 18$

$4(6) + 3y = 18$

$24 + 3y = 18$

$3y = -6$

$y = -2$

The solution set is $\{(6, -2)\}$.

143. $\dfrac{6x}{x^2 - 4} - \dfrac{3}{x+2}$

Factor the first denominator.

$x^2 - 4 = (x+2)(x-2)$

The LCD $= (x+2)(x-2)$.

$\dfrac{6x}{x^2 - 4} - \dfrac{3}{x+2}$

$= \dfrac{6}{(x+2)(x-2)} - \dfrac{3(x-2)}{(x+2)(x-2)}$

$= \dfrac{6x - 3(x-2)}{(x+2)(x-2)} = \dfrac{6x - 3x + 6}{(x+2)(x-2)}$

$= \dfrac{3x + 6}{(x+2)(x-2)} = \dfrac{3(x+2)}{(x+2)(x-2)}$

$= \dfrac{3}{x-2}$

144. $2x^3 - 16x^2 + 30x = 2x\left(x^2 - 8x + 15\right)$

$ = 2x(x-3)(x-5)$

145. a. $7x + 5x = (7+5)x = 12x$

     b. $7\sqrt{2} + 5\sqrt{2} = (7+5)\sqrt{2} = 12\sqrt{2}$

146. $4\sqrt{50x} = 4\sqrt{25 \cdot 2x} = 4 \cdot 5\sqrt{2x} = 20\sqrt{2x}$

147. a. $3(x+5) = 3x + 3 \cdot 5 = 3x + 15$

     b. $\sqrt{3}(\sqrt{7} + \sqrt{5}) = \sqrt{3}\sqrt{7} + \sqrt{3}\sqrt{5} = \sqrt{21} + \sqrt{15}$

9.3 Check Points

1. a. $8\sqrt{13} + 9\sqrt{13} = (8+9)\sqrt{13} = 17\sqrt{13}$

     b. $\sqrt{17x} - 20\sqrt{17x} = (1-20)\sqrt{17x} = -19\sqrt{17x}$

2. a. $5\sqrt{27} + \sqrt{12} = 5\sqrt{9 \cdot 3} + \sqrt{4 \cdot 3}$
$$= 5 \cdot 3\sqrt{3} + 2\sqrt{3}$$
$$= 15\sqrt{3} + 2\sqrt{3}$$
$$= 17\sqrt{3}$$

     b. $6\sqrt{18x} - 4\sqrt{8x} = 6\sqrt{9 \cdot 2x} - 4\sqrt{4 \cdot 2x}$
$$= 6 \cdot 3\sqrt{2x} - 4 \cdot 2\sqrt{2x}$$
$$= 18\sqrt{2x} - 8\sqrt{2x}$$
$$= 10\sqrt{2x}$$

3. a. $\sqrt{2}(\sqrt{5} + \sqrt{11}) = \sqrt{2}\sqrt{5} + \sqrt{2}\sqrt{11} = \sqrt{10} + \sqrt{22}$

     b. $(4+\sqrt{3})(2+\sqrt{3}) = 4 \cdot 2 + 4\sqrt{3} + 2\sqrt{3} + (\sqrt{3})^2$
$$= 8 + 4\sqrt{3} + 2\sqrt{3} + 3$$
$$= 11 + 6\sqrt{3}$$

     c. $(3+\sqrt{5})(8 - 4\sqrt{5})$
$$= 3 \cdot 8 - 3 \cdot 4\sqrt{5} + 8\sqrt{5} - 4(\sqrt{5})^2$$
$$= 24 - 12\sqrt{5} + 8\sqrt{5} - 4 \cdot 5$$
$$= 24 - 12\sqrt{5} + 8\sqrt{5} - 20$$
$$= 4 - 4\sqrt{5}$$

4. a. $(3+\sqrt{11})(3-\sqrt{11}) = 3^2 - (\sqrt{11})^2$
$$= 9 - 11$$
$$= -2$$

     b. $(\sqrt{7} - \sqrt{2})(\sqrt{7} + \sqrt{2}) = (\sqrt{7})^2 - (\sqrt{2})^2$
$$= 7 - 2$$
$$= 5$$

9.3 Exercise Set

1. $8\sqrt{3} + 5\sqrt{3} = (8+5)\sqrt{3} = 13\sqrt{3}$

3. $17\sqrt{6} - 2\sqrt{6} = (17-2)\sqrt{6} = 15\sqrt{6}$

5. $3\sqrt{13} - 8\sqrt{13} = (3-8)\sqrt{13} = -5\sqrt{13}$

7. $12\sqrt{x} + 3\sqrt{x} = (12+3)\sqrt{x} = 15\sqrt{x}$

9. $70\sqrt{y} - 76\sqrt{y} = (70-76)\sqrt{y}$
$$= -6\sqrt{y}$$

11. $7\sqrt{10x} + 2\sqrt{10x} = (7+2)\sqrt{10x}$
$$= 9\sqrt{10x}$$

13. $7\sqrt{5y} - \sqrt{5y} = 7\sqrt{5y} - 1\sqrt{5y}$
$$= (7-1)\sqrt{5y} = 6\sqrt{5y}$$

15. $\sqrt{5} + \sqrt{5} = 1\sqrt{5} + 1\sqrt{5} = (1+1)\sqrt{5}$
$$= 2\sqrt{5}$$

17. $4\sqrt{2} + 3\sqrt{2} + 5\sqrt{2} = (4+3+5)\sqrt{2}$
$$= 12\sqrt{2}$$

19. $4\sqrt{7} - 5\sqrt{7} + 8\sqrt{7} = (4-5+8)\sqrt{7}$
$$= 7\sqrt{7}$$

21. $4\sqrt{11} - 6\sqrt{11} + 2\sqrt{11} = (4-6+2)\sqrt{11}$
$$= 0\sqrt{11} = 0$$

23. $\sqrt{5} + \sqrt{20} = \sqrt{5} + \sqrt{4 \cdot 5} = \sqrt{5} + 2\sqrt{5}$
$$= 1\sqrt{5} + 2\sqrt{5} = 3\sqrt{5}$$

25. $\sqrt{8} - \sqrt{2} = \sqrt{4 \cdot 2} - \sqrt{2} = \sqrt{4}\sqrt{2} - \sqrt{2}$
$$= 2\sqrt{2} - 1\sqrt{2} = (2-1)\sqrt{2}$$
$$= \sqrt{2}$$

27. $\sqrt{50} + \sqrt{18} = \sqrt{25}\sqrt{2} + \sqrt{9}\sqrt{2}$
$$= 5\sqrt{2} + 3\sqrt{2} = 8\sqrt{2}$$

29. $7\sqrt{12} + \sqrt{75} = 7\sqrt{4}\sqrt{3} + \sqrt{25}\sqrt{3}$
$$= 7 \cdot 2\sqrt{3} + 5\sqrt{3}$$
$$= 14\sqrt{3} + 5\sqrt{3} = 19\sqrt{3}$$

31. $3\sqrt{27} - 2\sqrt{18} = 3\sqrt{9 \cdot 3} - 2\sqrt{9 \cdot 2}$
$$= 3 \cdot 3\sqrt{3} - 2 \cdot 3\sqrt{2}$$
$$= 9\sqrt{3} - 6\sqrt{2}$$
Because $\sqrt{3}$ and $\sqrt{2}$ are unlike radicals, it is not possible to combine terms and simplify further.

33. $2\sqrt{45x} - 2\sqrt{20x}$
$$= 2\sqrt{9}\sqrt{5x} - 2\sqrt{4}\sqrt{5x}$$
$$= 2 \cdot 3\sqrt{5x} - 2 \cdot 2\sqrt{5x}$$
$$= 6\sqrt{5x} - 4\sqrt{5x}$$
$$= (6-4)\sqrt{5x} = 2\sqrt{5x}$$

35. $\sqrt{8} + \sqrt{16} + \sqrt{18} + \sqrt{25}$
$$= \sqrt{4}\sqrt{2} + 4 + \sqrt{9}\sqrt{2} + 5$$
$$= 2\sqrt{2} + 4 + 3\sqrt{2} + 5$$
$$= (4+5) + (2\sqrt{2} + 3\sqrt{2})$$
$$= 9 + 5\sqrt{2}$$

37. $\sqrt{2} + \sqrt{11}$
These are unlike radicals, so the terms cannot be combined.

39. $2\sqrt{80} + 3\sqrt{75} = 2\sqrt{16}\sqrt{5} + 3\sqrt{25}\sqrt{3}$
$$= 2 \cdot 4\sqrt{5} + 3 \cdot 5\sqrt{3}$$
$$= 8\sqrt{5} + 15\sqrt{3}$$
Because $\sqrt{5}$ and $\sqrt{3}$ are unlike radicals, it is not possible to combine terms.

41. $3\sqrt{54} - 2\sqrt{20} + 4\sqrt{45} - \sqrt{24}$
$$= 3\sqrt{9}\sqrt{6} - 2\sqrt{4}\sqrt{5} + 4\sqrt{9}\sqrt{5} - \sqrt{4}\sqrt{6}$$
$$= 3 \cdot 3\sqrt{6} - 2 \cdot 2\sqrt{5} + 4 \cdot 3\sqrt{5} - 2\sqrt{6}$$
$$= 9\sqrt{6} - 4\sqrt{5} + 12\sqrt{5} - 2\sqrt{6}$$
$$= (9-2)\sqrt{6} + (-4+12)\sqrt{5}$$
$$= 7\sqrt{6} + 8\sqrt{5}$$

43. $\sqrt{2}(\sqrt{3} + \sqrt{5}) = \sqrt{2} \cdot \sqrt{3} + \sqrt{2} \cdot \sqrt{5}$
$$= \sqrt{6} + \sqrt{10}$$

45. $\sqrt{7}(\sqrt{6} - \sqrt{10}) = \sqrt{7} \cdot \sqrt{6} - \sqrt{7} \cdot \sqrt{10}$
$$= \sqrt{42} - \sqrt{70}$$

47. $\sqrt{3}(5 + \sqrt{3}) = \sqrt{3} \cdot 5 + \sqrt{3} \cdot \sqrt{3}$
$$= 5\sqrt{3} + 3$$

49. $\sqrt{3}(\sqrt{6} - \sqrt{3}) = \sqrt{3} \cdot \sqrt{6} - \sqrt{3} \cdot \sqrt{3}$
$$= \sqrt{18} - 3 = \sqrt{9}\sqrt{2} - 3$$
$$= 3\sqrt{2} - 3$$

51. $(5 + \sqrt{2})(6 + \sqrt{2})$
Use the FOIL method.
$$(5 + \sqrt{2})(6 + \sqrt{2})$$
$$= 5 \cdot 6 + 5\sqrt{2} + 6\sqrt{2} + \sqrt{2} \cdot \sqrt{2}$$
$$= 30 + 5\sqrt{2} + 6\sqrt{2} + 2$$
$$= (30 + 2) + (5 + 6)\sqrt{2}$$
$$= 32 + 11\sqrt{2}$$

53. $(4 + \sqrt{5})(10 - 3\sqrt{5})$
$$= 4 \cdot 10 + 4(-3\sqrt{5}) + \sqrt{5} \cdot 10 + \sqrt{5}(-3\sqrt{5})$$
$$= 40 + 12\sqrt{5} + 10\sqrt{5} - 3 \cdot 5$$
$$= 40 - 12\sqrt{5} + 10\sqrt{5} - 15$$
$$= (40 - 15) + (-12 + 10)\sqrt{5}$$
$$= 25 - 2\sqrt{5}$$

55. $\left(6-3\sqrt{7}\right)\left(2-5\sqrt{7}\right)$

$=6\cdot 2+6\left(-5\sqrt{7}\right)-3\sqrt{7}\left(2\right)-3\sqrt{7}\left(-5\sqrt{7}\right)$

$=12-30\sqrt{7}-6\sqrt{7}+15\cdot 7$

$=12-30\sqrt{7}-6\sqrt{7}+105$

$=\left(12+105\right)+\left(-30-6\right)\sqrt{7}$

$=117-36\sqrt{7}$

57. $\left(\sqrt{10}-3\right)\left(\sqrt{10}-5\right)$

$=\sqrt{10}\cdot\sqrt{10}+\sqrt{10}\left(-5\right)-3\sqrt{10}-3\left(-5\right)$

$=10-5\sqrt{10}-3\sqrt{10}+15$

$=25-8\sqrt{10}$

59. $\left(\sqrt{3}+\sqrt{6}\right)\left(\sqrt{3}+2\sqrt{6}\right)$

$=\sqrt{3}\cdot\sqrt{3}+\sqrt{3}\cdot 2\sqrt{6}+\sqrt{6}\cdot 3+\sqrt{6}\cdot 2\sqrt{6}$

$=3+2\sqrt{18}+\sqrt{18}+2\cdot 6$

$=3+2\sqrt{18}+\sqrt{18}+12$

$=15+3\sqrt{18}=15+3\sqrt{9}\sqrt{2}$

$=15+3\cdot 3\sqrt{2}$

$=15+9\sqrt{2}$

61. $\left(\sqrt{2}+1\right)\left(\sqrt{3}-6\right)$

$=\sqrt{2}\cdot\sqrt{3}+\sqrt{2}\left(-6\right)+1\cdot\sqrt{3}+1\left(-6\right)$

$=\sqrt{6}-6\sqrt{2}+\sqrt{3}-6$

63. $\left(3+\sqrt{5}\right)\left(3-\sqrt{5}\right)$

These two radical expressions are conjugates. Use the special-product formula.

$\left(A+B\right)\left(A-B\right)=A^2-B^2$

$\left(3+\sqrt{5}\right)\left(3-\sqrt{5}\right)=3^2-\left(\sqrt{5}\right)^2$

$=9-5$

$=4$

65. $\left(1-\sqrt{6}\right)\left(1+\sqrt{6}\right)=1^2-\left(\sqrt{6}\right)^2$

$=1-6$

$=-5$

67. $\left(\sqrt{11}+5\right)\left(\sqrt{11}-5\right)=\left(\sqrt{11}\right)^2-5^2$

$=11-25=-14$

69. $\left(\sqrt{7}-\sqrt{5}\right)\left(\sqrt{7}+\sqrt{5}\right)=\left(\sqrt{7}\right)^2-\left(\sqrt{5}\right)^2$

$=7-5=2$

71. $\left(2\sqrt{3}+7\right)\left(2\sqrt{3}-7\right)=\left(2\sqrt{3}\right)^2-7^2$

$=12-49$

$=-37$

73. $\left(2\sqrt{3}+\sqrt{5}\right)\left(2\sqrt{3}-\sqrt{5}\right)$

$=\left(2\sqrt{3}\right)^2-\left(\sqrt{5}\right)^2$

$=12-5$

$=7$

75. Use the special-product formula.

$\left(A+B\right)^2=A^2+2AB+B^2$

$\left(\sqrt{2}+\sqrt{3}\right)^2$

$=\left(\sqrt{2}\right)^2+2\cdot\sqrt{2}\cdot\sqrt{3}+\left(\sqrt{3}\right)^2$

$=2+2\sqrt{6}+3=5+2\sqrt{6}$

77. Use the special-product formula

$\left(A+B\right)^2=A^2-2AB+B^2$

$\left(\sqrt{x}-\sqrt{10}\right)^2$

$=\left(\sqrt{x}\right)^2-2\cdot\sqrt{x}\cdot\sqrt{10}+\left(\sqrt{10}\right)^2$

$=x-2\sqrt{10x}+10$

79. $5\sqrt{27x^3}-3x\sqrt{12x}$

$=5\sqrt{9x^2}\cdot\sqrt{3x}-3x\sqrt{4}\cdot\sqrt{3x}$

$=5\left(3x\right)\sqrt{3x}-3x\left(2\right)\sqrt{3x}$

$=15x\sqrt{3x}-6x\sqrt{3x}$

$=9x\sqrt{3x}$

81. $6y^2\sqrt{x^5y}+2x^2\sqrt{xy^5}$

$=6y^2\sqrt{x^4}\cdot\sqrt{xy}+2x^2\sqrt{y^4}\cdot\sqrt{xy}$

$=6y^2\left(x^2\right)\sqrt{xy}+2x^2\left(y^2\right)\sqrt{xy}$

$=6x^2y^2\sqrt{xy}+2x^2y^2\sqrt{xy}$

$=8x^2y^2\sqrt{xy}$

83. $3\sqrt[3]{54} - 4\sqrt[3]{16}$

$= 3\sqrt[3]{27} \cdot \sqrt[3]{2} - 4\sqrt[3]{8} \cdot \sqrt[3]{2}$

$= 3(3)\sqrt[3]{2} - 4(2)\sqrt[3]{2}$

$= 9\sqrt[3]{2} - 8\sqrt[3]{2}$

$= \sqrt[3]{2}$

85. $x\sqrt[3]{32x} + 9\sqrt[3]{4x^4}$

$= x\sqrt[3]{8}\sqrt[3]{4x} + 9\sqrt[3]{x^3} \cdot \sqrt[3]{4x}$

$= x(2)\sqrt[3]{4x} + 9(x)\sqrt[3]{4x}$

$= 2x\sqrt[3]{4x} + 9x\sqrt[3]{4x}$

$= 11x\sqrt[3]{4x}$

87. Use the formulas for perimeter and area of a square with $s = \sqrt{3} + \sqrt{5}$.

$P = 4x = 4\left(\sqrt{3} + \sqrt{5}\right)$

$\quad = 4\sqrt{3} + 4\sqrt{5}$

The perimeter is $\left(4\sqrt{3} + 4\sqrt{5}\right)$ inches.

$A = s^2$

$A = \left(\sqrt{3} + \sqrt{5}\right)^2$

$\quad = \left(\sqrt{3}\right)^2 + 2\sqrt{3}\sqrt{5} + \left(\sqrt{5}\right)^2$

$\quad = 3 + 2\sqrt{15} + 5$

$\quad = 8 + 2\sqrt{15}$

The area is $\left(8 + 2\sqrt{15}\right)$ square inches.

89. Use the formulas for the perimeter and area of a rectangle with $l = \sqrt{6} + 1$ and $w = \sqrt{6} - 1$.

$P = 2l + 2w = 2\left(\sqrt{6} + 1\right) + 2\left(\sqrt{6} - 1\right)$

$\quad = 2\sqrt{6} + 2 + 2\sqrt{6} - 2$

$\quad = 4\sqrt{6}$

The perimeter is $4\sqrt{6}$ inches.

$A = lw$

$A = \left(\sqrt{6} + 1\right)\left(\sqrt{6} - 1\right)$

$\quad = \left(\sqrt{6}\right)^2 - 1^2$

$\quad = 6 - 1$

$\quad = 5$

The area is 5 square inches.

91. To find the perimeter of a triangle, add the lengths of the three sides.

$P = \sqrt{2} + \sqrt{2} + 2 = 2 + 2\sqrt{2}$

The perimeter is $\left(2 + 2\sqrt{2}\right)$ inches.

Use the formula for the area of a triangle with $b = \sqrt{2}$ and $h = \sqrt{2}$.

$A = \dfrac{1}{2}bh$

$A = \dfrac{1}{2}\left(\sqrt{2}\right)\left(\sqrt{2}\right) = \dfrac{1}{2} \cdot 2 = 1$

The area is 1 square inch.

93. $\sqrt{2} + \sqrt{8}; a = 2, b = 8$

$\sqrt{a} + \sqrt{b} = \sqrt{(a+b) + 2\sqrt{ab}}$

$\sqrt{2} + \sqrt{8} = \sqrt{(2+8) + 2\sqrt{2 \cdot 8}}$

$\quad = \sqrt{10 + 2\sqrt{16}}$

$\quad = \sqrt{10 + 2 \cdot 4}$

$\quad = \sqrt{18} = \sqrt{9}\sqrt{2} = 3\sqrt{2}$

$\sqrt{2} + \sqrt{8} = \sqrt{2} + \sqrt{4 \cdot 2}$

$\quad = \sqrt{2} + \sqrt{4}\sqrt{2}$

$\quad = \sqrt{2} + 2\sqrt{2}$

$\quad = (1+2)\sqrt{2} = 3\sqrt{2}$

Explanations of preferences will vary.

95. a. $J = 1.4\sqrt{x} + 55 - \left(20 - 1.2\sqrt{x}\right)$

$\quad = 1.4\sqrt{x} + 55 - 20 + 1.2\sqrt{x}$

$\quad = 1.4\sqrt{x} + 1.2\sqrt{x} + 55 - 20$

$\quad = 2.6\sqrt{x} + 35$

b. $J = 2.6\sqrt{x} + 35$

$J = 2.6\sqrt{30} + 35 \approx 49$

49% of full-time college students had jobs in 2005.
This is the same as the actual percentage displayed in the bar graph.

97. a. 49% of full-time college students had jobs in 30 years after 1975, or 2005. This is represented by the point $(30, 49)$.

b. According to the graph, about 51% or 52% of full-time college students will have jobs in 2015.

99. – 105. Answers will vary.

107. does not make sense; Explanations will vary.
Sample explanation: After they are simplified, the
terms are not like radicals.

$$2\sqrt{20} + 4\sqrt{75} = 2\sqrt{4 \cdot 5} + 4\sqrt{25 \cdot 3}$$
$$= 2 \cdot 2\sqrt{5} + 4 \cdot 5\sqrt{3}$$
$$= 4\sqrt{5} + 20\sqrt{3}$$

109. does not make sense; Explanations will vary.
Sample explanation: This product will eliminate the
radicals.

111. false; Changes to make the statement true will vary.
A sample change is:

$$\left(\sqrt{5} + \sqrt{3}\right)^2 = \left(\sqrt{5}\right)^2 + 2\sqrt{5}\sqrt{3} + \left(\sqrt{3}\right)^2$$
$$= 5 + 2\sqrt{15} + 3$$
$$= 8 + 2\sqrt{15}.$$

113. false; Changes to make the statement true will vary.
A sample change is:

$$\left(\sqrt{7} + \sqrt{3}\right)\left(\sqrt{7} - \sqrt{3}\right) = \left(\sqrt{7}\right)^2 - \left(\sqrt{3}\right)^2$$
$$= 7 - 3$$
$$= 4.$$

115. $\left(\sqrt[3]{4} + 1\right)\left(\sqrt[3]{2} - 3\right)$

$$= \sqrt[3]{4} \cdot \sqrt[3]{2} - 3 \cdot \sqrt[3]{4} + 1 \cdot \sqrt[3]{2} - 1 \cdot 3$$
$$= \sqrt[3]{8} - 3\sqrt[3]{4} + \sqrt[3]{2} - 3$$
$$= 2 - 3\sqrt[3]{4} + \sqrt[3]{2} - 3$$
$$= -1 - 3\sqrt[3]{4} + \sqrt[3]{2}$$

117. $\left(4\sqrt{3x} + \sqrt{2y}\right)\left(4\sqrt{3x} - \sqrt{2y}\right)$

$$= \left(4\sqrt{3x}\right)^2 - \left(\sqrt{2y}\right)^2$$
$$= 4^2\left(\sqrt{3x}\right)^2 - \left(\sqrt{2y}\right)^2$$
$$= 16 \cdot 3x - 2y$$
$$= 48x - 2y$$

119. $\sqrt{16x} - \sqrt{9x} = \sqrt{7x}$

The graphs do not coincide so the simplification is
incorrect. The right side of the equation should be
$\sqrt{x}$.

$$\sqrt{16x} - \sqrt{9x} = \sqrt{16}\sqrt{x} - \sqrt{9}\sqrt{x}$$
$$= 4\sqrt{x} - 3\sqrt{x}$$
$$= (4 - 3)\sqrt{x}$$
$$= 1\sqrt{x} = \sqrt{x}$$

121. $\left(\sqrt{x} + 2\right)\left(\sqrt{x} - 2\right) = x^2 - 4$

The graphs do not coincide so the simplification is
incorrect. The right side of the equation should be
$x - 4$.

$$\left(\sqrt{x} + 2\right)\left(\sqrt{x} - 2\right) = \left(\sqrt{x}\right)^2 - 2^2 = x - 4$$

Note: the domain of the left side of the equation is
$x \geq 0$ while the domain of the right side is any real
number. Therefore, the two graphs are only
identical for $x \geq 0$.

122. $(5x + 3)(5x - 3) = (5x)^2 - 3^2$
$$= 25x^2 - 9$$

123. $64x^3 - x = x\left(64x^2 - 1\right)$

$$= x\left[(8x)^2 - 1^2\right]$$
$$= x(8x + 1)(8x - 1)$$

124. $y = -\dfrac{1}{4}x + 3$

slope $= -\dfrac{1}{4} = \dfrac{-1}{4}$; y-intercept $= 3$

Plot $(0,3)$. From this point, move 1 unit *down* and 4 units to the *right* to reach the point $(4,2)$. Draw a line through $(0,3)$ and $(4,2)$.

$y = -\dfrac{1}{4}x + 3$

125. $\dfrac{\sqrt{3}}{\sqrt{5}} \cdot \dfrac{\sqrt{5}}{\sqrt{5}} = \dfrac{\sqrt{15}}{\sqrt{25}} = \dfrac{\sqrt{15}}{5}$

126. $\left(5+\sqrt{3}\right)\left(5-\sqrt{3}\right) = 5^2 - \left(\sqrt{3}\right)^2 = 25 - 3 = 22$

127. $\left(\sqrt{6}-\sqrt{2}\right)\left(\sqrt{6}+\sqrt{2}\right) = \left(\sqrt{6}\right)^2 - \left(\sqrt{2}\right)^2 = 6 - 2 = 4$

Mid-Chapter Check Point

1. $\sqrt{50} \cdot \sqrt{6} = \sqrt{50 \cdot 6} = \sqrt{300}$
$= \sqrt{100} \cdot \sqrt{3} = 10\sqrt{3}$

2. $\sqrt{6} + 9\sqrt{6} = (1+9)\sqrt{6} = 10\sqrt{6}$

3. $\sqrt{96x^3} = \sqrt{16x^2} \cdot \sqrt{6x} = 4x\sqrt{6x}$

4. $\sqrt[5]{\dfrac{4}{32}} = \dfrac{\sqrt[5]{4}}{\sqrt[5]{32}} = \dfrac{\sqrt[5]{4}}{2}$

5. $\sqrt{27} + 3\sqrt{12} = \sqrt{9} \cdot \sqrt{3} + 3\sqrt{4} \cdot \sqrt{3}$
$= 3\sqrt{3} + 3(2)\sqrt{3}$
$= 3\sqrt{3} + 6\sqrt{3}$
$= 9\sqrt{3}$

6. $\left(\sqrt{10}+\sqrt{3}\right)\left(\sqrt{10}-\sqrt{3}\right)$
$= \left(\sqrt{10}\right)^2 - \left(\sqrt{3}\right)^2 = 10 - 3 = 7$

7. $\dfrac{\sqrt{5}}{2}\left(4\sqrt{3} - 6\sqrt{20}\right)$
$= \dfrac{4}{2}\sqrt{5 \cdot 3} - \dfrac{6}{2}\sqrt{5 \cdot 20}$
$= 2\sqrt{15} - 3\sqrt{100}$
$= 2\sqrt{15} - 3(10)$
$= 2\sqrt{15} - 30$

8. $-\sqrt{32x^{21}} = -\sqrt{16x^{20}} \cdot \sqrt{2x}$
$= -4x^{10}\sqrt{2x}$

9. $\sqrt{6x^3} \cdot \sqrt{2x^4} = \sqrt{6x^3 \cdot 2x^4}$
$= \sqrt{12x^7}$
$= \sqrt{4x^6} \cdot \sqrt{3x}$
$= 2x^3\sqrt{3x}$

10. $\dfrac{\sqrt[3]{32}}{\sqrt[3]{2}} = \sqrt[3]{\dfrac{32}{2}} = \sqrt[3]{16} = \sqrt[3]{8} \cdot \sqrt[3]{2} = 2\sqrt[3]{2}$

11. $-3\sqrt{90} - 5\sqrt{40}$
$= -3\sqrt{9} \cdot \sqrt{10} - 5\sqrt{4} \cdot \sqrt{10}$
$= -3(3)\sqrt{10} - 5(2)\sqrt{10}$
$= -9\sqrt{10} - 10\sqrt{10}$
$= -19\sqrt{10}$

12. $\left(2-\sqrt{3}\right)\left(5+2\sqrt{3}\right)$
$= 10 + 4\sqrt{3} - 5\sqrt{3} - 2\left(\sqrt{3}\right)^2$
$= 10 - \sqrt{3} - 6$
$= 4 - \sqrt{3}$

13. $\dfrac{\sqrt{56x^5}}{\sqrt{7x^3}} = \sqrt{\dfrac{56x^5}{7x^3}} = \sqrt{8x^2}$
$= \sqrt{4x^2} \cdot \sqrt{2} = 2x\sqrt{2}$

14. $-\sqrt[4]{32} = -\sqrt[4]{16} \cdot \sqrt[4]{2} = -2\sqrt[4]{2}$

15. $\left(\sqrt{2}+\sqrt{7}\right)^2$

$=\left(\sqrt{2}\right)^2+2\left(\sqrt{2}\right)\left(\sqrt{7}\right)+\left(\sqrt{7}\right)^2$

$=2+2\sqrt{2\cdot7}+7$

$=9+2\sqrt{14}$

16. $\sqrt[3]{\dfrac{1}{2}}\cdot\sqrt[3]{32}=\sqrt[3]{\dfrac{1}{2}\cdot32}=\sqrt[3]{16}$

$=\sqrt[3]{8}\cdot\sqrt[3]{2}=2\sqrt[3]{2}$

17. $\sqrt{5}+\sqrt{20}+\sqrt{45}$

$=\sqrt{5}+\sqrt{4}\cdot\sqrt{5}+\sqrt{9}\cdot\sqrt{5}$

$=1\sqrt{5}+2\sqrt{5}+3\sqrt{5}$

$=6\sqrt{5}$

18. $\dfrac{1}{3}\sqrt{\dfrac{90}{16}}=\dfrac{1}{3}\dfrac{\sqrt{90}}{\sqrt{16}}=\dfrac{\sqrt{9}\cdot\sqrt{10}}{3\cdot4}$

$=\dfrac{3\sqrt{10}}{12}=\dfrac{\sqrt{10}}{4}$

19. $3\sqrt{2}\left(\sqrt{2}+\sqrt{5}\right)$

$=3\sqrt{2}\cdot\sqrt{2}+3\sqrt{2}\cdot\sqrt{5}$

$=3\sqrt{2\cdot2}+3\sqrt{2\cdot5}$

$=3\sqrt{4}+3\sqrt{10}$

$=3(2)+3\sqrt{10}$

$=6+3\sqrt{10}$

20. $\left(5-\sqrt{2}\right)\left(5+\sqrt{2}\right)=5^2-\left(\sqrt{2}\right)^2$

$=25-2$

$=23$

9.4 Check Points

1. a. $\dfrac{25}{\sqrt{10}}\cdot\dfrac{\sqrt{10}}{\sqrt{10}}=\dfrac{25\sqrt{10}}{10}$

$=\dfrac{5\sqrt{10}}{2}$

b. $\sqrt{\dfrac{2}{7}}=\dfrac{\sqrt{2}}{\sqrt{7}}$

$=\dfrac{\sqrt{2}}{\sqrt{7}}\cdot\dfrac{\sqrt{7}}{\sqrt{7}}$

$=\dfrac{\sqrt{14}}{7}$

2. a. $\dfrac{15}{\sqrt{18}}=\dfrac{15}{3\sqrt{2}}=\dfrac{15}{3\sqrt{2}}\cdot\dfrac{\sqrt{2}}{\sqrt{2}}=\dfrac{15\sqrt{2}}{3\cdot2}=\dfrac{5\sqrt{2}}{2}$

b. $\sqrt{\dfrac{7x}{20}}=\dfrac{\sqrt{7x}}{\sqrt{20}}=\dfrac{\sqrt{7x}}{2\sqrt{5}}\cdot\dfrac{\sqrt{5}}{\sqrt{5}}=\dfrac{\sqrt{35x}}{2\cdot5}=\dfrac{\sqrt{35x}}{10}$

3. $\dfrac{8}{4+\sqrt{5}}=\dfrac{8}{4+\sqrt{5}}\cdot\dfrac{4-\sqrt{5}}{4-\sqrt{5}}$

$=\dfrac{32-8\sqrt{5}}{16-5}$

$=\dfrac{32-8\sqrt{5}}{11}$

4. $\dfrac{8}{\sqrt{7}-\sqrt{3}}=\dfrac{8}{\sqrt{7}-\sqrt{3}}\cdot\dfrac{\sqrt{7}+\sqrt{3}}{\sqrt{7}+\sqrt{3}}$

$=\dfrac{8\sqrt{7}+8\sqrt{3}}{\left(\sqrt{7}\right)^2-\left(\sqrt{3}\right)^2}$

$=\dfrac{8\sqrt{7}+8\sqrt{3}}{7-3}$

$=\dfrac{4\left(2\sqrt{7}+2\sqrt{3}\right)}{4}$

$=2\sqrt{7}+2\sqrt{3}$

9.4 Exercise Set

1. $\dfrac{1}{\sqrt{10}} = \dfrac{1}{\sqrt{10}} \cdot \dfrac{\sqrt{10}}{\sqrt{10}} = \dfrac{\sqrt{10}}{10}$

3. $\dfrac{5}{\sqrt{5}} = \dfrac{5}{\sqrt{5}} \cdot \dfrac{\sqrt{5}}{\sqrt{5}} = \dfrac{5\sqrt{5}}{5} = \sqrt{5}$

5. $\dfrac{2}{\sqrt{6}} = \dfrac{2}{\sqrt{6}} \cdot \dfrac{\sqrt{6}}{\sqrt{6}} = \dfrac{2\sqrt{6}}{6} = \dfrac{\sqrt{6}}{3}$

7. $\dfrac{28}{\sqrt{7}} = \dfrac{28}{\sqrt{7}} \cdot \dfrac{\sqrt{7}}{\sqrt{7}} = \dfrac{28\sqrt{7}}{7} = 4\sqrt{7}$

9. $\sqrt{\dfrac{3}{5}} = \dfrac{\sqrt{3}}{\sqrt{5}} = \dfrac{\sqrt{3}}{\sqrt{5}} \cdot \dfrac{\sqrt{5}}{\sqrt{5}} = \dfrac{\sqrt{15}}{5}$

11. $\sqrt{\dfrac{7}{3}} = \dfrac{\sqrt{7}}{\sqrt{3}} = \dfrac{\sqrt{7}}{\sqrt{3}} \cdot \dfrac{\sqrt{3}}{\sqrt{3}} = \dfrac{\sqrt{21}}{3}$

13. $\sqrt{\dfrac{x^2}{3}} = \dfrac{\sqrt{x^2}}{\sqrt{3}} = \dfrac{x}{\sqrt{3}} \cdot \dfrac{\sqrt{3}}{\sqrt{3}} = \dfrac{x\sqrt{3}}{3}$

15. $\sqrt{\dfrac{11}{x}} = \dfrac{\sqrt{11}}{\sqrt{x}} = \dfrac{\sqrt{11}}{\sqrt{x}} \cdot \dfrac{\sqrt{x}}{\sqrt{x}} = \dfrac{\sqrt{11x}}{x}$

17. $\sqrt{\dfrac{x}{y}} = \dfrac{\sqrt{x}}{\sqrt{y}} = \dfrac{\sqrt{x}}{\sqrt{y}} \cdot \dfrac{\sqrt{y}}{\sqrt{y}} = \dfrac{\sqrt{xy}}{y}$

19. $\sqrt{\dfrac{x^4}{2}} = \dfrac{\sqrt{x^4}}{\sqrt{2}} = \dfrac{x^2}{\sqrt{2}}$

$\qquad = \dfrac{x^2}{\sqrt{2}} \cdot \dfrac{\sqrt{2}}{\sqrt{2}} = \dfrac{x^2\sqrt{2}}{2}$

21. $\dfrac{\sqrt{7}}{\sqrt{5}} = \dfrac{\sqrt{7}}{\sqrt{5}} \cdot \dfrac{\sqrt{5}}{\sqrt{5}} = \dfrac{\sqrt{35}}{5}$

23. $\dfrac{\sqrt{3x}}{\sqrt{14}} = \dfrac{\sqrt{3x}}{\sqrt{14}} \cdot \dfrac{\sqrt{14}}{\sqrt{14}} = \dfrac{\sqrt{42x}}{14}$

25. $\dfrac{1}{\sqrt{20}} = \dfrac{1}{\sqrt{4}\sqrt{5}} = \dfrac{1}{2\sqrt{5}} = \dfrac{1}{2\sqrt{5}} \cdot \dfrac{\sqrt{5}}{\sqrt{5}}$

$\qquad = \dfrac{\sqrt{5}}{2\cdot 5} = \dfrac{\sqrt{5}}{10}$

27. $\dfrac{12}{\sqrt{32}} = \dfrac{12}{\sqrt{6}\sqrt{2}} = \dfrac{12}{4\sqrt{2}} = \dfrac{3}{\sqrt{2}}$

$\qquad = \dfrac{3}{\sqrt{2}} \cdot \dfrac{\sqrt{2}}{\sqrt{2}} = \dfrac{3\sqrt{2}}{2}$

29. $\dfrac{15}{\sqrt{12}} = \dfrac{15}{\sqrt{4}\sqrt{3}} = \dfrac{15}{2\sqrt{3}} = \dfrac{15}{2\sqrt{3}} \cdot \dfrac{\sqrt{3}}{\sqrt{3}}$

$\qquad = \dfrac{15\sqrt{3}}{2\cdot 3} = \dfrac{15\sqrt{3}}{6} = \dfrac{5\sqrt{3}}{2}$

31. $\sqrt{\dfrac{5}{18}} = \dfrac{\sqrt{5}}{\sqrt{18}} = \dfrac{\sqrt{5}}{\sqrt{9}\sqrt{2}} = \dfrac{\sqrt{5}}{3\sqrt{2}}$

$\qquad = \dfrac{\sqrt{5}}{3\sqrt{2}} \cdot \dfrac{\sqrt{2}}{\sqrt{2}} = \dfrac{\sqrt{10}}{3\cdot 2} = \dfrac{\sqrt{10}}{6}$

33. $\sqrt{\dfrac{x}{32}} = \dfrac{\sqrt{x}}{\sqrt{32}} = \dfrac{\sqrt{x}}{\sqrt{16}\sqrt{2}} = \dfrac{\sqrt{x}}{4\sqrt{2}}$

$\qquad = \dfrac{\sqrt{x}}{4\sqrt{2}} \cdot \dfrac{\sqrt{2}}{\sqrt{2}} = \dfrac{\sqrt{2x}}{4\cdot 2} = \dfrac{\sqrt{2x}}{8}$

35. $\sqrt{\dfrac{1}{45}} = \dfrac{\sqrt{1}}{\sqrt{45}} = \dfrac{1}{\sqrt{45}} = \dfrac{1}{\sqrt{9}\sqrt{5}} = \dfrac{1}{3\sqrt{5}}$

$\qquad = \dfrac{1}{3\sqrt{5}} \cdot \dfrac{\sqrt{5}}{\sqrt{5}} = \dfrac{\sqrt{5}}{3\cdot 5} = \dfrac{\sqrt{5}}{15}$

37. $\dfrac{\sqrt{7}}{\sqrt{12}} = \dfrac{\sqrt{7}}{\sqrt{4}\sqrt{3}} = \dfrac{\sqrt{7}}{2\sqrt{3}} \cdot \dfrac{\sqrt{3}}{\sqrt{3}}$

$\qquad = \dfrac{\sqrt{21}}{2\cdot 3} = \dfrac{\sqrt{21}}{6}$

39. $\dfrac{8x}{\sqrt{8}} = \dfrac{8x}{\sqrt{4}\sqrt{2}} = \dfrac{8x}{2\sqrt{2}} = \dfrac{4x}{\sqrt{2}}$

$\qquad = \dfrac{4x}{\sqrt{2}} \cdot \dfrac{\sqrt{2}}{\sqrt{2}} = \dfrac{4x\sqrt{2}}{2}$

$\qquad = 2x\sqrt{2}$

41. $\dfrac{\sqrt{7y}}{\sqrt{8}} = \dfrac{\sqrt{7y}}{\sqrt{4}\sqrt{2}} = \dfrac{\sqrt{7y}}{2\sqrt{2}} \cdot \dfrac{\sqrt{2}}{\sqrt{2}}$

$\qquad = \dfrac{\sqrt{14y}}{2\cdot 2} = \dfrac{\sqrt{14y}}{4}$

43. $\sqrt{\dfrac{7x}{12}} = \dfrac{\sqrt{7x}}{\sqrt{12}} = \dfrac{\sqrt{7x}}{\sqrt{4}\sqrt{3}} = \dfrac{\sqrt{7x}}{2\sqrt{3}}$

$\qquad = \dfrac{\sqrt{7x}}{2\sqrt{3}} \cdot \dfrac{\sqrt{3}}{\sqrt{3}} = \dfrac{\sqrt{21x}}{2\cdot 3}$

$\qquad = \dfrac{\sqrt{21x}}{6}$

45. $\sqrt{\dfrac{45}{x}} = \dfrac{\sqrt{45}}{\sqrt{x}} = \dfrac{\sqrt{9}\sqrt{5}}{\sqrt{x}} = \dfrac{3\sqrt{5}}{\sqrt{x}}$

$\qquad = \dfrac{3\sqrt{5}}{\sqrt{x}} \cdot \dfrac{\sqrt{x}}{\sqrt{x}} = \dfrac{3\sqrt{5x}}{x}$

47. $\dfrac{5}{\sqrt{x^3}} = \dfrac{5}{\sqrt{x^2}\sqrt{x}} = \dfrac{5}{x\sqrt{x}} = \dfrac{5}{x\sqrt{x}} \cdot \dfrac{\sqrt{x}}{\sqrt{x}}$

$\qquad = \dfrac{5\sqrt{x}}{x\cdot x} = \dfrac{5\sqrt{x}}{x^2}$

49. $\sqrt{\dfrac{27}{y^3}} = \dfrac{\sqrt{27}}{\sqrt{y^3}} = \dfrac{\sqrt{9}\sqrt{3}}{\sqrt{y^2}\sqrt{y}}$

$\qquad = \dfrac{3\sqrt{3}}{y\sqrt{y}} = \dfrac{3\sqrt{3}}{y\sqrt{y}} \cdot \dfrac{\sqrt{y}}{\sqrt{y}}$

$\qquad = \dfrac{3\sqrt{3y}}{y\cdot y} = \dfrac{3\sqrt{3y}}{y^2}$

51. $\dfrac{\sqrt{50x^2}}{\sqrt{12y^3}} = \dfrac{\sqrt{25x^2}\sqrt{2}}{\sqrt{4y^2}\sqrt{3y}} = \dfrac{5x\sqrt{2}}{2y\sqrt{3y}}$

$\qquad = \dfrac{5x\sqrt{2}}{2y\sqrt{3y}} \cdot \dfrac{\sqrt{3y}}{\sqrt{3y}} = \dfrac{5x\sqrt{6y}}{2y\cdot 3y}$

$\qquad = \dfrac{5x\sqrt{6y}}{6y^2}$

53. Multiply the numerator and denominator by the conjugate of the denominator, $4-\sqrt{3}$.

$\qquad \dfrac{1}{4+\sqrt{3}} \cdot \dfrac{4-\sqrt{3}}{4-\sqrt{3}} = \dfrac{1\left(4-\sqrt{3}\right)}{4^2-\left(\sqrt{3}\right)^2}$

$\qquad\qquad = \dfrac{4-\sqrt{3}}{16-3}$

$\qquad\qquad = \dfrac{4-\sqrt{3}}{13}$

55. $\dfrac{9}{2-\sqrt{7}} = \dfrac{9}{2-\sqrt{7}} \cdot \dfrac{2+\sqrt{7}}{2+\sqrt{7}}$

$\qquad = \dfrac{9\left(2+\sqrt{7}\right)}{2^2-\left(\sqrt{7}\right)^2} = \dfrac{9\left(2+\sqrt{7}\right)}{4-7}$

$\qquad = \dfrac{9\left(2+\sqrt{7}\right)}{-3}$

$\qquad = -3\left(2+\sqrt{7}\right)$

$\qquad -6-3\sqrt{7}$

57. $\dfrac{16}{\sqrt{11}+3} = \dfrac{16}{\sqrt{11}+3} \cdot \dfrac{\sqrt{11}-3}{\sqrt{11}-3}$

$\qquad = \dfrac{16\left(\sqrt{11}-3\right)}{\left(\sqrt{11}\right)^2-3^2} = \dfrac{16\left(\sqrt{11}-3\right)}{11-9}$

$\qquad = \dfrac{16\left(\sqrt{11}-3\right)}{2}$

$\qquad = 8\left(\sqrt{11}-3\right)$

$\qquad = 8\sqrt{11}-24$

59. $\dfrac{18}{3-\sqrt{3}} = \dfrac{18}{3-\sqrt{3}} \cdot \dfrac{3+\sqrt{3}}{3+\sqrt{3}}$

$\qquad = \dfrac{18\left(3+\sqrt{3}\right)}{3^2-\left(\sqrt{3}\right)^2} = \dfrac{18\left(3+\sqrt{3}\right)}{9-3}$

$\qquad = \dfrac{18\left(3+\sqrt{3}\right)}{6}$

$\qquad = 3\left(3+\sqrt{3}\right)$

$\qquad = 9+3\sqrt{3}$

61. $\dfrac{\sqrt{2}}{\sqrt{2}+1} = \dfrac{\sqrt{2}}{\sqrt{2}+1} \cdot \dfrac{\sqrt{2}-1}{\sqrt{2}-1}$

$\qquad = \dfrac{\sqrt{2}\left(\sqrt{2}-1\right)}{\left(\sqrt{2}\right)^2-1^2} = \dfrac{\sqrt{2}\left(\sqrt{2}-1\right)}{2-1}$

$\qquad = \dfrac{\sqrt{2}\left(\sqrt{2}-1\right)}{1}$

$\qquad = 2-\sqrt{2}$

63.
$$\frac{\sqrt{10}}{\sqrt{10}-\sqrt{7}} = \frac{\sqrt{10}}{\sqrt{10}-\sqrt{7}} \cdot \frac{\sqrt{10}+\sqrt{7}}{\sqrt{10}+\sqrt{7}}$$
$$= \frac{\sqrt{10}\left(\sqrt{10}+\sqrt{7}\right)}{\left(\sqrt{10}\right)^2 - \left(\sqrt{7}\right)^2}$$
$$= \frac{\sqrt{10}\left(\sqrt{10}+\sqrt{7}\right)}{10-7}$$
$$= \frac{\sqrt{10}\left(\sqrt{10}+\sqrt{7}\right)}{3}$$
$$= \frac{10+\sqrt{70}}{3}$$

65.
$$\frac{6}{\sqrt{6}+\sqrt{3}} = \frac{6}{\sqrt{6}+\sqrt{3}} \cdot \frac{\sqrt{6}-\sqrt{3}}{\sqrt{6}-\sqrt{3}}$$
$$= \frac{6\left(\sqrt{6}-\sqrt{3}\right)}{\left(\sqrt{6}\right)^2 - \left(\sqrt{3}\right)^2}$$
$$= \frac{6\left(\sqrt{6}-\sqrt{3}\right)}{6-3}$$
$$= \frac{6\left(\sqrt{6}-\sqrt{3}\right)}{3}$$
$$= 2\left(\sqrt{6}-\sqrt{3}\right)$$
$$= 2\sqrt{6}-2\sqrt{3}$$

67.
$$\frac{2}{\sqrt{5}-\sqrt{3}} = \frac{2}{\sqrt{5}-\sqrt{3}} \cdot \frac{\sqrt{5}+\sqrt{3}}{\sqrt{5}+\sqrt{3}}$$
$$= \frac{2\left(\sqrt{5}+\sqrt{3}\right)}{\left(\sqrt{5}\right)^2 - \left(\sqrt{3}\right)^2}$$
$$= \frac{2\left(\sqrt{5}+\sqrt{3}\right)}{5-3}$$
$$= \frac{2\left(\sqrt{5}+\sqrt{3}\right)}{2}$$
$$= \sqrt{5}+\sqrt{3}$$

69.
$$\frac{2}{4+\sqrt{x}} = \frac{2}{4+\sqrt{x}} \cdot \frac{4-\sqrt{x}}{4-\sqrt{x}}$$
$$= \frac{2\left(4-\sqrt{x}\right)}{4^2 - \left(\sqrt{x}\right)^2} = \frac{2\left(4-\sqrt{x}\right)}{16-x}$$
$$= \frac{8-2\sqrt{x}}{16-x}$$

71.
$$\frac{2\sqrt{3}}{\sqrt{15}+2} = \frac{2\sqrt{3}}{\sqrt{15}+2} \cdot \frac{\sqrt{15}-2}{\sqrt{15}-2}$$
$$= \frac{2\sqrt{3}\left(\sqrt{15}-2\right)}{\left(\sqrt{15}\right)^2 - 2^2}$$
$$= \frac{2\sqrt{3}\left(\sqrt{15}-2\right)}{15-4}$$
$$= \frac{2\sqrt{3}\left(\sqrt{15}-2\right)}{11}$$
$$= \frac{2\sqrt{45}-4\sqrt{3}}{11}$$
$$= \frac{2\sqrt{9}\sqrt{5}-4\sqrt{3}}{11}$$
$$= \frac{2\cdot3\sqrt{5}-4\sqrt{3}}{11}$$
$$= \frac{6\sqrt{5}-4\sqrt{3}}{11}$$

73.
$$\frac{\sqrt{5}+\sqrt{2}}{\sqrt{5}-\sqrt{2}} = \frac{\sqrt{5}+\sqrt{2}}{\sqrt{5}-\sqrt{2}} \cdot \frac{\sqrt{5}+\sqrt{2}}{\sqrt{5}+\sqrt{2}}$$
$$= \frac{\left(\sqrt{5}+\sqrt{2}\right)^2}{\left(\sqrt{5}\right)^2 - \left(\sqrt{2}\right)^2}$$
$$= \frac{\left(\sqrt{5}\right)^2 + 2\sqrt{5}\sqrt{2} + \left(\sqrt{2}\right)^2}{\left(\sqrt{5}\right)^2 - \left(\sqrt{2}\right)^2}$$
$$= \frac{5+2\sqrt{10}+2}{5-2}$$
$$= \frac{7+2\sqrt{10}}{3}$$

75. $\dfrac{\sqrt{36x^2y^5}}{\sqrt{2x^3y}} = \sqrt{\dfrac{36x^2y^5}{2x^3y}} = \sqrt{\dfrac{18y^4}{x}}$

$= \dfrac{\sqrt{9y^4}\sqrt{2}}{\sqrt{x}} = \dfrac{3y^2\sqrt{2}}{\sqrt{x}}$

$= \dfrac{3y^2\sqrt{2}}{\sqrt{x}} \cdot \dfrac{\sqrt{x}}{\sqrt{x}} = \dfrac{3y^2\sqrt{2x}}{x}$

77. $\dfrac{2}{\sqrt{x+2}-\sqrt{x}}$

$= \dfrac{2}{\sqrt{x+2}-\sqrt{x}} \cdot \dfrac{\sqrt{x+2}+\sqrt{x}}{\sqrt{x+2}+\sqrt{x}}$

$= \dfrac{2\left(\sqrt{x+2}+\sqrt{x}\right)}{\left(\sqrt{x+2}\right)^2 - \left(\sqrt{x}\right)^2}$

$= \dfrac{2\left(\sqrt{x+2}+\sqrt{x}\right)}{x+2-x}$

$= \dfrac{2\left(\sqrt{x+2}+\sqrt{x}\right)}{2}$

$= \sqrt{x+2}+\sqrt{x}$

79. $\dfrac{\sqrt{2}}{\sqrt{3}} + \dfrac{\sqrt{3}}{\sqrt{2}} = \dfrac{\sqrt{2}}{\sqrt{3}} \cdot \dfrac{\sqrt{3}}{\sqrt{3}} + \dfrac{\sqrt{3}}{\sqrt{2}} \cdot \dfrac{\sqrt{2}}{\sqrt{2}}$

$= \dfrac{\sqrt{6}}{3} + \dfrac{\sqrt{6}}{2} = \dfrac{2\sqrt{6}}{6} + \dfrac{3\sqrt{6}}{6}$

$= \dfrac{5\sqrt{6}}{6}$

81. $\dfrac{2x+4-2h}{\sqrt{x+2-h}} = \dfrac{2(x+2-h)}{\sqrt{x+2-h}} \cdot \dfrac{\sqrt{x+2-h}}{\sqrt{x+2-h}}$

$= \dfrac{2(x+2-h)\sqrt{x+2-h}}{x+2-h}$

$= 2\sqrt{x+2-h}$

83. a. $P = \dfrac{x\left(13+\sqrt{x}\right)}{5\sqrt{x}}; x = 25$

$P = \dfrac{25\left(13+\sqrt{25}\right)}{5\sqrt{25}}$

$= \dfrac{25+(13+5)}{5 \cdot 5}$

$= \dfrac{25 \cdot 18}{25} = 18$

According to the formula, 18% of 25-year-olds must pay more taxes.

b. $\dfrac{x\left(13+\sqrt{x}\right)}{5\sqrt{x}} \cdot \dfrac{\sqrt{x}}{\sqrt{x}} = \dfrac{x\sqrt{x}\left(13+\sqrt{x}\right)}{5\sqrt{x}\sqrt{x}}$

$= \dfrac{x\sqrt{x}\cdot 13 + x\sqrt{x}\sqrt{x}}{5\sqrt{x}\sqrt{x}}$

$= \dfrac{13x\sqrt{x} + x \cdot x}{5x}$

$= \dfrac{x\left(13\sqrt{x}+x\right)}{5x}$

$= \dfrac{13\sqrt{x}+x}{5}$

c. $\dfrac{13\sqrt{25}+25}{5} = \dfrac{13(5)+25}{5} = 18$

According to the formula, 18% of 25-year-olds must pay more taxes. This is the same result as in part (a).

85. $\dfrac{w}{h} = \dfrac{2}{\sqrt{5}-1}$

$= \dfrac{2}{\sqrt{5}-1} \cdot \dfrac{\sqrt{5}+1}{\sqrt{5}+1}$

$= \dfrac{2\left(\sqrt{5}+1\right)}{5-1}$

$= \dfrac{\sqrt{5}+1}{2} \approx 1.62$

87. Answers will vary.

89. $P = \dfrac{x\left(13+\sqrt{x}\right)}{5\sqrt{x}}$

$x = 30: \quad P = \dfrac{30\left(13+\sqrt{30}\right)}{5\sqrt{30}} \approx 20$

$x = 40: \quad P = \dfrac{40\left(13+\sqrt{40}\right)}{5\sqrt{40}} \approx 24$

$x = 50: \quad P = \dfrac{50\left(13+\sqrt{50}\right)}{5\sqrt{50}} \approx 28$

These results show that about 20% of 30-year-old taxpayers, 24% of 40-year-old taxpayers, and 28% of 50-year-old taxpayers must pay more taxes. The trend is for an increasing percentage of taxpayers to pay more taxes as the taxpayers get older. Explanations may vary.

91. makes sense

93. makes sense

95. true

97. false; Changes to make the statement true will vary. A sample change is: They may require more space.

99. $\sqrt{2} + \sqrt{\dfrac{1}{2}} = \sqrt{2} + \dfrac{\sqrt{1}}{\sqrt{2}} = \sqrt{2} + \dfrac{1}{\sqrt{2}}$

$\qquad = \sqrt{2} + \dfrac{1}{\sqrt{2}} \cdot \dfrac{\sqrt{2}}{\sqrt{2}}$

$\qquad = \sqrt{2} + \dfrac{\sqrt{2}}{2}$

$\qquad = \dfrac{2\sqrt{2}}{2} + \dfrac{\sqrt{2}}{2} = \dfrac{3\sqrt{2}}{2}$

101. $\dfrac{4}{2 + \sqrt{\square}} = 8 - 4\sqrt{3}$

$\dfrac{4}{2 + \sqrt{\square}} \cdot \dfrac{2 - \sqrt{\square}}{2 - \sqrt{\square}} = 8 - 7\sqrt{3}$

$\dfrac{4\left(2 - \sqrt{\square}\right)}{2^2 - \left(\sqrt{\square}\right)^2} = 8 - 4\sqrt{3}$

$\dfrac{8 - 4\sqrt{\square}}{4 - \square} = 8 - 4\sqrt{3}$

If the missing number is 3, the last equation becomes $\dfrac{8 - 4\sqrt{3}}{4 - 3} = 8 - 4\sqrt{3}$, which is true. Thus, 3 goes in the box.

102. $6x^2 - 11x + 5 = 0$

$(6x - 5)(x - 1) = 0$

$6x - 5 = 0 \quad$ or $\quad x - 1 = 0$

$6x = 5 \qquad\qquad x = 1$

$x = \dfrac{5}{6}$

The solution set is $\left\{\dfrac{5}{6}, 1\right\}$.

103. $\left(2x^2\right)^{-3} = \dfrac{1}{\left(2x^2\right)^3} = \dfrac{1}{2^3\left(x^2\right)^3} = \dfrac{1}{8x^6}$

104. $\dfrac{x^2 - 6x + 9}{12} \cdot \dfrac{3}{x^2 - 9}$

$= \dfrac{(x-3)(x-3)}{12} \cdot \dfrac{3}{(x+3)(x-3)}$

$= \dfrac{x-3}{4(x+3)}$

105. $7 = -2.5x + 17$

$-10 = -2.5x$

$\dfrac{-10}{-2.5} = \dfrac{-2.5x}{-2.5}$

$4 = x$

The solution set is $\{4\}$.

106. $2x - 1 = x^2 - 4x + 4$

$0 = x^2 - 6x + 5$

$0 = (x - 5)(x - 1)$

$x - 5 = 0 \quad$ or $\quad x - 1 = 0$

$x = 5 \qquad\qquad x = 1$

The solution set is $\{1, 5\}$.

107. The solutions of the equation in exercise 106 are 1 and 5.

Check 1:

$\sqrt{2x - 1} + 2 = x$

$\sqrt{2(1) - 1} + 2 = 1$

$\sqrt{1} + 2 = 1$

$1 + 2 = 1$

$3 = 1, \text{ false}$

Check 5:

$\sqrt{2x - 1} + 2 = x$

$\sqrt{2(5) - 1} + 2 = 5$

$\sqrt{9} + 2 = 5$

$3 + 2 = 5$

$5 = 5, \text{ true}$

5 is a solution of $\sqrt{2x - 1} + 2 = x$.

9.5 Check Points

1.　$\sqrt{2x+3} = 5$

$\left(\sqrt{2x+3}\right)^2 = 5^2$

$2x + 3 = 25$

$2x = 22$

$x = 11$

Check 11:

$\sqrt{2x+3} = 5$

$\sqrt{2\cdot 11 + 3} = 5$

$\sqrt{25} = 5$

$5 = 5, \text{ true}$

The solution set is $\{11\}$.

2.　$\sqrt{x+32} - 3\sqrt{x} = 0$

$\sqrt{x+32} = 3\sqrt{x}$

$\left(\sqrt{x+32}\right)^2 = \left(3\sqrt{x}\right)^2$

$x + 32 = 9x$

$-8x = -32$

$x = 4$

Check 4:

$\sqrt{x+32} - 3\sqrt{x} = 0$

$\sqrt{4+32} - 3\sqrt{4} = 0$

$\sqrt{36} - 3\cdot 2 = 0$

$6 - 6 = 0$

$0 = 0, \text{ true}$

The solution set is $\{4\}$.

3.　$\sqrt{x} + 1 = 0$

$\sqrt{x} = -1$

$\left(\sqrt{x}\right)^2 = (-1)^2$

$x = 1$

Check 4:

$\sqrt{x} + 1 = 0$

$\sqrt{1} + 1 = 0$

$1 + 1 = 0$

$2 = 0, \text{ false}$

The false statement indicates that 1 is not a solution.
The solution set is $\{\ \}$.

4.　$\sqrt{x+3} + 3 = x$

$\sqrt{x+3} = x - 3$

$\left(\sqrt{x+3}\right)^2 = (x-3)^2$

$x + 3 = x^2 - 6x + 9$

$0 = x^2 - 7x + 6$

$0 = (x-1)(x-6)$

$x - 1 = 0 \quad \text{or} \quad x - 6 = 0$

$x = 1 \qquad\qquad x = 6$

Check 1:　　　　　　Check 6:

$\sqrt{x+3} + 3 = x$　　$\sqrt{x+3} + 3 = x$

$\sqrt{1+3} + 3 = 1$　　$\sqrt{6+3} + 3 = 6$

$\sqrt{4} + 3 = 1$　　　$\sqrt{9} + 3 = 6$

$2 + 3 = 1$　　　　　$3 + 3 = 6$

$5 = 1, \text{ false}$　　　$6 = 6, \text{ true}$

The false statement indicates that 1 is not a solution.
The solution set is $\{6\}$.

5.　$p = -2.5\sqrt{t} + 17$

$4.5 = -2.5\sqrt{t} + 17$

$-12.5 = -2.5\sqrt{t}$

$\dfrac{-12.5}{-2.5} = \dfrac{-2.5\sqrt{t}}{-2.5}$

$5 = \sqrt{t}$

$5^2 = \left(\sqrt{t}\right)^2$

$25 = t$

Only 4.5% of Americans will favor laws prohibiting interracial marriage 25 years after 1993, or 2018.

9.5 Exercise Set

1.　$\sqrt{x} = 5$

$\left(\sqrt{x}\right)^2 = 5^2$

$x = 25$

Check:

$\sqrt{x} = 5$

$\sqrt{25} = 5$

$5 = 5, \text{ true}$

The solution set is $\{25\}$.

3. $\sqrt{x} - 4 = 0$

$\sqrt{x} = 4$

$\left(\sqrt{x}\right)^2 = 4^2$

$x = 16$

Check:

$\sqrt{x} - 4 = 0$

$\sqrt{16} - 4 = 0$

$4 - 4 = 0$

$0 = 0$, true

The solution set is $\{16\}$.

5. $\sqrt{x+2} = 3$

$\left(\sqrt{x+2}\right)^2 = 3^2$

$x + 2 = 9$

$x = 7$

Substitution confirms the solution set is $\{7\}$.

7. $\sqrt{x-3} - 11 = 0$

$\sqrt{x-3} = 11$

$\left(\sqrt{x-3}\right)^2 = 11^2$

$x - 3 = 121$

$x = 124$

Substitution confirms the solution set is $\{124\}$.

9. $\sqrt{3x-5} = 4$

$\left(\sqrt{3x-5}\right)^2 = 4^2$

$3x - 5 = 16$

$3x = 21$

$x = 7$

Substitution confirms the solution set is $\{7\}$.

11. $\sqrt{x+5} + 2 = 5$

$\sqrt{x+5} = 3$

$\left(\sqrt{x+5}\right)^2 = 3^2$

$x + 5 = 9$

$x = 4$

Substitution confirms the solution set is $\{4\}$.

13. $\sqrt{x+3} = \sqrt{4x-3}$

$\left(\sqrt{x+3}\right)^2 = \left(\sqrt{4x-3}\right)^2$

$x + 3 = 4x - 3$

$-3x + 3 = -3$

$-3x = -6$

$x = 2$

Substitution confirms the solution set is $\{2\}$.

15. $\sqrt{6x-2} = \sqrt{4x+4}$

$\left(\sqrt{6x-2}\right)^2 = \left(\sqrt{4x+4}\right)^2$

$6x - 2 = 4x + 4$

$2x - 2 = 4$

$2x = 6$

$x = 3$

Substitution confirms the solution set is $\{3\}$.

17. $11 = 6 + \sqrt{x+1}$

$5 = \sqrt{x+1}$

$5^2 = \left(\sqrt{x+1}\right)^2$

$25 = x + 1$

$24 = x$

Substitution confirms the solution set is $\{24\}$.

19. $\sqrt{x} + 10 = 0$

$\sqrt{x} = -10$

$\left(\sqrt{x}\right)^2 = (-10)^2$

$x = 100$

Check 100:

$\sqrt{x} + 10 = 0$

$\sqrt{100} + 10 = 0$

$10 + 10 = 0$

$20 = 0$, false

This false statement indicates that 100 is not a solution. Since the only proposed solution is extraneous, the given equation has no solution. The solution set is $\{\ \}$.

21. $\sqrt{x-1} = -3$

$\left(\sqrt{x-1}\right)^2 = (-3)^2$

$x-1 = 9$

$x = 10$

Check 10:

$\sqrt{x-1} = -3$

$\sqrt{10-1} = -3$

$\sqrt{9} = -3$

$3 = -3$, false

The false statement shows that 10 is an extraneous solution. Since it is the only proposed solution, the given equation has no solution. The solution set is $\{\ \}$.

23. $3\sqrt{x} = \sqrt{8x+16}$

$\left(3\sqrt{x}\right)^2 = \left(\sqrt{8x+16}\right)^2$

$9x = 8x+16$

$x = 16$

Check 16:

$3\sqrt{x} = \sqrt{8x+16}$

$3\sqrt{16} = \sqrt{8\cdot16+16}$

$3\cdot4 = \sqrt{128+16}$

$12 = \sqrt{144}$

$12 = 12$, true

The solution set is $\{16\}$.

25. $\sqrt{2x-3}+5 = 0$

$\sqrt{2x-3} = -5$

$\left(\sqrt{2x-3}\right)^2 = (-5)^2$

$2x-3 = 25$

$2x = 28$

$x = 14$

Check 14:

$\sqrt{2x-3}+5 = 0$

$\sqrt{2\cdot14-3}+5 = 0$

$\sqrt{28-3}+5 = 0$

$\sqrt{25}+5 = 0$

$5+5 = 0$

$10 = 0$, false

The false statement shows that 14 is an extraneous solution. The solution set is $\{\ \}$.

27. $\sqrt{3x+4}-2 = 3$

$\sqrt{3x+4} = 5$

$\left(\sqrt{3x+4}\right)^2 = 5^2$

$3x+4 = 25$

$3x = 21$

$x = 7$

Substitution confirms the solution set is $\{7\}$.

29. $3\sqrt{x-1} = \sqrt{3x+3}$

$\left(3\sqrt{x-1}\right)^2 = \left(\sqrt{3x+3}\right)^2$

$9(x-1) = 3x+3$

$9x-9 = 3x+3$

$6x = 12$

$x = 2$

Substitution confirms the solution set is $\{2\}$.

31. $\sqrt{x+7} = x+5$

Square both sides,

$\left(\sqrt{x+7}\right)^2 = (x+5)^2$

Square the binomial on the right.

$x+7 = x^2+10x+25$

Simplify and solve this quadratic equation.

$0 = x^2+9x+18$

$0 = (x+3)(x+6)$

$x+3 = 0$ or $x+6 = 0$

$x = -3$ $x = -6$

There are two proposed solutions. Each must be checked in the original equation.

Check -3:   Check -6:

$\sqrt{x+7} = x+5$ $\sqrt{x+7} = x+5$

$\sqrt{-3+7} = -3+5$ $\sqrt{-6+7} = -6+5$

$\sqrt{4} = 2$ $\sqrt{1} = -1$

$2 = 2$, true $1 = -1$, false

Thus -6 is an extraneous solution, while -3 satisfies the equation. The solution set is $\{-3\}$.

33.

$$\sqrt{2x+13} = x+7$$

$$\left(\sqrt{2x+13}\right)^2 = (x+7)^2$$

$$2x+13 = x^2+14x+49$$

$$0 = x^2+12x+36$$

$$0 = (x+6)^2$$

$$0 = x+6$$

$$-6 = x$$

Check -6:

$$\sqrt{2x+13} = x+7$$

$$\sqrt{2(-6)+13} = -6+7$$

$$\sqrt{-12+13} = 1$$

$$\sqrt{1} = 1$$

$$1 = 1, \text{ true}$$

The solution set is $\{-6\}$.

35.

$$\sqrt{9x^2+2x-4} = 3x$$

$$\left(\sqrt{9x^2+2x-4}\right)^2 = (3x)^2$$

$$9x^2+2x-4 = 9x^2$$

$$2x-4 = 0$$

$$2x = 4$$

$$x = 2$$

Substitution confirms the solution set is $\{2\}$.

37.

$$x = \sqrt{2x-2}+1$$

$$x-1 = \sqrt{2x-2}$$

$$(x-1)^2 = \left(\sqrt{2x-2}\right)^2$$

$$x^2+2x+1 = 2x-2$$

$$x^2-4x+3 = 0$$

$$(x-1)(x-3) = 0$$

$$x-1 = 0 \text{ or } x-3 = 0$$

$$x = 1 \qquad x = 3$$

Check 1: Check 3:

$$x = \sqrt{2x-2}+1 \qquad x = \sqrt{2x-2}+1$$

$$1 = \sqrt{2\cdot1-2}+1 \qquad 3 = \sqrt{2\cdot3-2}+1$$

$$1 = \sqrt{2-2}+1 \qquad 3 = \sqrt{6-2}+1$$

$$1 = 0+1 \qquad 3 = \sqrt{4}+1$$

$$1 = 1, \text{ true} \qquad 3 = 2+1$$

$$3 = 3, \text{ true}$$

Both proposed solutions, 1 and 3, satisfy the original equation. The solution set is $\{1,3\}$.

39.

$$x = \sqrt{8-7x}+2$$

$$x-2 = \sqrt{8-7x}$$

$$(x-2)^2 = \left(\sqrt{8-7x}\right)^2$$

$$x^2-4x+4 = 8-7x$$

$$x^2+3x-4 = 0$$

$$(x+4)(x-1) = 0$$

$$x+4 = 0 \text{ or } x-1 = 0$$

$$x = -4 \qquad x = 1$$

Check -4: Check 1:

$$x = \sqrt{8-7x}+2 \qquad x = \sqrt{8-7x}+2$$

$$-4 = \sqrt{8-7(-4)}+2 \qquad 1 = \sqrt{8-7\cdot1}+2$$

$$-4 = \sqrt{8+28}+2 \qquad 1 = \sqrt{8-7}+2$$

$$-4 = \sqrt{36}+2 \qquad 1 = \sqrt{1}+2$$

$$-4 = 6+2 \qquad 1 = 1+2$$

$$-4 = 8, \text{ false} \qquad 1 = 3, \text{ false}$$

Both of the proposed solutions are extraneous so the given equation has no solution. The solution set is $\{\ \}$.

41.

$$\sqrt{3x}+10 = x+4$$

$$\sqrt{3x} = x-6$$

$$\left(\sqrt{3x}\right)^2 = (x-6)^2$$

$$3x = x^2-12x+36$$

$$0 = x^2-15x+36$$

$$0 = (x-3)(x-12)$$

$$x-3 = 0 \text{ or } x-12 = 0$$

$$x = 3 \qquad x = 12$$

Check 3: Check 12:

$$\sqrt{3x}+10 = x+4 \qquad \sqrt{3x}+10 = x+4$$

$$\sqrt{3\cdot3}+10 = 3+4 \qquad \sqrt{3\cdot12}+10 = 12+4$$

$$\sqrt{9}+10 = 7 \qquad \sqrt{36}+10 = 16$$

$$3-10 = 7 \qquad 6+10 = 16$$

$$13 = 7, \text{ false} \qquad 16 = 16, \text{ true}$$

The proposed solution 3 is extraneous, while 12 satisfies the equation. The solution set is $\{12\}$.

43. $3\sqrt{x} + 5 = 2$

$$3\sqrt{x} = -3$$

$$\left(3\sqrt{x}\right)^2 = (-3)^2$$

$$9x = 9$$

$$x = 1$$

Check 1:

$$3\sqrt{x} + 5 = 2$$

$$3\sqrt{1} + 5 = 2$$

$$3 \cdot 1 + 5 = 2$$

$$3 + 5 = 2$$

$$8 = 2, \text{ false}$$

The proposed solution 1 is extraneous, so the equation has no solution. The solution set is { }.

45. Let x = the number.

$$2 + \sqrt{4x} = 10$$

$$\sqrt{4x} = 8$$

$$\left(\sqrt{4x}\right)^2 = 8^2$$

$$4x = 64$$

$$x = 16$$

Check 16:

$$2 + \sqrt{4(16)} = 10$$

$$2 + \sqrt{64} = 10$$

$$2 + 8 = 10$$

$$10 = 10, \text{ true}$$

The number is 16.

47. Let x = the number.

$$x = 4 + \sqrt{2x}$$

$$x - 4 = \sqrt{2x}$$

$$(x-4)^2 = \left(\sqrt{2x}\right)^2$$

$$x^2 - 8x + 16 = 2x$$

$$x^2 - 10x + 16 = 0$$

$$(x-8)(x-2) = 0$$

$$x - 8 = 0 \quad \text{or} \quad x - 2 = 0$$

$$x = 8 \qquad\qquad x = 2$$

Check 8:   Check 2

$$8 = 4 + \sqrt{2(8)} \qquad 2 = 4 + \sqrt{2(2)}$$

$$8 = 4 + \sqrt{16} \qquad 2 = 4 + \sqrt{4}$$

$$8 = 4 + 4 \qquad\qquad 2 = 4 + 2$$

$$8 = 8 \text{ true} \qquad\quad 2 = 6 \text{ false}$$

Discard 2. The number is 8.

49. $v = \sqrt{2gh}$

$$v^2 = \left(\sqrt{2gh}\right)^2$$

$$v^2 = 2gh$$

$$\frac{v^2}{2g} = \frac{2gh}{2g}$$

$$\frac{v^2}{2g} = h$$

51. $\sqrt{x} + 2 = \sqrt{x+8}$

$$\left(\sqrt{x} + 2\right)^2 = \left(\sqrt{x+8}\right)^2$$

$$\left(\sqrt{x}\right)^2 + 2(2)\left(\sqrt{x}\right) + 2^2 = x + 8$$

$$x + 4\sqrt{x} + 4 = x + 8$$

$$4\sqrt{x} = 4$$

$$\sqrt{x} = 1$$

$$\left(\sqrt{x}\right)^2 = 1^2$$

$$x = 1$$

Check: $\sqrt{1} + 2 = \sqrt{1+8}$

$$1 + 2 = \sqrt{9}$$

$$3 = 3, \text{ true}$$

The solution set is {1}.

53. $\sqrt{x-8} = \sqrt{x} - 2$

$$\left(\sqrt{x-8}\right)^2 = \left(\sqrt{x} - 2\right)^2$$

$$x - 8 = \left(\sqrt{x}\right)^2 - 2\left(\sqrt{x}\right)(2) + 2^2$$

$$x - 8 = x - 4\sqrt{x} + 4$$

$$4\sqrt{x} = 12$$

$$\sqrt{x} = 3$$

$$\left(\sqrt{x}\right)^2 = 3^2$$

$$x = 9$$

Check: $\sqrt{9-8} = \sqrt{9} - 2$

$$\sqrt{1} = 3 - 2$$

$$1 = 1, \text{ true}$$

The solution set is $\{9\}$.

55. $f = 120\sqrt{p}$

$$840 = 120\sqrt{p}$$

$$\frac{840}{120} = \frac{120\sqrt{p}}{120}$$

$$7 = \sqrt{p}$$

$$7^2 = \left(\sqrt{p}\right)^2$$

$$49 = p$$

A nozzle pressure of 49 pounds per square inch is needed.

57. The answer to Exercise 55 is represented by the point (49, 840).

59. a. $p = 3.6\sqrt{t} + 46$

$$p = 3.6\sqrt{24} + 46 \approx 63.6$$

According to the formula, 63.6% of adults were overweight or obese in 2004.

b. The formula underestimates the actual value shown in the bar graph by 0.3%.

c. $p = 3.6\sqrt{t} + 46$

$$66 = 3.6\sqrt{t} + 46$$

$$20 = 3.6\sqrt{t}$$

$$\frac{20}{3.6} = \frac{3.6\sqrt{t}}{3.6}$$

$$\frac{20}{3.6} = \sqrt{t}$$

$$\left(\frac{20}{3.6}\right)^2 = \left(\sqrt{t}\right)^2$$

$$31 \approx t$$

66% of adults will be overweight or obese 31 years after 1980, or 2011.

61. – 63. Answers will vary.

65. does not make sense; Explanations will vary. Sample explanation: Extraneous solutions can be generated as early as the first step. You should check the proposed solution in the original equation.

67. does not make sense; Explanations will vary. Sample explanation: One, both, or neither of the solutions may satisfy the equation.

69. false; Changes to make the statement true will vary. A sample change is: −5 is a solution of the first equation only.

71. false; Changes to make the statement true will vary. A sample change is: The first step is to isolate the radical.

73. Let x = the smaller integer.
Then $x+1$ = the larger integer.

$$\sqrt{x+(x+1)} = x-1$$

$$\sqrt{2x+1} = x-1$$

$$\left(\sqrt{2x+1}\right)^2 = (x-1)^2$$

$$2x+1 = x^2 - 2x + 1$$

$$0 = x^2 - 4x$$

$$0 = x(x-4)$$

$$x = 0 \quad \text{or} \quad x-4 = 0$$

$$x = 4$$

Check 0:　　　　　　　Check 4:

$$\sqrt{x+(x+1)} = x-1 \qquad \sqrt{x+(x+1)} = x-1$$

$$\sqrt{0+1} = 0-1 \qquad\qquad \sqrt{x+5} = 4-1$$

$$\sqrt{1} = -1 \qquad\qquad\qquad \sqrt{9} = 3$$

$$1 = -1, \text{ false} \qquad\qquad 3 = 3, \text{ true}$$

The only solution to the equation is 4.
If $x = 4$, $x+1 = 5$, so the consecutive integers are 4 and 5.

75. $\sqrt{2x+2} = \sqrt{3x-5}$

The graphs intersect at one point, $(7,4)$, so the x-coordinate of the intersection point is 7.
Check 7:

$$\sqrt{2x+2} = \sqrt{3x-5}$$

$$\sqrt{2\cdot 7+2} = \sqrt{3\cdot 7-5}$$

$$\sqrt{14+2} = \sqrt{21-5}$$

$$\sqrt{16} = \sqrt{16}, \text{ true}$$

The solution set is $\{7\}$.

77. $\sqrt{x^2+3} = x+1$

The graphs intersect at one point, $(1,2)$. Therefore, the x-coordinate of the intersection point is 1.
Check 1:

$$\sqrt{x^2+3} = x+1$$

$$\sqrt{1^2+3} = 1+1$$

$$\sqrt{4} = 2$$

$$2 = 2, \text{ true}$$

The solution set is $\{1\}$.

79. $\sqrt{x}+4 = 2$

The graphs do not intersect. This indicates that the equation has no solution.

81. Let x = the amount invested at 6%.
Then $9000 - x$ = the amount invested at 4%.
The investments earned a total of $500 in interest, so $0.06x + 0.04(9000-x) = 500$.

$$0.06x + 0.04(9000-x) = 500$$

$$0.06x + 360 - 0.04x = 500$$

$$0.02x + 360 = 500$$

$$0.02x = 140$$

$$\frac{0.02x}{0.02} = \frac{140}{0.02}$$

$$x = 7000$$

$$9000 - x = 2000$$

$7000 was invested at 6% and $2000 was invested at 4%.

82. Let x = the price of an orchestra seat.
Then y = the price of a mezzanine seat.
The given information leads to the system
$$4x + 2y = 22$$
$$2x + 3y = 16$$
Because both equations are written in the form
$Ax + By = C$, the addition method is a good choice
for solving this system. Because the problem only
asks for the price of an orchestra seat, it is only
necessary to solve the system for x. To do this, it is
necessary to eliminate y.
Multiply the first equation by 3 and the second
equation by -2. Then add the results.
$$12x + 6y = 66$$
$$\underline{-4x - 6y = -32}$$
$$8x = 34$$
$$x = \frac{34}{8} = 4.25$$
The price of an orchestra seat is \$4.25.

83. $2x + y = -4$
$x + y = -3$
Graph $2x + y = -4$ using its x-intercept -2 and its y-intercept -4.
Graph $x + y = -3$ using its x-intercept -3 and y-intercept -3.

The two lines intersect at the point $(-1, -2)$ so the
solution set is $\{(-1, -2)\}$.

84. $-\left(\sqrt[5]{32}\right)^4 = -2^4 = -16$

85. $\left(\sqrt[3]{27}\right)^2 = 3^2 = 9$

86. $\dfrac{1}{\left(\sqrt[4]{81}\right)^3} = \dfrac{1}{(3)^3} = \dfrac{1}{27}$

9.6 Check Points

1. a. $25^{\frac{1}{2}} = \sqrt{25} = 5$

   b. $8^{\frac{1}{3}} = \sqrt[3]{8} = 2$

   c. $-81^{\frac{1}{4}} = -\sqrt[4]{81} = -3$

   d. $(-8)^{\frac{1}{3}} = \sqrt[3]{-8} = -2$

2. a. $27^{\frac{4}{3}} = \left(\sqrt[3]{27}\right)^4 = 3^4 = 81$

   b. $4^{\frac{3}{2}} = \left(\sqrt{4}\right)^3 = 2^3 = 8$

   c. $-16^{\frac{3}{4}} = -\left(\sqrt[4]{16}\right)^3 = -2^3 = -8$

3. a. $25^{-\frac{1}{2}} = \dfrac{1}{25^{\frac{1}{2}}} = \dfrac{1}{\sqrt{25}} = \dfrac{1}{5}$

   b. $64^{-\frac{1}{3}} = \dfrac{1}{64^{\frac{1}{3}}} = \dfrac{1}{\sqrt[3]{64}} = \dfrac{1}{4}$

   c. $32^{-\frac{4}{5}} = \dfrac{1}{32^{\frac{4}{5}}} = \dfrac{1}{\left(\sqrt[5]{32}\right)^4} = \dfrac{1}{2^4} = \dfrac{1}{16}$

4. a. Since this is group 2, substitute 2 for x.
$$p = 15x^{-\frac{5}{4}}$$
$$p = 15(2)^{-\frac{5}{4}} \approx 6.3$$
6.3% of Americans between the ages of 18 and
34 kept blogs or maintained websites in 2005.

   b. The answer in part (a) underestimates the actual
percentage given by the bar graph by 1.6%.

9.6 Exercise Set

1. $49^{\frac{1}{2}} = \sqrt{49} = 7$

3. $121^{\frac{1}{2}} = \sqrt{121} = 11$

5. $27^{\frac{1}{3}} = \sqrt[3]{27} = 3$

7. $-125^{\frac{1}{3}} = -\left(\sqrt[3]{125}\right) = -5$

9. $16^{\frac{1}{4}} = \sqrt[4]{16} = 2$

11. $-32^{\frac{1}{5}} = -\left(\sqrt[5]{32}\right) = -2$

13. $\left(\frac{1}{9}\right)^{\frac{1}{2}} = \sqrt{\frac{1}{9}} = \frac{1}{3}$

15. $\left(\frac{27}{64}\right)^{\frac{1}{3}} = \sqrt[3]{\frac{27}{64}} = \frac{\sqrt[3]{27}}{\sqrt[3]{64}} = \frac{3}{4}$

17. $81^{\frac{3}{2}} = \left(\sqrt{81}\right)^3 = 9^3 = 729$

19. $125^{\frac{2}{3}} = \left(\sqrt[3]{125}\right)^2 = 5^2 = 25$

21. $9^{\frac{3}{2}} = \left(\sqrt{9}\right)^3 = 3^3 = 27$

23. $(-32)^{\frac{3}{5}} = \left(\sqrt[5]{-32}\right)^3 = (-2)^3 = -8$

25. $9^{-\frac{1}{2}} = \frac{1}{9^{\frac{1}{2}}} = \frac{1}{\sqrt{9}} = \frac{1}{3}$

27. $125^{-\frac{1}{3}} = \frac{1}{125^{\frac{1}{3}}} = \frac{1}{\sqrt[3]{125}} = \frac{1}{5}$

29. $32^{-\frac{1}{5}} = \frac{1}{32^{\frac{1}{5}}} = \frac{1}{\sqrt[5]{32}} = \frac{1}{2}$

31. $\left(\frac{1}{4}\right)^{-\frac{1}{2}} = \frac{1}{\left(\frac{1}{4}\right)^{\frac{1}{2}}} = \frac{1}{\sqrt{\frac{1}{4}}} = \frac{1}{\frac{1}{2}} = 2$

33. $16^{-\frac{3}{4}} = \frac{1}{16^{\frac{3}{4}}} = \frac{1}{\left(\sqrt[4]{16}\right)^3} = \frac{1}{2^3} = \frac{1}{8}$

35. $81^{-\frac{5}{4}} = \frac{1}{81^{\frac{5}{4}}} = \frac{1}{\left(\sqrt[4]{81}\right)^5} = \frac{1}{3^5} = \frac{1}{243}$

37. $8^{-\frac{2}{3}} = \frac{1}{8^{\frac{2}{3}}} = \frac{1}{\left(\sqrt[3]{8}\right)^2} = \frac{1}{2^2} = \frac{1}{4}$

39. $\left(\frac{4}{25}\right)^{-\frac{1}{2}} = \frac{1}{\left(\frac{4}{25}\right)^{\frac{1}{2}}} = \frac{1}{\sqrt{\frac{4}{25}}} = \frac{1}{\frac{2}{5}} = \frac{5}{2}$

41. $\left(\frac{8}{125}\right)^{-\frac{1}{3}} = \frac{1}{\left(\frac{8}{125}\right)^{\frac{1}{3}}} = \frac{1}{\sqrt[3]{\frac{8}{125}}} = \frac{1}{\frac{2}{5}} = \frac{5}{2}$

43. $(-8)^{-\frac{2}{3}} = \frac{1}{(-8)^{\frac{2}{3}}} = \frac{1}{\left(\sqrt[3]{-8}\right)^2}$

$= \frac{1}{(-2)^2} = \frac{1}{4}$

45. $27^{\frac{2}{3}} + 16^{\frac{3}{4}} = \left(\sqrt[3]{27}\right)^2 + \left(\sqrt[4]{16}\right)^3$

$= 3^2 + 2^3 = 9 + 8 = 17$

47. $25^{\frac{3}{2}} \cdot 81^{\frac{1}{4}} = \left(\sqrt{25}\right)^3 \cdot \left(\sqrt[4]{81}\right)$

$= 5^3 \cdot 3 = 125 \cdot 3$

$= 375$

49. $x^{\frac{1}{3}} \cdot x^{\frac{1}{4}} = x^{\frac{1}{3}+\frac{1}{4}} = x^{\frac{4}{12}+\frac{3}{12}} = x^{\frac{7}{12}}$

51. $\dfrac{x^{\frac{1}{6}}}{x^{\frac{5}{6}}} = x^{\frac{1}{6}-\frac{5}{6}} = x^{-\frac{4}{6}} = x^{-\frac{2}{3}} = \dfrac{1}{x^{\frac{2}{3}}}$

53. $\left(x^{1/4}y^3\right)^{2/3} = \left(x^{1/4}\right)^{2/3} \cdot \left(y^3\right)^{2/3}$

$= x^{\frac{1}{4} \cdot \frac{2}{3}} \cdot y^{3 \cdot \frac{2}{3}}$

$= x^{\frac{1}{6}}y^2$

55. $\left(\dfrac{x^{2/5}}{x^{6/5} \cdot x^{3/5}}\right)^5 = \dfrac{\left(x^{2/5}\right)^5}{\left(x^{6/5}\right)^5 \cdot \left(x^{3/5}\right)^5}$

$= \dfrac{x^2}{x^6 \cdot x^3} = \dfrac{x^2}{x^9}$

$= x^{2-9} = x^{-7} = \dfrac{1}{x^7}$

57. a. $h = 0.84d^{\frac{2}{3}}$

$h = 0.84(985)^{\frac{2}{3}} \approx 83.2$

The tree is approximately 83.2 meters.

b. $h = 0.84d^{\frac{2}{3}}$

$h = 0.84\left(\sqrt[3]{d}\right)^2$ or $h = 0.84\sqrt[3]{d^2}$

59. a. $N = \dfrac{a^{\frac{1}{2}}}{2\pi r^{\frac{1}{2}}}$

$N = \dfrac{(9.8)^{\frac{1}{2}}}{2\pi(1.7)^{\frac{1}{2}}} \approx 0.382$

It would need to rotate about 0.382 revolutions per second.

b. $0.382 \cdot 60 = 22.92$

0.382 revolutions per second is equivalent to 22.92 revolutions per minute.

c. $N = \dfrac{a^{\frac{1}{2}}}{2\pi r^{\frac{1}{2}}} \cdot \dfrac{r^{\frac{1}{2}}}{r^{\frac{1}{2}}}$

$= \dfrac{(ar)^{\frac{1}{2}}}{2\pi r}$

$= \dfrac{\sqrt{ar}}{2\pi r}$

61. – 65. Answers will vary.

67. does not make sense; Explanations will vary.

Sample explanation: $5^{\frac{1}{2}} \cdot 5^{\frac{1}{2}} = 5^{\frac{1}{2}+\frac{1}{2}} = 5^1 = 5.$

69. does not make sense; Explanations will vary.
Sample explanation: Because of the even index, the second equation is not correct.

71. false; Changes to make the statement true will vary.

A sample change is: $8^{-\frac{2}{3}} = \dfrac{1}{4}.$

73. false; Changes to make the statement true will vary.

A sample change is: $-3^{-2} = -\dfrac{1}{3^2} = -\dfrac{1}{9}.$

75. true

77. true

79. $\dfrac{3^{-1} \cdot 3^{\frac{1}{2}}}{3^{-\frac{3}{2}}} = \dfrac{3^{-1+\frac{1}{2}}}{3^{-\frac{3}{2}}}$

$= \dfrac{3^{-\frac{2}{2}+\frac{1}{2}}}{3^{-\frac{3}{2}}} = \dfrac{3^{-\frac{1}{2}}}{3^{-\frac{3}{2}}} = \dfrac{3^{\frac{3}{2}}}{3^{\frac{1}{2}}}$

$= 3^{\frac{3}{2}-\frac{1}{2}} = 3^{\frac{2}{2}} = 3^1$

$= 3$

81. a. $A = 6V^{\frac{2}{3}}$

b. The graph shows that a cube whose volume is 27 cubic units has a surface area of 54 square units.

c. The graph shows that the volume of a cube whose volume is 8 cubic units is 24 square units.

82. $7x - 3y = -14$

$\qquad y = 3x + 6$

To solve this system by the substitution method, substitute $3x + 6$ for y in the first equation and solve for x.

$7x - 3(3x + 6) = -14$

$\quad 7x - 9x - 18 = -14$

$\qquad -2x - 18 = -14$

$\qquad\qquad -2x = 4$

$\qquad\qquad\quad x = -2$

Back-substitute -2 for x into the second equation.

$y = 3x + 6$

$y = 3(-2) + 6 = -6 + 6 = 0$

The solution set is $\{(-2, 0)\}$.

83. $-3x + 4y \le 12$

$\qquad x \ge 2$

To graph the solutions of this system of inequalities, first graph $-3x + 4y = 12$ as a solid line using its x-intercept, -4, and its y-intercept 3. Use $(0,0)$ as a test point. Since $-3(0) + 4(0) \le 12$ is true, shade the half-plane containing $(0,0)$. Now graph $x = 2$ as a solid vertical line. Since $0 \ge 2$ is false, shade the half-plane *not* containing $(0,0)$, which is the half-plane to the right of the vertical line. The solution set of the system is the intersection (overlap) of the two shaded regions.

84. $\dfrac{(2x)^5}{x^3} = \dfrac{2^5 x^5}{x^3} = \dfrac{32x^5}{x^3} = 32x^2$

85. $\qquad 4x^2 = 20$

$\qquad 4\left(-\sqrt{5}\right)^2 = 20$

$\quad 4(-1)^2 \left(\sqrt{5}\right)^2 = 20$

$\qquad\quad 4 \cdot 1 \cdot 5 = 20$

$\qquad\qquad 20 = 20, \ \text{true}$

$-\sqrt{5}$ is a solution.

86. $\qquad (x - 1)^2 = 5$

$\qquad \left(1 + \sqrt{3} - 1\right)^2 = 5$

$\qquad\qquad \left(\sqrt{3}\right)^2 = 5$

$\qquad\qquad\qquad 3 = 5, \ \text{false}$

$1 + \sqrt{3}$ is not a solution.

87. $\sqrt{[6 - (-4)]^2 + [2 - (-3)]^2} = \sqrt{[6 + 4]^2 + [2 + 3]^2}$

$\qquad\qquad\qquad = \sqrt{10^2 + 5^2}$

$\qquad\qquad\qquad = \sqrt{100 + 25}$

$\qquad\qquad\qquad = \sqrt{125}$

$\qquad\qquad\qquad = \sqrt{25 \cdot 5}$

$\qquad\qquad\qquad = 5\sqrt{5}$

Chapter 9 Review

1. $\sqrt{121} = 11$
   The principal square root of 121 is 11.

2. $-\sqrt{121} = -11$
   The negative square root of 121 is -11.

3. $\sqrt{-121}$ is not a real number because the square of a real number is never negative.

4. $\sqrt[3]{\dfrac{8}{125}} = \dfrac{2}{5}$ because $\left(\dfrac{2}{5}\right)^3 = \dfrac{8}{125}$.

5. $\sqrt[5]{-32} = -2$ because $(-2)^5 = -32$.

6. $-\sqrt[4]{81} = -3$ because $3^4 = 81$.

7. $\sqrt{75} \approx 8.660$

8. $\sqrt{398-5} = \sqrt{393} \approx 19.824$

9. $M = 0.7\sqrt{t} + 12.5$
   $M = 0.7\sqrt{9} + 12.5 = 14.6$
   According to the model, 14.6 non-program minutes disrupted an hour of cable TV action in 2005.

10. Answers will vary. Example: The number of disruptive minutes is increasing, but the rate of increase is slowing down.

11. $d = \sqrt{\dfrac{3h}{2}}$

    $d = \sqrt{\dfrac{3 \cdot 1450}{2}} \approx 47$

    Visitors will be able to see about 47 miles from the top of the Sear's Tower.

12. $\sqrt{54} = \sqrt{9 \cdot 6} = \sqrt{9}\sqrt{6} = 3\sqrt{6}$

13. $6\sqrt{20} = 6\sqrt{4 \cdot 5} = 6\sqrt{4}\sqrt{5}$
    $= 6 \cdot 2\sqrt{5} = 12\sqrt{5}$

14. $\sqrt{63x^2} = \sqrt{9x^2}\sqrt{7} = 3x\sqrt{7}$

15. $\sqrt{48x^3} = \sqrt{16x^2}\sqrt{3x} = 4x\sqrt{3x}$

16. $\sqrt{x^8} = x^4$ because $\left(x^4\right)^2 = x^8$.

17. $\sqrt{75x^9} = \sqrt{25x^8}\sqrt{3x} = 5x^4\sqrt{3x}$

18. $\sqrt{45x^{23}} = \sqrt{9x^{22}}\sqrt{5x} = 3x^{11}\sqrt{5x}$

19. $\sqrt[3]{24} = \sqrt[3]{8 \cdot 3} = \sqrt[3]{8}\sqrt[3]{3} = 2\sqrt[3]{3}$

20. $\sqrt{7} \cdot \sqrt{11} = \sqrt{7 \cdot 11} = \sqrt{77}$

21. $\sqrt{3} \cdot \sqrt{12} = \sqrt{36} = 6$

22. $\sqrt{5x} \cdot \sqrt{10x} = \sqrt{50x^2} = \sqrt{25x^2}\sqrt{2}$
    $= 5x\sqrt{2}$

23. $\sqrt{3x^2} \cdot \sqrt{4x^3} = \sqrt{12x^5} = \sqrt{4x^4}\sqrt{3x}$
    $= 2x^2\sqrt{3x}$

24. $\sqrt[3]{6} \cdot \sqrt[3]{9} = \sqrt[3]{6 \cdot 9} = \sqrt[3]{54} = \sqrt[3]{27} \cdot \sqrt[3]{2}$
    $= 3\sqrt[3]{2}$

25. $\sqrt{\dfrac{5}{2}} \cdot \sqrt{\dfrac{3}{8}} = \sqrt{\dfrac{5 \cdot 3}{2 \cdot 8}} = \sqrt{\dfrac{15}{16}}$
    $= \dfrac{\sqrt{15}}{\sqrt{16}} = \dfrac{\sqrt{15}}{4}$

26. $\sqrt{\dfrac{121}{4}} = \dfrac{\sqrt{121}}{\sqrt{4}} = \dfrac{11}{2}$

27. $\sqrt{\dfrac{7x}{25}} = \dfrac{\sqrt{7x}}{\sqrt{25}} = \dfrac{\sqrt{7x}}{5}$

28. $\sqrt{\dfrac{18}{x^2}} = \dfrac{\sqrt{18}}{\sqrt{x^2}} = \dfrac{\sqrt{9}\sqrt{2}}{x} = \dfrac{3\sqrt{2}}{x}$

29. $\dfrac{\sqrt{200}}{\sqrt{2}} = \sqrt{\dfrac{200}{2}} = \sqrt{100} = 10$

30. $\dfrac{\sqrt{96}}{\sqrt{3}} = \sqrt{32} = \sqrt{16}\sqrt{2} = 4\sqrt{2}$

31. $\dfrac{\sqrt{72x^8}}{\sqrt{x^3}} = \sqrt{\dfrac{72x^8}{x^3}} = \sqrt{72x^5}$
    $= \sqrt{36x^4}\sqrt{2x} = 6x^2\sqrt{2x}$

32. $\sqrt[3]{\dfrac{5}{64}} = \dfrac{\sqrt[3]{5}}{\sqrt[3]{64}} = \dfrac{\sqrt[3]{5}}{4}$

33. $\sqrt[3]{\dfrac{40}{27}} = \dfrac{\sqrt[3]{40}}{\sqrt[3]{27}} = \dfrac{\sqrt[3]{8}\sqrt[3]{5}}{3} = \dfrac{2\sqrt[3]{5}}{3}$

34. $7\sqrt{5} + 13\sqrt{5} = (7+13)\sqrt{5} = 20\sqrt{5}$

35. $\sqrt{8} + \sqrt{50} = \sqrt{4}\sqrt{2} + \sqrt{25}\sqrt{2}$
$\qquad\qquad = 2\sqrt{2} + 5\sqrt{2}$
$\qquad\qquad = (2+5)\sqrt{2} = 7\sqrt{2}$

36. $\sqrt{75} - \sqrt{48} = \sqrt{25}\sqrt{3} - \sqrt{16}\sqrt{3}$
$\qquad\qquad = 5\sqrt{3} - 4\sqrt{3}$
$\qquad\qquad = (5-4)\sqrt{3} = \sqrt{3}$

37. $2\sqrt{80} + 3\sqrt{45} = 2\sqrt{16}\sqrt{5} + 3\sqrt{9}\sqrt{5}$
$\qquad\qquad = 2\cdot4\sqrt{5} + 3\cdot3\sqrt{5}$
$\qquad\qquad = 8\sqrt{5} + 9\sqrt{5} = 17\sqrt{5}$

38. $4\sqrt{72} - 2\sqrt{48} = 4\sqrt{36}\sqrt{2} - 2\sqrt{16}\sqrt{3}$
$\qquad\qquad = 4\cdot6\sqrt{2} - 2\cdot4\sqrt{3}$
$\qquad\qquad = 24\sqrt{2} - 8\sqrt{3}$

39. $2\sqrt{18} + 3\sqrt{27} - \sqrt{12}$
$\quad = 2\sqrt{9}\sqrt{2} + 3\sqrt{9}\sqrt{3} - \sqrt{4}\sqrt{3}$
$\quad = 2\cdot3\sqrt{2} + 3\cdot3\sqrt{3} - 2\sqrt{3}$
$\quad = 6\sqrt{2} + 9\sqrt{3} - 2\sqrt{3}$
$\quad = 6\sqrt{2} + 7\sqrt{3}$

40. $\sqrt{10}\left(\sqrt{5} + \sqrt{6}\right) = \sqrt{10}\cdot\sqrt{5} + \sqrt{10}\cdot\sqrt{6}$
$\qquad\qquad = \sqrt{50} + \sqrt{60}$
$\qquad\qquad = \sqrt{25}\sqrt{2} + \sqrt{4}\sqrt{15}$
$\qquad\qquad = 5\sqrt{2} + 2\sqrt{15}$

41. $\sqrt{3}\left(\sqrt{6} - \sqrt{12}\right) = \sqrt{3}\cdot\sqrt{6} - \sqrt{3}\cdot\sqrt{12}$
$\qquad\qquad = \sqrt{18} - \sqrt{36}$
$\qquad\qquad = \sqrt{9}\sqrt{2} - 6 = 3\sqrt{2} - 6$

42. $\left(9 + \sqrt{2}\right)\left(10 + \sqrt{2}\right)$
$\quad = 9\cdot10 + 9\sqrt{2} + 10\sqrt{2} + \sqrt{2}\cdot\sqrt{2}$
$\quad = 90 + 19\sqrt{2} + 2 = 92 + 19\sqrt{2}$

43. $\left(1 + 3\sqrt{7}\right)\left(4 - \sqrt{7}\right)$
$\quad = 1\cdot4 - 1\sqrt{7} + 3\sqrt{7}\cdot4 - 3\cdot\sqrt{7}\sqrt{7}$
$\quad = 4 - \sqrt{7} + 12\sqrt{7} - 3\cdot7$
$\quad = 4 + 11\sqrt{7} - 21$
$\quad = -17 + 11\sqrt{7}$

44. $\left(\sqrt{3} + 2\right)\left(\sqrt{6} - 4\right)$
$\quad = \sqrt{3}\cdot\sqrt{6} + 4\sqrt{3} + 2\sqrt{6} - 2\cdot4$
$\quad = \sqrt{18} - 4\sqrt{3} + 2\sqrt{6} - 8$
$\quad = \sqrt{9}\sqrt{2} - 4\sqrt{3} + 2\sqrt{6} - 8$
$\quad = 3\sqrt{2} - 4\sqrt{3} + 2\sqrt{6} - 8$

45. $\left(2 + \sqrt{7}\right)\left(2 - \sqrt{7}\right) = 2^2 - \left(\sqrt{7}\right)^2$
$\qquad\qquad\qquad = 4 - 7 = -3$

46. $\left(\sqrt{11} - \sqrt{5}\right)\left(\sqrt{11} + \sqrt{5}\right)$
$\quad = \left(\sqrt{11}\right)^2 - \left(\sqrt{5}\right)^2$
$\quad = 11 - 5 = 6$

47. $\left(1 + \sqrt{2}\right)^2 = 1^2 + 2\cdot1\cdot\sqrt{2} + \left(\sqrt{2}\right)^2$
$\qquad\qquad = 1 + 2\sqrt{2} + 2$
$\qquad\qquad = 3 + 2\sqrt{2}$

48. $\dfrac{30}{\sqrt{5}} = \dfrac{30}{\sqrt{5}}\cdot\dfrac{\sqrt{5}}{\sqrt{5}} = \dfrac{30\sqrt{5}}{5} = 6\sqrt{5}$

49. $\dfrac{13}{\sqrt{50}} = \dfrac{13}{\sqrt{25}\sqrt{2}} = \dfrac{13}{5\sqrt{2}}\cdot\dfrac{\sqrt{2}}{\sqrt{2}}$
$\qquad = \dfrac{13\sqrt{2}}{5\cdot2} = \dfrac{13\sqrt{2}}{10}$

50. $\sqrt{\dfrac{2}{3}} = \dfrac{\sqrt{2}}{\sqrt{3}} = \dfrac{\sqrt{2}}{\sqrt{3}}\cdot\dfrac{\sqrt{3}}{\sqrt{3}} = \dfrac{\sqrt{6}}{3}$

51. $\sqrt{\dfrac{3}{8}} = \dfrac{\sqrt{3}}{\sqrt{8}} = \dfrac{\sqrt{3}}{\sqrt{4}\sqrt{2}} = \dfrac{\sqrt{3}}{2\sqrt{2}}$

$\qquad = \dfrac{\sqrt{3}}{2\sqrt{2}} \cdot \dfrac{\sqrt{2}}{\sqrt{2}} = \dfrac{\sqrt{6}}{2 \cdot 2} = \dfrac{\sqrt{6}}{4}$

52. $\sqrt{\dfrac{17}{x}} = \dfrac{\sqrt{17}}{\sqrt{x}} = \dfrac{\sqrt{17}}{\sqrt{x}} \cdot \dfrac{\sqrt{x}}{\sqrt{x}} = \dfrac{\sqrt{17x}}{x}$

53. $\dfrac{11}{\sqrt{5}+2} = \dfrac{11}{\sqrt{5}+2} \cdot \dfrac{\sqrt{5}-2}{\sqrt{5}-2}$

$\qquad = \dfrac{11\left(\sqrt{5}-2\right)}{\left(\sqrt{5}\right)^2 - 2^2}$

$\qquad = \dfrac{11\left(\sqrt{5}-2\right)}{5-4}$

$\qquad = \dfrac{11\left(\sqrt{5}-2\right)}{1}$

$\qquad = 11\sqrt{5} - 22$

54. $\dfrac{21}{4-\sqrt{3}} = \dfrac{21}{4-\sqrt{3}} \cdot \dfrac{4+\sqrt{3}}{4+\sqrt{3}}$

$\qquad = \dfrac{21\left(4+\sqrt{3}\right)}{4^2 - \left(\sqrt{3}\right)^2}$

$\qquad = \dfrac{21\left(4+\sqrt{3}\right)}{16-3}$

$\qquad = \dfrac{21\left(4+\sqrt{3}\right)}{13}$

$\qquad = \dfrac{84+21\sqrt{3}}{13}$

55. $\dfrac{12}{\sqrt{5}+\sqrt{3}} = \dfrac{12}{\sqrt{5}+\sqrt{3}} \cdot \dfrac{\sqrt{5}-\sqrt{3}}{\sqrt{5}-\sqrt{3}}$

$\qquad = \dfrac{12\left(\sqrt{5}-\sqrt{3}\right)}{\left(\sqrt{5}\right)^2 - \left(\sqrt{3}\right)^2}$

$\qquad = \dfrac{12\left(\sqrt{5}-\sqrt{3}\right)}{5-3}$

$\qquad = \dfrac{12\left(\sqrt{5}-\sqrt{3}\right)}{2}$

$\qquad = 6\left(\sqrt{5}-\sqrt{3}\right)$

$\qquad = 6\sqrt{5} - 6\sqrt{3}$

56. $\dfrac{7\sqrt{2}}{\sqrt{2}-4} = \dfrac{7\sqrt{2}}{\sqrt{2}-4} \cdot \dfrac{\sqrt{2}+4}{\sqrt{2}+4}$

$\qquad = \dfrac{7\sqrt{2}\left(\sqrt{2}+4\right)}{\left(\sqrt{2}\right)^2 - 4^2} = \dfrac{7\sqrt{2}\left(\sqrt{2}+4\right)}{2-16}$

$\qquad = \dfrac{7\sqrt{2}\left(\sqrt{2}+4\right)}{-14} = \dfrac{7 \cdot \sqrt{2}\sqrt{2} + 7 \cdot \sqrt{2} \cdot 4}{-14}$

$\qquad = \dfrac{7 \cdot 2 + 28\sqrt{2}}{-14} = \dfrac{14 + 28\sqrt{2}}{-14}$

$\qquad = \dfrac{14\left(1+2\sqrt{2}\right)}{14(-1)} = -1\left(1+2\sqrt{2}\right)$

$\qquad = -1 - 2\sqrt{2}$

57. $\sqrt{x+3} = 4$

$\qquad \left(\sqrt{x+3}\right) = 4^2$

$\qquad\quad x+3 = 16$

$\qquad\qquad x = 13$

Check 13:

$\qquad \sqrt{x+3} = 4$

$\qquad \sqrt{13+3} = 4$

$\qquad\quad \sqrt{16} = 4$

$\qquad\qquad 4 = 4, \text{ true}$

The solution set is $\{13\}$.

58. $\sqrt{2x+3} = 5$

$\qquad \left(\sqrt{2x+3}\right)^2 = 5^2$

$\qquad\quad 2x+3 = 25$

$\qquad\qquad 2x + 22$

$\qquad\qquad\quad x = 11$

Check 11:

$\qquad \sqrt{2x+3} = 5$

$\qquad \sqrt{2(11)+3} = 5$

$\qquad\quad \sqrt{22+3} = 5$

$\qquad\qquad \sqrt{25} = 5$

$\qquad\qquad\quad 5 = 5, \text{ true}$

The solution set is $\{11\}$.

59. $3\sqrt{x} = \sqrt{6x+15}$

$\left(3\sqrt{x}\right)^2 = \left(\sqrt{6x+15}\right)^2$

$9x = 6x+15$

$3x = 15$

$x = 5$

Substitution confirms the solution set is $\{5\}$.

60. $\sqrt{5x+1} = x+1$

$\left(\sqrt{5x+1}\right)^2 = \left(x+1\right)^2$

$5x+1 = x^2+2x+1$

$0 = x^2-3x$

$0 = x(x-3)$

$x = 0$ or $x-3 = 0$

$x = 3$

Each of the proposed solutions must be checked separately in the original equation.

Check 0:   Check 3:

$\sqrt{5x+1} = x+1$ $\sqrt{5x+1} = x+1$

$\sqrt{5\cdot 0+1} = 0+1$ $\sqrt{5\cdot 3+1} = 3+1$

$\sqrt{1} = 0+1$ $\sqrt{15+1} = 4$

$1 = 1,$ true $\sqrt{16} = 4$

                $4 = 4,$ true

The solution set is $\{0,3\}$.

61. $\sqrt{x+1}+5 = x$

$\sqrt{x+1} = x-5$

$\left(\sqrt{x+1}\right)^2 = \left(x-5\right)^2$

$x+1 = x^2-10x+25$

$0 = x^2-11x+24$

$0 = (x-3)(x-8)$

$x-3 = 0$ or $x-8 = 0$

$x = 3$ $x = 8$

Check 3:   Check 8:

$\sqrt{x+1}+5 = x$ $\sqrt{x+1}+5 = x$

$\sqrt{3+1}+5 = 3$ $\sqrt{8+1}+5 = 8$

$\sqrt{4}+5 = 3$ $\sqrt{9}+5 = 8$

$2+5 = 3$ $3+5 = 8$

$7 = 3,$ false $8 = 8,$ true

The false statement indicates that 3 does not satisfy the original equation; it is an extraneous solution.
The solution set is $\{8\}$.

62. $\sqrt{x-2}+5 = 1$

$\sqrt{x-2} = -4$

$\left(\sqrt{x-2}\right)^2 = \left(-4\right)^2$

$x-2 = 16$

$x = 18$

Check 18:

$\sqrt{x-2}+5 = 1$

$\sqrt{18-2}+5 = 1$

$\sqrt{16}+5 = 1$

$4+5 = 1$

$9 = 1,$ false

The only proposed solution, 18, is extraneous, so the equation has no solution. The solution set is $\{\ \}$.

63. $x = \sqrt{x^2+4x+4}$

$x^2 = \left(\sqrt{x^2+4x+4}\right)^2$

$x^2 = x^2+4x+4$

$0 = 4x+4$

$-4 = 4x$

$-1 = x$

Check:

$x = \sqrt{x^2+4x+4}$

$-1 = \sqrt{(-1)^2+4(-1)+4}$

$-1 = \sqrt{1-4+4}$

$-1 = \sqrt{1}$

$-1 = 1,$ false

The only proposed solution, -1, is extraneous, so the equation has no solution. The solution set is $\{\ \}$.

64. $W = 4\sqrt{2x}$

$16 = 4\sqrt{2x}$

$\dfrac{16}{4} = \dfrac{4\sqrt{2x}}{4}$

$4 = \sqrt{2x}$

$4^2 = \left(\sqrt{2x}\right)^2$

$16 = 2x$

$8 = x$

The leg length is 8 feet.

65.

$$p = 3.5\sqrt{t} + 38$$
$$66 = 3.5\sqrt{t} + 38$$
$$28 = 3.5\sqrt{t}$$
$$\frac{28}{3.5} = \frac{3.5\sqrt{t}}{3.5}$$
$$8 = \sqrt{t}$$
$$64 = t$$

According to the formula, 66% of U.S. women will participate in the labor force 64 years after 1960, or 2024.

66. $16^{\frac{1}{2}} = \sqrt{16} = 4$

67. $125^{\frac{1}{3}} = \sqrt[3]{125} = 5$

68. $64^{\frac{2}{3}} = \left(\sqrt[3]{64}\right)^2 = 4^2 = 16$

69. $25^{-\frac{1}{2}} = \frac{1}{25^{\frac{1}{2}}} = \frac{1}{\sqrt{25}} = \frac{1}{5}$

70. $27^{-\frac{1}{3}} = \frac{1}{27^{\frac{1}{3}}} = \frac{1}{\sqrt[3]{27}} = \frac{1}{3}$

71.
$$(-8)^{-\frac{4}{3}} = \frac{1}{(-8)^{\frac{4}{3}}} = \frac{1}{\left(\sqrt[3]{-8}\right)^4}$$
$$= \frac{1}{(-2)^4} = \frac{1}{16}$$

72. $S = 28.6A^{\frac{1}{3}}; A = 8$

$$S = 28.6 \cdot 8^{\frac{1}{3}} = 28.6\sqrt[3]{8}$$
$$= 28.6 \cdot 2 = 57.2 \approx 57$$

There are approximately 57 species on a Galapagos island whose area is 8 square miles.

Chapter 9 Test

1. $-\sqrt{64} = -8$

The negative square root of 64 is −8.

2. $\sqrt[3]{64} = 4$ because $4^3 = 64$.

3. $\sqrt{48} = \sqrt{16 \cdot 3} = \sqrt{16}\sqrt{3} = 4\sqrt{3}$

4. $\sqrt{72x^3} = \sqrt{36x^2}\sqrt{2x} = 6x\sqrt{2x}$

5. $\sqrt{x^{29}} = \sqrt{x^{28} \cdot x} = \sqrt{x^{28}}\sqrt{x} = x^{14}\sqrt{x}$

6. $\sqrt{\frac{25}{x^2}} = \frac{\sqrt{25}}{\sqrt{x^2}} = \frac{5}{x}$

7.
$$\sqrt{\frac{75}{27}} = \frac{\sqrt{75}}{\sqrt{27}} = \frac{\sqrt{25}\sqrt{3}}{\sqrt{9}\sqrt{3}}$$
$$= \frac{5\sqrt{3}}{3\sqrt{3}} = \frac{5}{3}$$

8. $\sqrt[3]{\frac{5}{8}} = \frac{\sqrt[3]{5}}{\sqrt[3]{8}} = \frac{\sqrt[3]{5}}{2}$

9.
$$\frac{\sqrt{80x^4}}{\sqrt{2x^2}} = \sqrt{\frac{80x^4}{2x^2}} = \sqrt{40x^2}$$
$$= \sqrt{4x^2}\sqrt{10} = 2x\sqrt{10}$$

10.
$$\sqrt{10} \cdot \sqrt{5} = \sqrt{50} = \sqrt{25 \cdot 2}$$
$$= \sqrt{25}\sqrt{2} = 5\sqrt{2}$$

11.
$$\sqrt{6x} \cdot \sqrt{6y} = \sqrt{6x \cdot 6y}$$
$$= \sqrt{36xy}$$
$$= \sqrt{36} \cdot \sqrt{xy}$$
$$= 6\sqrt{xy}$$

12.
$$\sqrt{10x^2} \cdot \sqrt{2x^3} = \sqrt{20x^5} = \sqrt{4x^4}\sqrt{5x}$$
$$= 2x^2\sqrt{5x}$$

13.
$$\sqrt{24} + 3\sqrt{54} = \sqrt{4}\sqrt{6} + 3\sqrt{9}\sqrt{6}$$
$$= 2\sqrt{6} + 3 \cdot 3\sqrt{6}$$
$$= 2\sqrt{6} + 9\sqrt{6}$$
$$= 11\sqrt{6}$$

14. $7\sqrt{8} - 2\sqrt{32} = 7\sqrt{4}\sqrt{2} - 2\sqrt{16}\sqrt{2}$

$\qquad\qquad = 7 \cdot 2\sqrt{2} - 2 \cdot 4\sqrt{2}$

$\qquad\qquad = 14\sqrt{2} - 8\sqrt{2} = 6\sqrt{2}$

15. $\sqrt{3}\left(\sqrt{10} + \sqrt{3}\right) = \sqrt{3} \cdot \sqrt{10} + \sqrt{3} \cdot \sqrt{3}$

$\qquad\qquad\qquad = \sqrt{30} + 3$

16. $\left(7 - \sqrt{5}\right)\left(10 + 3\sqrt{5}\right)$

$\qquad = 7 \cdot 10 + 7 \cdot 3\sqrt{5} - 10\sqrt{5} - 3\sqrt{5} \cdot \sqrt{5}$

$\qquad = 70 + 21\sqrt{5} - 10\sqrt{5} - 3 \cdot 5$

$\qquad = 70 + 11\sqrt{5} - 15 = 55 + 11\sqrt{5}$

17. $\left(\sqrt{6} + 2\right)\left(\sqrt{6} - 2\right) = \left(\sqrt{6}\right)^2 - 2^2$

$\qquad\qquad\qquad\qquad = 6 - 4 = 2$

18. $\left(3 + \sqrt{7}\right)^2 = 3^2 + 2 \cdot 3 \cdot \sqrt{7} + \left(\sqrt{7}\right)^2$

$\qquad\qquad = 9 + 6\sqrt{7} + 7 = 16 + 6\sqrt{7}$

19. $\dfrac{4}{\sqrt{5}} = \dfrac{4}{\sqrt{5}} \cdot \dfrac{\sqrt{5}}{\sqrt{5}} = \dfrac{4\sqrt{5}}{5}$

20. $\dfrac{5}{4 + \sqrt{3}} = \dfrac{5}{4 + \sqrt{3}} \cdot \dfrac{4 - \sqrt{3}}{4 - \sqrt{3}}$

$\qquad = \dfrac{5\left(4 - \sqrt{3}\right)}{4^2 - \left(\sqrt{3}\right)^2}$

$\qquad = \dfrac{5\left(4 - \sqrt{3}\right)}{16 - 3}$

$\qquad = \dfrac{5\left(4 - \sqrt{3}\right)}{13}$

$\qquad = \dfrac{20 - 5\sqrt{3}}{13}$

21. $\sqrt{3x} + 5 = 11$

$\qquad \sqrt{3x} = 6$

$\qquad \left(\sqrt{3x}\right)^2 = 6^2$

$\qquad\qquad 3x = 36$

$\qquad\qquad x = 12$

Check the proposed solution in the original equation.

$\qquad \sqrt{3x} + 5 = 11$

$\qquad \sqrt{3 \cdot 12} + 5 = 11$

$\qquad\quad \sqrt{36} + 5 = 11$

$\qquad\qquad 6 + 5 = 11$

$\qquad\qquad\quad 11 = 11$

The solution set is $\{12\}$.

22. $\sqrt{2x - 1} = x - 2$

$\qquad \left(\sqrt{2x - 1}\right)^2 = (x - 2)^2$

$\qquad\qquad 2x - 1 = x^2 - 4x + 4$

$\qquad\qquad\quad 0 = x^2 - 6x + 5$

$\qquad\qquad\quad 0 = (x - 1)(x - 5)$

$\qquad x - 1 = 0 \quad \text{or} \quad x - 5 = 0$

$\qquad\quad x = 1 \qquad\qquad x = 5$

Check each proposed solution in the original equation.

Check 1:$\qquad\qquad$Check 5:

$\sqrt{2x - 1} = x - 2 \qquad \sqrt{2x - 1} = x - 2$

$\sqrt{2 \cdot 1 - 1} = 1 - 2 \qquad \sqrt{2 \cdot 5 - 1} = 5 - 2$

$\quad \sqrt{2 - 1} = 1 - 2 \qquad\quad \sqrt{10 - 1} = 3$

$\qquad\quad \sqrt{1} = -1 \qquad\qquad\quad \sqrt{9} = 3$

$\qquad\qquad 1 = -1, \text{ false} \qquad 3 = 3, \text{ true}$

The check shows that 1 is an extraneous solution. The solution set is $\{5\}$.

23.
$$p = -4.4\sqrt{x} + 38$$
$$16 = -4.4\sqrt{x} + 38$$
$$-22 = -4.4\sqrt{x}$$
$$\frac{-22}{-4.4} = \frac{-4.4\sqrt{x}}{-4.4}$$
$$5 = \sqrt{x}$$
$$25 = x$$

According to the formula, 16% of Americans with an income of $25 thousand report that their health is fair or poor.

24. $8^{\frac{2}{3}} = \left(\sqrt[3]{8}\right)^2 = 2^2 = 4$

25. $9^{-\frac{1}{2}} = \dfrac{1}{9^{\frac{1}{2}}} = \dfrac{1}{\sqrt{9}} = \dfrac{1}{3}$

Cumulative Review (Chapters 1-9)

1. $2x + 3x - 5 + 7 = 10x + 3 - 6x - 4$
$$5x + 2 = 4x - 1$$
$$x + 2 = -1$$
$$x = -3$$
The solution set is $\{-3\}$.

2.
$$2x^2 + 5x = 12$$
$$2x^2 + 5x - 12 = 0$$
$$(2x - 3)(x + 4) = 0$$
$$2x - 3 = 0 \quad \text{or} \quad x + 4 = 0$$
$$2x = 3 \qquad\qquad x = -4$$
$$x = \frac{3}{2}$$
The solution set is $\left\{-4, \dfrac{3}{2}\right\}$.

3.
$$8x - 5y = -4$$
$$2x + 15y = -66$$
Multiply the first equation by 3 and add the two equations.
$$24x - 15y = -12$$
$$\underline{2x + 15y = -66}$$
$$26x \qquad = -78$$
$$x \qquad = -3$$
Back-substitute $x = -3$ into the first equation and solve for y.
$$8(-3) - 5y = -4$$
$$-24 - 5y = -4$$
$$-5y = 20$$
$$y = -4$$
The solution set is $\{(-3, -4)\}$.

4. $\dfrac{15}{x} - 4 = \dfrac{6}{x} + 3$

Restriction: $x \neq 0$

Multiply both sides by the LCD, which is x.
$$x\left(\frac{15}{x} - 4\right) = x\left(\frac{6}{x} + 3\right)$$
$$x \cdot \frac{15}{x} - x \cdot 4 = x \cdot \frac{6}{x} + x \cdot 3$$
$$15 - 4x = 6 + 3x$$
$$15 - 7x = 6$$
$$-7x = -9$$
$$x = \frac{9}{7}$$
The solution set is $\left\{\dfrac{9}{7}\right\}$.

5. $-3x - 7 = 8$
$$-3x = 15$$
$$x = -5$$
The solution set is $\{-5\}$.

6. $\sqrt{2x-1}-x=-2$

$$\sqrt{2x-1}=x-2$$

$$\left(\sqrt{2x-1}\right)^2=\left(x-2\right)^2$$

$$2x-1=x^2-4x+4$$

$$0=x^2-6x+5$$

$$0=\left(x-1\right)\left(x-5\right)$$

$$x-1=0 \quad \text{or} \quad x-5=0$$

$$x=1 \qquad\qquad x=5$$

Check each proposed solution in the original equation.

Check 1: $\sqrt{2x-1}-x=-2$

$$\sqrt{2\cdot1-1}-1=-2$$

$$\sqrt{2-1}-1=-2$$

$$\sqrt{1}-1=-2$$

$$1-1=-2$$

$$0=-2, \text{ false}$$

Check 5: $\sqrt{2x-1}-x=-2$

$$\sqrt{2\cdot5-1}-5=-2$$

$$\sqrt{10-1}-5=-2$$

$$\sqrt{9}-5=-2$$

$$3-5=-2$$

$$-2=-2, \text{ true}$$

The check shows that 1 is an extraneous solution. The solution set is $\{5\}$.

7. $\dfrac{8x^3}{-4x^7}=\dfrac{8}{-4}\cdot x^{3-7}=-2x^{-4}$

$$=\dfrac{-2}{x^4}=-\dfrac{2}{x^4}$$

8. $6\sqrt{75}-4\sqrt{12}=6\sqrt{25}\sqrt{3}-4\sqrt{4}\sqrt{3}$

$$=6\cdot5\sqrt{3}-4\cdot2\sqrt{3}$$

$$=30\sqrt{3}-8\sqrt{3}$$

$$=22\sqrt{3}$$

9. $\dfrac{\dfrac{1}{x}-\dfrac{1}{2}}{\dfrac{1}{3}-\dfrac{x}{6}}$

LCD $= 6x$

$$\dfrac{\dfrac{1}{x}-\dfrac{1}{2}}{\dfrac{1}{3}-\dfrac{x}{6}}=\dfrac{6x}{6x}\cdot\dfrac{\left(\dfrac{1}{x}-\dfrac{1}{2}\right)}{\left(\dfrac{1}{3}-\dfrac{x}{6}\right)}$$

$$=\dfrac{6x\cdot\dfrac{1}{x}-6x\cdot\dfrac{1}{2}}{6x\cdot\dfrac{1}{3}-6x\cdot\dfrac{x}{6}}=\dfrac{6-3x}{2x-x^2}$$

$$=\dfrac{3\left(2-x\right)}{x\left(2-x\right)}=\dfrac{3}{x}$$

10. $\dfrac{4-x^2}{3x^2-5x-2}=\dfrac{\left(2+x\right)\left(2-x\right)}{\left(3x+1\right)\left(x-2\right)}$

$$=\dfrac{\left(2+x\right)\left(-1\right)\left(x-2\right)}{\left(3x+1\right)\left(x-2\right)}$$

$$=\dfrac{-1\left(2+x\right)}{3x+1}$$

$$=-\dfrac{2+x}{3x+1}$$

11. $-5-\left(-8\right)-\left(4-6\right)$

$$=-5-\left(-8\right)-\left(-2\right)$$

$$=-5+8+2$$

$$=3+2$$

$$=5$$

12. To factor this trinomial, find two integers whose product is 77 and whose sum is -18. These integers are -7 and -11.

$$x^2-18x+77=\left(x-7\right)\left(x-11\right)$$

13. $x^3-25x=x\left(x^2-25\right)$

$$=x\left(x+5\right)\left(x-5\right)$$

14.

$$x-2\overline{\smash{\big)}6x^3-19x^2+16x-4}$$

with quotient $6x^2-7x+2$

$$\underline{6x^3-12x^2}$$
$$-7x^2+16x$$
$$\underline{-7x^2+14x}$$
$$2x-4$$
$$\underline{2x-4}$$
$$0$$

$$\frac{6x^3-19x^2+16x-4}{x-2}=6x^2-7x+2$$

15. $(2x-3)(4x^2+6x+9)$

$$=2x(4x^2+6x+9)-3(4x^2+6x+9)$$

$$=8x^3+12x^2+18x-12x^2-18x-27$$

$$=8x^3-27$$

16. $\dfrac{3x}{x^2+x-2}-\dfrac{2}{x+2}$

$$=\frac{3x}{(x+2)(x-1)}-\frac{2}{x+2}$$

$$=\frac{3x}{(x+2)(x-1)}-\frac{2(x-1)}{(x+2)(x-1)}$$

$$=\frac{3x-2(x-1)}{(x+2)(x-1)}$$

$$=\frac{3x-2x+2}{(x+2)(x-1)}$$

$$=\frac{x+2}{(x+2)(x-1)}$$

$$=\frac{1}{x-1}$$

17. $\dfrac{5x^2-6x+1}{x^2-1}\div\dfrac{16x^2-9}{4x^2+7x+3}$

$$=\frac{5x^2-6x+1}{x^2-1}\cdot\frac{4x^2+7x+3}{16x^2-9}$$

$$=\frac{(5x-1)(x-1)}{(x+1)(x-1)}\cdot\frac{(4x+3)(x+1)}{(4x+3)(4x-3)}$$

$$=\frac{5x-1}{4x-3}$$

18. $\sqrt{12}-4\sqrt{75}=\sqrt{4}\cdot\sqrt{3}-4\sqrt{25}\cdot\sqrt{3}$

$$=2\sqrt{3}-4(5)\sqrt{3}$$

$$=2\sqrt{3}-20\sqrt{3}$$

$$=-18\sqrt{3}$$

19. $2x-y=4$

The graph is a line with *x*-intercept 2 and *y*-intercept −4. The point (1, −2) can be used as a checkpoint. Draw a line through (2,0), (0, −4), and (1, −2).

2x − y = 4

20. $y=-\dfrac{2}{3}x$

The graph is a line with slope $-\dfrac{2}{3}=\dfrac{-2}{3}$ and *y*-intercept 0. Plot (0,0). From the origin, move 2 units *down* and 3 units to the *right* to reach the point (3, −2). Draw a line through (0,0) and (3, −2).

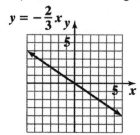

$y=-\dfrac{2}{3}x$

21. $x\ge-1$

Graph *x* = 1 as a solid vertical line. Use (0,0) as a test point. Since $0\ge-1$ is true, shade the half-plane that contains (0,0). This is the region to the right of the vertical line.

x ≥ −1

22. $m=\dfrac{y_2-y_1}{x_2-x_1}=\dfrac{-3-5}{2-(-1)}=\dfrac{-8}{3}=-\dfrac{8}{3}$

23. Slope 5, passing through $(-2, -3)$.
First, substitute 5 for m, -2 for x_1, and -3 for y_1 in the point-slope form.

$$y - y_1 = m(x - x_1)$$
$$y - (-3) = 5[x - (-2)]$$
$$y + 3 = 5(x + 2)$$

Now rewrite the equation in slope-intercept form.
$$y + 3 = 5x + 10$$
$$y = 5x + 7$$

24. Let x = the number.
$$5x - 7 = 208$$
$$5x = 215$$
$$x = 43$$
The number is 43.

25. Let x = the number of deer in the park.

$$\frac{\text{Original number of tagged deer}}{\text{Total number of deer}} = \frac{\text{Number of tagged deer in sample}}{\text{Number of deer in sample}}$$

$$\frac{318}{x} = \frac{56}{168}$$
$$(318)(168) = 56x$$
$$53,424 = 56x$$
$$954 = x$$

There are approximately 954 deer in the park.

Chapter 10
Quadratic Equations and Introduction to Functions

10.1 Check Points

1. a. $x^2 = 36$

$x = \sqrt{36}$ or $x = -\sqrt{36}$

$x = 6 \qquad x = -6$

The solution set is $\{\pm 6\}$.

b. $5x^2 = 15$

$x^2 = 3$

$x = \sqrt{3}$ or $x = -\sqrt{3}$

The solution set is $\left\{\pm\sqrt{3}\right\}$.

c. $2x^2 - 7 = 0$

$2x^2 = 7$

$x^2 = \dfrac{7}{2}$

$x = \sqrt{\dfrac{7}{2}}$ or $x = -\sqrt{\dfrac{7}{2}}$

$\pm\sqrt{\dfrac{7}{2}} = \pm\dfrac{\sqrt{7}}{\sqrt{2}} \cdot \dfrac{\sqrt{2}}{\sqrt{2}} = \pm\dfrac{\sqrt{14}}{2}$

The solution set is $\left\{\pm\dfrac{\sqrt{14}}{2}\right\}$.

2. $(x-3)^2 = 25$

$x - 3 = \sqrt{25}$ or $x - 3 = -\sqrt{25}$

$x - 3 = 5$ or $x - 3 = -5$

$x = 8 \qquad\qquad x = -2$

The solution set is $\{-2, 8\}$.

3. $(x-2)^2 = 7$

$x - 2 = \sqrt{7}$ or $x - 2 = -\sqrt{7}$

$x = 2 + \sqrt{7} \qquad\quad x = 2 - \sqrt{7}$

The solution set is $\left\{2 \pm \sqrt{7}\right\}$.

4. $w^2 + 20^2 = 50^2$

$w^2 + 400 = 2500$

$w^2 = 2100$

$w = \sqrt{2100}$ or $w = -\sqrt{2100}$

$w = 10\sqrt{21} \qquad\qquad w = -10\sqrt{21}$

$w \approx 45.8 \qquad\qquad w \approx -45.8$

The dimension must be positive. Reject -45.8. The width of the rectangle is $10\sqrt{21}$ inches or about 45.8 inches.

5. $d = \sqrt{(x_2 - x_1)^2 + (y_2 - y_1)^2}$

$= \sqrt{(1-(-4))^2 + (-3-9)^2}$

$= \sqrt{5^2 + (-12)^2}$

$= \sqrt{25 + 144}$

$= \sqrt{169}$

$= 13$

The distance between the two points is 13 units.

10.1 Exercise Set

1. $x^2 = 16$

$x = \sqrt{16}$ or $x = -\sqrt{16}$

$x = 4 \qquad x = -4$

The solution set is $\{\pm 4\}$.

3. $y^2 = 81$

$y = \sqrt{81}$ or $y = -\sqrt{81}$

$y = 9 \qquad y = -9$

The solution set is $\{\pm 9\}$.

5. $x^2 = 7$

$x = \sqrt{7}$ or $x = -\sqrt{7}$

The solution set is $\left\{\pm\sqrt{7}\right\}$.

7. $x^2 = 50$

$x = \sqrt{50}$ or $x = -\sqrt{50}$

Simplify $\sqrt{50}$:

$\sqrt{50} = \sqrt{25}\sqrt{2} = 5\sqrt{2}$

$x = 5\sqrt{2}$ or $x = -5\sqrt{2}$

The solution set is $\left\{\pm 5\sqrt{2}\right\}$.

9. $5x^2 = 20$

$x^2 = 4$

$x = \sqrt{4}$ or $x = -\sqrt{4}$

$x = 2$ or $x = -2$

The solution set is $\left\{\pm 2\right\}$.

11. $4y^2 = 49$

$y^2 = \dfrac{49}{4}$

$y = \sqrt{\dfrac{49}{4}}$ or $y = -\sqrt{\dfrac{49}{4}}$

$y = \dfrac{7}{2}$ or $y = -\dfrac{7}{2}$

The solution set is $\left\{\pm \dfrac{7}{2}\right\}$.

13. $2x^2 + 1 = 51$

$2x^2 = 50$

$x^2 = 25$

$x = \sqrt{25}$ or $x = -\sqrt{25}$

$x = 5$ or $x = -5$

The solution set is $\left\{\pm 5\right\}$.

15. $3x^2 - 2 = 0$

$3x = 2$

$x^2 = \dfrac{2}{3}$

$x = \sqrt{\dfrac{2}{3}}$ or $x = -\sqrt{\dfrac{2}{3}}$

Rationalize the denominators.

$\sqrt{\dfrac{2}{3}} = \dfrac{\sqrt{2}}{\sqrt{3}} = \dfrac{\sqrt{2}}{\sqrt{3}} \cdot \dfrac{\sqrt{3}}{\sqrt{3}} = \dfrac{\sqrt{6}}{3}$

$x = \dfrac{\sqrt{6}}{3}$ or $x = -\dfrac{\sqrt{6}}{3}$

The solution set is $\left\{\pm \dfrac{\sqrt{6}}{3}\right\}$.

17. $5z^2 - 7 = 0$

$5z^2 = 7$

$z^2 = \dfrac{7}{5}$

$z = \sqrt{\dfrac{7}{5}}$ or $z = -\sqrt{\dfrac{7}{5}}$

Rationalize the denominators.

$\sqrt{\dfrac{7}{5}} = \dfrac{\sqrt{7}}{\sqrt{5}} = \dfrac{\sqrt{7}}{\sqrt{5}} \cdot \dfrac{\sqrt{5}}{\sqrt{5}} = \dfrac{\sqrt{35}}{5}$

$z = \dfrac{\sqrt{35}}{5}$ or $z = -\dfrac{\sqrt{35}}{5}$

The solution set is $\left\{\pm \dfrac{\sqrt{35}}{5}\right\}$.

19. $(x-3)^2 = 16$

$x - 3 = \sqrt{16}$ or $x - 3 = -\sqrt{16}$

$x - 3 = 4$ or $x - 3 = -4$

$x = 7$ $x = -1$

The solution set is $\left\{-1, 7\right\}$.

21. $(x+5)^2 = 121$

$x + 5 = \sqrt{121}$ or $x + 5 = -\sqrt{121}$

$x + 5 = 11$ or $x + 5 = -11$

$x = 6$ $x = -16$

The solution set is $\left\{-16, 6\right\}$.

23. $(3x+2)^2 = 9$

$3x + 2 = \sqrt{9}$ or $3x + 2 = -\sqrt{9}$

$3x + 2 = 3$ or $3x + 2 = -3$

$3x = 1$ or $3x = -5$

$x = \dfrac{1}{3}$ $x = -\dfrac{5}{3}$

The solution set is $\left\{-\dfrac{5}{3}, \dfrac{1}{3}\right\}$.

25. $(x-5)^2 = 3$

$x - 5 = \sqrt{3}$ or $x - 5 = -\sqrt{3}$

$x = 5 + \sqrt{3}$ $x = 5 - \sqrt{3}$

The solution set is $\left\{5 \pm \sqrt{3}\right\}$.

27. $(y+8)^2 = 11$

$\quad y+8 = \sqrt{11} \qquad$ or $\quad y+8 = -\sqrt{11}$

$\quad\quad y = -8 + \sqrt{11} \qquad\quad y = -8 - \sqrt{11}$

The solution set is $\left\{-8 \pm \sqrt{11}\right\}$.

29. $(z-4)^2 = 18$

$\quad z-4 = \sqrt{18} \qquad$ or $z-4 = -\sqrt{18}$

$\quad z-4 = 3\sqrt{2} \qquad\quad z-4 = -3\sqrt{2}$

$\quad\quad z = 4 + 3\sqrt{2} \qquad\quad z = 4 - 3\sqrt{2}$

The solution set is $\left\{4 \pm 3\sqrt{2}\right\}$.

31. $x^2 + 4x + 4 = 16$

$\quad\quad (x+2)^2 = 16$

$\quad x+2 = \sqrt{16} \qquad$ or $\quad x+2 = -\sqrt{16}$

$\quad x+2 = 4 \qquad\quad$ or $\quad x+2 = -4$

$\quad\quad x = 2 \qquad\qquad\quad x = -6$

The solution set is $\{-6, 2\}$.

33. $x^2 - 6x + 9 = 36$

$\quad\quad (x-3)^2 = 36$

$\quad x-3 = \sqrt{36} \quad$ or $x-3 = -\sqrt{36}$

$\quad x-3 = 6 \qquad$ or $x-3 = -6$

$\quad\quad x = 9 \qquad\qquad x = -3$

The solution set is $\{-3, 9\}$.

35. $x^2 - 10x + 25 = 2$

$\quad\quad (x-5)^2 = 2$

$\quad x-5 = \sqrt{2} \quad$ or $x-5 = -\sqrt{2}$

$\quad\quad x = 5 + \sqrt{2} \qquad x = 5 - \sqrt{2}$

The solution set is $\left\{5 \pm \sqrt{2}\right\}$.

37. $x^2 + 2x + 1 = 5$

$\quad\quad (x+1)^2 = 5$

$\quad x+1 = \sqrt{5} \qquad$ or $x+1 = -\sqrt{5}$

$\quad\quad x = -1 + \sqrt{5} \qquad x = -1 - \sqrt{5}$

The solution set is $\left\{-1 \pm \sqrt{5}\right\}$.

39. $y^2 - 14y + 49 = 12$

$\quad\quad (y-7)^2 = 12$

$\quad y-7 = \sqrt{12} \qquad$ or $y-7 = -\sqrt{12}$

$\quad y-7 = 2\sqrt{3} \qquad$ or $y-7 = -2\sqrt{3}$

$\quad\quad y = 7 + 2\sqrt{3} \qquad\quad y = 7 - 2\sqrt{3}$

The solution set is $\left\{7 \pm 2\sqrt{3}\right\}$.

41. $8^2 + 15^2 = c^2$

$\quad 64 + 225 = c^2$

$\quad\quad 289 = c^2$

$\quad\quad\quad c = \sqrt{289} = 17$

The missing length is 17 meters.

43. $15^2 + 36^2 = c^2$

$\quad 225 + 1296 = c^2$

$\quad\quad 1521 = c^2$

$\quad\quad\quad c = \sqrt{1521}$

$\quad\quad\quad\quad = 39$

The missing length is 39 meters.

45. $a^2 + 16^2 = 20^2$

$\quad a^2 + 256 = 440$

$\quad\quad a^2 = 144$

$\quad\quad a = \sqrt{144}$

$\quad\quad\quad = 12$

The missing length is 12 centimeters.

47. $9^2 + b^2 = 16^2$

$\quad 81 + b^2 = 256$

$\quad\quad b^2 = 175$

$\quad\quad b = \sqrt{175}$

$\quad\quad\quad = \sqrt{25}\sqrt{7}$

$\quad\quad\quad = 5\sqrt{7}$

The missing length is $5\sqrt{7}$ meters.

49.
$$d = \sqrt{(x_2 - x_1)^2 + (y_2 - y_1)^2}$$
$$= \sqrt{(4-3)^2 + (1-5)^2}$$
$$= \sqrt{1^2 + (-4)^2}$$
$$= \sqrt{1+16} = \sqrt{17} \approx 4.12$$

The distance between the two points is $\sqrt{17} \approx 4.12$ units.

51.
$$d = \sqrt{(x_2 - x_1)^2 + (y_2 - y_1)^2}$$
$$= \sqrt{(4-(-4))^2 + (17-2)^2}$$
$$= \sqrt{8^2 + 15^2} = \sqrt{64 + 225}$$
$$= \sqrt{289} = 17$$

The distance between the two points is 17 units.

53.
$$d = \sqrt{(x_2 - x_1)^2 + (y_2 - y_1)^2}$$
$$= \sqrt{(9-6)^2 + (5-(-1))^2}$$
$$= \sqrt{3^2 + 6^2} = \sqrt{9 + 36}$$
$$= \sqrt{45} = 3\sqrt{5} \approx 6.71$$

The distance between the two points is $3\sqrt{5} \approx 6.71$ units.

55.
$$d = \sqrt{(x_2 - x_1)^2 + (y_2 - y_1)^2}$$
$$= \sqrt{(-2-(-7))^2 + (-1-(-5))^2}$$
$$= \sqrt{5^2 + 4^2} = \sqrt{25 + 16}$$
$$= \sqrt{41} \approx 6.40$$

The distance between the two points is $\sqrt{41} \approx 6.40$ units.

57.
$$d = \sqrt{(x_2 - x_1)^2 + (y_2 - y_1)^2}$$
$$= \sqrt{(4\sqrt{7} - (-2\sqrt{7}))^2 + (8-10)^2}$$
$$= \sqrt{(6\sqrt{7})^2 + (-2)^2} = \sqrt{252 + 4}$$
$$= \sqrt{256} = 16$$

The distance between the two points is 16 units.

59. Let x = the number.
$$(x-3)^2 = 25$$
$$x-3 = \sqrt{25} \quad \text{or} \quad x-3 = -\sqrt{25}$$
$$x = 3 + 5 \qquad\qquad x = 3 - 5$$
$$x = 8 \qquad\qquad\quad x = -2$$
The number is -2 or 8.

61. Let x = the number.
$$(3x+2)^2 = 49$$
$$3x+2 = \sqrt{49} \quad \text{or} \quad 3x+2 = -\sqrt{49}$$
$$3x+2 = 7 \qquad\qquad 3x+2 = -7$$
$$3x = 5 \qquad\qquad\quad 3x = -9$$
$$x = \frac{5}{3} \qquad\qquad\quad x = -3$$

The number is -3 or $\dfrac{5}{3}$.

63.
$$A = \pi r^2$$
$$\frac{A}{\pi} = r^2$$
$$r = \sqrt{\frac{A}{\pi}}$$
$$= \frac{\sqrt{A}}{\sqrt{\pi}} \cdot \frac{\sqrt{\pi}}{\sqrt{\pi}}$$
$$= \frac{\sqrt{A\pi}}{\pi}$$

65.
$$I = \frac{k}{d^2}$$
$$d^2 I = k$$
$$d^2 = \frac{k}{I}$$
$$d = \sqrt{\frac{k}{I}} = \frac{\sqrt{k}}{\sqrt{I}}$$
$$= \frac{\sqrt{k}}{\sqrt{I}} \cdot \frac{\sqrt{I}}{\sqrt{I}}$$
$$= \frac{\sqrt{kI}}{I}$$

67. Let x = the length of the ladder.
$$8^2 + 10^2 = x^2$$
$$64 + 100 = x^2$$
$$164 = x^2$$
$$x = \sqrt{164} = \sqrt{4}\sqrt{41} = 2\sqrt{41}$$
The length of the ladder is $2\sqrt{41}$ feet.

69.
$$90^2 + 90^2 = x^2$$
$$8100 + 8100 = x^2$$
$$16,200 = x^2$$
$$\sqrt{16,2000} = \sqrt{8100}\sqrt{2} = 90\sqrt{2}$$
The distance from home plate to second base is $90\sqrt{2}$ feet.

71. $A = \pi r^2 ; A = 36\pi$
$$36\pi = \pi r^2$$
$$36 = r^2$$
$$r = \sqrt{36} = 6$$
The radius is 6 inches.

73. $W = 3t^2 ; W = 108$
$$108 = 3t^2$$
$$36 = t^2$$
$$t = \sqrt{36} = 6$$
The fetus weighs 108 grams after 6 weeks.

75. $d = 16t^2 ; d = 400$
The rock must fall 400 feet to hit the water.
$$400 = 16t^2$$
$$25 = t^2$$
$$t = \sqrt{25} = 5$$
It will take 5 seconds for the rock to hit the water.

77. The length of each side of the original garden is x meters. Therefore, the length of each larger side is x + 4 meters since 2 meters were added to each side.
Larger square: $A = (x+4)^2 ; A = 144$
$$144 = (x+4)^2$$
$$x + 4 = \sqrt{144} \quad \text{or} \quad x + 4 = -\sqrt{144}$$
$$x + 4 = 12 \quad \text{or} \quad x + 4 = -12$$
$$x = 8 \qquad\qquad x = -16$$
Reject -16 because a length cannot be negative. The length of each side of the original square is 8 meters.

79. The volume of a rectangular solid is given by $V = lwh$. From the problem statement, we have $V = 200, l = x, w = x, h = 2$
$$200 = x \cdot x \cdot 2$$
$$200 = 2x^2$$
$$100 = x^2$$
$$x = \sqrt{100} = 10$$
The length and width of the open box are both 10 inches.

81. – 83. Answers will vary.

85. makes sense

87. makes sense

89. false; Changes to make the statement true will vary. A sample change is: They are not equivalent. The first equation has two solutions, $-5 \pm 2\sqrt{2}$, while the second equation is only satisfied by $-5 + 2\sqrt{2}$.

91. true

93.
$$d = \sqrt{(x_2 - x_1)^2 + (y_2 - y_1)^2}$$
$$5 = \sqrt{(x - (-3))^2 + (-5 - (-2))^2}$$
$$5 = \sqrt{(x+3)^2 + (-3)^2}$$
$$5^2 = (x+3)^2 + (-3)^2$$
$$25 = x^2 + 6x + 9 + 9$$
$$0 = x^2 + 6x - 7$$
$$0 = (x+7)(x-1)$$
$$x + 7 = 0 \quad \text{or} \quad x - 1 = 0$$
$$x = -7 \qquad\qquad x = 1$$
The possible values for x are -7 and 1.

95. $(x-1)^2 - 9 = 0$

Check -2:   Check 4:

$(-2-1)^2 - 9 = 0$ $(4-1)^2 - 9 = 0$

$(-3)^2 - 9 = 0$ $3^2 - 9 = 0$

$9 - 9 = 0$ $9 - 9 = 0$

$0 = 0$, true $0 = 0$ true

The solutions are $\{-2, 4\}$.

96. $12x^2 + 14x - 6 = 2(6x^2 + 7x - 3)$
$$= 2(2x+3)(3x-1)$$

97. $\dfrac{x^2-x-6}{3x-3} \div \dfrac{x^2-4}{x-1}$

$= \dfrac{x^2-x-6}{3x-3} \cdot \dfrac{x-1}{x^2-4}$

$= \dfrac{(x+2)(x-3)}{3(x-1)} \cdot \dfrac{(x-1)}{(x+2)(x-2)}$

$= \dfrac{x-3}{3(x-2)}$

98. $4(x-5) = 22 + 2(6x+3)$

$4x - 20 = 22 + 12x + 6$

$4x - 20 = 28 + 12x$

$-8x - 20 = 28$

$-8x = 48$

$x = -6$

The solution is set $\{-6\}$.

99. $x^2 + 8x + 16 = x^2 + 2 \cdot 4x + 4^2 = (x+4)^2$

100. $x^2 - 14x + 49 = x^2 - 2 \cdot 7x + 7^2 = (x-7)^2$

101. $x^2 + 5x + \dfrac{25}{4} = x^2 + 2 \cdot \dfrac{5}{2}x + \left(\dfrac{5}{2}\right)^2 = \left(x+\dfrac{5}{2}\right)^2$

10.2 Check Points

1. a. $x^2 + 10x$

The coefficient of the x-term is 10. Half of 10 is 5, and $5^2 = 25$. Add 25.

$x^2 + 10x + 25 = (x+5)^2$

b. $x^2 - 6x$

The coefficient of the x-term is -6. Half of -6 is -3, and $(-3)^2 = 9$. Add 9.

$x^2 - 6x + 9 = (x-3)^2$

c. $x^2 + 3x$

The coefficient of the x-term is 3. Half of 3 is $\dfrac{3}{2}$, and $\left(\dfrac{3}{2}\right)^2 = \dfrac{9}{4}$. Add $\dfrac{9}{4}$.

$x^2 + 3x + \dfrac{9}{4} = \left(x+\dfrac{3}{2}\right)^2$

2. a. The coefficient of the x-term is 6. Half of 6 is 3, and $3^2 = 9$. Add 9.

$x^2 + 6x = 7$

$x^2 + 6x + 9 = 7 + 9$

$(x+3)^2 = 16$

$x + 3 = \sqrt{16}$ or $x + 3 = -\sqrt{16}$

$x + 3 = 4$ $x + 3 = -4$

$x = 1$ $x = -7$

The solution set is $\{-7, 1\}$.

b. $x^2 - 10x + 18 = 0$

First subtract 18 from both sides to isolate the binomial $x^2 - 10x$.

$x^2 - 10x = -18$

Next, complete the square.

$x^2 - 10x + 25 = -18 + 25$

$x^2 - 10x + 25 = 7$

$(x-5)^2 = 7$

$x - 5 = \sqrt{7}$ or $x - 5 = -\sqrt{7}$

$x = 5 + \sqrt{7}$ $x = 5 - \sqrt{7}$

The solution set is $\left\{5 + \sqrt{7}\right\}$.

3. $2x^2 - 10x - 1 = 0$

First, divide both sides of the equation by 2 so that the coefficient of the x^2 term will be 1.

$$x^2 - 5x - \frac{1}{2} = 0$$

Next, add $\frac{1}{2}$ to both sides to isolate the binomial.

$$x^2 - 5x = \frac{1}{2}$$

Complete the square: The coefficient of the x-term is -5, and $\frac{1}{2}(-5) = -\frac{5}{2}$, so add $\left(-\frac{5}{2}\right)^2 = \frac{25}{4}$ to both sides.

$$x^2 - 5x + \frac{25}{4} = \frac{1}{2} + \frac{25}{4}$$

$$x^2 - 5x + \frac{25}{4} = \frac{2}{4} + \frac{25}{4}$$

$$\left(x - \frac{5}{2}\right)^2 = \frac{27}{4}$$

$$x - \frac{5}{2} = \sqrt{\frac{27}{4}} \qquad \text{or} \qquad x - \frac{5}{2} = -\sqrt{\frac{27}{4}}$$

$$x = \frac{5}{2} + \frac{\sqrt{27}}{2} \qquad\qquad x = \frac{5}{2} - \frac{\sqrt{27}}{2}$$

$$x = \frac{5}{2} + \frac{3\sqrt{3}}{2} \qquad\qquad x = \frac{5}{2} - \frac{3\sqrt{3}}{2}$$

$$x = \frac{5 + 3\sqrt{3}}{2} \qquad\qquad x = \frac{5 - 3\sqrt{3}}{2}$$

The solution set is $\left\{ \dfrac{5 \pm 3\sqrt{3}}{2} \right\}$.

10.2 Exercise Set

1. $x^2 + 10x$

The coefficient of the x-term is 10. Half of 10 is 5, and $5^2 = 25$. Add 25.

$$x^2 + 10x + 25 = (x + 5)^2$$

3. $x^2 - 2x$

The coefficient of the x-term is -2. Half of -2 is -1, and $(-1)^2 = 1$. Add 1.

$$x^2 - 2x + 1 = (x - 1)^2$$

5. $x^2 + 5x$

The coefficient of the x-term is 5. Half of 5 is $\frac{5}{2}$, and $\left(\frac{5}{2}\right)^2 = \frac{25}{4}$. Add $\frac{25}{4}$.

$$x^2 + 5x + \frac{25}{4} = \left(x + \frac{5}{2}\right)^2$$

7. $x^2 - 7x$

The coefficient of the x-term is -7. Half of -7 is $\frac{-7}{2}$, and $\left(\frac{-7}{2}\right)^2 = \frac{49}{4}$. Add $\frac{49}{4}$.

$$x^2 - 7x + \frac{49}{4} = \left(x - \frac{7}{2}\right)^2$$

9. $x^2 + \frac{1}{2}x$

The coefficient of the x-term is $\frac{1}{2}$. Half of $\frac{1}{2}$ is $\frac{1}{2}\left(\frac{1}{2}\right) = \frac{1}{4}$, and $\left(\frac{1}{4}\right)^2 = \frac{1}{16}$. Add $\frac{1}{16}$.

$$x^2 + \frac{1}{2}x + \frac{1}{16} = \left(x + \frac{1}{4}\right)^2$$

11. $x^2 - \frac{4}{3}x$

The coefficient of the x-term is $-\frac{4}{3}$. Half of $-\frac{4}{3}$ is $\frac{1}{2}\left(-\frac{4}{3}\right) = -\frac{2}{3}$, and $\left(-\frac{2}{3}\right)^2 = \frac{4}{9}$. Add $\frac{4}{9}$.

$$x^2 - \frac{4}{3}x + \frac{4}{9} = \left(x - \frac{2}{3}\right)^2$$

13. $x^2 + 4x = 5$

$$x^2 + 4x + 4 = 5 + 4$$

$$(x + 2)^2 = 9$$

$$x + 2 = \sqrt{9} \qquad \text{or} \quad x + 2 = -\sqrt{9}$$

$$x + 2 = 3 \qquad\qquad x + 2 = -3$$

$$x = 1 \qquad\qquad\quad x = -5$$

The solution set is $\{-5, 1\}$.

15. $x^2 - 10x = -24$

$x^2 - 10x + 25 = -24 + 25$

$(x-5)^2 = 1$

$x - 5 = \sqrt{1}$ or $x - 5 = -\sqrt{1}$

$x - 5 = 1$ $x - 5 = -1$

$x = 6$ $x = 4$

The solution set is $\{4, 6\}$.

17. $x^2 - 2x = 5$

$x^2 - 2x + 1 = 5 + 1$

$(x-1)^2 = 6$

$x - 1 = \sqrt{6}$ or $x - 1 = -\sqrt{6}$

$x = 1 + \sqrt{6}$ or $x = 1 - \sqrt{6}$

The solution set is $\left\{ 1 \pm \sqrt{6} \right\}$.

19. $x^2 + 4x + 1 = 0$

First subtract 1 from both sides to isolate the binomial $x^2 + 4x$.

$x^2 + 4x = -1$

Next, complete the square.

$x^2 + 4x + 4 = -1 + 4$

$(x+2)^2 = 3$

$x + 2 = \sqrt{3}$ or $x + 2 = -\sqrt{3}$

$x = -2 + \sqrt{3}$ or $x = -2 - \sqrt{3}$

The solution set is $\left\{ -2 \pm \sqrt{3} \right\}$.

21. $x^2 - 3x = 28$

$x^2 - 3x + \dfrac{9}{4} = 28 + \dfrac{9}{4}$

$\left(x - \dfrac{3}{2} \right)^2 = \dfrac{121}{4}$

$x - \dfrac{3}{2} = \sqrt{\dfrac{121}{4}}$ or $x - \dfrac{3}{2} = -\sqrt{\dfrac{121}{4}}$

$x - \dfrac{3}{2} = \dfrac{11}{2}$ or $x - \dfrac{3}{2} = -\dfrac{11}{2}$

$x = \dfrac{14}{2} = 7$ $x = -\dfrac{8}{2} = -4$

The solution set is $\{-4, 7\}$.

23. $x^2 + 3x - 1 = 0$

$x^2 + 3x = 1$

$x^2 + 3x + \dfrac{9}{4} = 1 + \dfrac{9}{4}$

$\left(x + \dfrac{3}{2} \right)^2 = \dfrac{13}{4}$

$x + \dfrac{3}{2} = \sqrt{\dfrac{13}{4}}$ or $x + \dfrac{3}{2} = -\sqrt{\dfrac{13}{4}}$

$x + \dfrac{3}{2} = \dfrac{\sqrt{13}}{2}$ or $x + \dfrac{3}{2} = -\sqrt{\dfrac{13}{2}}$

$x = -\dfrac{3}{2} + \dfrac{\sqrt{13}}{2}$ or $x = -\dfrac{3}{2} - \dfrac{\sqrt{13}}{2}$

$x = \dfrac{-3 + \sqrt{13}}{2}$ or $x = \dfrac{-3 - \sqrt{13}}{2}$

The solution set is $\left\{ \dfrac{-3 \pm \sqrt{13}}{2} \right\}$.

25. $x^2 = 7x - 3$

$x^2 - 7x = -3$

$x^2 - 7x + \dfrac{49}{4} = -3 + \dfrac{49}{4}$

$\left(x - \dfrac{7}{2} \right)^2 = \dfrac{-12}{4} + \dfrac{49}{4}$

$\left(x - \dfrac{7}{2} \right)^2 = \dfrac{37}{4}$

$x - \dfrac{7}{2} = \sqrt{\dfrac{37}{4}}$ or $x - \dfrac{7}{2} = -\sqrt{\dfrac{37}{4}}$

$x - \dfrac{7}{2} = \dfrac{\sqrt{37}}{2}$ or $x - \dfrac{7}{2} = -\dfrac{\sqrt{37}}{2}$

$x = \dfrac{7}{2} + \dfrac{\sqrt{37}}{2}$ or $x = \dfrac{7}{2} - \dfrac{\sqrt{37}}{2}$

$x = \dfrac{7 + \sqrt{37}}{2}$ or $x = \dfrac{7 - \sqrt{37}}{2}$

The solution set is $\left\{ \dfrac{7 \pm \sqrt{37}}{2} \right\}$.

27. $2x^2 - 2x - 6 = 0$

First, divide both sides of the equation by 2 so that the coefficient of the x^2 term will be 1.

$x^2 - x - 3 = 0$

Next, add 3 to both sides to isolate the binomial.

$x^2 - x = 3$

Complete the square: The coefficient of the x-term is -1, and $\frac{1}{2}(-1) = -\frac{1}{2}$, so add $\left(-\frac{1}{2}\right)^2 = \frac{1}{4}$ to both sides.

$x^2 - x + \frac{1}{4} = 3 + \frac{1}{4}$

$\left(x - \frac{1}{2}\right)^2 = \frac{13}{4}$

$x - \frac{1}{2} = \sqrt{\frac{13}{4}}$ or $x - \frac{1}{2} = -\sqrt{\frac{13}{4}}$

$x - \frac{1}{2} = \frac{\sqrt{13}}{2}$ or $x - \frac{1}{2} = -\frac{\sqrt{13}}{2}$

$x = \frac{1 + \sqrt{13}}{2}$ or $x = \frac{1 - \sqrt{13}}{2}$

The solution set is $\left\{ \frac{1 \pm \sqrt{13}}{2} \right\}$.

29. $2x^2 - 3x + 1 = 0$

$x^2 - \frac{3}{2}x + \frac{1}{2} = 0$

$x^2 - \frac{3}{2}x = -\frac{1}{2}$

$x^2 - \frac{3}{2}x + \frac{9}{16} = -\frac{1}{2} + \frac{9}{16}$

$\left(x - \frac{3}{4}\right)^2 = -\frac{8}{16} + \frac{9}{16}$

$\left(x - \frac{3}{4}\right)^2 = \frac{1}{16}$

$x - \frac{3}{4} = \sqrt{\frac{1}{16}}$ or $x - \frac{3}{4} = -\sqrt{\frac{1}{16}}$

$x - \frac{3}{4} = \frac{1}{4}$ or $x - \frac{3}{4} = -\frac{1}{4}$

$x = 1$ $\qquad x = \frac{2}{4} = \frac{1}{2}$

The solution set is $\left\{ \frac{1}{2}, 1 \right\}$.

31. $2x^2 + 10x + 11 = 0$

$x^2 + 5x + \frac{11}{2} = 0$

$x^2 + 5x = -\frac{11}{2}$

$x^2 + 5x + \frac{25}{4} = -\frac{11}{2} + \frac{25}{4}$

$\left(x + \frac{5}{2}\right)^2 = -\frac{22}{4} + \frac{25}{4}$

$\left(x + \frac{5}{2}\right)^2 = \frac{3}{4}$

$x + \frac{5}{2} = \sqrt{\frac{3}{4}}$ or $x + \frac{5}{2} = -\sqrt{\frac{3}{4}}$

$x + \frac{5}{2} = \frac{\sqrt{3}}{2}$ or $x + \frac{5}{2} = -\frac{\sqrt{3}}{2}$

$x = -\frac{5}{2} + \frac{\sqrt{3}}{2}$ or $x = -\frac{5}{2} - \frac{\sqrt{3}}{2}$

$x = \frac{-5 + \sqrt{3}}{2}$ or $x = \frac{-5 - \sqrt{3}}{2}$

The solution set is $\left\{ \frac{-5 \pm \sqrt{3}}{2} \right\}$.

33. $4x^2 - 2x - 3 = 0$

$x^2 - \frac{1}{2}x - \frac{3}{4} = 0$

$x^2 - \frac{1}{2}x = \frac{3}{4}$

$x^2 - \frac{1}{2}x + \frac{1}{16} = \frac{3}{4} + \frac{1}{16}$

$\left(x - \frac{1}{4}\right)^2 = \frac{12}{16} + \frac{1}{16}$

$\left(x - \frac{1}{4}\right)^2 = \frac{13}{16}$

$x - \frac{1}{4} = \sqrt{\frac{13}{16}}$ or $x - \frac{1}{4} = -\sqrt{\frac{13}{16}}$

$x - \frac{1}{4} = \frac{\sqrt{13}}{4}$ or $x - \frac{1}{4} = -\frac{\sqrt{13}}{4}$

$x = \frac{1}{4} + \frac{\sqrt{13}}{4}$ or $x = \frac{1}{4} - \frac{\sqrt{13}}{4}$

$x = \frac{1 + \sqrt{13}}{4}$ or $x = \frac{1 - \sqrt{13}}{4}$

The solution set is $\left\{ \frac{1 \pm \sqrt{13}}{4} \right\}$.

35. $\dfrac{x^2}{6} - \dfrac{x}{3} - 1 = 0$

Multiply both sides of the equation by 6 to obtain

$x^2 - 2x - 6 = 0$

$x^2 - 2x = 6$

The coefficient on x is -2. Divide this by 2 and square the result.

$\left(\dfrac{-2}{2}\right)^2 = (-1)^2 = 1$

Add 1 to both sides of the equation:

$x^2 - 2x + 1 = 6 + 1$

$(x-1)^2 = 7$

$x - 1 = \pm\sqrt{7}$

$x = 1 \pm \sqrt{7}$

The solution set is $\left\{1 \pm \sqrt{7}\right\}$.

37. $(x+2)(x-3) = 1$

$x^2 - x - 6 = 1$

$x^2 - x = 7$

The coefficient of x is -1. Divide this by 2 and square the result.

$\left(\dfrac{-1}{2}\right)^2 = \dfrac{1}{4}$

Add $\dfrac{1}{4}$ to both sides of the equation.

$x^2 - x + \dfrac{1}{4} = 7 + \dfrac{1}{4}$

$\left(x - \dfrac{1}{2}\right)^2 = \dfrac{29}{4}$

$x - \dfrac{1}{2} = \pm\sqrt{\dfrac{29}{4}}$

$x = \dfrac{1}{2} \pm \dfrac{\sqrt{29}}{2} = \dfrac{1 \pm \sqrt{29}}{2}$

The solution set is $\left\{\dfrac{1 \pm \sqrt{29}}{2}\right\}$.

39. $x^2 + 4bx = 5b^2$

The coefficient on x is $4b$. Divide this by 2 and square the result.

$\left(\dfrac{4b}{2}\right)^2 = (2b)^2 = 4b^2$

Add $4b^2$ to both sides of the equation:

$x^2 + 4bx + 4b^2 = 5b^2 + 4b^2$

$(x + 2b)^2 = 9b^2$

$x + 2b = \pm\sqrt{9b^2}$

$x = -2b \pm 3b$

$x = -2b - 3b$ or $x = -2b + 3b$

$= -5b$ $= b$

The solution set is $\left\{-5b, b\right\}$.

41. Answers will vary.

43. makes sense

45. makes sense

47. false; Changes to make the statement true will vary. A sample change is: Completing the square is a method used for changing a binomial into a perfect square trinomial.

49. false; Changes to make the statement true will vary. A sample change is: Although not every quadratic equation can be solved by factoring, they can all be solved by completing the square.

51. Half of -20 is -10, and $(-10)^2 = 100$. Therefore, the perfect square trinomial with middle term $-20x$ is $x^2 - 20x + 100$.

53. $x^2 + bx + c = 0$

Subtract c from both sides to isolate the binomial $x^2 + bx$.

$x^2 + bx = -c$

The coefficient of the x-term is b.

$\dfrac{1}{2}(b) = \dfrac{b}{2}$, and $\left(\dfrac{b}{2}\right)^2 = \dfrac{b^2}{4}$, so add $\dfrac{b^2}{4}$ to both sides.

$x^2 + bx + \dfrac{b^2}{4} = -c + \dfrac{b^2}{4}$

$\left(x + \dfrac{b}{2}\right)^2 = \dfrac{-4c}{4} - \dfrac{b^2}{4}$

$\left(x + \dfrac{b}{2}\right)^2 = \dfrac{b^2 - 4c}{4}$

$\dfrac{x + b}{2} = \sqrt{\dfrac{b^2 - 4c}{4}}$

$x + \dfrac{b}{2} = \dfrac{\sqrt{b^2 - 4c}}{2}$

$x = -\dfrac{b}{2} + \dfrac{\sqrt{b^2 - 4c}}{2} = \dfrac{-b + \sqrt{b^2 - 4c}}{2}$

or

$\dfrac{x + b}{2} = -\sqrt{\dfrac{b^2 - 4c}{4}}$

$x + \dfrac{b}{2} = -\dfrac{\sqrt{b^2 - 4c}}{2}$

$x = -\dfrac{b}{2} - \dfrac{\sqrt{b^2 - 4c}}{2} = \dfrac{-b - \sqrt{b^2 - 4c}}{2}$

The solution set is $\left\{\dfrac{-b \pm \sqrt{b^2 - 4c}}{2}\right\}$.

Note: If terms are not combined on the right and the radical is not simplified, the solutions will be written in a different, but equivalent form:

$\left\{-\dfrac{b}{2} \pm \sqrt{\dfrac{b^2}{4} - c}\right\}$.

55. $\dfrac{2x + 3}{x^2 - 7x + 12} - \dfrac{2}{x - 3}$

$= \dfrac{2x + 3}{(x-3)(x-4)} - \dfrac{2}{x-3}$

$= \dfrac{2x + 3}{(x-3)(x-4)} - \dfrac{2(x-4)}{(x-3)(x-4)}$

$= \dfrac{(2x-3) - 2(x-4)}{(x-3)(x-4)}$

$= \dfrac{2x + 3 - 2x + 8}{(x-3)(x-4)}$

$= \dfrac{11}{(x-3)(x-4)}$

56. $\dfrac{x - \dfrac{1}{3}}{3 - \dfrac{1}{x}}$

LCD $= 3x$

$\dfrac{x - \dfrac{1}{3}}{3 - \dfrac{1}{x}} = \dfrac{3x}{3x} \cdot \dfrac{\left(x - \dfrac{1}{3}\right)}{\left(3 - \dfrac{1}{x}\right)}$

$= \dfrac{3x \cdot x - 3x \cdot \dfrac{1}{3}}{3x \cdot 3 - 3x \cdot \dfrac{1}{x}}$

$= \dfrac{3x^2 - x}{9x - 3}$

$= \dfrac{x(3x - 1)}{3(3x - 1)}$

$= \dfrac{x}{3}$

57. $\sqrt{2x+3} = 2x-3$

Square both sides and solve for x:

$$\left(\sqrt{2x+3}\right)^2 = (2x-3)^2$$

$$2x+3 = (2x)^2 - 2\cdot 2x\cdot 3 + 3^2$$

$$2x+3 = 4x^2 - 12x + 9$$

$$0 = 4x^2 - 14x + 6$$

$$0 = 2\left(2x^2 - 7x + 3\right)$$

$$0 = 2(2x-1)(x-3)$$

$$2x-1 = 0 \quad \text{or} \quad x-3 = 0$$

$$x = \frac{1}{2} \qquad\qquad x = 3$$

Each of the proposed solutions must be checked in the original equation.

Check $\dfrac{1}{2}$: $\sqrt{2x+3} = 2x-3$

$$\sqrt{2\left(\frac{1}{2}\right)+3} = 2\left(\frac{1}{2}\right)-3$$

$$\sqrt{1+3} = 1-3$$

$$= \sqrt{4} = 1-3$$

$$2 = -2, \text{ false}$$

Check 3: $\sqrt{2x+3} = 2x-3$

$$\sqrt{2\cdot 3+3} = 2\cdot 3-3$$

$$\sqrt{6+3} = 6-3$$

$$\sqrt{9} = 3$$

$$3 = 3, \text{ true}$$

Thus, $\dfrac{1}{2}$ is an extraneous solution. The solution set is $\{3\}$.

58. $\dfrac{-b \pm \sqrt{b^2-4ac}}{2a} = \dfrac{-(9) \pm \sqrt{(9)^2 - 4(2)(-5)}}{2(2)}$

$$= \frac{-9 \pm \sqrt{81+40}}{4}$$

$$= \frac{-9 \pm \sqrt{121}}{4}$$

$$= \frac{-9 \pm 11}{4}$$

$$= \frac{-9+11}{4} \quad \text{or} \quad \frac{-9-11}{4}$$

$$= \frac{2}{4} \quad \text{or} \quad \frac{-20}{4}$$

$$= \frac{1}{2} \quad \text{or} \quad -5$$

59. $\dfrac{-b \pm \sqrt{b^2-4ac}}{2a} = \dfrac{-(-12) \pm \sqrt{(-12)^2 - 4(9)(4)}}{2(9)}$

$$= \frac{12 \pm \sqrt{144-144}}{18}$$

$$= \frac{12 \pm \sqrt{0}}{18}$$

$$= \frac{12 \pm 0}{18}$$

$$= \frac{12}{18}$$

$$= \frac{2}{3}$$

60. $\dfrac{-b \pm \sqrt{b^2-4ac}}{2a} = \dfrac{-(-2) \pm \sqrt{(-2)^2 - 4(1)(-6)}}{2(1)}$

$$= \frac{2 \pm \sqrt{4+24}}{2(1)}$$

$$= \frac{2 \pm \sqrt{28}}{2}$$

$$= \frac{2 \pm 2\sqrt{7}}{2}$$

$$= \frac{2(1 \pm \sqrt{7})}{2}$$

$$= 1 \pm \sqrt{7}$$

10.3 Check Points

1. $8x^2 + 2x - 1 = 0$

Identify the values of $a, b,$ and c:

$a = 8, b = 2,$ and $c = -1$.

Substitute these values into the quadratic formula and simplify to get the equation's solutions.

$$x = \frac{-b \pm \sqrt{b^2-4ac}}{2a}$$

$$x = \frac{-2 \pm \sqrt{2^2 - 4(8)(-1)}}{2(8)}$$

$$= \frac{-2 \pm \sqrt{4+32}}{16} = \frac{-2 \pm \sqrt{36}}{16} = \frac{-2 \pm 6}{16}$$

$$x = \frac{-2+6}{16} \quad \text{or} \quad x = \frac{-2-6}{16}$$

$$= \frac{4}{16} = \frac{1}{4} \qquad\qquad = \frac{-8}{16} = -\frac{1}{2}$$

The solution set is $\left\{-\dfrac{1}{2}, \dfrac{1}{4}\right\}$.

2.
$$x^2 = 6x - 4$$

$x^2 - 6x + 4 = 0$
Identify the values of $a, b,$ and c:
$a = 1, b = -6,$ and $c = 4.$
Substitute these values into the quadratic formula and simplify to get the equation's solutions.

$$x = \frac{-b \pm \sqrt{b^2 - 4ac}}{2a}$$

$$x = \frac{-(-6) \pm \sqrt{(-6)^2 - 4(1)(4)}}{2(1)}$$

$$= \frac{6 \pm \sqrt{36 - 16}}{2}$$

$$= \frac{6 \pm \sqrt{20}}{2}$$

$$= \frac{6 \pm 2\sqrt{5}}{2}$$

$$= 3 \pm \sqrt{5}$$

The solution set is $\left\{3 \pm \sqrt{5}\right\}.$

3.
$$p = 0.004x^2 - 0.37x + 14.1$$

$25 = 0.004x^2 - 0.37x + 14.1$

$0 = 0.004x^2 - 0.37x - 10.9$
Identify the values of $a, b,$ and c:
$a = 0.004, b = -0.37,$ and $c = -10.9.$
Substitute these values into the quadratic formula and simplify to get the equation's solutions.

$$x = \frac{-b \pm \sqrt{b^2 - 4ac}}{2a}$$

$$x = \frac{-(-0.37) \pm \sqrt{(-0.37)^2 - 4(0.004)(-10.9)}}{2(0.004)}$$

$$\approx -23 \ \text{or} \ 116$$

Reject the negative solution to the quadratic equation because the time cannot be negative. 25% of the United States population will be foreign-born 116 years after 1920, or 2036.

10.3 Exercise Set

1. $x^2 + 5x + 6 = 0$
Identify the values of $a, b,$ and c:
$a = 1, b = 5,$ and $c = 6.$
Substitute these values into the quadratic formula and simplify to get the equation's solutions.

$$x = \frac{-b \pm \sqrt{b^2 - 4ac}}{2a}$$

$$x = \frac{5 \pm \sqrt{5^2 - 4(1)(6)}}{2(1)}$$

$$= \frac{5 \pm \sqrt{25 - 24}}{2} = \frac{5 \pm \sqrt{1}}{2} = \frac{-5 \pm 1}{2}$$

$$x = \frac{-5 + 1}{2} \qquad \text{or} \ \ x = \frac{-5 - 1}{2}$$

$$= \frac{-4}{2} = -2 \qquad \qquad = \frac{-6}{2} = -3$$

The solution set is $\{-3, -2\}.$

3. $x^2 + 5x + 3 = 0$

$a = 1, b = 5, c = 3$

$$x = \frac{-b \pm \sqrt{b^2 - 4ac}}{2a}$$

$$x = \frac{-5 \pm \sqrt{5^2 - 4(1)(3)}}{2 \cdot 1}$$

$$x = \frac{-5 \pm \sqrt{25 - 12}}{2}$$

$$= \frac{-5 \pm \sqrt{13}}{2}$$

The solution set is $\left\{\dfrac{-5 \pm \sqrt{13}}{2}\right\}.$

5. $x^2 + 4x - 6 = 0$

$a = 1, b = 4, c = -6$

$x = \dfrac{-b \pm \sqrt{b^2 - 4ac}}{2a}$

$x = \dfrac{-4 \pm \sqrt{4^2 - 4(1)(-6)}}{2 \cdot 1}$

$= \dfrac{-4 \pm \sqrt{16 + 24}}{2}$

$= \dfrac{-4 \pm \sqrt{40}}{2}$

$= \dfrac{-4 \pm 2\sqrt{10}}{2}$

$= \dfrac{2\left(-2 \pm \sqrt{10}\right)}{2}$

$= -2 \pm \sqrt{10}$

The solution set is $\left\{-2 \pm \sqrt{10}\right\}$.

7. $x^2 + 4x - 7 = 0$

$a = 1, b = 4, c = -7$

$x = \dfrac{-b \pm \sqrt{b^2 - 4ac}}{2a}$

$= \dfrac{-4 \pm \sqrt{4^2 - 4(1)(-7)}}{2 \cdot 1}$

$= \dfrac{-4 \pm \sqrt{16 + 28}}{2}$

$= \dfrac{-4 \pm \sqrt{44}}{2}$

$= \dfrac{-4 \pm 2\sqrt{11}}{2}$

$= \dfrac{2\left(-2 \pm \sqrt{11}\right)}{2}$

$= -2 \pm \sqrt{11}$

The solution set is $\left\{-2 \pm \sqrt{11}\right\}$.

9. $x^2 - 3x - 18 = 0$

$a = 1, b = -3, c = -18$

$x = \dfrac{-b \pm \sqrt{b^2 - 4ac}}{2a}$

$= \dfrac{-(-3) \pm \sqrt{(-3)^2 - 4(1)(-18)}}{2 \cdot 1}$

$= \dfrac{3 \pm \sqrt{9 + 72}}{2}$

$= \dfrac{3 \pm \sqrt{81}}{2}$

$= \dfrac{3 \pm 9}{2}$

$x = \dfrac{3 + 9}{2}$ or $x = \dfrac{3 - 9}{2}$

$x = \dfrac{12}{2} = 6$ or $x = \dfrac{-6}{2} = -3$

The solution set is $\left\{-3, 6\right\}$.

11. $6x^2 - 5x - 6 = 0$

$a = 6, b = -5, c = -6$

$x = \dfrac{-b \pm \sqrt{b^2 - 4ac}}{2a}$

$= \dfrac{-(-5) \pm \sqrt{(-5)^2 - 4(6)(-6)}}{2 \cdot 6}$

$= \dfrac{5 \pm \sqrt{25 + 144}}{12}$

$= \dfrac{5 \pm \sqrt{169}}{12} = \dfrac{5 \pm 13}{12}$

$x = \dfrac{5 + 13}{12}$ or $x = \dfrac{5 - 13}{12}$

$x = \dfrac{18}{12} = \dfrac{3}{2}$ or $x = \dfrac{-8}{12} = -\dfrac{2}{3}$

The solution set is $\left\{-\dfrac{2}{3}, \dfrac{3}{2}\right\}$.

13. $x^2 - 2x - 10 = 0$

$a = 1, b = -2, c = -10$

$$x = \frac{-b \pm \sqrt{b^2 - 4ac}}{2a}$$

$$= \frac{-(-2) \pm \sqrt{(-2)^2 - 4(1)(-10)}}{2 \cdot 1}$$

$$= \frac{2 \pm \sqrt{4 + 40}}{2} = \frac{2 \pm \sqrt{44}}{2}$$

$$= \frac{2 \pm 2\sqrt{11}}{2}$$

$$= \frac{2(1 \pm \sqrt{11})}{2}$$

$$= 1 \pm \sqrt{11}$$

The solution set is $\left\{ 1 \pm \sqrt{11} \right\}$.

15. $x^2 - x = 14$

Rewrite the equation in standard form.
Identify *a*, *b*, and *c*.

$a = 1, b = -1, c = -14$

Substitute these values into the quadratic formula.

$$x = \frac{-b \pm \sqrt{b^2 - 4ac}}{2a}$$

$$= \frac{-(-1) \pm \sqrt{(-1)^2 - 4(1)(-14)}}{2 \cdot 1}$$

$$= \frac{1 \pm \sqrt{1 + 56}}{2} = \frac{1 \pm \sqrt{57}}{2}$$

The radical cannot be simplified.

The solution set is $\left\{ \dfrac{1 \pm \sqrt{57}}{2} \right\}$.

17. $6x^2 + 6x + 1 = 0$

$a = 6, b = 6, c = 1$

$$x = \frac{-b \pm \sqrt{b^2 - 4ac}}{2a}$$

$$= \frac{-6 \pm \sqrt{6^2 - 4(6)(1)}}{2 \cdot 6}$$

$$= \frac{-6 \pm \sqrt{36 - 24}}{12} = \frac{-6 \pm \sqrt{12}}{12}$$

$$= \frac{-6 \pm 2\sqrt{3}}{12} = \frac{2(-3 \pm \sqrt{3})}{12}$$

$$= \frac{-3 \pm \sqrt{3}}{6}$$

The solution set is $\left\{ \dfrac{-3 \pm \sqrt{3}}{6} \right\}$.

19. $9x^2 - 12x + 4 = 0$

$a = 9, b = -12, c = 4$

$$x = \frac{-b \pm \sqrt{b^2 - 4ac}}{2a}$$

$$= \frac{-(-12) \pm \sqrt{(-12)^2 - 4(9)(4)}}{2 \cdot 9}$$

$$= \frac{12 \pm \sqrt{144 - 144}}{18} = \frac{12 \pm \sqrt{0}}{18}$$

$$= \frac{12 \pm 0}{18} = \frac{12}{18}$$

$$= \frac{2}{3}$$

The solution set is $\left\{ \dfrac{2}{3} \right\}$.

21. $4x^2 = 2x + 7$

Rewrite the equation in standard form.

$4x^2 - 2x - 7 = 0$

$a = 4, b = -2, c = -7$

$x = \dfrac{-b \pm \sqrt{b^2 - 4ac}}{2a}$

$= \dfrac{-(-2) \pm \sqrt{(-2)^2 - 4(4)(-7)}}{2 \cdot 4}$

$= \dfrac{2 \pm \sqrt{4 + 112}}{8} = \dfrac{2 \pm \sqrt{116}}{8}$

$= \dfrac{2 \pm 2\sqrt{29}}{8} = \dfrac{2\left(1 \pm \sqrt{29}\right)}{8}$

$= \dfrac{1 \pm \sqrt{29}}{4}$

The solution set is $\left\{ \dfrac{1 \pm \sqrt{29}}{4} \right\}$.

23. $2x^2 - x = 1$

Write the equation in standard form.

$2x^2 - x - 1 = 0$

Factor the trinomial.

$(2x + 1)(x - 1) = 0$

Use the zero-product property.

$2x + 1 = 0 \quad$ or $\quad x - 1 = 0$

$\quad 2x = -1 \qquad\qquad x = 1$

$\quad\quad x = -\dfrac{1}{2}$

The solution set is $\left\{ -\dfrac{1}{2}, 1 \right\}$.

25. $5x^2 + 2 = 11x$

Write the equation in standard form.

$5x^2 - 11x + 2 = 0$

Factor the trinomial.

$(5x - 1)(x - 2) = 0$

Use the zero-product property.

$5x - 1 = 0 \quad$ or $\quad x - 2 = 0$

$\quad 5x = 1 \qquad\qquad x = 2$

$\quad\quad x = \dfrac{1}{5}$

The solution set is $\left\{ \dfrac{1}{5}, 2 \right\}$.

27. $3x^2 = 60$

$x^2 = 20$

Use the square root property.

$x = \sqrt{20} \quad$ or $\quad x = -\sqrt{20}$

$x = 2\sqrt{5} \qquad x = -2\sqrt{5}$

The solution set is $\left\{ \pm 2\sqrt{5} \right\}$.

29. $x^2 - 2x = 1$

Write the equation in standard form.

$x^2 - 2x - 1 = 0$

The trinomial is prime, so we cannot factor and use the zero-product property. Instead, use the quadratic formula with $a = 1, b = -2, c = -1$

$x = \dfrac{-b \pm \sqrt{b^2 - 4ac}}{2a}$

$= \dfrac{-(-2) \pm \sqrt{(-2)^2 - 4(1)(-1)}}{2 \cdot 1}$

$= \dfrac{2 \pm \sqrt{4 + 4}}{2} = \dfrac{2 \pm \sqrt{8}}{2}$

$= \dfrac{2 \pm 2\sqrt{2}}{2} = \dfrac{2\left(1 \pm \sqrt{2}\right)}{2}$

$= 1 \pm \sqrt{2}$

The solution set is $\left\{ 1 \pm \sqrt{2} \right\}$.

31. $(2x + 3)(x + 4) = 1$

Write the equation in standard form.

$2x^2 + 11x + 12 = 1$

$2x^2 + 11x + 11 = 0$

The trinomial cannot be factored, so use the quadratic formula with $a = 2, b = 11, c = 11$.

$x = \dfrac{-b \pm \sqrt{b^2 - 4ac}}{2a}$

$= \dfrac{-11 \pm \sqrt{11^2 - 4(2)(11)}}{2 \cdot 2}$

$= \dfrac{-11 \pm \sqrt{121 - 88}}{4}$

$= \dfrac{-11 \pm \sqrt{33}}{4}$

The solution set is $\left\{ \dfrac{-11 \pm \sqrt{33}}{4} \right\}$.

33. $(3x-4)^2 = 16$

Use the square root property.

$3x-4 = \sqrt{16}$ or $3x-4 = -\sqrt{16}$

$3x-4 = 4$ $\qquad$ $3x-4 = -4$

$3x = 8$ $\qquad\qquad$ $3x = 0$

$x = \dfrac{8}{3}$ $\qquad\qquad$ $x = 0$

The solution set is $\left\{0, \dfrac{8}{3}\right\}$.

35. $3x^2 - 12x + 12 = 0$

$3\left(x^2 - 4x + 4\right) = 0$

$3(x-2)^2 = 0$

$(x-2)^2 = 0$

$x-2 = 0$

$x = 2$

The solution set is $\{2\}$.

37. $4x^2 - 16 = 0$

$4\left(x^2 - 4\right) = 0$

$4(x+2)(x-2) = 0$

$x+2 = 0$ or $x-2 = 0$

$x = -2$ $\qquad$ $x = 2$

The solution set is $\{-2, 2\}$.

39. $x^2 + 9x = 0$

$x(x+9) = 0$

$x = 0$ or $x+9 = 0$

$\qquad\qquad$ $x = -9$

The solution set is $\{-9, 0\}$.

41. $\dfrac{3}{4}x^2 - \dfrac{5}{2}x - 2 = 0$

To clear fractions, multiply both sides by the LCD, 4.

$4\left(\dfrac{3}{4}x^2 - \dfrac{5}{2}x - 2\right) = 4 \cdot 0$

$3x^2 - 10x - 8 = 0$

$(3x+2)(x-4) = 0$

$3x+2 = 0$ $\qquad$ or $x-4 = 0$

$3x = -2$ $\qquad\qquad$ $x = 4$

$x = -\dfrac{2}{3}$

The solution set is $\left\{-\dfrac{2}{3}, 4\right\}$.

43. $(3x-2)^2 = 10$

Use the square root property.

$3x-2 = \sqrt{10}$ $\qquad$ $3x-2 = -\sqrt{10}$

$3x = 2+\sqrt{10}$ or $\quad 3x = 2-\sqrt{10}$

$x = \dfrac{2+\sqrt{10}}{3}$ $\qquad$ $x = \dfrac{2-\sqrt{10}}{3}$

The solution set is $\left\{\dfrac{2 \pm \sqrt{10}}{3}\right\}$.

45. $\dfrac{x^2}{x+7} - \dfrac{3}{x+7} = 0$

Multiply both sides by the LCD, $x+7$.

$x^2 - 3 = 0$

$x^2 = 3$

$x = \pm\sqrt{3}$

The solution set is $\left\{\pm\sqrt{3}\right\}$.

47. $(x+2)^2 + x(x+1) = 4$

$x^2 + 4x + 4 + x^2 + x = 4$

$2x^2 + 5x = 0$

$x(2x+5) = 0$

$x = 0$ or $2x+5 = 0$

$\qquad\qquad$ $2x = -5$

$\qquad\qquad$ $x = -\dfrac{5}{2}$

The solution set is $\left\{-\dfrac{5}{2}, 0\right\}$.

49. $2x^2 - 9x - 3 = 9 - 9x$

$$2x^2 - 12 = 0$$

$$x^2 - 6 = 0$$

$$x^2 = 6$$

$$x = \pm\sqrt{6}$$

The solution set is $\left\{\pm\sqrt{6}\right\}$.

51. $\dfrac{1}{x} + \dfrac{1}{x+3} = \dfrac{1}{4}$

Multiply both sides by the LCD, $4x(x+3)$.

$$4x(x+3)\left(\frac{1}{x} + \frac{1}{x+3}\right) = 4x(x+3)\frac{1}{4}$$

$$4(x+3) + 4x = x(x+3)$$

$$4x + 12 + 4x = x^2 + 3x$$

$$0 = x^2 - 5x - 12$$

Use the quadratic formula with $a = 1$, $b = -5$, and $c = -12$.

$$x = \frac{-(-5) \pm \sqrt{(-5)^2 - 4(1)(-12)}}{2(1)}$$

$$= \frac{5 \pm \sqrt{25 + 48}}{2}$$

$$= \frac{5 \pm \sqrt{73}}{2}$$

The solution set is $\left\{\dfrac{5 \pm \sqrt{73}}{2}\right\}$.

53. $h = -16t^2 + 60t + 4$

$$0 = -16t^2 + 60t + 4$$

$$16t^2 - 60t - 4 = 0$$

$$4\left(4t^2 - 15t - 1\right) = 0$$

$$4t^2 - 15t - 1 = 0$$

Note: Dividing both sides by 4 is not necessary, but it results in smaller numbers to be substituted in the quadratic formula.

$$a = 4, b = -15, c = -1$$

$$t = \frac{-b \pm \sqrt{b^2 - 4ac}}{2a}$$

$$= \frac{-(-15) \pm \sqrt{(-15)^2 - 4(4)(-1)}}{2(4)}$$

$$= \frac{15 \pm \sqrt{225 + 16}}{8} = \frac{15 \pm \sqrt{241}}{8}$$

$$t = \frac{15 + \sqrt{241}}{8} \quad \text{or} \quad t = \frac{15 - \sqrt{241}}{8}$$

$$t \approx 3.8 \qquad \text{or} \quad t \approx -0.1$$

Reject the negative solution to the quadratic equation because the time cannot be negative. It will take about 3.8 seconds for the football to hit the ground.

55. $h = -0.05x^2 + 27$

$$22 = -0.05x^2 + 27$$

$$-5 = -0.05x^2$$

$$\frac{-5}{-0.05} = \frac{-0.05x^2}{-0.05}$$

$$100 = x^2$$

$$\sqrt{100} = x$$

$$10 = x$$

The arch is 22 feet high at a point that is 10 feet to the right of the center.

57. a. 2006 is 18 years after 1988. Substitute 18 for x.

$$N = -0.095x^2 + 1.74x + 60$$

$$N = -0.095(18)^2 + 1.74(18) + 60 \approx 60.5$$

According to the model, there were 60.5 million visitors to national parks in 2006.
This overestimates the actual number displayed in the bar graph by 0.1 million.

b. $N = -0.095x^2 + 1.74x + 60$

$$41 = -0.095x^2 + 1.74x + 60$$

$$0 = -0.095x^2 + 1.74x + 19$$

$$a = -0.095, b = 1.74, c = 19$$

$$x = \frac{-b \pm \sqrt{b^2 - 4ac}}{2a}$$

$$x = \frac{-(1.74) \pm \sqrt{(1.74)^2 - 4(-0.095)(19)}}{2(-0.095)}$$

$$x \approx -8 \quad \text{or} \quad x \approx 26$$

Reject the negative solution to the quadratic equation because the time cannot be negative. If trends continue, there will be 41 million visitors to national parks 26 years after 1988, in 2014.

59. Let x = the width of the rectangle.
Then $x+3$ = the length.

$$A = l2$$
$$36 = (x+3) \cdot x$$
$$36 = x^2 + 3x$$
$$0 = x^2 + 3x - 36$$
$$a = 1, b = 3, c = -36$$
$$x = \frac{-b \pm \sqrt{b^2 - 4ac}}{2a}$$
$$= \frac{-3 \pm \sqrt{(-3)^2 - 4(1)(-36)}}{2 \cdot 1}$$
$$= \frac{-3 \pm \sqrt{9 + 144}}{2} = \frac{-3 \pm \sqrt{153}}{2}$$
$$x = \frac{-3 + \sqrt{153}}{2} \quad \text{or} \quad x = \frac{-3 - \sqrt{153}}{2}$$
$$x \approx 4.7 \qquad\qquad x \approx -7.7$$

Reject the negative solution of the quadratic equation because the width cannot be negative. If x = 4.7, then $x+3$ = 7.7. Thus, to the nearest tenth of a meter, the width is 4.7 meters and the length is 7.7 meters.

61. Let x = the length of the shorter leg.
Then $x+1$ = the length of the longer leg.
Use the Pythagorean Theorem.

$$x^2 + (x+1) = 4^2$$
$$x^2 + x^2 + 2x + 1 = 16$$
$$2x^2 + 2x - 15 = 0$$

Solve using the quadratic formula.
$$a = 2, b = 2, c = -15$$
$$x = \frac{-2 \pm \sqrt{2^2 - 4(2)(-15)}}{2 \cdot 2}$$
$$= \frac{2 \pm \sqrt{4 + 120}}{4}$$
$$= \frac{2 \pm \sqrt{124}}{4}$$
$$x = \frac{-2 + \sqrt{124}}{4} \quad \text{or} \quad x = \frac{-2 - \sqrt{124}}{4}$$
$$x \approx 2.3 \qquad\qquad x \approx -3.3$$

The length of a leg cannot be negative, so reject -3.3. If x = 2.3, then $x+1$ = 3.3. Thus, to the nearest tenth of a foot, the lengths of the legs are 2.3 feet and 3.3 feet.

63. Set the two formulas equal to each other and solve for A.

$$\frac{DA}{A+12} = \frac{D(A+1)}{24}$$
$$24DA = D(A+1)(A+12)$$
$$24A = (A+1)(A+12)$$
$$24A = A^2 + 13A + 12$$
$$0 = A^2 - 11A + 12$$

Solve using the quadratic formula.
$$A = \frac{-(-11) \pm \sqrt{(-11)^2 - 4(1)(12)}}{2(1)}$$
$$= \frac{11 \pm \sqrt{121 - 48}}{2} = \frac{11 \pm \sqrt{73}}{2}$$
$$A \approx 9.8 \quad \text{or} \quad A \approx 1.2$$

Discard 1.2 since this age is too young for the formulas to apply. The two formulas give the same child's dosage for a child that is about 9.8 years old.

65. – 67. Answers will vary.

69. does not make sense; Explanations will vary. Sample explanation: The factoring method would be quicker.

71. does not make sense; Explanations will vary. Sample explanation: The expression cannot be simplified because 2 is not a factor of 3.

73. false; Changes to make the statement true will vary.
A sample change is: $\dfrac{4 \pm \sqrt{3}}{2}$ cannot be simplified.

75. true

77. $x^2 + 2\sqrt{3}x - 9 = 0$

Here, the coefficient of the x-term is an irrational number. The quadratic formula can still be used.

$a = 1, b = 2\sqrt{3}, c = -9$

$x = \dfrac{-b \pm \sqrt{b^2 - 4ac}}{2a}$

$= \dfrac{-2\sqrt{3} \pm \sqrt{\left(2\sqrt{3}\right)^2 - 4(1)(-9)}}{2 \cdot 1}$

$= \dfrac{-2\sqrt{3} \pm \sqrt{12 + 36}}{2} = \dfrac{-2\sqrt{3} \pm \sqrt{48}}{2}$

$= \dfrac{-2\sqrt{3} \pm 4\sqrt{3}}{2}$

$x = \dfrac{-2\sqrt{3} + 4\sqrt{3}}{2}$ or $= \dfrac{-2\sqrt{3} - 4\sqrt{3}}{2}$

$= \dfrac{2\sqrt{3}}{2} = \sqrt{3}$ $= \dfrac{-6\sqrt{3}}{2} = -3\sqrt{3}$

The solution set is $\left\{-3\sqrt{3}, \sqrt{3}\right\}$.

79. $y = -16x^2 + 60x + 4$

To find when the football hits the ground, we need to solve $0 = -16x^2 + 60x + 4$.

From the graph, we see that the football will hit the ground after about 3.8 seconds which matches with the solution for Exercise 53.

81. $125^{-\frac{2}{3}} = \dfrac{1}{125^{\frac{2}{3}}} = \dfrac{1}{\left(\sqrt[3]{125}\right)^2}$

$= \dfrac{1}{5^2} = \dfrac{1}{25}$

82. To rationalize the denominator, multiply numerator and denominator by the conjugate of the denominator.

$\dfrac{12}{3 + \sqrt{5}} = \dfrac{12}{3 + \sqrt{5}} \cdot \dfrac{3 - \sqrt{5}}{3 - \sqrt{5}}$

$= \dfrac{12\left(3 - \sqrt{5}\right)}{3^2 - \left(\sqrt{5}\right)^2}$

$= \dfrac{12\left(3 - \sqrt{5}\right)}{9 - 5}$

$= \dfrac{12\left(3 - \sqrt{5}\right)}{4}$

$= 3\left(3 - \sqrt{5}\right)$

$= 9 - 3\sqrt{5}$

83. $(x - y)\left(x^2 + xy + y^2\right)$

$= x\left(x^2 + xy + y^2\right) - y\left(x^2 + xy + y^2\right)$

$= x^3 + x^2 y + xy^2 - x^2 y - xy^2 - y^3$

$= x^3 - y^3$

84. No, squaring a real number cannot result in a negative number. Neither $\sqrt{-1}$ nor $\sqrt{-4}$ are real numbers.

85. a. $-\sqrt{4} = -2$, $\sqrt{1} = 1$

b. $-\sqrt{5}$, $\sqrt{5}$

c. $-\sqrt{5}$, $-\sqrt{4}$, $\sqrt{1}$, $\sqrt{5}$

d. $\sqrt{-1}$, $\sqrt{-4}$

86. a. $-\sqrt{9} = -3$, $\sqrt{0} = 0$, $\sqrt{9} = 3$

b. $-\sqrt{7}$, $\sqrt{7}$

c. $-\sqrt{9}$, $-\sqrt{7}$, $\sqrt{0}$, $\sqrt{7}$, $\sqrt{9}$

d. $\sqrt{-9}$, $\sqrt{-7}$

Mid-Chapter Check Point

1. $(3x-2)^2 = 100$

$$3x - 2 = \pm\sqrt{100}$$

$$3x - 2 = \pm 10$$

$$3x = 2 \pm 10$$

$$x = \frac{2 \pm 10}{3}$$

$$x = \frac{2+10}{3} = 4 \quad \text{or} \quad x = \frac{2-10}{3} = -\frac{8}{3}$$

The solution set is $\left\{-\dfrac{8}{3}, 4\right\}$.

2. $15x^2 = 5x$

$$15x^2 - 5x = 0$$

$$5x(3x-1) = 0$$

$$5x = 0 \quad \text{or} \quad 3x - 1 = 0$$

$$x = 0 \qquad\qquad 3x = 1$$

$$x = \frac{1}{3}$$

The solution set is $\left\{0, \dfrac{1}{3}\right\}$.

3. $x^2 - 2x - 10 = 0$

$a = 1, b = -2, c = -10$

$$x = \frac{-(-2) \pm \sqrt{(-2)^2 - 4(1)(-10)}}{2(1)}$$

$$= \frac{2 \pm \sqrt{4+40}}{2} = \frac{2 \pm \sqrt{44}}{2}$$

$$= \frac{2 \pm 2\sqrt{11}}{2} = 1 \pm \sqrt{11}$$

The solution set is $\left\{1 \pm \sqrt{11}\right\}$.

4. $x^2 - 8x + 16 = 7$

$$x^2 - 8x + 9 = 0$$

$a = 1, b = -8, c = 9$

$$x = \frac{-(-8) \pm \sqrt{(-8)^2 - 4(1)(9)}}{2(1)}$$

$$= \frac{8 \pm \sqrt{64-36}}{2} = \frac{8 \pm \sqrt{28}}{2}$$

$$= \frac{8 \pm 2\sqrt{7}}{2} = 4 \pm \sqrt{7}$$

The solution set is $\left\{4 \pm \sqrt{7}\right\}$.

5. $3x^2 - x - 2 = 0$

$$(3x+2)(x-1) = 0$$

$$3x + 2 = 0 \quad \text{or} \quad x - 1 = 0$$

$$3x = -2 \qquad\qquad x = 1$$

$$x = -\frac{2}{3}$$

The solution set is $\left\{-\dfrac{2}{3}, 1\right\}$.

6. $6x^2 = 10x - 3$

$$6x^2 - 10x + 3 = 0$$

$a = 6, b = -10, c = 3$

$$x = \frac{-(-10) \pm \sqrt{(-10)^2 - 4(6)(3)}}{2(6)}$$

$$= \frac{10 \pm \sqrt{100-72}}{12} = \frac{10 \pm \sqrt{28}}{12}$$

$$= \frac{10 \pm 2\sqrt{7}}{12} = \frac{5 \pm \sqrt{7}}{6}$$

The solution set is $\left\{\dfrac{5 \pm \sqrt{7}}{6}\right\}$.

7. $x^2 + (x+1)^2 = 25$

$$x^2 + x^2 + 2x + 1 = 25$$

$$2x^2 + 2x - 24 = 0$$

$$x^2 + x - 12 = 0$$

$$(x+4)(x-3) = 0$$

$$x + 4 = 0 \quad \text{or} \quad x - 3 = 0$$

$$x = -4 \qquad\qquad x = 3$$

The solution set is $\left\{-4, 3\right\}$.

8. $(x+5)^2 = 40$

$$x + 5 = \pm\sqrt{40}$$

$$x + 5 = \pm 2\sqrt{10}$$

$$x = -5 \pm 2\sqrt{10}$$

The solution set is $\left\{-5 \pm 2\sqrt{10}\right\}$.

9. $2\left(x^2-8\right)=11-x^2$

$2x^2-16=11-x^2$

$3x^2=27$

$x^2=9$

$x=\pm\sqrt{9}$

$x=\pm3$

The solution set is $\{\pm3\}$.

10. $2x^2+5x+1=0$

$a=2$, $b=5$, $c=1$

$x=\dfrac{-5\pm\sqrt{5^2-4(2)(1)}}{2(2)}$

$=\dfrac{-5\pm\sqrt{25-8}}{4}=\dfrac{-5\pm\sqrt{17}}{4}$

The solution set is $\left\{\dfrac{-5\pm\sqrt{17}}{4}\right\}$.

11. $(x-8)(2x-3)=34$

$2x^2-16x-3x+24=34$

$2x^2-19x-10=0$

$(2x+1)(x-10)=0$

$2x+1=0$ or $x-10=0$

$2x=-1$ $x=10$

$x=-\dfrac{1}{2}$

The solution set is $\left\{-\dfrac{1}{2},10\right\}$.

12. $x+\dfrac{16}{x}=8$

Multiply both sides of the equation by x.

$x\left(x+\dfrac{16}{x}\right)=x(8)$

$x^2+16=8x$

$x^2-8x+16=0$

$(x-4)^2=0$

$x=4$

The solution set is $\{4\}$.

13. $x^2+14x-32=0$

$x^2+14x=32$

The coefficient on x is 14. Divide this by 2 and square the result.

$\left(\dfrac{14}{2}\right)^2=7^2=49$

Add 49 to both sides.

$x^2+14x+49=32+49$

$(x+7)^2=81$

$x+7=\pm\sqrt{81}$

$x+7=\pm9$

$x=-7\pm9$

$x=-7+9=2$ or $x=-7-9=-16$

The solution set is $\{-16,2\}$.

14. Let a = the length of the missing side.

$a^2+6^2=8^2$

$a^2+36=64$

$a^2=28$

$a=\sqrt{28}=2\sqrt{7}$

The missing length is $2\sqrt{7}$ cm.

15. $d=\sqrt{\left(x_2-x_1\right)^2+\left(y_2-y_1\right)^2}$

$=\sqrt{\left(9-(-3)\right)^2+\left(-3-2\right)^2}$

$=\sqrt{\left(12\right)^2+\left(-5\right)^2}=\sqrt{144+25}$

$=\sqrt{169}=13$

The distance is 13 units.

16. $(4x)^2+(3x)^2=20^2$

$16x^2+9x^2=400$

$25x^2=400$

$x^2=16$

$x=\sqrt{16}$

$x=4$

$3x=12$

$4x=16$

The lengths of the legs are 12 inches and 16 inches.

10.4 Check Points

1. a. $\sqrt{-16} = \sqrt{16(-1)} = \sqrt{16}\sqrt{-1} = 4i$

b. $\sqrt{-5} = \sqrt{5(-1)} = \sqrt{5}\sqrt{-1} = i\sqrt{5}$

c. $\sqrt{-50} = \sqrt{50(-1)} = \sqrt{25 \cdot 2}\sqrt{-1} = 5i\sqrt{2}$

2. $(x+2)^2 = -25$

$\quad x+2 = \sqrt{-25} \qquad$ or $\qquad x+2 = -\sqrt{-25}$

$\quad x+2 = 5i \qquad\qquad\qquad x+2 = -5i$

$\qquad x = -2+5i \qquad\qquad\qquad x = -2-5i$

The solution set is $\{-2 \pm 5i\}$.

3. $x^2 + 6x + 13 = 0$

$\quad a=1, \ b=6, \ c=13$

$x = \dfrac{-b \pm \sqrt{b^2 - 4ac}}{2a}$

$\quad = \dfrac{-6 \pm \sqrt{6^2 - 4(1)(13)}}{2 \cdot 1}$

$\quad = \dfrac{-6 \pm \sqrt{36 - 52}}{2} = \dfrac{-6 \pm \sqrt{-16}}{2}$

$\quad = \dfrac{-6 \pm 4i}{2} = \dfrac{2(-3 \pm 2i)}{2}$

$\quad = -3 \pm 2i$

The solution set is $\{-3 \pm 2i\}$.

10.4 Exercise Set

1. $\sqrt{-36} = \sqrt{36(-1)} = \sqrt{36}\sqrt{-1} = 6i$

3. $\sqrt{-13} = \sqrt{13(-1)} = \sqrt{13}\sqrt{-1} = i\sqrt{13}$

5. $\sqrt{-50} = \sqrt{50(-1)} = \sqrt{25 \cdot 2}\sqrt{-1} = 5i\sqrt{2}$

7. $\sqrt{-20} = \sqrt{20(-1)} = \sqrt{4 \cdot 5}\sqrt{-1} = 2i\sqrt{5}$

9. $-\sqrt{-28} = -\sqrt{28(-1)}$

$\qquad = -\sqrt{4 \cdot 7}\sqrt{-1}$

$\qquad = -2i\sqrt{7}$

11. $7 + \sqrt{-16} = 7 + \sqrt{16}\sqrt{-1} = 7 + 4i$

13. $10 + \sqrt{-3} = 10 + \sqrt{3}\sqrt{-1} = 10 + i\sqrt{3}$

15. $6 - \sqrt{-98} = 6 - \sqrt{98}\sqrt{-1}$

$\qquad = 6 - \sqrt{49 \cdot 2}\sqrt{-1}$

$\qquad = 6 - 7i\sqrt{2}$

17. $(x-3)^2 = -9$

$\quad x-3 = \sqrt{-9} \qquad$ or $\qquad x-3 = -\sqrt{-9}$

$\quad x-3 = 3i \qquad\qquad\qquad x-3 = -3i$

$\qquad x = 3+3i \qquad\qquad\qquad x = 3-3i$

The solution set is $\{3 \pm 3i\}$.

19. $(x+7)^2 = -64$

$\quad x+7 = \sqrt{-64} \qquad$ or $\qquad x+7 = -\sqrt{-64}$

$\quad x+7 = 8i \qquad\qquad\qquad x+7 = -8i$

$\qquad x = -7+8i \qquad\qquad\qquad x = -7-8i$

The solution set is $\{-7 \pm 8i\}$.

21. $(x-2)^2 = -7$

$\quad x-2 = \sqrt{-7} \qquad$ or $\qquad x-2 = -\sqrt{-7}$

$\quad x-2 = i\sqrt{7} \qquad\qquad\qquad x-2 = -i\sqrt{7}$

$\qquad x = 2+i\sqrt{7} \qquad\qquad\qquad x = 2-i\sqrt{7}$

The solution set is $\{2 \pm i\sqrt{7}\}$.

23. $(y+3)^2 = -18$

$\quad x+3 = \sqrt{-18} \qquad$ or $\qquad x+3 = -\sqrt{-18}$

$\quad x+3 = 3i\sqrt{2} \qquad\qquad\qquad x+3 = -3i\sqrt{2}$

$\qquad x = -3+3i\sqrt{2} \qquad\qquad\qquad x = -3-3i\sqrt{2}$

The solution set is $\{-3 \pm 3i\sqrt{2}\}$.

25. $x^2 + 4x + 5 = 0$

$a = 1, b = 4, c = 5$

$x = \dfrac{-b \pm \sqrt{b^2 - 4ac}}{2a}$

$ = \dfrac{-4 \pm \sqrt{4^2 - 4(1)(5)}}{2 \cdot 1}$

$ = \dfrac{-4 \pm \sqrt{16 - 20}}{2} = \dfrac{-4 \pm \sqrt{-4}}{2}$

$ = \dfrac{-4 \pm 2i}{2} = \dfrac{2(-2 \pm i)}{2}$

$ = -2 \pm i$

The solution set is $\{-2 \pm i\}$.

27. $x^2 - 6x + 13 = 0$

$a = 1, b = -6, c = 13$

$x = \dfrac{-b \pm \sqrt{b^2 - 4ac}}{2a}$

$ = \dfrac{-(-6) \pm \sqrt{(-6)^2 - 4(1)(13)}}{2 \cdot 1}$

$ = \dfrac{6 \pm \sqrt{36 - 52}}{2} = \dfrac{6 \pm \sqrt{-16}}{2}$

$ = \dfrac{6 \pm 4i}{2} = \dfrac{2(3 \pm 2i)}{2}$

$ = 3 \pm 2i$

The solution set is $\{3 \pm 2i\}$.

29. $x^2 - 12x + 40 = 0$

$a = 1, b = -12, c = 40$

$x = \dfrac{-b \pm \sqrt{b^2 - 4ac}}{2a}$

$ = \dfrac{-(-12) \pm \sqrt{(-12)^2 - 4(1)(40)}}{2 \cdot 1}$

$ = \dfrac{12 \pm \sqrt{144 - 160}}{2} = \dfrac{12 \pm \sqrt{-16}}{2}$

$ = \dfrac{12 \pm 4i}{2} = \dfrac{2(6 \pm 2i)}{2}$

$ = 6 \pm 2i$

The solution set is $\{6 \pm 2i\}$.

31. $x^2 = 10x - 27$

Write the equation in standard form; then identify a, b, and c.

$x^2 - 10x + 27 = 0$

$a = 1, b = -10, c = 27$

$x = \dfrac{-b \pm \sqrt{b^2 - 4ac}}{2a}$

$ = \dfrac{-(-10) \pm \sqrt{(-10)^2 - 4(1)(27)}}{2 \cdot 1}$

$ = \dfrac{10 \pm \sqrt{100 - 108}}{2} = \dfrac{10 \pm \sqrt{-8}}{2}$

$ = \dfrac{10 \pm 2i\sqrt{2}}{2} = \dfrac{2(5 \pm i\sqrt{2})}{2}$

$ = 5 \pm i\sqrt{2}$

The solution set is $\{5 \pm i\sqrt{2}\}$.

33. $5x^2 = 2x - 3$

Write the equation in standard form.

$5x^2 - 2x + 3 = 0$

$a = 5, b = -2, c = 3$

$x = \dfrac{-b \pm \sqrt{b^2 - 4ac}}{2a}$

$ = \dfrac{-(-2) \pm \sqrt{(-2)^2 - 4(5)(3)}}{2 \cdot 5}$

$ = \dfrac{2 \pm \sqrt{4 - 60}}{10} = \dfrac{2 \pm \sqrt{-56}}{10}$

$ = \dfrac{2 \pm 2i\sqrt{14}}{10} = \dfrac{2(1 \pm i\sqrt{14})}{10}$

$ = \dfrac{1 \pm i\sqrt{14}}{5}$

The solution set is $\left\{\dfrac{1 \pm i\sqrt{14}}{5}\right\}$.

35. $2y^2 = 4y - 5$

Write the equation in standard form.

$2y^2 - 4y + 5 = 0$

$a = 2, b = -4, c = 5$

$y = \dfrac{-b \pm \sqrt{b^2 - 4ac}}{2a}$

$= \dfrac{-(-4) \pm \sqrt{(-4)^2 - 4(2)(5)}}{2 \cdot 2}$

$= \dfrac{4 \pm \sqrt{16 - 40}}{4} = \dfrac{4 \pm \sqrt{-24}}{4}$

$= \dfrac{4 \pm 2i\sqrt{6}}{4} = \dfrac{2(2 \pm i\sqrt{6})}{2 \cdot 2}$

$= \dfrac{2 \pm i\sqrt{6}}{2}$

The solution set is $\left\{ \dfrac{2 \pm i\sqrt{6}}{2} \right\}$.

37. $12x^2 + 35 = 8x^2 + 15$

$4x^2 + 35 = 15$

$4x^2 = -20$

$x^2 = -5$

$x = \pm\sqrt{-5} = \pm i\sqrt{5}$

The solution set is $\left\{ \pm i\sqrt{5} \right\}$.

39. $\dfrac{x+3}{5} = \dfrac{x-2}{x}$

$5x\left(\dfrac{x+3}{5}\right) = 5x\left(\dfrac{x-2}{x}\right)$

$x(x+3) = 5(x-2)$

$x^2 + 3x = 5x - 10$

$x^2 - 2x + 10 = 0$

$a = 1, b = -2, c = 10$

$x = \dfrac{-(-2) \pm \sqrt{(-2)^2 - 4(1)(10)}}{2(1)}$

$= \dfrac{2 \pm \sqrt{4 - 40}}{2} = \dfrac{2 \pm \sqrt{-36}}{2}$

$= \dfrac{2 \pm 6i}{2} = 1 \pm 3i$

The solution set is $\left\{ 1 \pm 3i \right\}$.

41. $\dfrac{1}{x+1} - \dfrac{1}{2} = \dfrac{1}{x}$

Multiply both sides by the LCD, $2x(x+1)$.

$2x(x+1)\left(\dfrac{1}{x+1} - \dfrac{1}{2}\right) = 2x(x+1)\left(\dfrac{1}{x}\right)$

$2x - x(x+1) = 2(x+1)$

$2x - x^2 - x = 2x + 2$

$-x^2 - x - 2 = 0$

$x^2 + x + 2 = 0$

$a = 1, b = 1, c = 2$

$x = \dfrac{-1 \pm \sqrt{(1)^2 - 4(1)(2)}}{2(1)}$

$= \dfrac{-1 \pm \sqrt{1 - 8}}{2} = \dfrac{-1 \pm \sqrt{-7}}{2}$

$= \dfrac{-1 \pm i\sqrt{7}}{2}$

The solution set is $\left\{ \dfrac{-1 \pm i\sqrt{7}}{2} \right\}$.

43. $R = -2x^2 + 36x$

$200 = -2x^2 + 36x$

$2x^2 + 36x + 200 = 0$

$x^2 + 18x + 100 = 0$

$a = 1, b = 18, c = 100$

$x = \dfrac{-b \pm \sqrt{b^2 - 4ac}}{2a}$

$= \dfrac{-18 \pm \sqrt{18^2 - 4(1)(100)}}{2 \cdot 1}$

$= \dfrac{-18 \pm \sqrt{324 - 400}}{2}$

$= \dfrac{-18 \pm \sqrt{-76}}{2} = \dfrac{-18 \pm 2i\sqrt{19}}{2}$

$= \dfrac{2(-9 \pm i\sqrt{19})}{2} = 9 \pm i\sqrt{19}$

The solutions of the equation are $9 \pm i\sqrt{19}$, which are not real numbers. Because the equation has no real number solution, it is not possible to generate $200,000 in weekly revenue. The job applicant has guaranteed to do something that is impossible, so this person will not be hired.

45. – 49. Answers will vary.

476

51. does not make sense; Explanations will vary. Sample explanation: Imaginary numbers are not *undefined*.

53. does not make sense; Explanations will vary. Sample explanation: It is not a variable, $i = \sqrt{-1}$.

55. false; Changes to make the statement true will vary. A sample change is: $-\sqrt{-9} = -(3i) = -3i$.

57. false; Changes to make the statement true will vary. A sample change is: $2 + \sqrt{-4} = 2 + 2i$.

59. $x^2 - 2x + 2 = 0$
To show that $1 + i$ is a solution of this equation substitute $1 + i$ for x.
$$x^2 - 2x + 2 = 0$$
$$(1+i)^2 - 2(1+i) + 2 = 0$$
$$1 + 2i + i^2 - 2 - 2i + 2 = 0$$
$$1 + 2i + (-1) - 2 - 2i + 2 = 0$$
$$(1 - 1 - 2 + 2) + (2i - 2i) = 0$$
$$0 + 0 = 0$$
$$0 = 0, \text{ true}$$
To show that $1 - i$ is the other solution, substitute $1 - i$ for x.
$$x^2 - 2x + 2 = 0$$
$$(1-i)^2 - 2(1-i) + 2 = 0$$
$$1 - 2i + i^2 - 2 + 2i + 2 = 0$$
$$1 - 2i + (-1) - 2 + 2i + 2 = 0$$
$$(1 - 1 - 2 + 2) + (-2i + 2i) = 0$$
$$0 + 0 = 0$$
$$0 = 0, \text{ true}$$

61. The graph shows that the parabola and the horizontal line do not intersect. The vertex, which is the maximum point on the graph, has a *y*-coordinate that is less than 80. Therefore, the ball will never reach a height of 80 feet.

63. $y = \dfrac{1}{3}x - 2$

slope $= \dfrac{1}{3}$; *y*-intercept $= -2$

Plot $(0, -2)$. From this point, go 1 unit *up* and 3 units to the *right* to reach the point $(3, -1)$

64. $2x - 3y = 6$
x-intercept: 3
y-intercept: −2
checkpoint: $(-3, -4)$
Draw a line through $(3,0)$, $(0, -2)$, and $(-3, -4)$.

65. $x = -2$
Draw a vertical line with *x*-intercept −2.

66. $y = x^2 + 4x + 3$

x	$x^2 + 4x + 3$	(x, y)
-5	$(-5)^2 + 4(-5) + 3 = 8$	$(-5, 8)$
-4	$(-4)^2 + 4(-4) + 3 = 3$	$(-4, 3)$
-3	$(-3)^2 + 4(-3) + 3 = 0$	$(-3, 0)$
-2	$(-2)^2 + 4(-2) + 3 = -1$	$(-2, -1)$
-1	$(-1)^2 + 4(-1) + 3 = 0$	$(-1, 0)$
0	$(0)^2 + 4(0) + 3 = 3$	$(0, 3)$
1	$(1)^2 + 4(1) + 3 = 8$	$(1, 8)$

67. $y = x^2 - 2x - 3$

$0 = x^2 - 2x - 3$

$0 = (x + 1)(x - 3)$

$x + 1 = 0 \quad$ or $\quad x - 3 = 0$

$\quad x = -1 \qquad\qquad x = 3$

The x-intercepts are -1 and 3.

68. $y = (0)^2 - 2(0) - 3 = -3$

The y-intercept is -3.

10.5 Check Points

1. a. $y = x^2 - 6x + 8$

Because a, the coefficient of x^2, is 1, which is greater than 0, the parabola opens upward.

b. Make a table.

x	$y = x^2 - 6x + 8$	(x, y)
0	$y = (0)^2 - 6(0) + 8 = 8$	$(0, 8)$
1	$y = (1)^2 - 6(1) + 8 = 3$	$(1, 3)$
2	$y = (2)^2 - 6(2) + 8 = 0$	$(2, 0)$
3	$y = (3)^2 - 6(3) + 8 = -1$	$(3, -1)$
4	$y = (4)^2 - 6(4) + 8 = 0$	$(4, 0)$
5	$y = (5)^2 - 6(5) + 8 = 3$	$(5, 3)$
6	$y = (6)^2 - 6(6) + 8 = 8$	$(6, 8)$

Plot the points and connect them with a smooth curve.

2. $y = x^2 - 6x + 8$

To find the x-intercepts, replace y with 0 and solve the resulting equation.

$0 = x^2 - 6x + 8$

$0 = (x - 4)(x - 2)$

$x - 4 = 0 \quad$ or $\quad x - 2 = 0$

$\quad x = 4 \qquad\qquad x = 2$

The x-intercepts are 2 and 4.

3. $y = x^2 - 6x + 8$

To find the y-intercept, replace x with 0.

$y = 0^2 - 6(0) + 8 = 8$

The y-intercept is 8.

4. $y = x^2 - 6x + 8$

$a = 1, b = -6, c = 8$

x-coordinate of vertex

$$x = \frac{-b}{2a} = \frac{-(-6)}{2(1)} = \frac{6}{2} = 3$$

y-coordinate of vertex

$y = 3^2 - 6(3) + 8 = 9 - 18 + 8 = -1$

The vertex is $(3, -1)$.

5. $y = x^2 + 6x + 5$

Step 1 Determine how the parabola opens.

Here a, the coefficient of x^2, is 1.

Because $a > 0$, the parabola opens upward.

Step 2 Find the vertex.
For this equation, $a = 1, b = 6$, and $c = 5$.
x-coordinate of vertex
$$= \frac{-b}{2a} = \frac{-6}{2(1)} = \frac{-6}{2} = -3$$
y-coordinate of vertex
$$= (-3)^2 + 6(-3) + 5 = 9 - 18 + 5 = -4$$
The vertex is $(-3, -4)$.

Step 3 Find the x-intercepts.
Replace y with 0 in $y = x^2 + 6x + 5$ and solve for x.
$$x^2 + 6x + 5 = 0$$
$$(x + 5)(x + 1) = 0$$
$$x + 5 = 0 \quad \text{or} \quad x + 1 = 0$$
$$x = -5 \qquad x = -1$$
The x-intercepts are -5 and -1.

Step 4 Find the y-intercept.
Replace x with 0 and solve for y.
$$y = 0^2 + 6(0) + 5 = 5$$
The y-intercept is 5.

Steps 5 and 6 Plot the intercepts and the vertex.
Plot $(-3, -4), (-5, 0), (-1, 0)$, and $(0, 5)$, and connect them with a smooth curve.

6. $y = -x^2 - 2x + 5$

Step 1 Determine how the parabola opens.
$a = -1 < 0$, so the parabola opens downward.

Step 2 Find the vertex.
$a = -1, \ b = -2, \ c = 5$
x-coordinate of vertex
$$x = \frac{-b}{2a} = \frac{-(-2)}{2(-1)} = \frac{2}{-2} = -1$$
y-coordinate of vertex
$$y = -(-1)^2 - 2(-1) + 5 = -1 + 2 + 5 = 6$$
The vertex is $(-1, 6)$.

Step 3 Find the x-intercepts.
$$y = -x^2 - 2x + 5$$
$$0 = -x^2 - 2x + 5$$
$$a = -1, \ b = -2, \ c = 5$$
$$x = \frac{-b \pm \sqrt{b^2 - 4ac}}{2a}$$
$$x = \frac{-(-2) \pm \sqrt{(-2)^2 - 4(-1)(5)}}{2(-1)}$$
$$x = \frac{2 \pm \sqrt{4 + 20}}{-2}$$
$$x = \frac{2 \pm \sqrt{24}}{-2}$$
$$x = \frac{2 \pm 2\sqrt{6}}{-2}$$
$$x = -1 \pm \sqrt{6}$$
$$x \approx -3.4 \quad \text{or} \quad x \approx 1.4$$
The x-intercepts are approximately -3.4 and 1.4.

Step 4 Find the y-intercept.
$$y = -x^2 - 2x + 5$$
$$y = -0^2 - 2(0) + 5 = 5$$
The y-intercept is 5.

Steps 5 and 6
Plot $(-1, 6), (-3.4, 0), (1.4, 0)$, and $(0, 5)$, and connect them with a smooth curve.

7. $y = -0.005x^2 + 2x + 5$

a. The information needed is found at the vertex.
x-coordinate of vertex
$$x = \frac{-b}{2a} = \frac{-2}{2(-0.005)} = 200$$
y-coordinate of vertex
$$y = -0.005(200)^2 + 2(200) + 5 = 205$$
The vertex is $(200, 205)$.
The maximum height of the arrow is 205 feet. This occurs 200 feet from its release.

b. The arrow will hit the ground when the height reaches 0.

$$y = -0.005x^2 + 2x + 5$$
$$0 = -0.005x^2 + 2x + 5$$
$$x = \frac{-b \pm \sqrt{b^2 - 4ac}}{2a}$$
$$x = \frac{-2 \pm \sqrt{2^2 - 4(-0.005)(5)}}{2(-0.005)}$$
$$x \approx -2 \quad \text{or} \quad x \approx 402$$

The arrow travels 402 feet before hitting the ground.

c. The starting point occurs when $x = 0$. Find the corresponding y-coordinate.
$$y = -0.005(0)^2 + 2(0) + 5 = 5$$

Plot $(0,5)$, $(402,0)$, and $(200,205)$, and connect them with a smooth curve.

10.5 Exercise Set

1. $y = x^2 - 4x + 3$

Because a, the coefficient of x^2, is 1, which is greater than 0, the parabola opens upward.

3. $y = -2x^2 + x + 6$

Because $a = -2$, which is less than 0, the parabola opens downward.

5. $y = x^2 - 4x + 3$

To find the x-intercepts, replace y with 0 and solve the resulting equation.
$$x^2 - 4x + 3 = 0$$
$$(x-1)(x-3) = 0$$
$$x - 1 = 0 \quad \text{or} \quad x - 3 = 0$$
$$x = 1 \qquad\qquad x = 3$$
The x-intercepts are 1 and 3.

7. $y = -x^2 + 8x - 12$

To find the x-intercepts, replace y with 0 and solve the resulting equation.
$$0 = -x^2 + 8x - 12$$
$$x^2 - 8x + 12 = 0$$
$$(x-2)(x-6) = 0$$
$$x - 2 = 0 \quad \text{or} \quad x - 6 = 0$$
$$x = 2 \qquad\qquad x = 6$$
The x-intercepts are 2 and 6.

9. $y = x^2 + 2x - 4$

To find the x-intercepts, replace y with 0 and solve the resulting equation.
$$0 = x^2 + 2x - 4$$
This equation cannot be solved by factoring, so use the quadratic formula with $a = 1, b = 2,$ and $c = -4$.
$$x = \frac{-b \pm \sqrt{b^2 - 4ac}}{2a}$$
$$= \frac{-2 \pm \sqrt{2^2 - 4(1)(-4)}}{2(1)}$$
$$= \frac{-2 \pm \sqrt{4 + 16}}{2} = \frac{-2 \pm \sqrt{20}}{2}$$
$$= \frac{-2 \pm 2\sqrt{5}}{2} = -1 \pm \sqrt{5}$$
$$x = -1\sqrt{5} \approx -3.2 \quad \text{or} \quad x = -1 - \sqrt{5} \approx 1.2$$
The x-intercepts are approximately -3.2 and 1.2.

11. $y = x^2 - 4x + 3$

To find the y-intercept, replace x with 0.
$$y = 0^2 - 4 \cdot 0 + 3 = 0 - 0 + 3 = 3$$
The y-intercept is 3.

13. $y = -x^2 + 8x - 12$
$$y = -0^2 + 8 \cdot 0 - 12 = 0 + 0 - 12 = -12$$
The y-intercept is -12.

15. $y = x^2 + 2x - 4$
$$y = 0^2 + 2 \cdot 0 - 4 = -4$$
The y-intercept is -4.

17. $y = x^2 + 6x$
$$y = 0^2 + 6 \cdot 0 = 0$$
The y-intercept is 0.

19. $y = x^2 - 4x + 3$

$a = 1, b = -4, c = 3$

x-coordinate of vertex

$= \dfrac{-b}{2a} = \dfrac{-(-4)}{2(1)} = \dfrac{4}{2} = 2$

y-coordinate of vertex

$= 2^2 - 4(2) + 3 = 4 - 8 + 3 = -1$

The vertex is $(2, -1)$.

21. $y = 2x^2 + 4x - 6$

$a = 2, b = 4, c = -6$

x-coordinate of vertex

$= \dfrac{-b}{2a} = \dfrac{-4}{2(2)} = \dfrac{-4}{4} = -1$

y-coordinate of vertex

$= 2(-1)^2 + 4(-1) - 6 = 2 - 4 - 6 = -8$

The vertex is $(-1, -8)$.

23. $y = x^2 + 6x$

$a = 1, b = 6, c = 0$

x-coordinate of vertex

$= \dfrac{-b}{2a} = \dfrac{-6}{2(1)} = \dfrac{-6}{2} = -3$

y-coordinate of vertex

$= (-3)^2 + 6(-3) = 9 - 18 = -9$

The vertex is $(-3, -9)$.

25. $y = x^2 + 8x + 7$

Step 1 Determine how the parabola opens.

Here a, the coefficient of x^2, is 1.

Because $a > 0$, the parabola opens upward.

Step 2 Find the vertex.

For this equation, $a = 1, b = 8$, and $c = 7$.

x-coordinate of vertex

$= \dfrac{-b}{2a} = \dfrac{-8}{2(1)} = \dfrac{-8}{2} = -4$

y-coordinate of vertex

$= (-4)^2 + 8(-4) + 7 = 16 - 32 + 7 = -9$

The vertex is $(-4, -9)$.

Step 3 Find the x-intercepts.

Replace y with 0 in $y = x^2 + 8x + 7$ and solve for x.

$x^2 + 8x + 7 = 0$

$(x + 7)(x + 1) = 0$

$x + 7 = 0$ or $x + 1 = 0$

$x = -7$ $x = -1$

The x-intercepts are -7 and -1.

Step 4 Find the y-intercept.

Replace x with 0 and solve for y.

$y = 0^2 + 8(0) + 7 = 0 + 0 + 7 = 7$

The y-intercept is 7.

Steps 5 and 6 Plot the intercepts and the vertex. Connect these points with a smooth curve.

Plot $(-4, -9), (-7, 0), (-1, 0)$, and $(0, 7)$, and connect them with a smooth curve.

$y = x^2 + 8x + 7$

27. $y = x^2 - 2x - 8$

Step 1 $a = 1 > 0$, so the parabola opens upward.

Step 2 $a = 1, b = -2, c = -8$

x-coordinate of vertex

$= \dfrac{-b}{2a} = \dfrac{-2(-2)}{2(1)} = \dfrac{2}{2} = 1$

y-coordinate of vertex

$= 1^2 - 2(1) - 8 = 1 - 2 - 8 = -9$

The vertex is $(1, -9)$

Step 3

$x^2 - 2x - 8 = 0$

$(x + 2)(x - 4) = 0$

$x + 2 = 0$ or $x - 4 = 0$

$x = -2$ $x = 4$

The x-intercepts are -2 and 4.

Step 4 $y = 0^2 - 2(0) - 8 = 8$

The y-intercept is -8.

Steps 5 and 6 Plot

$(1, -9), (-2, 0), (4, 0)$, and $(0, -8)$, and connect them with a smooth curve.

$y = x^2 - 2x - 8$

29. $y = -x^2 + 4x - 3$

Step 1 $a = -1 < 0$, so the parabola opens downward.

Step 2 $a = -1, b = 4, c = -3$

x-coordinate of vertex

$$= \frac{-b}{2a} = \frac{-4}{2(-1)} = \frac{-4}{-2} = 2$$

y-coordinate of vertex

$$= -2^2 + 4 \cdot 2 - -4 + 8 - 3 = 1$$

The vertex is $(2, 1)$.

Step 3

$$-x^2 + 4x - 3 = 0$$
$$0 = x^2 - 4x + 3$$
$$0 = (x - 1)(x - 3)$$
$$x - 1 = 0 \quad \text{or} \quad x - 3 = 0$$
$$x = 1 \qquad x = 3$$

The x-intercepts are 1 and 3.

Step 4 $y = -0^2 + 4(0) - 3 = -3$

The y-intercept is -3.

Steps 5 and 6 Plot $(2, 1), (1, 0), (3, 0)$, and $(0, -3)$, and connect them with a smooth curve.

$y = -x^2 + 4x - 3$

31. $y = x^2 - 1$

Step 1 $a = 1 > 0$, so the parabola opens upward.

Step 2 $a = 1, b = 0, c = -1$

x-coordinate of vertex

$$= \frac{-b}{2a} = \frac{-0}{2(1)} = \frac{0}{2} = 0$$

y-coordinate of vertex

$$= 0^2 - 1 = -1$$

The vertex is $(0, 1)$.

Step 3

$$x^2 - 1 = 0$$
$$(x + 1)(x - 1) = 0$$
$$x + 1 = 0 \quad \text{or} \quad x - 1 = 0$$
$$x = -1 \qquad x = 1$$

The x-intercepts are -1 and 1.

Step 4 $y = 0^2 - 1 = -1$

The y-intercept is -1. Notice that this gives the same point as the vertex, $(0, -1)$.

Steps 5 and 6 Plot $(0, -1), (-1, 0)$, and $(1, 0)$, and connect them with a smooth curve.

$y = x^2 - 1$

33. $y = x^2 + 2x + 1$

Step 1 $a - 1 > 0$, so the parabola opens upward.

Step 2 $a = 1, b = 2, c = 1$

x-coordinate of vertex

$$= \frac{-b}{2a} = \frac{-2}{2(1)} = \frac{-2}{2} = -1$$

y-coordinate of vertex

$$= (-1)^2 + 2(-1) + 1 = 1 - 2 + 1 = 0$$

The vertex is $(-1, 0)$.

Step 3

$$x^2 + 2x + 1 = 0$$
$$(x + 1)^2 = 0$$
$$x + 1 = 0$$
$$x = -1$$

There is only one x-intercept, -1. Notice that this gives the same point as the vertex, $(-1, 0)$.

Step 4 $y = 0^2 + 2 \cdot 0 + 1 = 1$

The y-intercept is 1.

The work in Steps 1-4 has produced only two points, $(-1, 0)$ and $(0, 1)$. At least one additional point is needed. In order to have at least one point on each side of the vertex, choose an x-value less than -1 and find the corresponding y-value.

If $x = -2$, $y = (-2)^2 + 2(-2) + 1 = 4 - 4 + 1 = 1$.

Steps 5 and 6 Plot $(-2, 1), (-1, 0)$, and $(0, 1)$, and connect them with a smooth curve.

$y = x^2 + 2x + 1$

35. $y = -2x^2 + 4x + 5$

Step 1 $a = -2 < 0$, so the parabola opens downward.

Step 2 $a = -2, b = 4, c = 5$

x-coordinate of vertex

$$= \frac{-b}{2a} = \frac{-4}{2(-2)} = \frac{-4}{-4} = 1$$

y-coordinate of vertex

$$= -2(1)^2 + 4(1) + 5 = -2 + 4 + 5 = 7$$

The vertex is $(1, 7)$

Step 3

$-2x^2 + 4x + 5 = 0$

$$0 = 2x^2 - 4x - 5$$

The trinomial cannot be factored, so use the quadratic formula with $a = 2, b = -4$, and $c = -5$.

$$x = \frac{-b \pm \sqrt{b^2 - 4ac}}{2a}$$

$$= \frac{-(-4) \pm \sqrt{(-4)^2 - 4(2)(-5)}}{2 \cdot 2}$$

$$= \frac{4 \pm \sqrt{16 + 40}}{4} = \frac{4 \pm \sqrt{56}}{4}$$

$$x = \frac{4 + \sqrt{56}}{4} \approx 2.9 \quad \text{or} \quad x = \frac{4 - \sqrt{56}}{4} \approx -0.9$$

The x-intercepts are approximately 2.9 and -0.9.

Step 4 $y = -2 \cdot 0^2 + 4 \cdot 0 + 5 = 5$

The y-intercept is 5.

Steps 5 and 6 Plot

$(1,7), (2.9, 0), (-0.9, 0)$, and $(0, 5)$, and connect them with a smooth curve.

$y = -2x^2 + 4x + 5$

37. $y = (x - 3)^2 + 2$

$y = (x^2 - 6x + 9) + 2$

$y = x^2 - 6x + 11$

$a = 1, b = -6, c = 11$

$$x = -\frac{b}{2a} = -\frac{(-6)}{2(1)} = \frac{6}{2} = 3$$

$$y = (3)^2 - 6(3) + 11 = 9 - 18 + 11 = 2$$

The vertex is $(3, 2)$.

39. $y = (x + 5)^2 - 4$

$y = (x^2 + 10x + 25) - 4$

$y = x^2 + 10x + 21$

$a = 1, b = 10, c = 21$

$$x = -\frac{b}{2a} = -\frac{10}{2(1)} = -5$$

$$y = (-5)^2 + 10(-5) + 21$$

$$= 25 - 50 + 21 = -4$$

The vertex is $(-5, -4)$.

41. $y = 2(x - 1)^2 - 3$

$y = 2(x^2 - 2x + 1) - 3$

$y = 2x^2 - 4x + 2 - 3$

$y = 2x^2 - 4x - 1$

$a = 2, b = -4, c = -1$

$$x = -\frac{b}{2a} = -\frac{(-4)}{2(2)} = \frac{4}{4} = 1$$

$$y = 2(1)^2 - 4(1) - 1 = 2 - 4 - 1 = -3$$

The vertex is $(1, -3)$.

43. $y = -3(x + 2)^2 + 5$

$y = -3(x^2 + 4x + 4) + 5$

$y = -3x^2 - 12x - 12 + 5$

$y = -3x^2 - 12x - 7$

$a = -3, b = -12, c = -7$

$$x = -\frac{b}{2a} = -\frac{(-12)}{2(-3)} = -\frac{12}{6} = -2$$

$$y = -3(-2)^2 - 12(-2) - 7$$

$$= -12 + 24 - 7 = 5$$

The vertex is $(-2, 5)$.

45. For a parabola whose equation is $y = a(x - h)^2 + k$, the vertex is the point (h, k).

47. **a.** $y = -0.01x^2 + 0.7x + 6.1$

$a = -0.01, \ b = 0.7, \ c = 6.1$

x-coordinate of vertex

$= \dfrac{-b}{2a} = \dfrac{-0.7}{2(-0.01)} = 35$

y-coordinate of vertex

$y = -0.01x^2 + 0.7x + 6.1$

$y = -0.01(35)^2 + 0.7(35) + 6.1 = 18.35$

The maximum height of the shot is about 18.35 feet. This occurs 35 feet from its point of release.

b. The ball will reach the maximum horizontal distance when its height returns to 0.

$y = -0.01x^2 + 0.7x + 6.1$

$0 = -0.01x^2 + 0.7x + 6.1$

$a = -0.01, \ b = 0.7, \ c = 6.1$

$x = \dfrac{-b \pm \sqrt{b^2 - 4ac}}{2a}$

$x = \dfrac{-0.7 \pm \sqrt{0.7^2 - 4(-0.01)(6.1)}}{2(-0.01)}$

$x \approx 77.8$ or $x \approx -7.8$

The maximum horizontal distance is 77.8 feet.

c. The initial height can be found at $x = 0$.

$y = -0.01x^2 + 0.7x + 6.1$

$y = -0.01(0)^2 + 0.7(0) + 6.1 = 6.1$

The shot was released at a height of 6.1 feet.

49. **a.** 1999 is 0 years after 1999. Substitute 0 for *x*.

$y = 0.22x^2 - 0.50x + 7.68$

$y = 0.22(0)^2 - 0.50(0) + 7.68 = 7.68$

According to the model, 7.68 million households received food stamps in 1999.
This underestimates the actual number shown in the graph by 0.02 million.

b. According to the graph, the number of households receiving food stamps over this time period was at a minimum in 2000, namely 7.4 million.

c. The information needed occurs at the vertex.

$y = 0.22x^2 - 0.50x + 7.68$

$a = 0.22, \ b = -0.50, \ c = 7.68$

x-coordinate of vertex

$= \dfrac{-b}{2a} = \dfrac{-(-0.50)}{2(0.22)} \approx 1$

y-coordinate of vertex

$y = 0.22x^2 - 0.50x + 7.68$

$y = 0.22(1)^2 - 0.50(1) + 7.68 = 7.4$

According to the model, the number of households receiving food stamps over this time period was at a minimum 1 year after 1999, or 2000, namely 7.4 million. This is the same as part (b).

51. $A = l \cdot w$

$= x(50 - x)$

$= -x^2 + 50x$

The leading coefficient is negative, so the graph of the area equation opens down and the vertex is at the highest point.

$x = -\dfrac{b}{2a} = -\dfrac{50}{2(-1)} = 25$

$y = -(25)^2 + 50(25)$

$= 625$

The vertex is $(25, 625)$.

The area reaches a maximum value of 625 square yards if length is $x = 25$ yards and the width is $50 - 25 = 25$ yards.

53. – 57. Answers will vary.

59. makes sense

61. does not make sense; Explanations will vary. Sample explanation: Over the short portion of the path shown, it may appear linear. However the path is best described by a quadratic model.

63. true

65. false; Changes to make the statement true will vary. A sample change is: Since $a \geq 0$, the parabola opens upward and its vertex will be the lowest point on the graph.

67. Intersection points: $(-2, 0)$ and $(2, 0)$.

484

69. Answers will vary.

71. $y = -0.25x^2 + 40x$

$a = -0.25$, $b = 40$, $c = 0$

$x = -\dfrac{b}{2a} = -\dfrac{40}{2(-0.25)} = \dfrac{40}{0.5} = 80$

$y = -0.25(80)^2 + 40(80) = 1600$

The vertex is $(80, 1600)$.

The y-intercept is 0 and the graph opens down.
Window settings will vary. One example would be:

73. $y = 5x^2 + 40x + 600$

$a = 5$, $b = 40$, $c = 600$

$x = -\dfrac{b}{2a} = -\dfrac{40}{2(5)} = -\dfrac{40}{10} = -4$

$y = 5(-4)^2 + 40(-4) + 600 = 520$

The vertex is $(-4, 520)$.

The y-intercept is 600 and the graph opens up.
Window settings will vary. One example would be:

75. $7(x-2) = 10 - 2(x+3)$

$7x - 14 = 10 - 2x - 6$

$7x - 14 = 4 - 2x$

$9x - 14 = 4$

$9x = 18$

$x = 2$

The solution set is $\{2\}$.

76. $\dfrac{7}{x+2}+\dfrac{2}{x+3}=\dfrac{1}{x^2+5x+6}$

$\dfrac{7}{x+2}+\dfrac{2}{x+3}=\dfrac{1}{(x+2)(x+3)}$

Restrictions: $x \neq -2, x \neq -3$

LCD $=(x+2)(x+3)$

$(x+2)(x+3)\left[\dfrac{7}{x+2}+\dfrac{2}{x+3}\right]=(x+2)(x+3)\left[\dfrac{1}{(x+2)(x+3)}\right]$

$\qquad 7(x+3)+2(x+2)=1$

$\qquad 7x+21+2x+4=1$

$\qquad\qquad 9x+25=1$

$\qquad\qquad\quad 9x=-24$

$\qquad\qquad\quad\;\; x=\dfrac{-24}{9}=-\dfrac{8}{3}$

The solution set is $\left\{-\dfrac{8}{3}\right\}$.

77. $5x-3y=-13$

$x=2-4y$

To solve this system by the substitution method, substitute $2-4y$ for x in the first equation.

$\qquad\quad 5x-3y=-13$

$\quad 5(2-4y)-3y=-13$

$\quad 10-20y-3y=-13$

$\qquad 10-23y=-13$

$\qquad\quad -23y=-23$

$\qquad\qquad\;\; y=1$

Back-substitute 1 for y in the second equation of the given system.

$x=2-4y=2-4(1)=-2$

The solution set is $\{(-2,1)\}$.

78. In set 1 each x-coordinate is paired with one and only one y-coordinate.

79. Graph (a) has each x-coordinate paired with one and only one y-coordinate.

80. $x^2+3x+5=(-3)^2+3(-3)+5$

$\qquad\qquad\quad\;\; =9-9+5$

$\qquad\qquad\quad\;\; =5$

10.6 Check Points

1. Domain: {golf, lawn mowing, water skiing, hiking, bicycling}
   Range: {250, 325, 430, 720}

2. a. This relation is not a function because the two ordered pairs (5,6) and (5,8) have the same first component but different second components.

   b. This relation is a function because no two ordered pairs have the same first component and different second components.

3. a. $f(x) = 4x + 3$
   $f(5) = 4(5) + 3 = 20 + 3 = 23$

   b. $f(x) = 4x + 3$
   $f(-2) = 4(-2) + 3 = -8 + 3 = -5$

   c. $f(x) = 4x + 3$
   $f(0) = 4(0) + 3 = 0 + 3 = 3$

4. a. $g(x) = x^2 + 4x + 3$
   $g(5) = (5)^2 + 4(5) + 3$
   $= 25 + 20 + 3$
   $= 48$

   b. $g(x) = x^2 + 4x + 3$
   $g(-4) = (-4)^2 + 4(-4) + 3$
   $= 16 - 16 + 3$
   $= 3$

   c. $g(x) = x^2 + 4x + 3$
   $g(0) = 0^2 + 4(0) + 3$
   $= 0 + 0 + 3$
   $= 3$

5. The first two graphs pass the vertical line and thus y is a function of x. The last graph fails the vertical line and thus y is not a function of x.

6. a. $f(x) = -2.9x + 286$
   $f(90) = -2.9(90) + 286 = 25$
   According to the linear function, a 60-year-old has a 25% chance to survive to age 90.

   b. $g(x) = 0.01x^2 - 4.9x + 370$
   $g(90) = 0.01(90)^2 - 4.9(90) + 370 = 10$
   According to the quadratic function, a 60-year-old has a 10% chance to survive to age 90.

   c. According to the bar graph, a 60-year-old has a 24% chance to survive to age 90. Thus the linear function serves as a better description of this data.

10.6 Exercise Set

1. $\{(1,2),(3,4),(5,5)\}$ This relation is a function because no two ordered pairs have the same first component and different second components. The domain is the set of all first components: {1,3,5}. The range is the set of second components: {2,4,5}.

3. $\{(3,4),(3,5),(4,4),(4,5)\}$ This relation is not a function because the first two ordered pairs have the same first component but different second components. (The same applies to the third and fourth ordered pairs.)
   Domain: {3,4}
   Range: {4,5}

5. $\{(-3,-3),(-2,-2),(-1,-1),(0,0)\}$
   This relation is a function.
   Domain: {-3, -2, -1,0}
   Range: {-3, -2, -1,0}

7. $\{(1,4),(1,5),(1,6)\}$
   This relation is not a function because all three ordered pairs have the same first component.
   Domain: {1}
   Range: {4,5,6}

9. $f(x) = x + 5$

   a. $f(7) = 7 + 5 = 12$

   b. $f(-6) = -6 + 5 = -1$

   c. $f(0) = 0 + 5 = 5$

11. $f(x) = 7x$

  a $f(10) = 7 \cdot 10 = 70$

  b $f(-4) = 7(-4) = -28$

  c. $f(0) = 7 \cdot 0 = 0$

13. $f(x) = 8x - 3$

  a. $f(12) = 8(12) - 3 = 96 - 3 = 93$

  b. $f\left(-\dfrac{1}{2}\right) = 8\left(-\dfrac{1}{2}\right) - 3 = -4 - 3 = -7$

  c. $f(0) = 8(0) - 3 = 0 - 3 = -3$

15. $g(x) = x^2 + 3x$

  a. $g(2) = 2^2 + 3(2) = 4 + 6 = 10$

  b. $g(-2) = (-2)^2 + 3(-2) = 4 - 6 = -2$

  c. $g(0) = 0^2 + 3(0) = 0 + 0 = 0$

17. $h(x) = x^2 - 2x + 3$

  a. $h(4) = 4^2 - 2 \cdot 4 + 3 = 16 - 8 + 3 = 11$

  b. $h(-4) = (-4)^2 - 2(-4) + 3$
      $= 16 + 8 + 3 = 27$

  c. $h(0) = 0^2 - 2 \cdot 0 + 3 = 3$

19. $f(x) = 5$

The value of this function is 5 for every value of x.

  a. $f(9) = 5$

  b. $f(-9) = 5$

  c. $f(0) = 5$

21. $f(r) = \sqrt{r + 6} + 3$

  a. $f(-6) = \sqrt{-6 + 6} + 3 = \sqrt{0} + 3$
      $= 0 + 3 = 3$

  b. $f(10) = \sqrt{10 + 6} + 3 = \sqrt{16} + 3$
      $= 4 + 3 = 7$

23. $f(x) = \dfrac{x}{|x|}$

  a. $f(6) = \dfrac{6}{|6|} = \dfrac{6}{6} = 1$

  b. $f(-6) = \dfrac{-6}{|-6|} = \dfrac{-6}{6} = -1$

25. No vertical line will intersect this graph in more than one point so y is a function of x.

27. No vertical line will intersect this graph in more than one point, so y is a function of x.

29. Many vertical lines will intersect this graph in two points. One such line is the y-axis. Therefore, y is not a function of x.

31. No vertical line will intersect this graph in more than one point, so y is a function of x.

33. $f(x) = 2x + 3$; $\{-1, 0, 1\}$
  $f(-1) = 2(-1) + 3 = -2 + 3 = 1$
  $f(0) = 2(0) + 3 = 0 + 3 = 3$
  $f(1) = 2(1) + 3 = 2 + 3 = 5$
  $\{(-1, 1), (0, 3), (1, 5)\}$

35. $g(x) = x - x^2$; $\{-2, -1, 0, 1, 2\}$
  $g(-2) = (-2) - (-2)^2$
      $= -2 - 4 = -6$
  $g(-1) = (-1) - (-1)^2$
      $= -1 - 1 = -2$
  $g(0) = 0 - 0^2 = 0$
  $g(1) = 1 - 1^2 = 1 - 1 = 0$
  $g(2) = 2 - 2^2 = 2 - 4 = -2$
  $\{(-2, -6), (-1, -2), (0, 0), (1, 0), (2, -2)\}$

37. $\dfrac{f(x)-f(h)}{x-h}=\dfrac{[6x+7]-[6h+7]}{x-h}$

$\qquad\qquad =\dfrac{6x+7-6h-7}{x-h}$

$\qquad\qquad =\dfrac{6x-6h}{x-h}=\dfrac{6(x-h)}{(x-h)}$

$\qquad\qquad =6$

where $x\neq h$.

39. $\dfrac{f(x)-f(h)}{x-h}=\dfrac{\left[x^2-1\right]-\left[h^2-1\right]}{x-h}$

$\qquad\qquad =\dfrac{x^2-1-h^2+1}{x-h}$

$\qquad\qquad =\dfrac{x^2-h^2}{x-h}$

$\qquad\qquad =\dfrac{(x-h)(x+h)}{x-h}$

$\qquad\qquad =x+h$

where $x\neq h$.

41. a. $\{(\text{U.S., }80\%),(\text{Japan, }64\%),$
$\quad(\text{France, }64\%),(\text{Germany, }61\%),$
$\quad(\text{England, }59\%),(\text{China,}47\%)\}$

b. Yes, the relation is a function. Each element in the domain corresponds to only one element in the range.

43. $f(x)=0.76x+171.4$

$f(20)=0.76(20)+171.4=186.6$

This means that at age 20, the average cholesterol level for an American man is 186.6, or approximately 187.

45. a. $T(x)=-0.125x^2+5.25x+72$

$T(20)=-0.125(20)^2+5.25(20)+72=127$

Americans ordered an average of 127 takeout meals per person 20 years after 1984, or 2004. This is represented on the graph by the point $(20,127)$.

b. $R(x)=-0.6x+94$

$R(0)=-0.6(0)+94=94$

Americans ordered an average of 94 meals in restaurants per person 0 years after 1984, or 1984.
This is represented on the graph by the point $(0,94)$.

47. According to the graphs, the average number of takeout orders approximately equaled the average number of in-restaurant meals 4 years after 1984, or 1988.

$T(x)=-0.125x^2+5.25x+72$

$T(4)=-0.125(4)^2+5.25(4)+72=91$

In 1988 Americans ordered an average of 91 takeout meals per person.

$R(x)=-0.6x+94$

$R(4)=-0.6(4)+94=91.6$

In 1988 Americans ordered an average of 91.6 meals in restaurants per person.

49. – 51. Answers will vary.

53. makes sense

55. does not make sense; Explanations will vary. Sample explanation: The notation $f(x)$ does not mean multiplication of f by x.

57. false; Changes to make the statement true will vary. A sample change is: Not every relation is a function (e.g. $x^2+y^2=4$).

59. false; Changes to make the statement true will vary. A sample change is: The graph of a vertical line is not the graph of a function.

61. Since $f(0)=7$, we know the y-intercept is $b=7$ and that the point $(0,7)$ is on the graph. Since $f(1)=10$, we know the point $(1,10)$ is also on the graph. Using the two points, we can obtain the slope of the line:

$$m=\frac{10-7}{1-0}=\frac{3}{1}=3$$

Since we have the y-intercept and the slope, we can write the equation of the line as $f(x)=3x+7$.

63. Since the car decreases in value by $3200 each year, we have a linear function with slope $m = -3200$. The initial value of the car is $22,500 which is the y-intercept (i.e. the value of the car after $x = 0$ years). Therefore, we can write

$V(x) = -3200x + 22,500$ for $0 \le x \le 7$

$V(3) = -3200(3) + 22,500$

$\quad\quad = -9600 + 22,500$

$\quad\quad = 12,900$

This indicates that the value of the car will be $12,900 after 3 years.

64. 0.00397

To write this number in scientific notation, move the decimal point 3 places to the right. Because the number is between 0 and 1, the exponent will be positive.

$0.00397 = 3.97 \times 10^{-3}$

65.

$$\begin{array}{r} x^2 + 9x + 16 \\ x-2\overline{\smash{\big)}\,x^3 + 7x^2 - 2x + 3} \\ \underline{x^3 - 2x^2} \\ 9x^2 - 2x \\ \underline{9x^2 - 18x} \\ 16x + 3 \\ \underline{16x - 32} \\ 35 \end{array}$$

$$\frac{x^3 + 7x^2 - 2x + 3}{x - 2} = x^2 + 9x + 16 + \frac{35}{x - 2}$$

66. $3x + 2y = 6$

$8x - 3y = 1$

To solve this system by the addition method, multiply the first equation by 3 and then second equation by 2; then add the equations.

$\quad 9x + 6y = 18$

$\underline{16x - 6y = 2}$

$25x \quad\quad = 20$

$\quad\quad x = \dfrac{20}{25} = \dfrac{4}{5}$

Instead of substituting $\dfrac{4}{5}$ for x for working with fractions, go back to the original system and eliminate x.

To do this, multiply the first equation by 8 and the second equation by -3; then add.

$\quad 24x + 16y = 48$

$\underline{-24x + 9y = -3}$

$\quad\quad 25y = 45$

$\quad\quad\quad y = \dfrac{45}{25} = \dfrac{9}{5}$

The solution is $\left(\dfrac{4}{5}, \dfrac{9}{5}\right)$.

Chapter 10 Review

1. $x^2 = 64$

$x = \sqrt{64}$ or $x = -\sqrt{64}$

$x = 8 \quad\quad\quad x = -8$

The solution set is $\{-8, 8\}$.

2. $x^2 = 17$

$x = \sqrt{17}$ or $x = -\sqrt{17}$

The solution set is $\{\pm\sqrt{17}\}$.

3. $2x^2 = 150$

$\quad x^2 = 75$

$\quad x = \sqrt{75}$ or $x = -\sqrt{75}$

Simplify $\sqrt{75}$:

$\quad \sqrt{75} = \sqrt{25}\sqrt{3} = 5\sqrt{3}$

$\quad x = 5\sqrt{3}$ or $x = -5\sqrt{3}$

The solution set is $\{\pm 5\sqrt{3}\}$.

4. $(x-3)^2 = 9$

$x - 3 = \sqrt{9}$ or $x - 3 = -\sqrt{9}$

$x - 3 = 3 \quad\quad\quad x - 3 = -3$

$\quad x = 6 \quad\quad\quad\quad x = 0$

The solution set is $\{0, 6\}$.

5. $(y+4)^2 = 5$

$y + 4 = \sqrt{5} \quad$ or $\quad y + 4 = -\sqrt{5}$

$\quad y = -4 + \sqrt{5} \quad\quad y = -4 - \sqrt{5}$

The solution set is $\{-4 \pm \sqrt{5}\}$.

6. $3y^2 - 5 = 0$

$$3y^2 = 5$$

$$y^2 = \frac{5}{3}$$

$$y = \sqrt{\frac{5}{3}} \text{ or } y = -\sqrt{\frac{5}{3}}$$

Rationalize the denominators.

$$\sqrt{\frac{5}{3}} = \frac{\sqrt{5}}{\sqrt{3}} \cdot \frac{\sqrt{3}}{\sqrt{3}} = \frac{\sqrt{15}}{3}$$

$$y = \frac{\sqrt{15}}{3} \text{ or } y = -\frac{\sqrt{15}}{3}$$

The solution set is $\left\{ \pm \frac{\sqrt{15}}{3} \right\}$.

7. $(2x-7)^2 = 25$

$2x - 7 = \sqrt{25}$ or $2x - 7 = -\sqrt{25}$

$2x - 7 = 5 \qquad\qquad 2x - 7 = -5$

$2x = 12 \qquad\qquad\quad 2x = 2$

$x = 6 \qquad\qquad\quad\ x = 1$

The solution set is $\{1, 6\}$.

8. $(x+5)^2 = 12$

$x + 5 = \sqrt{12} \qquad$ or $\ x + 5 = -\sqrt{12}$

$x + 5 = 2\sqrt{3} \qquad\qquad x + 5 = -2\sqrt{3}$

$x = -5 + 2\sqrt{3} \qquad\ x = -5 - 2\sqrt{3}$

The solution set is $\left\{ -5 \pm 2\sqrt{3} \right\}$.

9. Let c = the length of the hypotenuse.

$$6^2 + 8^2 = c^2$$

$$36 + 64 = c^2$$

$$100 = c^2$$

$$c = \sqrt{100} = 10$$

The missing length is 10 feet.

10. Let c = the length of the hypotenuse.

$$4^2 + 6^2 = c^2$$

$$16 + 36 = c^2$$

$$c = \sqrt{52} = \sqrt{4}\sqrt{13} = 2\sqrt{13}$$

The missing length is $2\sqrt{13}$ inches.

11. Let b = the missing length (length of one of the legs).

$$11^2 + b^2 = 15^2$$

$$121 + b^2 = 225$$

$$b^2 = 104$$

$$b = \sqrt{104} = \sqrt{4}\sqrt{26} = 2\sqrt{26}$$

The missing length is $2\sqrt{26}$ centimeters.

12. Let x = the distance between the base of the building and the bottom of the ladder.

$$x^2 + 20^2 = 25^2$$

$$x^2 + 400 = 625$$

$$x = 225$$

$$x = \sqrt{225} = 15$$

The bottom of the ladder is 15 feet away from the building.

13. Let h = the distance up the pole that the wires should be attached.

In the figure, the pole and one of the wires are shown.

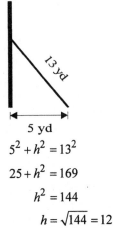

13 yd

5 yd

$$5^2 + h^2 = 13^2$$

$$25 + h^2 = 169$$

$$h^2 = 144$$

$$h = \sqrt{144} = 12$$

The wires will be attached 12 yards up the pole.

14. $W = 3t^2; W = 1200$

$$1200 = 3t^2$$

$$400 = t^2$$

$$t = \sqrt{400} = 20$$

The fetus weighs 1200 grams after 20 weeks.

15. $d = 16t^2; d = 100$

$$100 = 16t^2$$

$$6.25 = t^2$$

$$t = \sqrt{6.25} = 2.5$$

It will take the object 2.5 seconds to hit the water.

16. $d = \sqrt{(x_2 - x_1)^2 + (y_2 - y_1)^2}$

$= \sqrt{[1 - (-3)]^2 + [-5 - (-2)]^2}$

$= \sqrt{4^2 + (-3)^2}$

$= \sqrt{16 + 9}$

$= \sqrt{25}$

$= 5$

17. $d = \sqrt{(x_2 - x_1)^2 + (y_2 - y_1)^2}$

$= \sqrt{(5 - 3)^2 + (4 - 8)^2}$

$= \sqrt{2^2 + (-4)^2}$

$= \sqrt{4 + 16}$

$= \sqrt{20} = \sqrt{4 \cdot 5} = 2\sqrt{5} \approx 4.47$

18. $x^2 + 16x$

The coefficient of the x-term is 16. Half of 16 is 8, and $8^2 = 64$. Add 64.

$x^2 + 16x + 64 = (x + 8)^2$

19. $x^2 - 6x$

The coefficient of the x-term is –6. Half of –6 is –3, and $(-3)^2 = 9$. Add 9.

$x^2 - 6x + 9 = (x - 3)^2$

20. $x^2 + 3x$

The coefficient of the x-term is 3. Half of 3 is $\dfrac{3}{2}$

and $\left(\dfrac{3}{2}\right)^2 = \dfrac{9}{4}$. Add $\dfrac{9}{4}$.

$x^2 + 3x + \dfrac{9}{4} = \left(x + \dfrac{3}{2}\right)^2$

21. $x^2 - 5x$

The coefficient of the x-term is –5. Half of –5 is

$\dfrac{-5}{2}$ and $\left(\dfrac{-5}{2}\right)^2 = \dfrac{25}{4}$. Add $\dfrac{25}{4}$.

$x^2 - 5x + \dfrac{25}{4} = \left(x - \dfrac{5}{2}\right)^2$

22. $x^2 - 12x + 27 = 0$

First, subtract 27 from both sides to isolate the binomial $x^2 - 12x$.

$x^2 - 12x = -27$

Next, complete the square.

The coefficient of the x-term is –12. Half of –12 is –6 and $(-6)^2 = 36$. Add 36.

$x^2 - 12x + 36 = -27 + 36$

$(x - 6)^2 = 9$

$x - 6 = \sqrt{9}$ or $x - 6 = -\sqrt{9}$

$x - 6 = 3$ $\qquad x - 6 = -3$

$x = 9$ $\qquad\quad x = 3$

The solution set is $\{3, 9\}$.

23. $x^2 - 6x + 4 = 0$

$x^2 - 6x = -4$

$x^2 - 6x + 9 = -4 + 9$

$(x - 3)^2 = 5$

$x - 3 = \sqrt{5}$ $\qquad$ or $x - 3 = -\sqrt{5}$

$x = 3 + \sqrt{5}$ $\qquad x = 3 - \sqrt{5}$

The solution set is $\left\{3 \pm \sqrt{5}\right\}$.

24. $3x^2 - 12x + 11 = 0$

First, divide both sides of the equation by 3 so that the coefficient of the x^2-term will be 1.

$$x^2 - 4x + \frac{11}{3} = 0$$

$$x^2 - 4x = -\frac{11}{3}$$

$$x^2 - 4x + 4 = -\frac{11}{3} + 4$$

$$(x-2)^2 = -\frac{11}{3} + \frac{12}{3}$$

$$(x-2)^2 = \frac{1}{3}$$

$$x - 2 = \sqrt{\frac{1}{3}} \text{ or } x - 2 = -\sqrt{\frac{1}{3}}$$

Simplify the radicals.

$$\sqrt{\frac{1}{3}} = \frac{\sqrt{1}}{\sqrt{3}} = \frac{1}{\sqrt{3}} \cdot \frac{\sqrt{3}}{\sqrt{3}} = \frac{\sqrt{3}}{3}$$

$$x - 2 = \frac{\sqrt{3}}{3} \quad \text{ or } \quad x - 2 = -\frac{\sqrt{3}}{3}$$

$$x = 2 + \frac{\sqrt{3}}{3} \qquad x = 2 - \frac{\sqrt{3}}{3}$$

$$x = \frac{6}{3} + \frac{\sqrt{3}}{3} \qquad x = \frac{6}{3} - \frac{\sqrt{3}}{3}$$

$$x = \frac{6 + \sqrt{3}}{3} \qquad x = \frac{6 - \sqrt{3}}{3}$$

The solution set is $\left\{ \frac{6 \pm \sqrt{3}}{3} \right\}$.

25. $2x^2 + 5x - 3 = 0$

$a = 2, b = 5, c = -3$

Substitute these values into the quadratic formula.

$$x = \frac{-b \pm \sqrt{b^2 - 4ac}}{2a}$$

$$x = \frac{-5 \pm \sqrt{5^2 - 4(2)(-3)}}{2(2)}$$

$$= \frac{-5 \pm \sqrt{25 + 24}}{4} = \frac{-5 \pm \sqrt{49}}{4} = \frac{-5 \pm 7}{4}$$

$$x = \frac{-5 + 7}{4} \text{ or } x = \frac{-5 - 7}{4}$$

$$= \frac{2}{4} = \frac{1}{2} \qquad = \frac{-12}{4} = -3$$

The solution set is $\left\{ -3, \frac{1}{2} \right\}$.

26. $x^2 = 2x + 4$

Rewrite the equation in standard form.

$$x^2 - 2x - 4 = 0$$

Identify $a, b,$ and c.

$$a = 1, b = -2, c = -4$$

Substitute these values into the quadratic formula.

$$x = \frac{-b \pm \sqrt{b^2 - 4ac}}{2a}$$

$$= \frac{-(-2) \pm \sqrt{(-2)^2 - 4(1)(-4)}}{2(1)}$$

$$= \frac{2 \pm \sqrt{4 + 16}}{2} = \frac{2 \pm \sqrt{20}}{2}$$

$$= \frac{2 \pm 2\sqrt{5}}{2} = \frac{2 \pm \sqrt{20}}{2}$$

$$= 1 \pm \sqrt{5}$$

The solution set is $\left\{ 1 \pm \sqrt{5} \right\}$.

27. $3x^2 + 5 = 9x$

Rewrite the equation in standard form.

$$3x^2 - 9x + 5 = 0$$

$$a = 3, b = -9, c = 5$$

$$x = \frac{-b \pm \sqrt{b^2 - 4ac}}{2a}$$

$$= \frac{-(-9) \pm \sqrt{(-9)^2 - 4(3)(5)}}{2 \cdot 3}$$

$$= \frac{9 \pm \sqrt{81 - 60}}{6} = \frac{9 \pm \sqrt{21}}{6}$$

The solution set is $\left\{ \frac{9 \pm \sqrt{21}}{6} \right\}$.

28. $2x^2 - 11x + 5 = 0$

This equation can be solved by the factoring method. Factor the trinomial.

$$(2x - 1)(x - 5) = 0$$

Use the zero-product principle.

$$2x - 1 = 0 \text{ or } x - 5 = 0$$

$$2x = 1 \qquad x = 5$$

$$x = \frac{1}{2}$$

The solution set is $\left\{ \frac{1}{2}, 5 \right\}$.

29. $(3x+5)(x-3) = 5$

Write the equation in standard form.

$3x^2 - 4x - 15 = 5$

$3x^2 - 4x - 20 = 0$

This equation can be solved by the factoring method.

$(3x-10)(x+2) = 0$

$3x - 10 = 0 \quad$ or $\quad x + 2 = 0$

$3x = 10 \qquad\qquad x = -2$

$x = \dfrac{10}{3}$

The solution set is $\left\{-2, \dfrac{10}{3}\right\}$.

30. $3x^2 - 7x + 1 = 0$

The trinomial cannot be factored, so use the quadratic formula with $a = 3, b = -7,$ and $c = 1$.

$x = \dfrac{-b \pm \sqrt{b^2 - 4ac}}{2a}$

$= \dfrac{-(-7) \pm \sqrt{(-7)^2 - 4(3)(1)}}{2(3)}$

$= \dfrac{7 \pm \sqrt{49 - 12}}{6}$

$= \dfrac{7 \pm \sqrt{37}}{6}$

The solution set is $\left\{\dfrac{7 \pm \sqrt{37}}{6}\right\}$.

31. $x^2 - 9 = 0$

Solve by the factoring method.

$(x+3)(x-3) = 0$

$x + 3 = 0 \quad$ or $\quad x - 3 = 0$

$x = -3 \qquad\qquad x = 3$

The solution set is $\{-3, 3\}$.

32. $(2x-3)^2 = 5$

Use the square root property.

$2x - 3 = \sqrt{5} \qquad$ or $\quad 2x - 3 = -\sqrt{5}$

$2x = 3 + \sqrt{5} \qquad\qquad 2x = 3 - \sqrt{5}$

$x = \dfrac{3 + \sqrt{5}}{2} \qquad\qquad x = \dfrac{3 - \sqrt{5}}{2}$

The solution set is $\left\{\dfrac{3 \pm \sqrt{5}}{2}\right\}$.

33. a. 2007 is 4 years after 2003.

$T = 0.6x^2 + 5.4x + 28$

$T = 0.6(4)^2 + 5.4(4) + 28 = 59.2$

$59.2 billion was spent in 2007.

b. Let $T = 160$ and solve for x.

$T = 0.6x^2 + 5.4x + 28$

$160 = 0.6x^2 + 5.4x + 28$

$0 = 0.6x^2 + 5.4x - 132$

$x = \dfrac{-b \pm \sqrt{b^2 - 4ac}}{2a}$

$x = \dfrac{-5.4 \pm \sqrt{5.4^2 - 4(0.6)(-132)}}{2(0.6)}$

$x = \dfrac{-5.4 \pm \sqrt{345.96}}{1.2}$

$x = \dfrac{-5.4 \pm 18.6}{1.2}$

$x = -20$ or $x = 11$

The amount spent to fight terrorism is expected to reach $160 billion 11 years after 2003, or 2014.

34. $\sqrt{-81} = \sqrt{81(-1)} = \sqrt{81}\sqrt{-1} = 9i$

35. $\sqrt{-23} = \sqrt{-23(-1)} = \sqrt{23}\sqrt{-1} = i\sqrt{23}$

36. $\sqrt{-48} = \sqrt{48}\sqrt{-1} = \sqrt{16 \cdot 3}\sqrt{-1} = 4i\sqrt{3}$

37. $3 + \sqrt{-49} = 3 + \sqrt{49}\sqrt{-1} = 3 + 7i$

38. $x^2 = -100$

Use the square root property.

$x = \sqrt{-100}$ or $x = -\sqrt{-100}$

$x = 10i \qquad\qquad x = -10i$

The solutions are $\pm 10i$.

39. $5x^2 = -125$

$x^2 = -25$

$x = \sqrt{-25}$ or $x = -\sqrt{-25}$

$x = 5i \qquad\qquad x = -5i$

The solution set is $\{\pm 5i\}$.

40. $(2x+1)^2 = -8$

$2x+1 = \pm\sqrt{-8}$

$2x+1 = \pm 2i\sqrt{2}$

$2x = -1 \pm 2i\sqrt{2}$

$x = \dfrac{-1 \pm 2i\sqrt{2}}{2}$

The solution set is $\left\{\dfrac{-1 \pm 2i\sqrt{2}}{2}\right\}$.

41. $x^2 - 4x + 13 = 0$

Use the quadratic formula with
$a = 1, b = -4,$ and $c = 13$.

$x = \dfrac{-b \pm \sqrt{b^2 - 4ac}}{2a}$

$= \dfrac{-(-4) \pm \sqrt{(-4)^2 - 4(1)(13)}}{2 \cdot 1}$

$= \dfrac{4 \pm \sqrt{16 - 52}}{2} = \dfrac{4 \pm \sqrt{-36}}{2}$

$= \dfrac{4 \pm 6i}{2} = \dfrac{2(2 \pm 3i)}{2}$

$= 2 \pm 3i$

The solution set is $\{2 \pm 3i\}$.

42. $3x^2 - x + 2 = 0$

$a = 3, b = -1, c = 2$

$x = \dfrac{-b \pm \sqrt{b^2 - 4ac}}{2a}$

$= \dfrac{-(-1) \pm \sqrt{(-1)^2 - 4(3)(2)}}{2 \cdot 3}$

$= \dfrac{1 \pm \sqrt{1 - 24}}{6} = \dfrac{1 \pm \sqrt{-23}}{6}$

$= \dfrac{1 \pm i\sqrt{23}}{6}$

The solution set is $\left\{\dfrac{1 \pm i\sqrt{23}}{6}\right\}$.

43. $y = x^2 - 6x - 7$

a. Because a, the coefficient of x^2, is 1, which is greater than 0, the parabola opens upward.

b. $x^2 - 6x - 7 = 0$

$(x+1)(x-7) = 0$

$x + 1 = 0$ or $x - 7 = 0$

    $x = -1$ $x = 7$

The x-intercepts are -1 and 7.

c. $y = 0^2 - 6 \cdot 0 - 7 = -7$

The y-intercept is -7.

d. $a = 1, b = -6$

x-coordinate of vertex

$= \dfrac{-b}{2a} = \dfrac{-(-6)}{2(1)} = \dfrac{6}{2} = 3$

y-coordinate of vertex

$= 3^2 - 6 \cdot 3 - 7$

$= 9 - 18 - 7$

$= -16$

The vertex is $(3, -16)$.

e. Plot the points $(-1, 0), (7, 0), (0, -7)$,
and $(3, -16)$, and connect these points with a smooth curve.

44. $y = -x^2 - 2x + 3$

a. $a = -1 < 0$, so the parabola opens downward.

b. $-x^2 - 2x + 3 = 0$

$0 = x^2 + 2x - 3$

$0 = (x+3)(x-1)$

$x + 3 = 0$ or $x - 1 = 0$

    $x = -3$ $x = 1$

The x-intercepts are -3 and 1.

c. $y = -0^2 - 2 \cdot 0 + 3 = 3$

The y-intercept is 3.

d. $a = -1, b = -2$

x-intercept of vertex

$= \dfrac{-b}{2a} = \dfrac{-(-2)}{2(-1)} = \dfrac{2}{-2} = -1$

y-coordinate of vertex

$= -(-1)^2 - 2(-1) + 3$

$= -1 + 2 + 3$

$= 4$

The vertex is $(-1, 4)$.

e. Plot the points $(-3, 0), (1, 0), (0, 3),$ and $(-1, 4)$, and connect them with a smooth curve.

$y = -x^2 - 2x + 3$

45. $y = -3x^2 + 6x + 1$

a. $a = -3 < 0$, so the parabola opens downward.

b. $-3x^2 + 6x + 1 = 0$

$$0 = 3x^2 - 6x - 1$$

The trinomial cannot be factored, so use the quadratic formula with $a = 3, b = -6,$ and $c = -1$.

$x = \dfrac{-b \pm \sqrt{b^2 - 4ac}}{2a}$

$= \dfrac{-(-6) \pm \sqrt{(-6)^2 - 4(3)(-1)}}{2 \cdot 3}$

$= \dfrac{6 \pm \sqrt{36 + 12}}{6} = \dfrac{6 \pm \sqrt{48}}{6}$

$= \dfrac{6 \pm 4\sqrt{3}}{6} = \dfrac{2(3 \pm 2\sqrt{3})}{6}$

$= \dfrac{3 \pm 2\sqrt{3}}{3}$

$x = \dfrac{3 + 2\sqrt{3}}{3}$ or $x = \dfrac{3 - 2\sqrt{3}}{3}$

$x \approx 2.2 \qquad\qquad x \approx -0.2$

The x-intercepts are approximately 2.2 and -0.2.

c. $y = -3 \cdot 0^2 + 6 \cdot 0 + 1 = 1$

The y-intercept is 1.

d. $a = -3, b = 6$

$x = \dfrac{-b}{2a} = \dfrac{-6}{2(-3)} = \dfrac{-6}{-6} = 1$

$y = -3(1)^2 + 6(1) + 1 = -3 + 6 + 1 = 4$

The vertex is $(1, 4)$.

e. Plot the points $(2.2, 0), (-0.2, 0), (0, 1),$ and $(1, 4)$, and connect them with a smooth curve.

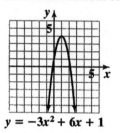

$y = -3x^2 + 6x + 1$

46. $y = x^2 - 4x$

a. $a = 1 > 0$, so the parabola opens upward.

b. $x^2 - 4x = 0$

$x(x - 4) = 0$

$x = 0$ or $x - 4 = 0$

$\qquad\qquad x = 4$

The x-intercepts are 0 and 4.

c. $y = 0^2 - 4 \cdot 0 = 0$

The y-intercept is 0. This does not provide an additional point because part (b) already showed that the parabola passes through the origin.

d. $a = 1, b = -4$

$x = \dfrac{-b}{2a} = \dfrac{-(-4)}{2(1)} = \dfrac{4}{2} = 2$

$y = 2^2 - 4 \cdot 2 = 4 - 8 = -4$

The vertex is $(2, -4)$.

e. Plot the points $(0, 0), (4, 0),$ and $(2, -4)$, and draw a smooth curve through them.

$y = x^2 - 4x$

47. The information needed occurs at the vertex.
x-coordinate.

$$x = \frac{-b}{2a} = \frac{-200}{2(-16)} = 6.25$$

y-coordinate.

$$y = -16x^2 + 200x + 4$$

$$y = -16(6.25)^2 + 200(6.25) + 4 = 629$$

The fireworks reach their greatest height 6.25 seconds after they are launched. The height reached is 629 feet.

48. a. The information needed occurs at the vertex.
x-coordinate.

$$x = \frac{-b}{2a} = \frac{-1}{2(-0.025)} = 20$$

y-coordinate.

$$y = -0.025x^2 + x + 6$$

$$y = -0.025(20)^2 + 20 + 6 = 16$$

The football will reach its greatest height 20 yards after it is tossed. The height reached is 16 feet.

b. $y = -0.025x^2 + x + 6$

$$y = -0.025(38)^2 + 38 + 6 = 7.9$$

The defender must reach 7.9 feet.

c. The football will hit the ground when $y = 0$.

$$y = -0.025x^2 + x + 6$$

$$0 = -0.025x^2 + x + 6$$

$$x = \frac{-b \pm \sqrt{b^2 - 4ac}}{2a}$$

$$x = \frac{-1 \pm \sqrt{1^2 - 4(-0.025)(6)}}{2(-0.025)}$$

$$x \approx -5.3 \text{ or } x \approx 45.3$$

The football will go 45.3 yards before it hits the ground.

d. Find the initial height.

$$y = -0.025x^2 + x + 6$$

$$y = -0.025(0)^2 + 0 + 6 = 6$$

Plot $(20,16)$, $(45.3,0)$, and $(0,6)$. Connect the points with a smooth curve.

49. $\{(2,7),(3,7),(5,7)\}$

This relation is a function because no two ordered pairs have the same first component and different second components.
The domain is the set of first components: $\{2, 3, 5\}$.
The range is the set of second components: $\{7\}$

50. $\{(1,10),(2,500),(3,\pi)\}$

This relation is a function.
Domain: $\{1,2,3\}$
Range: $\{10,500,\pi\}$

51. $\{(12,13),(14,15),(12,19)\}$

This relation is not a function because two of the ordered pairs have the same first component, 12, but different second components.
Domain: $\{12,14\}$
Range: $\{13,15,19\}$

52. $f(x) = 3x - 4$

a. $f(-5) = 3(-5) - 4 = -15 - 4 = -19$

b. $f(6) = 3 \cdot 6 - 4 = 18 - 4 = 14$

c. $f(0) = 3 \cdot 0 - 4 = 0 - 4 = -4$

53. $g(x) = x^2 - 5x + 2$

    a. $g(-4) = (-4)^2 - 5(-4) + 2$

           $= 16 + 20 + 2 = 38$

    b. $g(3) = 3^2 - 5 \cdot 3 + 2$

           $= 9 - 15 + 2 = -4$

    c. $g(0) = 0^2 - 5 \cdot 0 + 2 = -0 + 2 = 2$

54. Many vertical lines will intersect the graph in two points, so y is not a function of x.

55. No vertical line will intersect this graph in more than one point, so y is a function of x.

56. No vertical line will intersect this graph in more than one point, so y is a function of x.

57. Many vertical lines will intersect the graph in two points, so y is not a function of x.

58. **a.** $f(x) = 0.06x^2 + 0.8x + 3.6$

        $f(0) = 0.06(0)^2 + 0.8(0) + 3.6 = 3.6$

        In 1997, sales of organic foods were \$3.6 billion. This is represented by the point (0, 3.6).

    b. $f(x) = 0.06x^2 + 0.8x + 3.6$

        $f(8) = 0.06(8)^2 + 0.8(8) + 3.6 = 13.84$

        8 years after 1997, or 2005, sales of organic foods were \$13.84 billion. This is represented by the point (8, 13.84).

Chapter 10 Test

1. $3x^2 = 48$

    $x^2 = 16$

    $x = \sqrt{16}$ or $x = -\sqrt{16}$

    $x = 4$ or $x = -4$

    The solution set is $\{-4, 4\}$.

2. $(x - 3)^2 = 5$

    $x - 3 = \sqrt{5}$ or $x - 3 = -\sqrt{5}$

      $x = 3 + \sqrt{5}$ $x = 3 - \sqrt{5}$

    The solution set is $\{3 \pm \sqrt{5}\}$.

3. Let $b =$ distance PQ across the lake. Use the Pythagorean Theorem.

$$8^2 + b^2 = 12^2$$

$$64 + b^2 = 144$$

$$b^2 = 80$$

$$b = \sqrt{80} = \sqrt{16}\sqrt{5} = 4\sqrt{5}$$

The distance across the lake is $4\sqrt{5}$ yards.

4. $d = \sqrt{(x_2 - x_1)^2 + (y_2 - y_1)^2}$

    $= \sqrt{(-4 - 3)^2 + [1 - (-2)]^2}$

    $= \sqrt{(-7)^2 + 3^2}$

    $= \sqrt{49 + 9} = \sqrt{58} \approx 7.62$

5. $x^2 + 4x - 3 = 0$

    $x^2 + 4x \qquad = 3$ ← complete the square

    $x^2 + 4x + 4 = 3 + 4$

    $(x + 2)^2 = 7$

    $x + 2 = \sqrt{7}$ or $x + 2 = -\sqrt{7}$

      $x = -2 + \sqrt{7}$ $x = -2 - \sqrt{7}$

    The solution set is $\{-2 \pm \sqrt{7}\}$.

6. $3x^2 + 5x + 1 = 0$

The trinomial cannot be factored, so use the quadratic formula with $a = 3, b = 5,$ and $c = 1$.

$$x = \frac{-b \pm \sqrt{b^2 - 4ac}}{2a}$$

$$= \frac{-5 \pm \sqrt{5^2 - 4(3)(1)}}{2 \cdot 3}$$

$$= \frac{-5 \pm \sqrt{25 - 12}}{6}$$

$$= \frac{-5 \pm \sqrt{13}}{6}$$

The solution set is $\left\{\dfrac{-5 \pm \sqrt{13}}{6}\right\}$.

7. $(3x-5)(x+2) = -6$

Write the equation in standard form.

$3x^2 + x - 10 = -6$

$3x^2 + x - 4 = 0$

Factor the trinomial and use the zero-product principle.

$(3x+4)(x-1) = 0$

$3x+4 = 0$　　or $x-1 = 0$

$3x = -4$　　　　$x = 1$

$x = -\dfrac{4}{3}$

The solution set is $\left\{-\dfrac{4}{3}, 1\right\}$.

8. $(2x+1)^2 = 36$

$2x+1 = \sqrt{36}$　or　$2x+1 = -\sqrt{36}$

$2x+1 = 6$　　　　$2x+1 = -6$

$2x = 5$　　　　　$2x = -7$

$x = \dfrac{5}{2}$　　　　　$x = -\dfrac{7}{2}$

The solution set is $\left\{-\dfrac{7}{2}, \dfrac{5}{2}\right\}$.

9. $2x^2 = 6x - 1$

Write the equation in standard form.

$2x^2 - 6x + 1 = 0$

The trinomial cannot be factored so use the quadratic formula with $a = 2, b = -6,$ and $c = 1$.

$x = \dfrac{-b \pm \sqrt{b^2 - 4ac}}{2a}$

$= \dfrac{-(-6) \pm \sqrt{(-6)^2 - 4(2)(1)}}{2 \cdot 2}$

$= \dfrac{6 \pm \sqrt{36 - 8}}{4} = \dfrac{6 \pm \sqrt{28}}{4}$

$= \dfrac{6 \pm 2\sqrt{7}}{4} = \dfrac{2(3 \pm \sqrt{7})}{4}$

$= \dfrac{3 \pm \sqrt{7}}{2}$

The solution set is $\left\{\dfrac{3 \pm \sqrt{7}}{2}\right\}$.

10. $2x^2 + 9x = 5$

Write the equation in standard form.

$2x^2 + 9x - 5 = 0$

Solve by the factoring method.

$(2x-1)(x+5) = 0$

$2x-1 = 0$　or $x+5 = 0$

$2x = 2$　　　　$x = -5$

$x = \dfrac{1}{2}$

The solution set is $\left\{-5, \dfrac{1}{2}\right\}$.

11. $\sqrt{-121} = \sqrt{121(-1)} = \sqrt{121}\sqrt{-1} = 11i$

12. $\sqrt{-75} = \sqrt{75(-1)} = \sqrt{25 \cdot 3}\sqrt{-1}$

$= 5i\sqrt{3}$

13. $x^2 + 36 = 0$

$x^2 = -36$

$x = \sqrt{-36}$　or $x = -\sqrt{-36}$

$x = 6i$　　　　$x = -6i$

The solution set is $\{\pm 6i\}$.

14. $(x-5)^2 = 25$

$x-5 = \sqrt{-25}$　or $x-5 = -\sqrt{-25}$

$x-5 = 5i$　　　or $x-5 = -5i$

$x = 5 + 5i$　　　　$x = 5 - 5i$

The solution set is $\{5 \pm 5i\}$.

15. $x^2 - 2x + 5 = 0$

The trinomial cannot be factored, so use the quadratic formula with $a = 1, b = -2$, and $c = 5$.

$x = \dfrac{-b \pm \sqrt{b^2 - 4ac}}{2a}$

$= \dfrac{-(-2) \pm \sqrt{(-2)^2 - 4(1)(5)}}{2 \cdot 1}$

$= \dfrac{2 \pm \sqrt{4 - 20}}{2} = \dfrac{2 \pm \sqrt{-16}}{2}$

$= \dfrac{2 \pm 4i}{2} = \dfrac{2(1 \pm 2i)}{2}$

$= 1 \pm 2i$

The solution set is $\{1 \pm 2i\}$.

16. $y = x^2 + 2x - 8$

Step 1 $a = 1 > 0$, so the parabola opens upward.

Step 2 $a = 1, b = 2, c = -8$

x-coordinate of vertex

$$= \frac{-b}{2a} = \frac{-2}{2(1)} = \frac{-2}{2} = -1$$

y-coordinate of vertex

$$= (-1)^2 + 2(-1) - 8 = 1 - 2 - 8 = -9$$

The vertex is $(-1, -9)$.

Step 3 $x^2 + 2x - 8 = 0$

$$(x+4)(x-2) = 0$$

$$x + 4 = 0 \quad \text{or} \quad x - 2 = 0$$

$$x = -4 \qquad x = 2$$

The x-intercepts are -4 and 2.

Step 4 $y = 0^2 + 2 \cdot 0 - 8 = -8$

The y-intercept is -8.

Steps 5 and 6 Plot $(-1, -9), (-4, 0), (2, 0)$, and $(0, -8)$, then connect them with a smooth curve.

17. $y = -2x^2 + 16x - 24$

Step 1 $a = -2 < 0$, so the parabola opens downward.

Step 2 $a = -2, b = 16, c = -24$

$$x = \frac{-b}{2a} = \frac{-16}{2(-2)} = \frac{-16}{-4} = 4$$

$$y = -2 \cdot 4^2 + 16 \cdot 4 - 24$$

$$= -32 + 64 - 24 = 8$$

The vertex is $(4, 8)$.

Step 3

$$-2x^2 + 16x - 24 = 0$$

$$0 = 2x^2 - 16x + 24$$

$$0 = 2(x^2 - 8x + 12)$$

$$0 = 2(x-2)(x-6)$$

$$x - 2 = 0 \quad \text{or} \quad x - 6 = 0$$

$$x = 2 \qquad x = 6$$

The x-intercepts are 2 and 6.

Step 4

$$y = -2 \cdot 0^2 + 16 \cdot 0 - 24 = -24$$

The y-intercept is -24.

Steps 5 and 6 Plot $(4, 8), (2, 0), (6, 0)$, and $(0, -24)$, then connect them with a smooth curve.

18. $y = -16x^2 + 64x + 5$

The graph of this equation is a parabola opening downward, so its vertex is a maximum point. Find the coordinates of the vertex by using $a = -16, b = 64$.

$$x = \frac{-b}{2a} = \frac{-64}{2(-16)} = \frac{-64}{-32} = 2$$

$$y = -16 \cdot 2^2 + 64 \cdot 2 + 5$$

$$= -64 + 128 + 5 = 69$$

The baseball reaches its maximum height 2 seconds after it is hit. The maximum height is 69 feet.

19. The baseball will hit the ground when $y = 0$, so solve the quadratic equation $0 = -16x^2 + 64x + 5$ or $16x^2 - 64x - 5 = 0$.

The trinomial cannot be factored, so use the quadratic formula with $a = 16$, $b = -64$, and $c = -5$.

$$x = \frac{-b \pm \sqrt{b^2 - 4ac}}{2a}$$

$$= \frac{-(-64) \pm \sqrt{(-64)^2 - 4(16)(-5)}}{2 \cdot 16}$$

$$= \frac{64 \pm \sqrt{4096 + 320}}{32} = \frac{64 \pm \sqrt{4416}}{32}$$

$$x = \frac{64 + \sqrt{4416}}{32} \quad \text{or} \quad x = \frac{64 - \sqrt{4416}}{32}$$

$$x \approx 4.1 \qquad\qquad x \approx -0.08$$

Reject -0.08 because it represents a time before the baseball was hit. The baseball hit the ground 4.1 seconds after it was hit.

20. $\{(1,2),(3,4),(5,6),(6,6)\}$

This relation is a function because no two ordered pairs have the same first component and different second components.
Domain: $\{1,3,5,6\}$
Range: $\{2,4,6\}$

21. $\{(2,1),(4,3),(6,5),(6,6)\}$

This relation is not a function because two ordered pairs have the same first component, 6, but different second components.
Domain: $\{2,4,6\}$
Range: $\{1,3,5,6\}$

22. $f(x) = 7x - 3$
$f(10) = 7 \cdot 10 - 3 = 70 - 3 = 67$

23. $g(x) = x^2 - 3x + 7$
$g(-2) = (-2)^2 - 3(-2) + 7$
$= 4 + 6 + 7 = 17$

24. No vertical line will intersect this graph in more than one point, so y is a function of x.

25. Many vertical lines will intersect this graph in more than one point. One such line is the y-axis. Therefore, y is not a function of x.

26. $f(x) = \dfrac{x^2 - x}{2}$

$f(9) = \dfrac{9^2 - 9}{2} = \dfrac{81 - 9}{2} = \dfrac{72}{2} = 36$

This means that in a tournament with 9 chess players, 36 games must be played.

Cumulative Review (Chapters 1-10)

1. $2 - 4(x + 2) = 5 - 3(2x + 1)$
$2 - 4x - 8 = 5 - 6x - 3$
$-4x - 6 = 2 - 6x$
$2x - 6 = 2$
$2x = 8$
$x = 4$
The solution set is $\{4\}$.

2. $\dfrac{x}{2} - 3 = \dfrac{x}{5}$

Multiply both sides by the LCD, 10.
$10\left(\dfrac{x}{2} - 3\right) = 10\left(\dfrac{x}{5}\right)$
$5x - 30 = 2x$
$3x - 30 = 0$
$3x = 30$
$x = 10$
The solution set is $\{10\}$.

3. $3x + 9 \geq 5(x - 1)$
$3x + 9 \geq 5x - 5$
$-2x + 9 \geq -5$
$-2x \geq -14$
$\dfrac{-2x}{-2} \leq \dfrac{-14}{-2}$
$x \leq 7$
$(-\infty, 7]$

4. $2x + 3y = 6$
$x + 2y = 5$

To solve this system by the addition method, multiply the second equation by -2; then add the equations.
$$2x + 3y = 6$$
$$\underline{-2x - 4y = -10}$$
$$-y = -4$$
$$y = 4$$
Back-substitute 4 for y into the second original equation and solve for x.
$x + 2y = 5$
$x + 2 \cdot 4 = 5$
$x + 8 = 5$
$x = -3$
The solution set is $\{(-3, 4)\}$.

5. $3x - 2y = 1$

$y = 10 - 2x$

To solve this system by the substitution method, substitute $10 - 2x$ for y into the first equation.

$$3x - 2y = 1$$
$$3x - 2(10 - 2x) = 1$$
$$3x - 20 + 4x = 1$$
$$7x - 20 = 1$$
$$7x = 21$$
$$x = 3$$

Back-substitute 3 for x into the second equation of the given system to find in value of y.

$$y = 10 - 2(3) = 10 - 6 = 4$$

The ordered pair solution is $(3, 4)$ and the solution set is $\{(3, 4)\}$.

6. $\dfrac{3}{x+5} - 1 = \dfrac{4-x}{2x+10}$

$$\dfrac{3}{x+5} - 1 = \dfrac{4-x}{2(x+5)}$$

Restriction: $x \neq -5$

LCD = $2(x+5)$

$$2(x+5)\left[\dfrac{3}{x+5} - 1\right] = 2(x+5)\left[\dfrac{4-x}{2(x+5)}\right]$$
$$6 - 2(x+5) = 4 - x$$
$$6 - 2x - 10 = 4 - x$$
$$-4 - 2x = 4 - x$$
$$-4 - x = 4$$
$$-x = 8$$
$$x = -8$$

The solution set is $\{-8\}$.

7. $x + \dfrac{6}{x} = -5$

Restriction: $x \neq 0$

LCD = x

$$x\left(x + \dfrac{6}{x}\right) = x(-5)$$
$$x^2 + 6 = -5x$$
$$x^2 + 5x + 6 = 0$$
$$(x+3)(x+2) = 0$$
$$x + 3 = 0 \quad \text{or} \quad x + 2 = 0$$
$$x = -3 \qquad\qquad x = -2$$

The solution set is $\{-3, -2\}$.

8. $\qquad x - 5 = \sqrt{x+7}$

$$(x-5)^2 = \left(\sqrt{x+7}\right)^2$$
$$x^2 - 10x + 25 = x + 7$$
$$x^2 - 11x + 18 = 0$$
$$(x-9)(x-2) = 0$$
$$x - 9 = 0 \quad \text{or} \quad x - 2 = 0$$
$$x = 9 \qquad\qquad x = 2$$

Check each proposed solution in the original equation.

Check 9:   Check 2:

Check 9:	Check 2:
$x - 5 = \sqrt{x+7}$	$x - 5 = \sqrt{x+7}$
$9 - 5 = \sqrt{9+7}$	$2 - 5 = \sqrt{2+7}$
$4 = \sqrt{16}$	$-3 = \sqrt{9}$
$4 = 4$, true	$-3 = 3$, false

The checks show that 9 satisfies the equation, while 2 is an extraneous solution. The solution set is $\{9\}$.

9. $(x-2)^2 = 20$

To solve this quadratic equation, use the square root property.

$$x - 2 = \sqrt{20} \qquad \text{or} \quad x - 2 = -\sqrt{20}$$
$$x - 2 = 2\sqrt{5} \qquad\qquad x - 2 = -2\sqrt{5}$$
$$x = 2 + 2\sqrt{5} \qquad\qquad x = 2 - 2\sqrt{5}$$

The solution set is $\{2 \pm 2\sqrt{5}.\}$.

10. $3x^2 - 6x + 2 = 0$

Use the quadratic formula with $a = 3$, $b = -6$, and $c = 2$.

$$x = \dfrac{-b \pm \sqrt{b^2 - 4ac}}{2a}$$
$$= \dfrac{-(-6) \pm \sqrt{(-6)^2 - 4(3)(2)}}{2 \cdot 3}$$
$$= \dfrac{6 \pm \sqrt{36 - 24}}{6} = \dfrac{6 \pm \sqrt{12}}{6}$$
$$= \dfrac{6 \pm 2\sqrt{3}}{6} = \dfrac{2(3 \pm \sqrt{3})}{6}$$
$$= \dfrac{3 \pm \sqrt{3}}{3}$$

The solution set is $\left\{\dfrac{3 \pm \sqrt{3}}{3}\right\}$.

11. $A = \dfrac{5r+2}{t}$ for t

$$tA = t\left(\dfrac{5r+2}{t}\right)$$

$$tA = 5r+2$$

$$\dfrac{tA}{A} = \dfrac{5r+2}{A}$$

$$t = \dfrac{5r+2}{A}$$

12. $\dfrac{12x^3}{3x^{12}} = \dfrac{12}{3} \cdot \dfrac{x^3}{x^{12}}$

$$= 4x^{3-12}$$

$$= 4x^{-9}$$

$$= \dfrac{4}{x^9}$$

13. $4 \cdot 6 \div 2 \cdot 3 + (-5)$

$$= 24 \div 2 \cdot 3 + (-5)$$

$$= 12 \cdot 3 + (-5)$$

$$= 36 + (-5) = 31$$

14. $\left(6x^2 - 8x + 3\right) - \left(-4x^2 + x - 1\right)$

$$= \left(6x^2 - 8x + 3\right) + \left(4x^2 - x + 1\right)$$

$$= \left(6x^2 + 4x^2\right) + (-8x - x) + (3 + 1)$$

$$= 10x^2 - 9x + 4$$

15. $(7x+4)(3x-5)$

$$= 7x(3x) + 7x(-5) + 4(3x) + 4(-5)$$

$$= 21x^2 - 35x + 12x - 20$$

$$= 21x^2 - 23x - 20$$

16. $(5x-2)^2 = (5x)^2 - 2 \cdot 5x \cdot 2 + 2^2$

$$= 25x^2 - 20x + 4$$

17. $(x+y)\left(x^2 - xy + y^2\right)$

$$= x\left(x^2 - xy + y^2\right) + y\left(x^2 - xy + y^2\right)$$

$$= x^3 - x^2 y + xy^2 + x^2 y - xy^2 + y^3$$

$$= x^3 + y^3$$

18. $\dfrac{x^2 + 6x + 8}{x^2} \div \left(3x^2 + 6x\right)$

$$= \dfrac{x^2 + 6x + 8}{x^2} \cdot \dfrac{1}{3x^2 + 6x}$$

$$= \dfrac{(x+2)(x+4)}{x^2} \cdot \dfrac{1}{3x(x+2)}$$

$$= \dfrac{x+4}{3x^3}$$

19. $\dfrac{x}{x^2 + 2x - 3} - \dfrac{x}{x^2 - 5x + 4}$

To find the LCD, factor the denominators.

$$x^2 + 2x - 3 = (x+3)(x-1)$$

$$x^2 - 5x + 4 = (x-1)(x-4)$$

$$\text{LCD} = (x+3)(x-1)(x-4)$$

$$\dfrac{x}{(x+3)(x-1)} - \dfrac{x}{(x-1)(x-4)}$$

$$= \dfrac{x(x-4)}{(x+3)(x-1)(x-4)}$$

$$- \dfrac{x(x+3)}{(x+3)(x-1)(x-4)}$$

$$= \dfrac{x(x-4) - x(x+3)}{(x+3)(x-1)(x-4)}$$

$$= \dfrac{x^2 - 4x - x^2 - 3x}{(x+3)(x-1)(x-4)}$$

$$= \dfrac{-7x}{(x+3)(x-1)(x-4)}$$

20. $\dfrac{x - \dfrac{1}{5}}{5 - \dfrac{1}{x}}$

LCD = $5x$

$\dfrac{x - \dfrac{1}{5}}{5 - \dfrac{1}{x}} = \dfrac{5x}{5x} \cdot \dfrac{\left(x - \dfrac{1}{5}\right)}{\left(5 - \dfrac{1}{x}\right)}$

$= \dfrac{5x \cdot x - 5x \cdot \dfrac{1}{5}}{5x \cdot 5 - 5x \cdot \dfrac{1}{x}}$

$= \dfrac{5x^2 - x}{25x - 5}$

$= \dfrac{x(5x-1)}{5(5x-1)} = \dfrac{x}{5}$

21. $3\sqrt{20} + 2\sqrt{45} = 3\sqrt{4}\sqrt{5} + 2\sqrt{9}\sqrt{5}$

$= 3 \cdot 2\sqrt{5} + 2 \cdot 3\sqrt{5}$

$= 6\sqrt{5} + 6\sqrt{5} = 12\sqrt{5}$

22. $\sqrt{3x} \cdot \sqrt{6x} = \sqrt{18x^2} = \sqrt{9x^2}\sqrt{2}$

$= 3x\sqrt{2}$

23. $\dfrac{2}{\sqrt{3}} = \dfrac{2}{\sqrt{3}} \cdot \dfrac{\sqrt{3}}{\sqrt{3}} = \dfrac{2\sqrt{3}}{3}$

24. $\dfrac{8}{3 - \sqrt{5}} = \dfrac{8}{3 - \sqrt{5}} \cdot \dfrac{3 + \sqrt{5}}{3 + \sqrt{5}}$

$= \dfrac{8\left(3 + \sqrt{5}\right)}{3^2 - \left(\sqrt{5}\right)^2}$

$= \dfrac{8\left(3 + \sqrt{5}\right)}{9 - 5}$

$= \dfrac{8\left(3 + \sqrt{5}\right)}{4}$

$= 2\left(3 + \sqrt{5}\right) = 6 + 2\sqrt{5}$

25. $4x^2 - 49 = (2x)^2 - 7^2$

$= (2x + 7)(2x - 7)$

26. Factor by grouping.

$x^3 + 3x^2 - x - 3 = \left(x^3 + 3x^2\right) + (-x - 3)$

$= x^2(x + 3) - 1(x + 3)$

$= (x + 3)\left(x^2 - 1\right)$

$= (x + 3)(x + 1)(x - 1)$

27. $2x^2 + 8x - 42 = 2\left(x^2 + 4x - 21\right)$

$= 2(x - 3)(x + 7)$

28. $x^5 - 16x = x\left(x^4 - 16\right)$

$= \left[\left(x^2\right)^2 - 4^2\right]$

$= x\left(x^2 + 4\right)\left(x^2 - 4\right)$

$= x\left(x^2 + 4\right)(x + 2)(x - 2)$

29. $x^3 - 10x^2 + 25x = x\left(x^2 - 10x + 25\right)$

$= x(x - 5)^2$

30. $x^3 - 8$

Use the formula for factoring the difference of two cubes.

$x^3 - 8 = x^3 - 2^3$

$= (x - 2)\left(x^2 + 2 \cdot x + 2^2\right)$

$= (x - 2)\left(x^2 + 2x + 4\right)$

31. $8^{-\frac{2}{3}} = \dfrac{1}{8^{\frac{2}{3}}} = \dfrac{1}{\left(\sqrt[3]{8}\right)^2} = \dfrac{1}{2^2} = \dfrac{1}{4}$

32. $y = \dfrac{1}{3}x - 1$

slope $= \dfrac{1}{3}$; y-intercept $= -1$

Plot $(0,-1)$. From the point, move 1 unit *up* and 3
units to the *right* to reach the point $(3,0)$. Draw a
line through $(0,-1)$ and $(3,0)$.

$y = \dfrac{1}{3}x - 1$

33. $3x + 2y = -6$

x-intercept: -2
y-intercept: -3
checkpoint: $(-4,3)$
Draw a line through $(-2,0), (0,-3)$, and $(-4,3)$.

$3x + 2y = -6$

34. $y = -2$

The graph is a horizontal line with y-intercept -2.

$y = -2$

35. $3x - 4y \le 12$

Graph $3x - 4y = 12$ as a solid line using its x-
intercept, 4, and its y-intercept -3. Use $(0,0)$ as a
test point. Because $3 \cdot 0 - 4 \cdot 0 \le 12$ is true, shade the
half-plane containing $(0,0)$.

$3x - 4y \le 12$

36. $y = x^2 - 2x - 3$

The graph is a parabola opening upward.
Find the vertex: $a = 1, b = -2$

$$x = \dfrac{-b}{2a} = \dfrac{-(-2)}{2(1)} = \dfrac{2}{2} = 1$$

$$y = 1^2 - 2 \cdot 1 - 3 = 1 - 2 - 3 = -4$$

The vertex is $(1,-4)$.
Find the x-intercepts:

$$x^2 - 2x - 3 = 0$$
$$(x+1)(x-3) = 0$$
$$x + 1 = 0 \quad \text{or} \quad x - 3 = 0$$
$$x = -1 \qquad\quad x = 3$$

The x-intercepts are -1 and 3.
Find the y-intercept:

$$y = 0^2 - 2 \cdot 0 - 3 = 3$$

The y-intercept is -3.
Plot the points $(1,-4), (-1,0), (3,0)$, and $(0,-3)$,
then connect them with a smooth curve.

$y = x^2 - 2x - 3$

37. $2x + y < 4$

$\quad x > 2$

Graph $2x + y = 4$ as a dashed line using its x-intercept, 2, and y-intercept, 4.

Because $2 \cdot 0 + 0 < 4$ is true, shade the half-plane containing $(0,0)$.

Graph $x = 2$ as a dashed vertical line with x-intercept 2. Because $0 > 2$ is false, shade the half-plane *not* containing $(0,0)$.

This is the region to the right of the vertical line. The solution set is the intersection of the two shaded regions. The open circle at $(2,0)$ shows that is not included in the graph.

2x + y < 4

x > 2

38. $(-1,3)$ and $(2,-3)$

$$m = \frac{y_2 - y_1}{x_2 - x_1} = \frac{-3-3}{2-(-1)} = \frac{-6}{3} = -2$$

39. Line passing through $(1,2)$ and $(3,6)$

First find the slope.

$$m = \frac{6-2}{3-1} = \frac{4}{2} = 2$$

Use the slope and either point in the point-slope form.

$$y - y_1 = m(x - x_1) \quad \text{or} \quad y - y_1 = m(x - x_1)$$
$$y - 2 = 2(x-1) \qquad y - 6 = 2(x-3)$$

Rewrite either of these equations in slope-intercept form.

$$y - 2 = 2(x-1) \quad \text{or} \quad y - 6 = 2(x-3)$$
$$y - 2 = 2x - 2 \qquad\quad y - 6 = 2x - 6$$
$$y = 2x \qquad\qquad\quad y = 2x$$

Notice that the results are the same. The slope-intercept form is $y = 2x$.

40. Let x = the unknown number.

$$5x - 7 = 208$$
$$5x = 215$$
$$x = 43$$

The number is 43.

41. Let x = the price of the camera before the reduction.

$$x - 0.20x = 256$$
$$1x - 0.20x = 256$$
$$0.80x = 256$$
$$\frac{0.80x}{0.80} = \frac{256}{0.80}$$
$$x = 320$$

The price before the reduction was \$320.

42. Let x = the width of the rectangle.

Then $3x$ = the length.

$$2x + 2(3x) = 400$$
$$2x + 6x = 400$$
$$8x = 400$$
$$x = 50$$
$$3x = 150$$

The length is 150 yards and the width is 50 yards.

43. Let x = amount invested at 7%

Then $20,000 - x$ = amount invested at 9%.

The total interest earned in one year is 1550, so the equation is

$$0.07x + 0.09(20,000 - x) = 1550.$$

Solve this equation.

$$0.07x + 1800 - 0.09x = 1550$$
$$-0.02x + 1800 = 1550$$
$$-0.02x = -250$$
$$\frac{-0.02x}{-0.02} = \frac{-250}{-0.02}$$
$$x = 12,000$$

\$12,500 was invested at 7% and \$20,000 − \$12,500 = \$7500 was invested at 9%.

44. Let x = the number of liters of 40% acid solution.
Then $12 - x$ = the number of liters of 70% acid solution.

	Number of liters $\times$	Percent of Acid $=$	Amount of Acid
40% Acid solution	x	0.40	$0.4x$
70% Acid solution	$12-x$	0.70	$0.7(12-x)$
50% Acid solution	12	0.50	$0.5(12)$

$$0.40x + 0.70(12 - x) = 0.50(12)$$
$$0.40x + 8.4 - 0.70x = 6$$
$$-0.30x + 8.4 = 6$$
$$-0.30x = -2.4$$
$$\frac{-0.30x}{-0.30} = \frac{-2.4}{-0.30}$$
$$x = 8$$

8 liters of 40% acid solution and $12 - 8 = 4$ liters of 70% acid solution should be used.

45. Let x = the time it will take for the boats to be 232 miles apart.

	Rate	Time	Distance
Boat going east	13	x	$13x$
Boat going west	19	x	$19x$

$$13x + 19x = 232$$
$$32x = 232$$
$$x = 7.25$$

The boats will be 232 miles apart after 7.25 hours or 7 hours, 15 minutes.

46. Let x = the number of students to be enrolled.
$$\frac{x \text{ students}}{176 \text{ faculty members}} = \frac{23}{2}$$
$$\frac{x}{176} = \frac{23}{2}$$
$$2x = 176 \cdot 23$$
$$2x = 4048$$
$$x = 2024$$

The university should enroll 2024 students.

47. Let x = the height of the sail.
Use the formula for the area of a triangle.
$$A = \frac{1}{2}bh$$
$$120 = \frac{1}{2} \cdot 15 \cdot x$$
$$2 \cdot 120 = 2\left(\frac{1}{2} \cdot 15 \cdot x\right)$$
$$240 = 15x$$
$$16 = x$$
The height of the sail is 16 feet.

48. Let x = the measure of the second angle.
Then $x + 10$ = the measure of the first angle.
$4x + 20$ = the measure of the third angle.
$$x + (x + 10) + (4x + 20) = 180$$
$$6x + 30 = 180$$
$$6x = 150$$
$$x = 25$$

Measure of the first angle = $x + 10 = 35°$
Measure of the second angle = $x = 25°$
Measure of the third angle = $4x + 20 = 120°$

49. Let x = the price of a TV.
Then y = the price of a stereo.
$$3x + 4y = 2530$$
$$4x + 3y = 2510$$
To solve this system by the addition method, multiply the first equation by 4 and the second equation by -3; then add the resulting equations.
$$\begin{aligned} 12x + 16y &= 10,120 \\ -12x - 9y &= -7530 \\ \hline 7y &= 2590 \\ y &= 370 \end{aligned}$$

Back-substitute 370 for y in the first equation of the original system.
$$3x + 4y = 2530$$
$$3x + 4(370) = 2530$$
$$3x + 1480 = 2530$$
$$3x = 1050$$
$$x = 350$$

The price of a TV is $350 and the price of a stereo is $370.

50. Let $x =$ the width of the rectangle.

Then $x + 6 =$ the length of the rectangle.

The area of the rectangle is 55 square meters, so the equation is $(x + 6)(x) = 55$.

Solve this equation.

$$x^2 + 6x = 55$$

$$x^2 + 6x - 55 = 0$$

$$(x + 11)(x - 5) = 0$$

$$x + 11 = 0 \quad \text{or} \quad x - 5 = 0$$

$$x = -11 \qquad x = 5$$

Reject 11 because the width cannot be negative. The width is 5 meters and the length is 11 meters.

Appendix

Check Points Appendix

1. **a.** $\dfrac{10+20+30+40+50}{5} = \dfrac{150}{5} = 30$

   b. $\dfrac{3+10+10+10+117}{5} = \dfrac{150}{5} = 30$

2. **a.** First arrange the data items from smallest to largest: 25, 28, <u>35</u>, 40, 42.
   The number of data items is odd, so the median is the middle number. The median is 35.

   b. First arrange the data items from smallest to largest: 61, 72, <u>79</u>, <u>85</u>, 87, 93.
   The number of data items is even, so the median is the mean of the two middle data items.
   The median is $\dfrac{79+85}{2} = \dfrac{164}{2} = 82$.

3. **a.** Mean $= \dfrac{417.4+46.9+37.1+35.0+32.8+27.2+20.8+19.2+19.1+13.9}{10} = \$66.94$ billion

   b. Position of mean: $\dfrac{n+1}{2} = \dfrac{10+1}{2} = 5.5$ position
   The median is the mean of the data items in positions 5 and 6.
   Thus, the median is $\dfrac{27.2+32.8}{2} = \$30$ billion.

   c. The mean is so much greater than the median because one data item ($417.4) is much greater than the others.

4. **a.** 3, 8, 5, 8, 9, 10
   8 occurs most often. The mode is 8.

   b. 3, 8, 5, 8, 9, 3
   Both 3 and 8 occur most often. The modes are 3 and 8.

   c. 3, 8, 5, 6, 9, 10
   Each data item occurs the same number of times. There is no mode.

5. *Mean:* Mean $= \dfrac{107+136+138+138+172+173+190+191}{8} = \dfrac{1245}{8} \approx 155.6$
   Median: The data items are arranged in order: 107, 136, 138, <u>138</u>, <u>172</u>, 173, 190, 191
   The number of data items is even, so the median is the mean of the two middle data items.
   The median is $\dfrac{138+172}{2} = \dfrac{310}{2} = 155$.
   Mode: The number 138 occurs more often than any other. The mode is 138.

Exercise Set Appendix

1. $\dfrac{7+4+3+2+8+5+1+3}{8} = \dfrac{33}{8} = 4.125$

3. $\dfrac{91+95+99+97+93+95}{6} = \dfrac{570}{6} = 95$

5. $\dfrac{100+40+70+40+60}{5} = \dfrac{310}{5} = 62$

7. $\dfrac{1.6+3.8+5.0+2.7+4.2+4.2+3.2+4.7+3.6+2.5+2.5}{11} = \dfrac{38}{11} \approx 3.45$

9. First arrange the data items from smallest to largest: 1, 2, 3, 3, 4, 5, 7, 8
   The number of data items is even, so the median is the mean of the two middle data items. The median is 3.5.

11. First arrange the data items from smallest to largest: 91, 93, 95, 95, 97, 99
    The number of data items is even, so the median is the mean of the two middle data items.
    $\text{Median} = \dfrac{95+95}{2} = 95$

13. First arrange the data items from smallest to largest: 40, 40, 60, 70, 100
    The number of data items is odd, so the median is the middle number. The median is 60.

15. First arrange the data items from smallest to largest: 1.6, 2.5, 2.5, 2.7, 3.2, 3.6, 3.8, 4.2, 4.2, 4.7, 5.0
    The number of data items is odd, so the median is the middle number. The median is 3.6.

17. The mode is 3.

19. The mode is 95.

21. The mode is 40.

23. The modes are 2.5 and 4.2.

25. The data items are 52, 56, 59, 68, 69, 71, 71, 74, 87.
    Mean: $\text{Mean} = \dfrac{52+56+59+68+69+71+71+74+87}{9} = \dfrac{607}{9} \approx 67.4$
    Median: The data items are arranged in order. The number of data items is odd, so the median is the middle number. The median is 69.
    Mode: The number 71 occurs more often than any other. The mode is 71.

27. The data items are $17,500, $19,000, $22,000, $27,500, $98,500
    Mean: $\text{Mean} = \dfrac{\$17,500+\$19,000+\$22,000+\$27,500+\$98,500}{5} = \dfrac{\$184,500}{5} \approx \$36,900$
    Median: The data items are arranged in order. The number of data items is odd, so the median is the middle number. The median is $22,000.
    The median is more representative. Explanations will vary.